FEATURES AND BENEFITS
Core-Plus Mathematics, Course 2 TEACHER'S GUIDE PART B ©2008

Content and Organization

See page(s):

• Alignment to the NCTM Grades 9–12 Content Standards.	x
• Introduction and Organization of Course 2.	xi–xvii
• Access, Equity, and Differentiation.	xvi–xvii
• Implementing the Curriculum.	xvii–xxviii

Student and Teacher Friendly

• Engaging student-centered applications invite students to read and do more mathematics on their own. Read about summer jobs and Supply and Demand.	359–360
• Lesson development organizes problems for students into easy-to-understand instructions. See *Designing Parabolas*, Investigation 2.	332–334
• Full color *Student Edition* page alongside *Teacher's Guide* page for easy reference.	458–T458
• Effective *Teacher's Guide* design provides point-of-use support to make it easier for you to focus on managing students' progress in completing investigations.	325–T331

Extensive and Varied Practice

• **Applications** tasks help students use and apply ideas from each lesson.	345–349
• **Connections** tasks connect each lesson's topics with other mathematics students know.	349–352
• **Reflections** tasks help students avoid developing misconceptions and help them rethink key ideas that were developed in the lesson.	352–353
• **Extensions** tasks provide opportunities to explore further or more deeply important ideas developed in the lesson.	353–356
• **Review** tasks help students maintain important skills.	356–358

Test Preparation and Assessment

• **Think About This Situation** assesses students' prior knowledge before the start of the lesson.	327
• **Summarizing the Mathematics** assesses students' ability to correctly articulate the mathematics developed after each investigation in the lesson.	331
• **Check Your Understanding** assesses students' ability to solve problems based upon the mathematics developed in each investigation in the lesson.	331
• **Looking Back** lessons help students review and practice key ideas that were developed in the unit.	393–398

Technology

• *CPMP-Tools*™ expands student use of technology by including software tools for algebra, geometry, statistics, and discrete mathematics and time-saving access to selected lesson data sets.	xi
• *StudentWorks*™ **CD-ROM** includes the *Student Edition* and more on one convenient CD.	
• *ExamView*® *Assessment Suite* **CD-ROM** is a powerful state-of-the art test generator that combines ease of use with enormous flexibility in creating customized assessments.	
• *TeacherWorks*™ *Plus* **CD-ROM** is the latest in all-in-one planners and teaching resource center including the ability to edit many of your print resources.	
• *Core-Plus Mathematics* Web site resources at **www.cpmp.glencoe.com**.	

Course 2 Core-Plus Mathematics

Contemporary Mathematics in Context

2nd Edition

**Christian R. Hirsch • James T. Fey • Eric W. Hart
Harold L. Schoen • Ann E. Watkins**

with

**Beth E. Ritsema • Rebecca K. Walker • Sabrina Keller
Robin Marcus • Arthur F. Coxford • Gail Burrill**

New York, New York   Columbus, Ohio   Chicago, Illinois   Woodland Hills, California

 **Glencoe**

The McGraw·Hill Companies

 This material is based upon work supported, in part, by the National Science Foundation under grant no. ESI 0137718. Opinions expressed are those of the authors and not necessarily those of the Foundation.

Send all inquiries to:
Glencoe/McGraw-Hill
8787 Orion Place
Columbus, OH 43240-4027

ISBN: 978-0-07-877259-7   **Core-Plus Mathematics**
MHID: 0-07-877259-1   *Contemporary Mathematics in Context*
                             Course 2 Teacher Edition, Part A

ISBN: 978-0-07-877260-3   **Core-Plus Mathematics**
MHID: 0-07-877260-5   *Contemporary Mathematics in Context*
                             Course 2 Teacher Edition, Part B

Printed in the United States of America.

2 3 4 5 6 7 8 9 10 079/043 16 15 14 13 12 11 10 09 08

Core-Plus Mathematics 2 Development Team

Senior Curriculum Developers

Christian R. Hirsch (Director)
Western Michigan University

James T. Fey
University of Maryland

Eric W. Hart
Maharishi University of Management

Harold L. Schoen
University of Iowa

Ann E. Watkins
California State University, Northridge

Contributing Curriculum Developers

Beth E. Ritsema
Western Michigan University

Rebecca K. Walker
Grand Valley State University

Sabrina Keller
Michigan State University

Robin Marcus
University of Maryland

Arthur F. Coxford (deceased)
University of Michigan

Gail Burrill
Michigan State University
(First edition only)

Principal Evaluator

Steven W. Ziebarth
Western Michigan University

Advisory Board

Diane Briars
Pittsburgh Public Schools

Jeremy Kilpatrick
University of Georgia

Robert E. Megginson
University of Michigan

Kenneth Ruthven
University of Cambridge

David A. Smith
Duke University

Mathematical Consultants

Deborah Hughes-Hallett
University of Arizona / Harvard University

Stephen B. Maurer
Swarthmore College

William McCallum
University of Arizona

Doris Schattschneider
Moravian College

Richard Scheaffer
University of Florida

Evaluation Consultant

Norman L. Webb
University of Wisconsin-Madison

Technical Coordinator

James Laser
Western Michigan University

Collaborating Teachers

Mary Jo Messenger
Howard County Public Schools, Maryland

Jacqueline Stewart
Okemos, Michigan

Graduate Assistants

Allison BrckaLorenz
Christopher Hlas
University of Iowa

Michael Conklin
University of Maryland

Dana Grosser
Anna Kruizenga
Nicole Lanie
Diane Moore
Western Michigan University

Undergraduate Assistants

Cassie Durgin
University of Maryland

Rachael Kaluzny
Jessica Tucker
Ashley Wiersma
Western Michigan University

Core-Plus Mathematics 2 Field-Test Sites

Core-Plus Mathematics 2 builds on the strengths of the 1st edition which was shaped by multi-year field tests in 36 high schools in Alaska, California, Colorado, Georgia, Idaho, Iowa, Kentucky, Michigan, Ohio, South Carolina, and Texas. Each revised text is the product of a three-year cycle of research and development, pilot testing and refinement, and field testing and further refinement. Special thanks are extended to the following teachers and their students who participated in the testing and evaluation of 2nd Edition Course 2.

Hickman High School
Columbia, Missouri
  Melissa Hundley
  Stephanie Krawczyk
  Cheryl Lightner
  Amy McCann
  Tiffany McCracken
  Ryan Pingrey
  Michael Westcott

Holland Christian High School
Holland, Michigan
  Tim Laverell
  Brian Lemmen
  Betsi Roelofs
  John Timmer
  Mike Verkaik

Jefferson Junior High School
Columbia, Missouri
  Lori Kilfoil

Malcolm Price Lab School
Cedar Falls, Iowa
  Megan Balong
  Dennis Kettner
  James Maltas

Oakland Junior High School
Columbia, Missouri
  Dana Sleeth

Riverside University High School
Milwaukee, Wisconsin
  Cheryl Brenner
  Dave Cusma
  Alice Lanphier
  Ela Kiblawi
  Ulices Sepulveda

Rock Bridge High School
Columbia, Missouri
  Nancy Hanson
  Emily Hawn
  Lisa Holt
  Betsy Launder
  Linda Shumate

Sauk Prairie High School
Prairie du Sac, Wisconsin
  Joel Amidon
  Shane Been
  Kent Jensen
  Joan Quenan
  Scott Schutt
  Mary Walz

Washington High School
Milwaukee, Wisconsin
  Anthony Amoroso

West Junior High School
Columbia, Missouri
  Katie Bihr

Overview of Course 2

UNIT 1 FUNCTIONS, EQUATIONS, AND SYSTEMS

Functions, Equations, and Systems reviews and extends student ability to recognize, describe, and use functional relationships among quantitative variables, with special emphasis on relationships that involve two or more independent variables.

Topics include direct and inverse variation and joint variation; power functions; linear equations in standard form; and systems of two linear equations with two variables, including solution by graphing, substitution, and elimination.

Lesson 1 Direct and Inverse Variation

Lesson 2 Multivariable Functions

Lesson 3 Systems of Linear Equations

Lesson 4 Looking Back

UNIT 2 MATRIX METHODS

Matrix Methods develops student understanding of matrices and ability to use matrices to represent and solve problems in a variety of real-world and mathematical settings.

Topics include constructing and interpreting matrices, row and column sums, matrix addition, scalar multiplication, matrix multiplication, powers of matrices, inverse matrices, properties of matrices, and using matrices to solve systems of equations.

Lesson 1 Constructing, Interpreting, and Operating on Matrices

Lesson 2 Multiplying Matrices

Lesson 3 Matrices and Systems of Linear Equations

Lesson 4 Looking Back

UNIT 3 COORDINATE METHODS

Coordinate Methods develops student understanding of coordinate methods for representing and analyzing properties of geometric shapes, for describing geometric change, and for producing animations.

Topics include representing two-dimensional figures and modeling situations with coordinates, including computer-generated graphics; distance in the coordinate plane, midpoint of a segment, and slope; coordinate and matrix models of rigid transformations (translations, rotations, and line reflections), of size transformations, and of similarity transformations; animation effects.

Lesson 1 A Coordinate Model of a Plane

Lesson 2 Coordinate Models of Transformations

Lesson 3 Transformations, Matrices, and Animation

Lesson 4 Looking Back

Overview of Course 2

4 REGRESSION AND CORRELATION

Regression and Correlation develops student understanding of the characteristics and interpretation of the least squares regression equation and of the use of correlation to measure the strength of the linear association between two variables.

Topics include interpreting scatterplots; least squares regression, residuals and errors in prediction, sum of squared errors; Pearson's correlation coefficient, lurking variables, and cause and effect.

Lesson 1 Bivariate Relationships

Lesson 2 Least Squares Regression and Correlation

Lesson 3 Looking Back

5 NONLINEAR FUNCTIONS AND EQUATIONS

Nonlinear Functions and Equations introduces function notation, reviews and extends student ability to construct and reason with functions that model parabolic shapes and other quadratic relationships in science and economics, with special emphasis on formal symbolic reasoning methods, and introduces common logarithms and algebraic methods for solving exponential equations.

Topics include formalization of function concept, notation, domain and range; factoring and expanding quadratic expressions, solving quadratic equations by factoring and the quadratic formula, applications to supply and demand, break-even analysis; common logarithms and solving exponential equations using base 10 logarithms.

Lesson 1 Quadratic Functions, Expressions, and Equations

Lesson 2 Nonlinear Systems of Equations

Lesson 3 Common Logarithms and Exponential Equations

Lesson 4 Looking Back

6 NETWORK OPTIMIZATION

Network Optimization develops student understanding of vertex-edge graphs and ability to use these graphs to solve network optimization problems.

Topics include optimization, mathematical modeling, algorithmic problem solving, digraphs, trees, minimum spanning trees, distance matrices, Hamilton circuits and paths, the Traveling Salesperson Problem, critical paths, and the PERT technique.

Lesson 1 Optimum Spanning Networks

Lesson 2 Scheduling Projects Using Critical Paths

Lesson 3 Looking Back

Overview of Course 2

UNIT 7 TRIGONOMETRIC METHODS

Trigonometric Methods develops student understanding of trigonometric functions and the ability to use trigonometric methods to solve triangulation and indirect measurement problems.

Topics include sine, cosine, and tangent functions of measures of angles in standard position in a coordinate plane and in a right triangle; indirect measurement; analysis of variable-sided triangle mechanisms; Law of Sines and Law of Cosines.

Lesson 1 Trigonometric Functions

Lesson 2 Using Trigonometry in Any Triangle

Lesson 3 Looking Back

UNIT 8 PROBABILITY DISTRIBUTIONS

Probability Distributions further develops student ability to understand and visualize situations involving chance by using simulation and mathematical analysis to construct probability distributions.

Topics include Multiplication Rule, independent events, conditional probability, probability distributions and their graphs, waiting-time distributions, expected value, and rare events.

Lesson 1 Probability Models

Lesson 2 Expected Value

Lesson 3 The Waiting-Time Distribution

Lesson 4 Looking Back

Contents

Contents

NCTM Standards

Core-Plus Mathematics and the instructional and assessment practices it promotes address the focal points of the National Council of Teachers of Mathematics' *Principles and Standards for School Mathematics*. By design, the **process standards** on Problem Solving, Reasoning and Proof, Communication, Connections, and Representation are an integral part of each lesson of every unit in the curriculum. The chart below correlates Course 2 units with the **content standards** for grades 9–12 in terms of focus (Ⓕ) and connections (Ⓒ).

Correlation of Course 2 to NCTM Standards

NCTM Grades 9–12 Content Standards	Unit 1 Functions, Equations, and Systems	Unit 2 Matrix Methods	Unit 3 Coordinate Methods	Unit 4 Regression and Correlation	Unit 5 Nonlinear Functions and Equations	Unit 6 Network Optimization	Unit 7 Trigonometric Methods	Unit 8 Probability Distributions
Number and Operations								
Understand numbers, ways of representing numbers, relationships among numbers, and number systems		Ⓒ	Ⓒ	Ⓒ	Ⓕ		Ⓒ	Ⓒ
Understand meanings of operations and how they relate to one another		Ⓒ	Ⓒ		Ⓒ		Ⓒ	Ⓒ
Compute fluently and make reasonable estimates		Ⓒ	Ⓒ	Ⓒ	Ⓒ		Ⓒ	
Algebra								
Understand patterns, relations, and functions	Ⓕ	Ⓒ		Ⓕ	Ⓕ		Ⓕ	Ⓒ
Represent and analyze mathematical situations and structures using algebraic symbols	Ⓕ	Ⓕ	Ⓒ	Ⓕ	Ⓕ		Ⓕ	Ⓒ
Use mathematical models to represent and understand quantitative relationships	Ⓕ	Ⓕ	Ⓒ	Ⓕ	Ⓕ	Ⓒ	Ⓕ	Ⓕ
Analyze change in various contexts	Ⓕ	Ⓒ		Ⓕ	Ⓕ		Ⓒ	Ⓒ
Geometry								
Analyze characteristics and properties of two- and three-dimensional geometric shapes and develop mathematical arguments about geometric relationships			Ⓕ			Ⓕ	Ⓕ	
Specify locations and describe spatial relationships using coordinate geometry and other representational systems			Ⓕ			Ⓒ	Ⓕ	
Apply transformations and use symmetry to analyze mathematical situations			Ⓕ	Ⓒ			Ⓒ	
Use visualization, spatial reasoning, and geometric modeling to solve problems	Ⓒ		Ⓕ	Ⓒ		Ⓕ	Ⓕ	Ⓒ
Measurement								
Understand measurable attributes of objects and the units, systems, and processes of measurement			Ⓒ	Ⓒ			Ⓕ	
Apply appropriate techniques, tools, and formulas to determine measurements			Ⓒ	Ⓒ			Ⓕ	Ⓒ
Data Analysis and Probability								
Formulate questions that can be addressed with data and collect, organize, and display relevant data to answer them		Ⓒ		Ⓕ			Ⓒ	Ⓒ
Select and use appropriate statistical methods to analyze data				Ⓕ			Ⓒ	Ⓒ
Develop and evaluate inferences and predictions that are based on data				Ⓕ			Ⓒ	Ⓕ
Understand and apply basic concepts of probability				Ⓒ			Ⓒ	Ⓕ

Overview

Introduction

The first three courses in *Core-Plus Mathematics* provide a significant common core of broadly useful mathematics for all students. They were developed to prepare students for success in college, in careers, and in daily life in contemporary society. Course 4 continues the preparation of students for success in college mathematics and statistics courses. The program builds upon the theme of mathematics as sense-making. Through investigations of real-life contexts, students develop a rich understanding of important mathematics that makes sense to them and which, in turn, enables them to make sense out of new situations and problems.

Each course in *Core-Plus Mathematics* shares the following mathematical and instructional features.

- ## Integrated Content

  Each year, the curriculum advances students' understanding of mathematics along interwoven strands of algebra and functions, statistics and probability, geometry and trigonometry, and discrete mathematics. These strands are unified by fundamental themes, by common topics, and by mathematical habits of mind or ways of thinking. Developing mathematics each year along multiple strands helps students develop diverse mathematical insights and nurtures their differing strengths and talents.

- ## Mathematical Modeling

  The curriculum emphasizes mathematical modeling including the processes of data collection, representation, interpretation, prediction, and simulation. The modeling perspective permits students to experience mathematics as a means of making sense of data and problems that arise in diverse contexts within and across cultures.

- ## Access and Challenge

  The curriculum is designed to make mathematics accessible to more students, while at the same time challenging the most able students. Differences in students' performance and interest can be accommodated by the depth and level of abstraction to which core mathematics topics are pursued, by the nature and degree of difficulty of applications, and by providing opportunities for student choice of homework tasks and projects.

- ## Technology

  Numeric, graphic, and programming capabilities such as those found on many graphing calculators are assumed and appropriately used throughout the curriculum. The curriculum materials also include a suite of computer software called *CPMP-Tools* that provide powerful aids to learning mathematics and solving mathematical problems. (See pages xvii–xviii for further details.) This use of technology permits the curriculum and instruction to emphasize multiple representations (verbal, numerical, graphical, and symbolic) and to focus on goals in which mathematical thinking and problem solving are central.

- ## Active Learning

  Instructional materials promote active learning and teaching centered around collaborative investigations of problem situations followed by teacher-led whole-class summarizing activities that lead to analysis, abstraction, and further application of underlying mathematical ideas and principles. Students are actively engaged in exploring, conjecturing, verifying, generalizing, applying, proving, evaluating, and communicating mathematical ideas.

- ## Multi-dimensional Assessment

  Comprehensive assessment of student understanding and progress through both curriculum-embedded assessment opportunities and supplementary assessment tasks supports instruction and enables monitoring and evaluation of each student's performance in terms of mathematical processes, content, and dispositions.

Core-Plus Mathematics is designed to make mathematics accessible and more meaningful to more students. Developing mathematics along multiple strands nurtures the differing strengths and talents of students and simultaneously helps them to develop diverse mathematical insights. Developing mathematics from a modeling perspective permits students to experience mathematics as a means of making sense of data and problems that arise in diverse contexts within and across cultures. Engaging students in collaborating on tasks in small groups develops their ability to both deal with, and find commonality in, diversity of ideas. Using technology as a means for learning and doing mathematics enables students to develop versatile ways of dealing with realistic situations and reduces the manipulative skill filter which has prevented large numbers of students from continuing their study of significant mathematics. In addition, technology-produced graphics offer powerful new ways of visualizing mathematics across each of the strands.

Integrated Mathematics

Core-Plus Mathematics replaces the traditional Algebra-Geometry-Advanced Algebra/Trigonometry-Precalculus sequence of high school mathematics courses with a sequence of courses that features concurrent and connected development of important mathematics drawn from four strands.

Algebra and Functions

The Algebra and Functions strand develops student ability to recognize, represent, and solve problems involving relations among quantitative variables. Central to the development is the use of functions as mathematical models. The key algebraic models in the curriculum are linear, exponential, power, polynomial, logarithmic, rational, and trigonometric functions. Modeling with systems of equations, both linear and nonlinear, is developed. Attention is also given to symbolic reasoning and manipulation.

Geometry and Trigonometry

The primary goal of the Geometry and Trigonometry strand is to develop visual thinking and ability to construct, reason with, interpret, and apply mathematical models of patterns in visual and physical contexts. The focus is on describing

Overview

patterns in shape, size, and location; representing patterns with drawings, coordinates, or vectors; predicting changes and invariants in shapes under transformations; and organizing geometric facts and relationships through deductive reasoning.

Statistics and Probability

The primary goal of the Statistics and Probability strand is to develop student ability to analyze data intelligently, to recognize and measure variation, and to understand the patterns that underlie probabilistic situations. The ultimate goal is for students to understand how inferences can be made about a population by looking at a sample from that population. Graphical methods of data analysis, simulations, sampling, and experience with the collection and interpretation of real data are featured.

Discrete Mathematics

The Discrete Mathematics strand develops student ability to solve problems using vertex-edge graphs, recursion, matrices, systematic counting methods (combinatorics), and voting methods. Key themes are discrete mathematical modeling, optimization, and algorithmic problem-solving.

Connected Strands

Each of these four strands of mathematics is developed within focused units connected by fundamental ideas such as symmetry, matrices, functions, data analysis, and curve-fitting. The strands also are connected across units by mathematical habits of mind such as visual thinking, recursive thinking, searching for and explaining patterns, making and checking conjectures, reasoning with multiple representations, inventing mathematics, and providing convincing arguments and proofs.

The strands are unified further by the fundamental themes of data, representation, shape, and change. Important mathematical ideas are frequently revisited through this attention to connections within and across strands, enabling students to develop a robust and connected understanding of mathematics.

Organization of Course 2

Course 2 consists of eight units. Each of the units is comprised of two to four multi-day lessons in which major ideas are developed through investigation of rich applied problems. Units vary in length from approximately two to six weeks.

Unit 1 *Functions, Equations, and Systems*
Unit 2 *Matrix Methods*
Unit 3 *Coordinate Methods*
Unit 4 *Regression and Correlation*
Unit 5 *Nonlinear Functions and Equations*
Unit 6 *Network Optimization*
Unit 7 *Trigonometric Methods*
Unit 8 *Probability Distributions*

The 2nd Edition of Course 2 builds on the strengths of the 1st Edition. It includes mathematical content which the developers believed is the most important mathematics all ninth-grade students should have the opportunity to learn. In particular, the content of the last units in the text are not viewed as optional as is often the case with traditional textbooks. Depending on the mathematics standards and content expectations for your state, you may wish to have students complete all Course 1 units before they embark on Course 2 of the *Core-Plus Mathematics* series.

Instructional Model

The manner in which students encounter mathematical ideas can contribute significantly to the quality of their learning and the depth of their understanding. *Core-Plus Mathematics* units are designed around multi-day lessons centered on big ideas. Each lesson includes 2–4 focused mathematical investigations that engage students in a four-phase cycle of classroom activities, described in the following paragraph—*Launch, Explore, Share and Summarize,* and *Apply.* This cycle is designed to engage students in investigating and making sense of problem situations, in constructing important mathematical concepts and methods, in generalizing and proving mathematical relationships, and in communicating, both orally and in writing, their thinking and the results of their efforts. Most classroom activities are designed to be completed by students working collaboratively in groups of two to four students.

LAUNCH class discussion

Think About This Situation

The lesson launch promotes a teacher-led discussion of a problem situation and of related questions to think about. This discussion sets the context for the student work to follow and helps to generate student interest. It also provides an opportunity for the teacher to assess student knowledge and to clarify directions for the investigation to follow.

EXPLORE group investigation

Investigation

Classroom activity then shifts to investigating focused problems and questions related to the launching situation by gathering data, looking for and explaining patterns, constructing models and meanings, and making and verifying conjectures. As students collaborate in pairs or small groups, the teacher circulates among students providing guidance and support, clarifying or asking questions, giving hints, providing encouragement, and drawing group members into the discussion to help groups collaborate more effectively. The investigations and related questions posed by students and teachers drive the learning.

SHARE AND SUMMARIZE class discussion

Summarize the Mathematics

This investigative work is followed by a teacher-led class discussion (referred to as Summarize the Mathematics) in which students summarize mathematical ideas developed in their groups, providing an opportunity to construct a shared understanding of important concepts, methods, and approaches. This discussion leads to a class summary of important ideas or to further exploration of a topic if competing perspectives remain. Varying points of view and differing conclusions that can be justified should be encouraged.

APPLY individual tasks

Check Your Understanding

Students are given a task to complete on their own to check and reinforce their initial understanding of concepts and methods.

Overview

Homework

In addition to the classroom investigations, *Core-Plus Mathematics* provides sets of On Your Own tasks, which are designed to engage students in applying, connecting, reflecting on, extending, and reviewing their evolving mathematical knowledge. On Your Own tasks are provided for each lesson in the materials and are central to the learning goals of each lesson. These tasks are intended primarily for individual work outside of class. Selection of homework tasks should be based on student performance and the availability of time and technology. Also, students should exercise some choice of tasks to pursue, and at times, should be given the opportunity to pose their own problems and questions to investigate. The chart below describes the types of tasks in a typical On Your Own set.

On Your Own: Homework Tasks	
Applications	These tasks provide opportunities for students to use and strengthen their understanding of the ideas they have learned in the lesson.
Connections	These tasks help students to build links between mathematical topics they have studied in the lesson and to connect those topics with other mathematics that they know.
Reflections	These tasks provide opportunities for students to re-examine their thinking about ideas in the lesson.
Extensions	These tasks provide opportunities for students to explore further or more deeply the mathematics they are learning.
Review	These tasks provide opportunities for just-in-time review and distributed practice of mathematical skills to maintain procedural fluency.

Additional Summarizing Activities

In *Core-Plus Mathematics*, students learn mathematics by doing mathematics. However, it is important that students prepare and maintain summaries of important concepts and methods that are developed. Students should create a Math Toolkit that organizes important class-generated ideas and selected Summarize the Mathematics responses as they complete investigations. Math Toolkit Prompts are provided in this *Teacher's Guide* to assist in identifying and summarizing key concepts and methods as they are developed by students.

In addition, the final lesson in each unit is a Looking Back lesson that helps students review and synthesize the key mathematical concepts and techniques developed in the unit. The Summarize the Mathematics questions in this lesson are focused on key ideas of the unit. The Check Your Understanding asks students to prepare a summary of the important concepts and skills developed in the unit. Templates to guide preparation of these unit summaries can be found in the *Unit Resource Masters*. Completed Unit Summaries should become part of students' Math Toolkits.

Students should retain their Math Toolkits as they continue on to Courses 3 and 4. In some districts, teachers collect these resources at the end of the school year and return them to students in the fall.

Multiple Approaches to Assessment

Assessing what students know and are able to do is an integral part of *Core-Plus Mathematics*. There are opportunities for assessment in each phase of the instructional cycle. Initially, as students pursue the investigations that comprise the curriculum, the teacher is able to informally assess student understanding of mathematical processes and content and their disposition toward mathematics. At the end of each investigation, a class discussion to Summarize the Mathematics provides an opportunity for the teacher to assess levels of understanding that various groups of students have reached as they share and explain their findings. Finally, the Check Your Understanding tasks and the tasks in the On Your Own sets provide further opportunities to assess the level of understanding of each individual student. Quizzes, in-class tests, take-home assessment tasks, and extended projects are included in the teacher resource materials.

A more detailed description of the complete assessment program is given on pages xxi–xv of this text and in *Implementing Core-Plus Mathematics*.

Practicing for Standardized Tests

Opportunities for additional review and practice are provided in eight Preparing for Standardized Tests practice sets included in the *Unit Resource Masters*. Each Practicing for Standardized Tests master presents 10 questions and a test-taking tip. The questions are presented in the form of test items similar to how they often appear in standardized tests such as state assessments tests, the Preliminary Scholastic Aptitude Test (PSAT), or the ACT PLAN. By using these practice sets, students can become familiar with the formats of standardized tests and develop effective test-taking strategies for performing well on such tests.

Access, Equity, and Differentiation

Several research studies have provided evidence that introducing activities through class discussion, teaching students to explain and justify, and making real-world contexts accessible to students promote greater access and equity in mathematics classrooms. (Boaler, J. "Learning from Teaching: Exploring the Relationship Between Reform Curriculum and Equity," *Journal for Research in Mathematics Education*, 2002, Vol. 33, No. 4, 239–258, and Brown, C.A., Stein, M.K., and Forman, E. A. "Assisting teachers and students to reform their mathematics classroom," *Education Studies in Mathematics*, 1996, 31–93). These practices that help promote equity are briefly discussed below.

Introducing Activities Through Class Discussions Group and class discussions of the aim of activities, the meaning of contexts, the challenging points within problems, and possible problem access points to which students might turn make tasks more evenly accessible to all students.

Teaching Students to Explain and Justify their Thinking Giving explicit attention to explaining thinking and evaluating what makes a good piece of work helps students improve their work.

Making Real-world Contexts Accessible Considering the constraints that real situations involve and connecting these situations with issues and topics in their own lives helps students view mathematics as something that will help them interpret their world.

Other Practices that Promote Equity Mixed-ability classes, a focus on problems solving, high expectations for all students, attention to a broad array of mathematical topics, and allowing students to restate problems in their own words also appear to help students from different racial, ethnic, and linguistic groups be more successful in mathematics.

Overview

Core-Plus Mathematics offers many opportunities for teachers to incorporate these practices into daily routines. One such built-in opportunity is the Think About This Situation (TATS) used to introduce lessons through discussions. Although no TATS questions are in the student text for individual investigations, there are often suggestions in the *Teacher's Guide* for class launches of investigations. Since much of the mathematical content is based on real contexts, it is important that all students understand the contexts and draw on their own or a classmate's background knowledge. Opportunities for students to explain and justify their thinking are built into all curriculum features. Look for opportunities to encourage the habit of mind of justifying one's thinking as students work individually and participate in small-group or class discussions.

The *Teacher's Guide* periodically includes notes that provide specific ideas for differentiation at point of use. Look for the margin notes.

Implementing the Curriculum

Considering mathematics topics and knowledge presented at each grade level and how that knowledge is built upon in succeeding grades is key to improving student learning. To support building the teacher expertise to effectively implement *Core-Plus Mathematics*, the developers recommend that districts begin adoption with Course 1 and add a course level each year. Encourage teachers to progress from Course 1 to Course 4 in stages so they can develop an understanding of the growth of mathematical ideas in the curriculum. Realize that teachers will need time and support to improve instruction for their students.

Additional advice related to successful implementation is on the Core-Plus Mathematics Project (CPMP) Web site at www.wmich.edu/cpmp under Implementation.

Planning for Instruction

The *Core-Plus Mathematics* curriculum is not only changing what mathematics all students have the opportunity to learn but is also changing how that learning occurs and is assessed. Active learning is most effective when accompanied with active teaching. Just as the student text is designed to actively engage students in doing mathematics, the teacher's resource materials are designed to support teachers in planning for instruction: in observing, listening, questioning, and facilitating student work; in orchestrating classroom discussion; and in managing the classroom.

The *Teacher's Guide* provides suggestions, based on the experiences of field-test teachers, for implementing this exciting new curriculum in your classroom. You probably will find new ideas that can at first be overwhelming. The developers highly recommend that teachers who are teaching *Core-Plus Mathematics* for the first time do so at least in pairs who share a common planning period.

Each of the items listed below is included in the *Teacher's Guide* for each unit.
- Unit Overview
- Objectives, suggested timeline, and materials needed
- Instructional notes and suggestions
- Suggested assignments for each homework set
- Solutions for investigations and homework tasks

Overview

Each *Unit Resource Masters* includes reproducible masters for teaching, student activities, technology tips, a unit summary, and practicing for standardized tests. Also included in each *Unit Resource Masters* is the assessment package for the unit as outlined on pages xxi–xxiv.

A first step toward planning the teaching of a unit is to review the scope and sequence of the unit. This review provides an overall feel for the goals and coherence of the unit. The *Scope and Sequence* guide shows where specific mathematical topics fit in the complete four-year curriculum. Working through the student investigations, if possible with a colleague, provides help in thinking about possible student responses and understanding mathematical ideas that may be unfamiliar.

In the *Teacher's Guide*, at the beginning of each unit, you will find a Planning Guide to assist in overall planning. This resource gives a quick overview of lessons, suggested assignments, materials needed, and pacing suggestions.

You will also find teaching notes for each lesson, including instructional suggestions and sample student responses to investigations and homework sets. Thinking about the range of possible responses and solutions to problems proves to be very helpful in facilitating student work.

Some teachers choose to post the homework assignment at the beginning of a lesson along with the due date—usually a day or two following planned completion of the lesson. Other teachers prefer to assign particular tasks at appropriate points during the course of the multiday investigation and then assign the remaining tasks toward the end of the lesson. Review tasks can be assigned before the completion of the investigation. Note that all recommended assignments include provision for student choice of some tasks. This is but one of many ways in which this curriculum is designed to accommodate and support differences in students' interests and performance levels.

It is strongly recommended that student solutions to Connections tasks be discussed in class. These tasks help students organize and formalize the mathematics developed in context and connect it to other mathematics they have studied. Structuring the underlying mathematics and building connections are best accomplished by comparing and discussing student work and synthesizing key ideas within the classroom.

Some recommended assignments include Just-in-Time Review tasks. It is important that these tasks be assigned as indicated in the Planning Guide to help ensure understanding of ideas or procedures needed in the next investigation.

Technology in Course 2

In the 21st century, anyone who faces the challenge of learning mathematics or using mathematics to solve problems can draw on the resources of powerful information technology tools. Calculators and computers can help with calculations, drawing, and data analysis in mathematical explorations and solving mathematical problems.

Graphing Calculators: Graphing calculators with iteration capabilities are assumed for class work and homework. Computer algebra system (CAS) capabilities are desirable.

Overview

Computers: Periodically, it would be valuable to have one classroom computer for whole class discussions, 4–6 classroom computers for groups to use as stations during investigations, portable classroom sets of computers, or computer lab access. For some homework tasks, school or home computer availability is also desirable.

Computer software: The use of spreadsheet, interactive geometry, data analysis, and vertex-edge graph software, and computer algebra systems (CAS) is incorporated into Course 2 units. The curriculum materials include computer software called *CPMP-Tools* specifically designed to support student learning and problem solving.

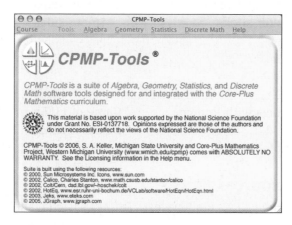

The software toolkit includes four families of programs:

Algebra The software for work on algebra problems includes an electronic spreadsheet and a computer algebra system (CAS) that produces tables and graphs of functions, manipulates algebraic expressions, and solves equations and inequalities.

Geometry The software for work on geometry problems includes an interactive drawing program for constructing, measuring, and manipulating geometric figures and a set of custom tools for studying computer animation and geometric models of physical mechanisms.

Statistics The software for work on data analysis and probability problems provides tools for graphic display and analysis of data, simulation of probabilistic situations, and mathematical modeling of quantitative relationships.

Discrete Mathematics The software for work on graph theory problems provides tools for constructing, manipulating, and analyzing vertex-edge graphs.

In addition to the general purpose tools provided for work on tasks in each strand of *Core-Plus Mathematics*, *CPMP-Tools* includes files that provide electronic copies of most data sets essential for work on problems in each *Core-Plus Mathematics* course. When students see an opportunity to use computer tools for work on a particular investigation, they can select the *CPMP-Tools* menu corresponding to the content involved in the problem. Then they can select the sub-menu items corresponding to the required mathematical operations and data sets. Each unit overview in the Teacher's Guide provides general information related to *CPMP-Tools* use in the unit. Technology notes at point of use alert teachers to applicable software and specific data sets included in the software.

Materials Needed for Course 2

The following is a complete list of items used in the eight units of Course 2. Each unit Planning Guide indicates the items used in that unit.

Necessary

Balls	Stop watches
Ramp materials	Graph poster paper
Tape measures	Spaghetti
Protractors	Colored pencils
Rulers, centimeter and inches	Linkage strips that allow 12-cm and
Yardsticks or meter sticks	16-cm sides
Dice	

Optional:

Household products with known pH levels	Game of LIFE®
Game of Monopoly®	Decks of cards

Electronic Resources

The *Core-Plus Mathematics* student text, *Teacher's Guide,* and *Unit Resource Masters* are included for viewing and printing from the *Core-Plus Mathematics TeacherWorks Plus* CD-ROM. Custom tailoring of assessment items can be accomplished by using the *ExamView* Assessment Suites. *CPMP-Tools* is available on both the *StudentWorks* and *TeacherWorks Plus* CD-ROMs.

Orchestrating Lessons

Core-Plus Mathematics is designed to engage students in a four-phase cycle of classroom activities. The activities in Course 2, as in Course 1, often require both students and teachers to assume roles quite different than those in more traditional mathematics classrooms. Students successfully completing Course 1 should have become accustomed to these new roles. Although realistic problem solving and investigative work by students are the heart of the curriculum, how teachers orchestrate the launching of an investigation and the sharing and summarizing of results is critical to successful implementation.

Students enter the classroom with differing strengths, experience, and knowledge. These differences can be viewed as assets. Engaging the class in a free-flowing give-and-take discussion of how students think about the launch situations serves to connect lessons with the informal understandings of data, shape, change, and chance that students bring to the classroom. Try to maximize the participation of students in these discussions by emphasizing that their ideas and possible approaches are valued and important and that definitive answers are not necessarily expected at this time.

Overview

Once launched, an investigation may involve students working together collaboratively in small groups for a period of days punctuated occasionally by brief class discussion of questions students have raised. In this setting, the investigation becomes driven primarily by the instructional materials themselves. Rather than orchestrating class discussion, the teacher shifts to circulating among the groups and observing, listening, and interacting with students by asking guiding or probing questions. These small-group investigations lead to (re)invention of important mathematics that make sense to students. Sharing and agreeing as a class on the mathematical ideas that groups are developing is the purpose of the Summarizing the Mathematics (STM) in the instructional materials.

Class discussions at STMs are orchestrated somewhat differently than during the launch of a lesson. At this stage, mathematical ideas and methods still may be under development and may vary for individual groups. So, class discussion should involve groups comparing their methods and results, analyzing their work, and arriving at conclusions agreed upon by the class.

Periodically, you will find samples of class discussions centered around Think About This Situation or Summarize the Mathematics questions at point of use. These sample discussions, called Promoting Mathematical Discourse, may provide some ideas for your class discussions. These sample discussions are indicated by PROMOTING MATHEMATICAL DISCOURSE .

Assessment

Throughout the *Core-Plus Mathematics* curriculum, the term "assessment" is meant to include all instances of gathering information about students' levels of understanding and their disposition toward mathematics for purposes of making decisions about instruction. You may want to consult the extended section on assessment in *Implementing Core-Plus Mathematics*.

The dimensions of student performance that are assessed in this curriculum (see chart below) are consistent with the assessment recommendations of the National Council of Teachers of Mathematics in the *Assessment Standards for School Mathematics* (NCTM, 1995). They are more comprehensive than those of a typical testing program.

Assessment Dimensions		
Process	**Content**	**Disposition**
Problem Solving	Concepts	Beliefs
Reasoning	Applications	Perseverance
Communication	Mathematical Representation	Confidence
Connections	Procedures	Enthusiasm

Sources of Assessment Information

Several kinds of assessment are available to teachers using *Core-Plus Mathematics*. Some of these sources reside within the student text itself, some of them are student-generated, and some are materials designed specifically for assessment. Understanding the nature of these sources is a prerequisite for selecting assessment tools, establishing guidelines on how to score assessments, making judgments about what students know and are able to do, and assigning grades.

Curriculum Sources

Two features of the curriculum, questioning and observation by the teacher, provide fundamental and particularly useful ways of gathering formative assessment information. The student text uses questions to facilitate student understanding of new concepts, of how these concepts fit with earlier ideas and with one another, and of how they can be applied in problem situations. Whether students are working individually or in groups, the teacher is given a window to watch how the students think about and apply mathematics as they attempt to answer the questions posed in the curriculum materials. In fact, by observing how students respond to the curriculum-embedded questions, the teacher can assess student performance across all process, content, and attitude dimensions described in the chart on page xxi.

Specific features in the student material that focus on different ways students respond to questions are the Summarize the Mathematics, Check Your Understanding, and the On Your Own homework sets. Summarize the Mathematics features are intended to bring students together, usually after they have been working in small groups, so they may share and discuss the progress each group has made during a sequence of related activities. The questions in the Summarize the Mathematics are focused on the mathematical concepts and procedures developed in the investigation. They should help the teacher and the students identify and formalize the key ideas of the investigation. Each Summarize the Mathematics is intended to be treated as a whole-class discussion, so it should provide an opportunity for teachers to assess, informally, the levels of understanding that the various groups of students have reached.

Following each Summarize the Mathematics, the Check Your Understanding tasks are meant to be completed by students working individually. Student responses to these tasks provide an opportunity for teachers to assess the level of understanding of each student.

The tasks in the On Your Own homework sets serve many purposes, including post-investigation assessment. Each type of task in the On Your Own homework sets has a different instructional purpose. Applications tasks provide opportunities for students to demonstrate how well they understand and can use the ideas they learned in the investigations of the lesson. Work on Connections tasks demonstrates how well the students understand links between mathematical topics they studied in the lesson and their ability to connect those topics with other mathematics that they know. Reflections tasks provide insight into students' mathematical thinking and strategic competence. Extensions tasks reveal how well students are able to extend the present content beyond the level addressed in the investigations. The Review tasks allow for pre-assessment of students' understanding of ideas or procedures needed in the upcoming lessons and also provide information on how well students are retaining previously learned mathematics. The performance of students or groups of students on each of these types of tasks provides the teacher with further information to help assess each student's evolving ability to use, connect, and extend the mathematics of the lesson.

Finally, an opportunity for group self-assessment is provided in the last element of each unit, the Looking Back lesson. These tasks help students pull together and demonstrate what they have learned in the unit and at the same time provide helpful review and confidence-building for students.

Student-Generated Sources

Mathematics Toolkits Students should create a Math Toolkit that organizes important class-generated ideas and selected Summarize the Mathematics responses as they complete investigations. Constructing a Math Toolkit prompts are provided in the *Teacher's Guide* to assist in identifying key concepts and methods as they are developed by students.

Unit Summaries A summary template intended to help students organize and record the main ideas learned in the unit is provided in each *Unit Resource Masters*. The synthesis of ideas that occurs during completion of the "Looking Back" lesson and the final unit Summarize the Mathematics discussion should provide the background for student completion of the unit summary.

Assessment Resources

Each *Unit Resource Masters* includes lesson quizzes and unit assessments in the form of tests, take-home tasks, and projects. There are also banks of questions and projects from which you can form end of semester exams following the Unit 4 and Unit 8 assessment masters. Calculators are assumed in most cases and are intended to be available to students. Teacher discretion should be used regarding student access to their textbook and Math Toolkit for assessments. In general, if the goals to be assessed are problem solving and reasoning, while memory of facts and procedural skill are of less interest, resources may be allowed. However, if automaticity of procedures or unaided recall are being assessed, it is appropriate to prohibit resource materials.

The *ExamView* software can be used to modify the curriculum provided assessment items or to create formal assessments using a combination of curriculum supplied items and ones by the teacher.

Lesson Quizzes Two forms of a quiz covering the main ideas of each lesson are provided. These quizzes are comprised of problems meant to determine if students have developed understanding of the important concepts and procedures of each lesson. The two forms of each quiz are not necessarily equivalent, although they assess essentially the same mathematical ideas. Since many rich opportunities for assessing students are embedded in the curriculum itself, you may choose not to use a quiz at the end of every lesson.

Overview

Unit Tests Two forms of tests are provided for each unit and are intended to be completed in a 50-minute class period. The two forms of each test are not necessarily equivalent, although they assess essentially the same mathematical ideas. Teachers should preview the two versions carefully to be sure that the unit assessment aligns with the learning goals emphasized.

Take-Home Assessments Take-home assessment tasks are included for each unit. The students or the teacher should choose one or, at most, two of these tasks. These assessments, some of which are best done by students working in pairs or small groups, provide students with the opportunity to organize the information from the completed unit, to work with another student or group of students, to engage in in-depth problem solving, to grapple with new and more complex situations related to the mathematics of the unit, and to avoid the time pressure often generated by in-class exams. These problems may also require more extensive use of technology than is often available in the regular classroom during testing situations. You may wish to use these more in-depth problems as a replacement for a portion of an in-class end-of-unit exam.

Projects Assessment has traditionally been based on evaluating work that students have completed in a very short time period and under restricted conditions. Some assessment, however, should involve work done over a longer time period and with the aid of resources. Thus, assessment projects are included in unit assessments. These projects, which are intended to be completed by small groups of students, provide an opportunity for students to conduct an investigation that extends and applies the main ideas from the unit and to write a summary of their findings. Many of these might also allow for students to present their work in a variety of ways. You may have students who would rather prepare and present their work orally or visually using computers and/or video equipment. In this way, the projects can provide an opportunity for students to use their creativity while demonstrating their understanding of mathematics.

Midterm and Final Assessments A bank of assessment tasks from which to construct midterm and final exams that fit your particular class needs and emphases are provided in the Unit 4 and Unit 8 *Unit Resource Masters*. In addition to problems similar in form to those on the quizzes and tests, these assessment banks include several multiple-choice problems for each unit.

Extended assessment projects are also included with the end-of-year assessments. These projects are investigations that make use of many of the main ideas encountered in the curriculum. They require use of material from more than one unit. The projects are intended to be completed by small groups of students working over a period of time. You may wish to have different groups work on different projects and then give presentations or create posters of their work.

Portfolios The *Core-Plus Mathematics* assessment program provides many tasks that can be placed in students' portfolios, including reports of individual and group projects, Math Toolkits, teacher-completed observation checklists, unit assessments (especially the take-home tasks), and projects. See *Implementing Core-Plus Mathematics* for additional portfolio information.

Overview

Scoring Assessments

High expectations of the quality of students' written work will encourage students to reach their potential. Assigning scores to open-ended assessments and to observations of students' performance requires more subjective judgment by the teacher than does grading short-answer or multiple-choice tests. It is therefore not possible to provide a complete set of explicit guidelines for scoring open-ended assessment items and written or oral reports. However, some general guidelines may be helpful. When scoring student work on open-ended assessment tasks, the goal is to reward, in a fair and consistent way, the kinds of thinking and understanding that the task is meant to measure. To score open-ended assessment tasks, teachers should have a general rubric, or scoring scheme, with several response levels in mind; a specific rubric and anchor items. (See *Implementing Core-Plus Mathematics* for more details.) The general rubric is the foundation for scoring across a wide range of types of open-ended tasks. The following general rubric can be used for most assessment tasks provided with *Core-Plus Mathematics*.

General Scoring Rubric	
4 points	Contains complete response with clear, coherent, and unambiguous explanation; includes clear and simple diagram, if appropriate; communicates effectively to identified audience; shows understanding of question's mathematical ideas and processes; identifies all important elements of question; includes examples and counterexamples; gives strong supporting arguments
3 points	Contains good solid response with some, but not all, of the characteristics above; explains less completely; may include minor error of execution but not of understanding
2 points	Contains complete response, but explanation is muddled; presents incomplete arguments; includes diagrams that are inappropriate or unclear, or fails to provide a diagram when it would be appropriate; indicates some understanding of mathematical ideas, but in an unclear way; shows clear evidence of understanding some important ideas while also making one or more fundamental, specific errors
1 point	Omits parts of question and response; has major errors; uses inappropriate strategies
0 points	No response; frivolous or irrelevant response

Assigning Grades

Since the *Core-Plus Mathematics* approach and materials provide a wide variety of assessment information, the teacher will be in a good position to assign appropriate grades. With such a wide choice for assessment, a word of caution is appropriate. *It is easy to overassess students.* The developers believe it is best to vary assessment methods from lesson to lesson, and from unit to unit. If information on what students understand and are able to do is available from their homework and in-class work, it may not be necessary to take the time for a formal quiz after each lesson. Similarly, information from take-home assessments or project work may replace all or portions of an in-class test.

Deciding exactly how to weigh the various kinds of assessment information is a decision that the teacher will need to make and communicate clearly to students.

Managing Classroom Activities

Active Learning and Collaborative Work

The *Core-Plus Mathematics* curriculum materials are designed to promote active, collaborative learning and group work for two important reasons. First, a collaborative environment fosters students' ability to make sense of mathematics and develop deep mathematical understandings. Collaborative learning is an effective method for engaging all the students in the learning process, particularly students who have been under represented in mathematics classes. Second, practice in collaborative learning in the classroom is practice for real life: students develop and exercise the same skills in the classroom that they need in their lives at home, in the community, and in the workplace.

Value of Individuals

Perhaps the most fundamental belief underlying the use of collaborative learning is that every student is viewed as a valuable resource and contributor. In other words, every student participates in group work and is given the opportunity and time to voice ideas and opinions. Implementing this concept is not easy nor does it happen automatically. In order to set a tone that will promote respect for individuals and their contributions, classroom norms should be established. Teachers should initiate a discussion and together write all the student formulated classroom rules for both individual and group behavior. The positively stated rules of behavior should be posted in the classroom and every member of the learning community should be held responsible for adhering to them.

Importance of Social Connections

Even in classrooms in which the rules for showing respect have been clearly established, experience has shown that students still cannot talk with one another about mathematics (or social studies, or literature, or any other subject) if they do not first have positive social connections.

One way to develop this kind of common base is through team-building activities. These short activities may be used at the beginning of the year to help students get acquainted with the whole class, and may be used during the year whenever new groups are formed to help groupmates know one another better. Team-building activities help students learn new and positive things about classmates with whom they may have attended classes for years, but have not known in depth. The time taken for these quick team builders pays off later in helping students feel comfortable enough to work with the members of their group.

Need for Teaching Social Skills

Experience also has shown that social skills are critical to the successful functioning of any small group. Because there is no guarantee that students of any particular age will have the social skills necessary for effective group work, it often is necessary to teach these skills to build a collaborative learning environment.

These social skills are specific skills, not general goals. Examples of specific social skills that the teacher can teach in the classroom include responding to ideas respectfully, keeping track of time, disagreeing in an agreeable way, involving everyone, and following directions. Though goals such as cooperating and listening are important, they are too general to teach.

One of the premises of collaborative learning is that by developing the appropriate skills through practice, anyone in the class can learn to work in a group with anyone else. Learning to work in groups is a continuous process, however, and the process can be helped by decisions that the teacher makes.

One method of teaching social skills is to begin by selecting a specific skill and then having the class brainstorm to develop a script for practicing that skill. Next, the students practice that skill during their group work. Finally, in what is called the processing, the students discuss within their groups how well they performed the assigned social skill. Effective teaching of social skills requires practicing and processing; merely describing a specific social skill is not enough. The *Teacher's Guide* includes specific collaborative skills to practice and processing prompts for student self-assessment.

The culture and teaching-learning norms created within the classroom are crucial to the success of this curriculum. It is important to inculcate in students a sense of inquiry and responsibility for their own learning. Without this commitment, active, collaborative learning by students cannot be effective. Some students seem satisfied with the rationale that collaboration is important in workplace. Others may need to understand that the struggle of verbalizing their thinking, listening to others' thinking, questioning themselves and other group members, and coming to an agreement increases their understanding and retention of the mathematics while contributing to the formation of important thinking skills or habits of mind.

Issues of helping students to work collaboratively will become less pressing as both you and your students experience this type of learning. *Implementing Core-Plus Mathematics* provides additional information related to the challenge of facilitating collaborative work including support to help teachers make decisions about group size, composition, method of selection, the duration of groups and dealing with student absences. This resource also offers a number of practical suggestions from *Core-Plus Mathematics* teachers on effectively pacing instruction in a student-centered classroom.

Additional Resources

Implementing Core-Plus Mathematics contains expanded information on:
- the scope and sequence of Courses 1–4,
- managing classroom activities,
- differentiation built into the program,
- the assessment program,
- communication with parents, and
- mathematics program evaluation.

You will find it useful to have the implementation guide available for reference throughout the school year.

Math Link articles related to *Core-Plus Mathematics* written by developers and teachers are available on the *Core-Plus Mathematics* Project Web site at www.wmich.edu/cpmp under Publications. These articles were written based on first edition experiences, but in many cases are still applicable to the second edition materials.

Overview

Topics include:
- selecting and implementing *Core-Plus Mathematics*,
- effectively using collaborative groups,
- the four-year mathematics program,
- options for acceleration paths to AP Calculus or AP Statistics,
- meeting the needs of ELL and LEP students,
- college placement,
- the International Baccalaureate Program, and
- achievement in Science.

Annotated Bibliography Available on the CPMP Web site under Publications are references to articles, book chapters, dissertations, papers presented at conferences, and field-test reports based on the program. Some of these resources can be downloaded.

Professional Development Opportunities A variety of professional development opportunities are provided by Glencoe and the Core-Plus Mathematics Project. Workshops are listed on the CPMP Web site www.wmich.edu/cpmp under Implementation. Experienced *Core-Plus Mathematics* teacher-consultants can be contracted to provide onsite inservice. Contact your Glencoe sales representative or the CPMP office (cpmp@wmich.edu) for provider names.

Parent Support Information and resources for parents including helping with homework, research supporting *Core-Plus Mathematics*, evidence of success, and frequently asked questions is available at www.wmich.edu/cpmp/parentresource/index.html.

UNIT 5

NONLINEAR FUNCTIONS AND EQUATIONS

In earlier *Core-Plus Mathematics* units, you studied nonlinear functions that are useful in solving problems related to projectile motion, exponential growth and decay, and profit of business ventures. In this unit, you will extend your ability to use quadratic functions to solve scientific, technical, and business problems that involve algebraic systems comprised of linear and nonlinear functions. You will also develop understanding of logarithms—another important tool for modeling nonlinear patterns and for solving problems related to exponential functions.

Key ideas will be developed through your work on problems in three lessons.

Lessons

1 Quadratic Functions, Expressions, and Equations

Use function notation to express relationships between variables. Use the connection between quadratic functions and graphs to solve design problems. Extend understanding and skill in expanding and factoring quadratic expressions and solving quadratic equations.

2 Nonlinear Systems of Equations

Develop numeric, graphic, and symbolic reasoning strategies for solving systems of equations that locate intersections of linear and inverse variation function graphs and intersections of linear and quadratic function graphs.

3 Common Logarithms and Exponential Functions

Use common logarithms to represent patterns of change in quantities, like sound intensity and pH of liquids, and to solve equations that involve exponential functions.

NONLINEAR FUNCTIONS AND EQUATIONS

Unit Overview

This is the second unit whose primary focus is quadratic functions and equations. The Course 1 unit *Quadratic Functions* was intended to help students begin to develop a clear and connected understanding of the numeric, graphic, verbal, and symbolic representations of quadratic functions and the ways that those representations can be applied to quantitative problems and patterns in data. Students should bring an intuitive understanding of quadratic patterns of change and some technical skills for reasoning with the various representations of those patterns to this unit.

Students will review and practice previously learned concepts and skills related to quadratic functions and equations, as well as expand their symbol manipulation skills to more sophisticated problems both in and out of context, through two lessons in this unit.

The first lesson reviews and extends students' skills in constructing quadratic function rules to match a graph or stated conditions, expanding and factoring quadratic expressions, and solving quadratic equations algebraically. Lesson 2 develops numeric, graphic, and algebraic strategies for solving (quadratic) equations and inequalities that arise out of problems involving comparisons between a linear and either an inverse variation or quadratic function. Lesson 3 introduces the idea of logarithm from an algebraic viewpoint. Base 10 (common) logarithms are used as a tool in solving exponential equations. Only common logarithms are developed here; logarithms with other bases will be developed in *Core-Plus Mathematics* Courses 3 and 4. The final lesson takes a look back and reviews the key concepts and skills of the unit.

Further work toward developing proficiency with manipulating symbols and transforming function representation occurs in subsequent units and courses. Additional practice for the skills developed in this unit is incorporated in Review tasks of the On Your Own homework sets of later units.

Unit Objectives

- Generalize the definition of function and introduce "$f(x)$" notation for functions and the concepts of domain and range
- Construct rules for quadratic functions based on given properties such as x-intercepts, y-intercept, and maximum/minimum point
- Write quadratic expressions in equivalent expanded or factored form
- Solve quadratic equations by factoring, by applying the quadratic formula, and by a CAS
- Write and solve equations that represent questions about "real-life" situations involving comparison of a linear function and either an inverse variation or quadratic function
- Estimate solutions to equations in the form $ax + b = \dfrac{k}{x}$ by using tables or graphs and solve those kinds of equations algebraically
- Estimate solutions to equations in the form $mx + d = ax^2 + bx + c$ using tables or graphs and solve those equations algebraically
- Use common logarithms to "linearize" exponential patterns of growth that occur in measurement of sound intensity, acidity (or alkalinity) of liquids, and earthquake intensity
- Use logarithms to solve exponential equations

Unit 5

Lesson Objectives	On Your Own Assignments*	Suggested Pacing	Materials
Lesson 1 *Quadratic Functions, Expressions, and Equations* • Distinguish relationships between variables that are functions from those that are not • Use $f(x)$ notation to represent functions and the common questions about functions that arise in applied problems • Identify domain and range of functions • Construct rules for quadratic functions based on given properties such as x-intercepts, y-intercept, and maximum/minimum point • Write quadratic expressions in equivalent expanded or factored form • Solve quadratic equations by factoring, by applying the quadratic formula, or by a CAS	**After Investigation 1:** A1–A3, A4 or A5, A6, C16, C17, choose one of R25–R27, E34 or E35 **After Investigation 2:** A7–A10, C17, R28, R29, Rv43–Rv47 **After Investigation 3:** A11, A12, choose three of C18–C23, R30, E36 or E37, E38, Rv48–Rv50 **After Investigation 4:** A13–A15, C24, choose two of R31–R33, choose one of E39–E42, Rv51, Rv52	10 days (including assessment)	• Computer software or calculators with CAS capatability such as the *CPMP-Tools* algebra software • Unit Resources
Lesson 2 *Nonlinear Systems of Equations* • Write an equation or inequality to represent a question about a "real-life" situation involving a comparison between a linear function and either an inverse variation or quadratic function • Estimate solutions to equations in the form $ax + b = \frac{k}{x}$ using tables or graphs and solve algebraically • Estimate solutions to equations in the form $mx + d = ax^2 + bx + c$ using tables or graphs and solve algebraically	**After Investigation 1:** A1–A4, R15, R16, E19, Rv25–Rv28 **After Investigation 2:** A5 or A6, A7, A8, choose two of C11–C14, R17, R18, choose two of E20–E24, Rv29	6 days (including assessment)	• Computer software or calculators with CAS capatability such as the *CPMP-Tools* algebra software • Unit Resources
Lesson 3 *Common Logarithms and Exponential Equations* • Recognize what is meant by "taking the common logarithm" of a real number • Be able to rewrite any real number as a power of 10 by finding common logarithms • Use common logarithms to solve exponential equations, both in and out of context	**After Investigation 1:** A1–A4, C12, R16, R17, E20 or E21, Rv28–Rv30 **After Investigation 2:** A5, choose two of A6–A11, C13–C15, R18, R19, choose two of E22–E27, Rv31–Rv34	5 days (including assessment)	• Computer software or calculators with CAS capatability such as the *CPMP-Tools* algebra software • *Optional:* Household products with known pH levels • Unit Resources
Lesson 4 *Looking Back* • Review and synthesize the major objectives of the unit		3 days (including assessment)	• Unit Resources

* When choice is indicated, it is important to leave the choice to the student.

Note: It is best if Connections and Reflections tasks are discussed as a whole class after they have been assigned as homework.

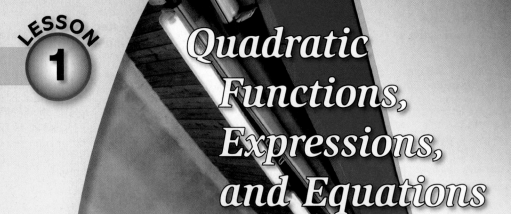

LESSON
1

Quadratic Functions, Expressions, and Equations

Luge is a winter sports event in which competitors slide down an ice-covered course at speeds of up to 70 mph, lying on their backs on a small sled. Luge races are timed to the thousandth of a second, reflecting the narrow margin between victory and defeat.

Along with the skill of the athletes, gravity is the major factor affecting the time of each run. Theory about the effects of gravity on falling objects (ignoring friction) predicts the following run times for a 1,000-meter run, straight downhill.

Vertical Drop (in meters)	Run Time (in seconds)
10	143
20	101
30	82
40	71
50	64
60	58
70	54
80	51
90	48
100	45

Quadratic Functions, Expressions, and Equations

As a result of work in Course 1 or prior study of algebra, students should have some familiarity with both the symbolic form and graphical structure of a quadratic function. In this lesson, students will begin to "dissect" quadratic functions by getting more comfortable with the expanding and factoring of quadratic expressions. Later in the lesson, students will use these skills to solve quadratic equations in the forms $ax^2 + b = c$, $ax^2 + bx = c$, and $ax^2 + bx + c = 0$. Students will also become familiar with the convention and convenience of function notation, as in $f(x)$. Such notation will be introduced in the first investigation and referred to throughout the remainder of the lesson and the unit.

Lesson Objectives

- Distinguish relationships between variables that are functions from those that are not
- Use $f(x)$ notation to represent functions and the common questions about functions that arise in applied problems
- Identify domain and range of functions
- Construct rules for quadratic functions based on given properties such as x-intercepts, y-intercept, and maximum/minimum point
- Write quadratic expressions in equivalent expanded or factored form
- Solve quadratic equations by factoring, by applying the quadratic formula, or by a CAS

Think About This Situation

Inspecting the (*vertical drop, run time*) data makes it clear that *run time* depends on *vertical drop* of the luge course.

a What kind of function would you expect to provide a mathematical model for the relationship of those variables?

b How would you go about finding a rule for such a function?

c How would you expect run times to change if, like most luge courses, the path downhill had a number of sharp, banked curves?

In work on investigations of this lesson, you will learn about mathematical notation for expressing functions. Then you will apply that new knowledge to extend your understanding of quadratic functions and your skill in solving problems that involve quadratics.

Investigation 1 — Functions and Function Notation

The graph and table below show the dependence of run time y on vertical drop x in a luge run. For each x value, there is exactly one corresponding value of y. In such cases, we say that y **is a function of** x or that the relationship between run time y and vertical drop x is a **function**.

Theoretical 1,000-m Luge Run Times

Vertical Drop (in meters)	Run Time (in seconds)
10	143
20	101
30	82
40	71
50	64
60	58
70	54
80	51
90	48
100	45

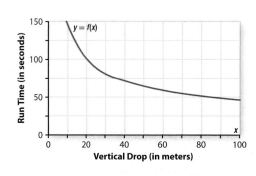

As is often the case in the TATS, it is not necessary that all students are able to come up with a rule for the (*vertical drop, run time*) data at this stage. They should, however, be able to articulate quite specific ideas, particularly in Part c.

Think About This Situation

a) Students might suggest an inverse or exponential rule as an appropriate model because of the nonlinear decreases in the table. Some students may suggest a quadratic model based on the title of the lesson or the connection of gravity to quadratic rules.

b) Students may suggest trial and error, algebraic reasoning, or a curve-fitting tool on a graphing calculator to aid in finding a rule.

c) Students should suggest that the run times will increase as curves are added to the course.

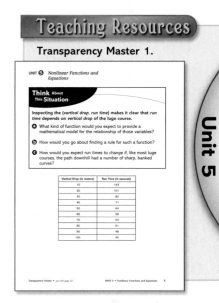

Teaching Resources

Transparency Master 1.

Unit 5

Investigation 1 Functions and Function Notation

The concept of a function is one of the most important mathematical tools for describing and reasoning about relationships between quantitative variables in a wide variety of problem situations. Students in *Core-Plus Mathematics* Course 1 studied a variety of specific examples and standard families of functions (especially linear, exponential, and quadratic functions) and used numeric, graphic, and symbolic function representations to solve a variety of standard problems. In those early units, we did not pay much attention to the formal defining criterion for a mathematical function—for each value of the independent variable, there is exactly one corresponding value of the dependent variable—and we did not introduce either the $f(x)$ notation or the formal concepts of domain and range.

At this point in *Core-Plus Mathematics* Course 2, with students having a repertoire of examples to draw on as concept images, it seems appropriate to introduce some of the standard formal language associated with functions as they are used in advanced mathematics. Thus, the purpose of this investigation is to directly address three questions:

• Which relationships between variables do mathematicians call functions?

• What is the standard notation used to represent information about functions?

• What do the terms *domain* and *range* mean when referring to functions?

The investigation uses three real-world contexts to illustrate uses of function notation, an additional question to contrast functions with non-function relationships, and a closer look at the sound intensity function to develop the concepts of domain and range.

COLLABORATION SKILL
Help our group check our thinking or solutions.

To show that y is a function of x, mathematicians and other professional users of mathematics commonly write "$y = f(x)$." Then facts and questions about the function can also be written in symbolic shorthand form. For example, to express the fact that a vertical drop of 30 meters will lead to a run time of 82 seconds, you could write "$f(30) = 82$" and say "f of 30 equals 82." (Written in this form, "$f(30)$" does *not* mean "f times 30.")

As you work on this investigation, keep in mind these basic questions:

What types of relationships between variables are called functions?

How is function notation used to express facts and questions about functions and the situations they describe?

1. Use information in the table and graph relating downhill run times to vertical drop of the luge course to answer the following questions. In each case, explain what the answer to the question tells about the luge run variables.

   a. How is the fact $f(50) = 64$ shown on the graph?

   b. What value of y satisfies the equation $y = f(40)$?

   c. What value of x satisfies the equation $51 = f(x)$?

   d. What value of y satisfies the equation $y = f(10)$?

   e. What value of x satisfies the equation $45 = f(x)$?

Bouncing Balls Gravity has the same effect on all objects, whether it is an athlete on an ice-covered luge course or a ball dropped from a tall building. However, gravity brings luge athletes down to stay, while it has to bring the bouncing balls down again and again. The following graph shows how the height of one type of bouncing ball changes over time after it is dropped onto a hard surface.

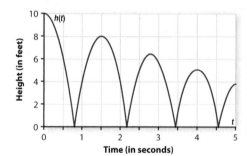

It is common to choose letter names for functions and variables that indicate the quantities involved in the relationship. In this case, it is helpful to use the notation $h(t)$ to represent the height of the ball in feet t seconds after it is dropped.

2. Use the graph above to estimate answers for the following questions about the function relating height of the ball to time. In each case, explain what the answer tells about the bouncing ball.

   a. What information is expressed by $h(0) = 10$?

   b. What is the value of $h(4)$?

1 **INSTRUCTIONAL NOTE** Watch for opportunities to connect functions in this unit to direct and inverse relationships studied in Course 2, Unit 1. Here, luge times are directly related to length of the luge course and inversely related to the vertical drop of the course.

a. $f(50) = 64$ is displayed on a graph of $f(x)$ by the point $(50, 64)$. If a 1,000-meter luge course has a vertical drop of 50 meters, then the predicted run time for experts is 64 seconds.

b. $y = 71$. On a 1,000-meter luge course with vertical drop of 40 meters, the predicted run time for experts will be 71 seconds.

c. $x = 80$. If a 1,000-meter luge course is to produce predicted expert run times of 51 seconds, then the vertical drop should be 80 meters.

d. $y = 143$. On a 1,000-meter luge course with vertical drop of 10 meters, the predicted expert run time is 143 seconds.

e. $x = 100$. To produce expert run times of 45 seconds on a 1,000-meter luge course, there should be a vertical drop of about 100 meters.

2 **a.** $h(0) = 10$ means that the ball starts ($t = 0$) at a height of 10 feet.

b. $h(4) \approx 5$ means that the ball is about 5 feet above the ground 4 seconds after it is dropped.

> **POSSIBLE MISCONCEPTION**
> Though it is noted in the text, some students may read $f(x)$ as "f times x." It may be worthwhile to discuss the different uses of parentheses and strategies to determine the contexts in which those different uses are found.

Unit 5

c. What values of t satisfy the equation $h(t) = 8$?

d. What is the value of $h(1)$?

e. What values of t satisfy the equation $h(t) = 0$?

 Recall that in a relationship between two variables x and y, y is a function of x when there is exactly one y value corresponding to each given x value.

a. Explain why the height of a bouncing ball is a function of time since it was dropped.

b. Explain why light intensity is a function of distance from light source to receiving surface.

c. Explain why length of the shadow cast by a tall building is a function of the time of day and time of the year.

d. Explain why the sales tax on a purchase is a function of the selling price of the item.

Sound Intensity The intensity of sound, like intensity of light, is inversely proportional to the square of the distance from the source.

 The rule $I(d) = \dfrac{8}{d^2}$ gives intensity of sound from a stereo speaker (in watts per square meter) as a function of distance (in meters) from the speaker.

a. Evaluate and explain the meaning of each of the following:

    i. $I(1)$ **ii.** $I(2)$

    iii. $I(0.5)$ **iv.** $I(10)$

b. Consider the equation $I(d) = 0.5$.

    i. What values of d will satisfy the equation?

    ii. What do those values tell you about the sound?

Nonfunctions At this point, it may seem that all relations between variables are functions. That is not the case. You can recognize "nonfunctions" by studying patterns in tables and graphs of (x, y) values and rules relating variables.

 The relationships between variables in Parts a–d are *not* functions. For each, explain why y is not a function of x.

a. The relationship between height (in cm) y and age (in years) x for a group of 20 young people that is shown in the scatterplot at the right

b. The relation between fuel efficiency y (in mpg) and weight x of a car or truck (in lbs)

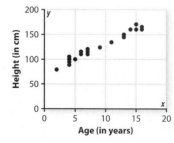

c. $h(t) = 8$ when $t \approx 0.35$ and when $t \approx 1.5$. This means that the ball is 8 feet above the ground at two times—0.35 seconds and 1.5 seconds after being dropped.

d. $h(1) \approx 4$ means that the ball is approximately 4 feet above the ground 1 second after it is dropped.

e. $h(t) = 0$ when $t \approx 0.8$, $t \approx 2.2$, $t \approx 3.4$, and $t \approx 4.6$ (for the part of the function graph shown in the diagram). This means that the ball hits the ground approximately 0.8 seconds, 2.2 seconds, 3.4 seconds, and 4.6 seconds after it is dropped.

3 **a.** Height is a function of time because for any given time, the ball is at exactly one height.

b. Intensity of light is a function of distance from the light source because for any given distance, the light has exactly one intensity.

c. Length of a shadow cast by a tall building is a function of the time of day and the time of the year because at any given time on any given day the shadow has exactly one length.

d. Sales tax is a function of the selling price of an item since for any selling price there is exactly one sales tax amount.

4 **INSTRUCTIONAL NOTE** Intensity of sound from a speaker is inversely proportional to the square of the distance from source to receiver. The various observations of relationships between change in distance and change in sound intensity in Problem 4 are connected with the fact that if two figures are similar and related by a scale factor of k, then their surface areas are related by the square of that scale factor. If your students would benefit from a review of these relationships, you could draw their attention to this here or during the STM discussion.

a. **i.** $I(1) = 8$. The sound intensity 1 meter from the source is 8 watts per square meter.

ii. $I(2) = 2$. The sound intensity 2 meters from the source is 2 watts per square meter.

iii. $I(0.5) = 32$. The sound intensity 0.5 meters from the source is 32 watts per square meter.

iv. $I(10) = 0.08$. The sound intensity 10 meters from the source is 0.08 watts per square meter.

b. **i.** 4 and -4

ii. The 4 means that the sound intensity will be one-half watt per square meter at a distance 4 meters from the source. The -4 has no meaning in this situation.

5 **a.** The relationship between height and age for 20 young people is not a function because there is more than one height corresponding to a given age. (There is generally a relationship between age and height (up to about age 16) for boys or for girls. The relationship is not precise enough or consistent enough to merit the mathematical term function.)

b. Fuel efficiency is not a function of weight of car because it is quite possible that two cars of the same weight could have different fuel efficiency. (This is another case where there is probably a general relation between the variables, but it is not precise enough to earn the name function from a mathematical perspective.)

INSTRUCTIONAL NOTE
Though it is common to present a "vertical line test" when discussing functionality of graphs, it is best if students come up with such a test on their own.

c.

x	−1	0	1	1	2
y	3	5	7	9	11

d.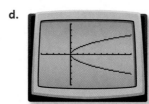

e. Explain why time is not a function of height in the bouncing ball experiment.

Domain and Range For any function $f(x)$, it is customary to refer to the variable x as the *input* and the function value $f(x)$ as the *output*. Many functions are only defined for some input values. Those numbers make up what is called the **domain** of the function. Similarly, only some numbers will occur as outputs of the function. Those numbers make up what is called the **range** of the function.

There are two ways to think about domain and range for a function that models a real-world situation. On one hand, you might ask what numbers are realistic or *practical* as inputs and outputs. On the other hand, you might ask what numbers *theoretically* can be used as inputs for a given function rule and what numbers will result as outputs (regardless of whether they make sense in the specific situation).

6 Consider again the function rule $I(d) = \dfrac{8}{d^2}$ relating sound intensity and distance from a speaker.

a. Which variable represents inputs? Which variable represents outputs?

b. Give an example of a number that theoretically cannot be used as an input to the rule. Give an example of a number that cannot possibly be an output from the rule.

c. Evaluate each of the following, if possible.

    i. $I(-1)$ **ii.** $I(-2)$ **iii.** $I(0)$ **iv.** $I(-10)$

d. Find the values of d that will satisfy the following equations, if possible.

    i. $I(d) = 8$ **ii.** $I(d) = -0.5$ **iii.** $I(d) = 0$ **iv.** $I(d) = 32$

e. When $I(d)$ is used as a model of the relationship between sound intensity and distance from a source, what might seem to be practical limits on the domain and range of the function?

f. What are the theoretical domain and range of the function $I(d)$? In other words, what values of d can be used as inputs to the rule for $I(d)$ and what range of output values will occur over that domain?

g. Look at a table and a graph of the function $I(d)$ and explain how such tables and graphs can be used to help determine the domain and range of a function.

c. The relationship shown by values in the table is not a function because two different *y* values (7 and 9) correspond to the *x* value 1.

d. The graph of the relationship shows that there are two different *y* values for all values of *x* except $x = 0$. Therefore, the relationship shown by the graph is not a function of *x*.

e. For any given height of the bouncing ball, there are multiple times after its drop where the ball reaches that height. A good example is at the height of 0 feet (refer to Problem 2 Part e).

 a. The variable *d* represents input.
The variable *I* represents output.

b. The only number that cannot theoretically be used as an input is $x = 0$.
Students could choose any negative number or 0 as one that cannot be used as output.

c. **i.** $I(-1) = 8$ **ii.** $I(-2) = 2$
   iii. $I(0)$ undefined   **iv.** $I(-10) = 0.08$

d. **i.** $d = \pm 1$ **ii.** No such *d*
   iii. No such *d*   **iv.** $d = \pm\frac{1}{2}$

e. The practical domain is certainly restricted to positive numbers and probably to some distances less than a few hundred meters (depending on the intensity of the sound from the speaker at its source). The practical range is $0 < I(d) < $ *some large number*; as one's ear gets closer and closer to the sound source, the intensity in watts per square meter grows rapidly.

f. The theoretical domain of the function $I(d)$ is all numbers except 0. The theoretical range is all positive numbers.

g. One can get clues to the domain by scanning tables and/or graphs for *x* values from negative to positive and noting any places where the table shows "error" in the *y*-value column or where the graph has a gap. One can get clues to the range by scanning a table to see the pattern of *y* values that occurs or by scanning a graph to see which *y*-coordinates seem to occur. This exploratory approach to understanding domain and range of a function has limitations; one cannot ever look at *all possible* input or output values, and thus may be overlooking values that are or are not input and output values.

Summary

As you discuss the STM, help students recognize that not all functions have correspondences between independent and dependent variables that can be described by algebraic rules. However, when verbal conditions or data patterns suggest such a rule, the calculation of function values is often made easier.

Examples from the investigation will help make this idea explicit for students. In addition, the *(age, height)* data in Problem 5 is a nice example of a situation that is not continuous (measurements to integer years and centimeters) and also has more than one *y* value for a given *x* value (not a function) that can be modeled by a function rule.

INSTRUCTIONAL NOTE
The distinction between *theoretical* and *practical* domains and ranges may be a source of confusion for some students. It would be worthwhile to stop and discuss the domains and ranges, both theoretical and practical, for the luge and bouncing ball examples earlier in the investigation.

Unit 5

Summarize
the Mathematics

In this investigation, you gained experience in identifying functions and using function notation.

a What does it mean for y to be a function of x?

b What examples would you use to illustrate the difference between relationships of variables that are functions and those that are not?

c How can you tell from a graph whether the relationship of variables displayed is a function or not?

d How can you determine the theoretical domain and range of a function? The practical domain and range?

Be prepared to share your thinking with the whole class.

✓ Check Your Understanding

The graph below shows the height of a basketball from a player's free throw attempt on its path to the basket that is 15 feet from the foul line.

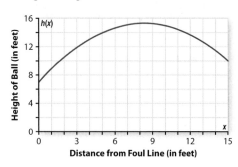

a. Explain why the height of the ball is a function of distance from the foul line.

b. Explain why the distance from the foul line is not a function of height of the ball.

c. If $h(x)$ gives the height in feet of the ball when it is above a spot x feet from the foul line:

   i. What information is expressed by $h(5) = 14$?

   ii. What value of y satisfies the equation $y = h(10)$? What does that fact tell about the flight of the player's shot?

   iii. What value(s) of x satisfy the equation $10 = h(x)$? What do the value(s) tell about the flight of the player's shot?

LESSON 1 • Quadratic Functions, Expressions, and Equations **331**

Summarize
the Mathematics

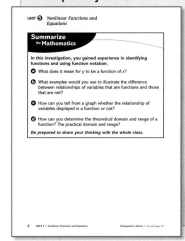

a A variable *y* is said to be a function of *x* when there is exactly one *y* value corresponding to each given *x* value.

b Student examples and non-examples of functions might draw on the situations studied throughout this lesson. (See summary on page T330.)

c You can tell from a graph of a relation whether the relation is a function by looking to see that no point (*x*, *y*) has a second point of the graph directly above or below it.

d The theoretical domain can be found by examining the function rule to see if there are any numbers that cannot be used in evaluating *f*(*x*). The range is found by considering the output values for the domain. If finding these values is not straightforward from the rule, you can examine a graph of the function to find restrictions on the *x* values and the output *y* values. To find the practical domain, you consider the context to find whether or not domain (*x* values) should be deleted because these values do not make sense for the situation. Practical range values are then the output values for the practical domain values.

MATH TOOLKIT Give a graphical example of a function and a relationship that is not a function. For the function example, use function notation to write a rule that represents your example. Then, describe the theoretical domain and range.

COLLABORATION PROMPT We helped our group check our thinking or solutions on Problems … by … .

✔ Check Your Understanding

a. On any particular shot for any horizontal distance from the foul line, the ball will be at exactly one position.

b. The ball reaches each height between 10 and about 15 feet at two different distances from the foul line.

c. **i.** When the ball is 5 feet from the foul line, it is at a height of 14 feet above the ground.

ii. $h(10) = 15$. Since the ball is higher 5 feet from the basket as it is when it is 5 feet from the goal line, it will arrive at the basket at a higher distance above the ground than when it left her hand. This can be seen in the graph through observation that the vertex of the parabola is slightly right of center.

iii. Reading an approximate solution from the graph, one gets $h(10) = 15$, meaning that at a point 10 feet horizontally from the foul line, the ball is about 15 feet above the floor.

iv. What are the practical domain and range of the function as shown on the graph?

v. What kind of function rule would you expect to provide a good algebraic model of the relationship shown in the graph?

vi. What would be the theoretical domain and range of such a function?

Investigation 2 Designing Parabolas

In the *Quadratic Functions* unit of Course 1, you explored quadratic patterns of change and developed skill in reasoning with the various representations of those patterns—tables, graphs, and symbolic rules. In this investigation, you will extend your understanding and skill in use of quadratic functions. As an example, consider the type of problem often faced by architects.

Developers of a new Magic Moments restaurant were intrigued by the design of a restaurant at the Los Angeles International Airport. In a meeting with their architect, they showed her a picture of the airport restaurant and asked if she could design something similar for them.

Like the airport structure, the Magic Moments restaurant was to be suspended above the ground by two giant parabolic arches—each 120 feet high and meeting the ground at points 200 feet apart. To prepare plans for the restaurant building, the designers had to develop and use functions whose graphs would match the planned arches.

One way to tackle this design problem is to imagine a parabola drawn on a coordinate grid as shown below. Any parabola can be described as the graph of some quadratic function.

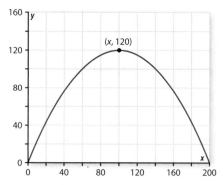

As you work on the problems of this investigation and the next, look for answers to this question:

What strategies can be used to find functions that model specific parabolic shapes?

iv. The practical domain is $0 \leq x \leq 15$. The practical range is
$7 \leq h \leq 15.333\ldots$.

v. Students should expect a quadratic function to model the relationship.

vi. The parabola would have a theoretical domain of all real numbers and
a theoretical range of all real numbers less than or equal to $15.333\ldots$.

Investigation 2 Designing Parabolas

In this investigation, students will explore the relationship of quadratic
expressions in factored form to the graph intercepts and maximum or minimum
points. Students may find relative comfort in writing functions in the
$f(x) = (x - m)(x - n)$ form based on the x-intercepts; however, the additional
work involved in writing those in the form $f(x) = a(x - m)(x - n)$, based on
specific intercepts and a vertex, may pose a more substantial challenge.
Students should not use the regression capabilities of their calculators for
these problems.

It is important to keep in mind that in this investigation, writing functions
in the $f(x) = a(x - m)(x - n)$ form is done algebraically and not with
transformations. Such operations on the graphs of quadratic functions will be
addressed in the Course 4 *Core-Plus Mathematics* unit, *Families of Functions*.

1 Using ideas from your earlier study of quadratic functions and their graphs, write the rule for a function with parabolic graph that contains points (0, 0), (200, 0), and a maximum point whose y-coordinate is 120. Use the hints in Parts a–d as needed.

   a. The graph of the desired function has x-intercepts (0, 0) and (200, 0). How do you know that the graph of the function $f(x) = x(x - 200)$ has those same x-intercepts?

   b. What is the x-coordinate of the maximum point on this graph?

   c. Suppose that $g(x)$ has a rule in the form $g(x) = k[x(x - 200)]$, for some particular value of k. What value of k will guarantee that $g(x) = 120$ at the maximum point of the graph?

   d. Write the rule for $g(x)$ in equivalent expanded form using the k value you found in Part c.

2 The logo chosen for Magic Moments continued the parabola theme with a large letter M drawn using two intersecting parabolas. The idea is shown in the next graph.

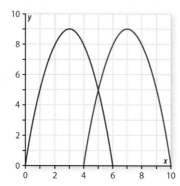

   a. Modify the strategy outlined in Problem 1 to find a quadratic function that will produce the leftmost parabola in the M.

   • Start with a function $f(x)$ that has x-intercepts at (0, 0) and (6, 0).

   • Find coordinates of the maximum point on the graph.

   • Find the rule for a related function $g(x)$ that has the same x-intercepts as $f(x)$ but passes through the desired maximum point.

   • Write the function rule for $f(x)$ using an equivalent expanded form of the quadratic expression involved.

   b. Use a similar strategy to find a function $g(x)$ that will produce the rightmost parabola.

   • Start with a function that has a graph with x-intercepts (4, 0) and (10, 0).

   • Then adjust the rule so that the function graph also passes through the required maximum point.

   • Finally, write the function rule using an equivalent expanded form of the quadratic expression involved.

a. Students may suggest solving the equation $x(x - 200) = 0$ and noting that the solutions ($x = 0$ or $x = 200$) indicate the x-intercepts. Some may suggest graphing $f(x)$ and showing that a graph of $f(x)$ also has x-intercepts of $(0, 0)$ and $(200, 0)$.

b. The symmetry of the parabola can be used to find the x-coordinate of the maximum point. Find the mean of the x-intercepts' x-coordinates, which is 100 in this case.

c. $k = -0.012$ would guarantee that $g(100) = 120$.

d. $g(x) = -0.012x^2 + 2.4x$

DIFFERENTIATION
Students could be asked to write the rule for the parabola prior to reading Problem 1. Then, if some groups seem to be struggling too much, refer them to Parts a–d.

 a. • $f(x) = ax(x - 6)$

   • We want $f(3) = 9$:

$$9 = a \cdot 3(3 - 6)$$
$$a = -1$$

   • $f(x) = -x(x - 6)$

   • $f(x) = -x^2 + 6x$

b. • $g(x) = a(x - 4)(x - 10)$

   • $g(7) = 9$
    $a = -1$
    So, $g(x) = -(x - 4)(x - 10)$.

   • $g(x) = -x^2 + 14x - 40$

INSTRUCTIONAL NOTE
You may wish to conduct a class summary of the method of finding the quadratic function rules before students work on the remainder of the investigation.

Unit 5

Your solutions to Problems 1 and 2 illustrate important and useful connections between rules and graphs for quadratic functions. Work on Problems 3, 4, and 5 will develop your understanding and skill in using those ideas.

③ Explain why the next diagram does or does not show the graph of $f(x) = (x - 3)(x + 1)$.

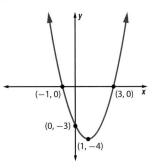

④ Use reasoning alone to sketch graphs of the following functions. Label these key points with their coordinates on the graphs:

- x-intercept(s),
- y-intercept, and
- maximum or minimum point.

Then check results of your reasoning using a graphing tool.

a. $f(x) = (x + 3)(x - 1)$
b. $f(x) = (x - 1)(x - 3)$
c. $f(x) = (x + 1)(x + 5)$
d. $f(x) = -2(x + 2)(x - 3)$
e. $f(x) = 0.5(x - 6)^2$

⑤ Write rules for quadratic functions whose graphs have the following properties. If possible, write more than one function rule that meets the given conditions.

a. x-intercepts at $(4, 0)$ and $(-1, 0)$
b. x-intercepts at $(7, 0)$ and $(1, 0)$ and graph opening upward
c. x-intercepts at $(7, 0)$ and $(1, 0)$ and minimum point at $(4, -10)$
d. x-intercepts at $(-5, 0)$ and $(0, 0)$ and graph opening downward
e. x-intercepts at $(3, 0)$ and $(-5, 0)$ and maximum point at $(-1, 8)$
f. x-intercepts at $(3.5, 0)$ and $(0, 0)$ and graph opening upward
g. x-intercepts at $(4.5, 0)$ and $(1, 0)$ and y-intercept at $(0, 9)$
h. x-intercepts at $(m, 0)$ and $(n, 0)$
i. only one x-intercept at $(0, 0)$
j. only one x-intercept at $(2, 0)$ and y-intercept at $(0, 6)$

3 Students may reason that the coordinates of the 4 points, when substituted in the rule $y = (x - 3)(x + 1)$, result in a true statement. Or, using the ideas from Problems 1 and 2, they may reason that $f(x) = a(x - 3)(x + 1)$; and since the minimum occurs at $x = 1$ and $y = -4$, that $-4 = a(1 - 3)(1 + 1)$. So, $a = 1$. Therefore, $f(x) = 1(x - 3)(x + 1)$.

4 **INSTRUCTIONAL NOTE** Listen carefully to student reasoning about the *x*-coordinate of the maximum/minimum point to be sure that they are reasoning based on the symmetry of the parabola.

Some students may need a question along the following lines as a reminder of how to find the *y*-intercept: What is the *x*-coordinate of any *y*-intercept?

a.

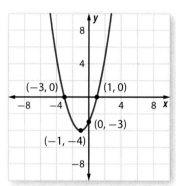

b.

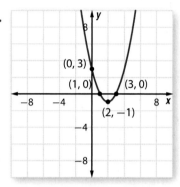

c.

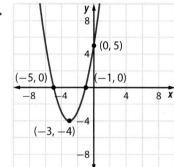

d.

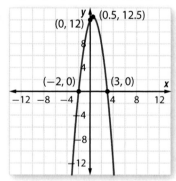

e.

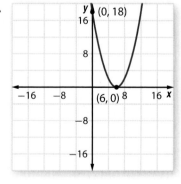

⑤ **INSTRUCTIONAL NOTE** Each of the following functions is written in factored form, but the expanded form is certainly acceptable.

a. $f(x) = a(x - 4)(x + 1)$, where a is any real number

b. $f(x) = a(x - 7)(x - 1)$, where a is any positive real number

c. $f(x) = \frac{10}{9}(x - 7)(x - 1)$

d. $f(x) = ax(x + 5)$, where a is any negative real number

e. $f(x) = -\frac{1}{2}(x - 3)(x + 5)$

f. $f(x) = ax(x - 3.5)$, where a is any positive real number

g. $f(x) = 2(x - 4.5)(x - 1)$

h. $f(x) = a(x - m)(x - n)$, where a is any real number

i. $f(x) = ax^2$, where a is any real number

j. $f(x) = \frac{3}{2}(x - 2)^2$

Teacher Notes

Summarize the Mathematics

In this investigation, you explored the ways in which factored forms, graphs, and intercepts are related for quadratic functions.

a How can the factored expression of a quadratic function be used to locate the *x*-intercept(s) and *y*-intercept of its graph?

b How can the factored expression of a quadratic function be used to locate the maximum or minimum point of its graph?

c How can the *x*-intercept(s), *y*-intercept, and maximum or minimum point of a parabola be used to write a rule for the corresponding quadratic function?

Be prepared to share your ideas, strategies, and reasoning with the class.

✓ Check Your Understanding

Use your understanding of connections between rules and graphs for quadratic functions to complete the following tasks.

a. Use reasoning alone to sketch graphs of these functions. Label *x*-intercepts, *y*-intercepts, and maximum or minimum points with their coordinates. Then check your sketches with a graphing tool.

   i. $f(x) = x(x + 6)$

   ii. $f(x) = -(x + 3)(x - 5)$

   iii. $f(x) = 3(x - 2)(x - 6)$

b. Find rules for quadratic functions with graphs meeting these conditions. In any case where it is possible, write more than one rule that meets the given conditions.

   i. *x*-intercepts at $(4, 0)$ and $(-1, 0)$ and opening upward

   ii. *x*-intercepts at $(2, 0)$ and $(6, 0)$ and maximum point at $(4, 12)$

   iii. only one *x*-intercept at $(-3, 0)$ and *y*-intercept at $(0, 18)$

Summarize
the Mathematics

(a) The x-intercept(s) can be found by determining the x values that make each factor equal to zero. The y-intercept can be found by evaluating the function for $x = 0$.

(b) Because of the symmetry of a parabola, the x-coordinate of the maximum or minimum will be the average of the x-coordinates of the x-intercepts.

(c) The important idea here is that knowing any 3 of these 4 "key" points will make writing a corresponding quadratic function possible. If the x-intercepts are known, the function can be set up in the form $f(x) = a(x - p)(x - q)$, where p and q are the x-coordinates of the x-intercepts. If the minimum or maximum values are known, then the coordinates for the minimum or maximum can be substituted for the $(x, f(x))$ coordinates in the function. This will result in an equation with a as the only variable. Solving this for a will provide the last piece of information needed for the function. A similar substitution process can be done if the y-intercept is known instead of the maximum or minimum.

Teaching Resources

Transparency Master 3.

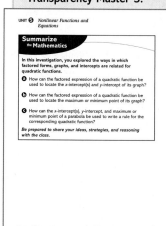

MATH TOOLKIT Give an example of how to use the x-intercepts and y-intercept or maximum (or minimum) point to write the function rule for the parabola.

✓ Check Your Understanding

a.

i. $f(x) = x(x + 6)$

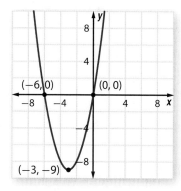

ii. $f(x) = -(x + 3)(x - 5)$

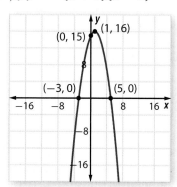

iii. $f(x) = 3(x - 2)(x - 6)$

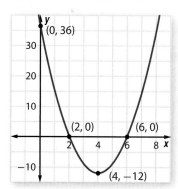

b.

i. $f(x) = a(x - 4)(x + 1)$, where a is any positive real number

ii. $g(x) = -3(x - 2)(x - 6)$

iii. $h(x) = 2(x + 3)(x + 3)$

Promoting Mathematical Discourse

Summarize the Mathematics, *page 335*

Teacher: It looks like most of you are finished with Problem 5, so let's take a few minutes to synthesize the skills we have been developing in this investigation. I would like each of you to pair with one other person to discuss the answers to the questions in the Summarize the Mathematics on page 335. *(The teacher gives students about 5 minutes to discuss Parts a–c.)*

Teacher: Johanna, please tell us how you and Randall responded to the question, "How can the factored form of a quadratic function be used to locate the x-intercept(s) and y-intercept of its graph?"

Johanna: Well, for the x-intercepts, you just look at each factor separately, like $(x - 7)$ and $(x + 3)$ and find what numbers make these zero. So, for that example, one x-intercept is at 7 and the other is at $x = -3$.

Teacher: Anyone have a question or something to add? *(No response.)* Will someone give us an example of a quadratic function in factored form that has only one x-intercept?

Placido: $(x - 7)^2$ is one.

Teacher: How do you know that?

Placido: Well, the graph of $y = (x - 7)^2$ has only one x-intercept because it really has the same factor twice. It is $(x - 7)(x - 7)$. Since it is shaped up, the minimum is at $(7, 0)$.

Teacher: Okay, it sounds like you all agree that we have a method for finding the x-intercepts when the factored form of the quadratic function is given. But you know that, in this class, we not only want methods, but we want to understand *why* they work. Think for a minute about *why* Johanna's method of looking at each factor to determine the value that makes the factor equal to zero actually locates the x-coordinate of the x-intercept. *(Pause.)* Ian, why does this method work?

Ian: It works because when one of the factors is zero, the result of the calculation is also zero. Multiplying by zero gives an answer of zero. An answer of zero means that the y value is zero. So, the point is exactly on the x-axis.

Teacher: Thanks, Ian. I know you were all listening intently to Ian's explanation, so will someone volunteer to use the specific function $f(x) = -(x - 4)(x + 10)$ and show why using $x = 4$ gives us an x-intercept. Alanna, as you explain, please sketch a graph of the function.

Alanna: Here is the graph. *(She sketches a graph.)* Now, if you plug 4 into $-(x - 4)(x + 10)$, it becomes -0×14, which equals 0. This means that $f(x)$, or y, is 0 and the point is $(4, 0)$— the x-intercept.

Teacher: Now, how do you use the factored form to find the y-intercept? Alanna, please explain your method using the same function $f(x) = -(x - 4)(x + 10)$?

Alanna: Since the x-coordinate for the y-intercept is 0, to find the y-coordinate, you just find $-(-4)(10) = 40$; so, the y-intercept is $(0, 40)$.

Teacher: Any questions or clarifications?

Curtis: I agree with Alanna. And she really explained "why" the method works when she said, "Since the x-coordinate for the y-intercept is 0 . . . ."

Delia: Finding the y-intercept helps us to sketch a better graph. The graph of the function that we have on the board could now have scales on the y-axis and show the y-intercept $(0, 40)$. It makes sense because the parabola should be shaped down.

Teacher: Let's connect the y-intercept idea to our new notation, function notation. How do you express that the x-coordinate of the y-intercept is 0 in function notation?

Delia: Oh, yeah, Alanna was finding $f(0)$ to get the y-intercept.

James: Well, how do you use function notation to talk about the x-intercept then? Let's see . . . . Since we are finding x values that give y values of 0, it seems that we are finding when $f(x) = 0$. Is that right?

Teacher: What do others think?

Chad: Sounds right. You are finding when the function crosses the x-axis or when it's value is 0.

Teacher: Any other comments? *(No comments offered.)* Now let's hear what you are thinking about how to find the maximum or minimum point of the graph from the factored form of the quadratic expression. Takoda?

Takoda: Well, once you have the x-intercepts from the factored form, you just use the x-coordinates to find the halfway point on the x-axis between the two. See here *(points to graph on board)*, use the 4 and -10 from our function $f(x)$ to find the x-coordinate of the max or min point. For $f(x)$, it is at $x = -3$. Then find $f(-3) = 49$.

Teacher: Any questions of Takoda? *(No questions surface.)* Then what was your thinking about using the intercepts and max or min point of the graph of a parabola to write a rule for the corresponding quadratic function. Rodney?

Rodney: If you know the two x-intercepts, then you can write the factored form of the quadratic function like $f(x) = a(x - p)(x - q)$.

Then to find the value of a, you use a third point, either the y-intercept or the max or min point. Put these values in for x and $f(x)$ and solve for a.

Teacher: Rodney, you said that rather quickly and it was a lot for me to process at one time. Would you please explain again, slower this time? Also, when you use letters such as p and q, we will need to know what those represent.

Rodney: Okay. I'll write it on the board. Let's say that you know the two x-intercepts $(p, 0)$ and $(q, 0)$. Then the rule must look like $f(x) = a(x - p)(x - q)$. To find out the value of a we need a third point. If we know the y-intercept, we can evaluate $f(x)$ at this point and solve for a. Any questions?

Dannish: Can you point to a problem where we did that?

Rodney: We did that in Problem 5 Part g.

Dannish: Okay, I see that.

Rodney: We could also use either the maximum or minimum point as a third point to find a. The idea is the same—you plug the x and y (or $f(x)$) values into the function and solve for a. We did this in Problem 5 Part c.

Teacher: Good job, students. Now one more question. What do you notice about the processes we described in Parts a and b compared to the processes we described in Part c?

Gia: Like it is the opposite process. In Parts a and b, we talked about getting information from the factored form of the rule— intercepts and max or min points. In Part c, we talked about using these points to write the rule. You can go either way.

Teacher: For your assignment for tonight, you should write a math toolkit summary of these two processes and provide an example for your reference. Also, complete the Check Your Understanding and take a look at Reflections Task 29 that extends our thinking in Part c. In particular, consider if it is ever possible to write a quadratic rule when you are given only two points on the parabola? *(The teacher judges that this extension is appropriate for this particular class. In general, you need three points to write a quadratic rule. One case where knowing two special points allows you to use the symmetry of a parabola to find a third point follows. If you know that a function has two distinct x-intercepts, know one x-intercept, and the maximum or minimum point, you can find the second x-intercept and write the rule.)*

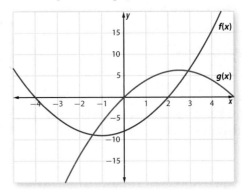

Investigation 3 — Expanding and Factoring

The standard form of rules for quadratic functions is $f(x) = ax^2 + bx + c$. But, as you have seen in problems of Investigation 2, rules for quadratics often occur naturally as products of linear expressions. Those factored quadratic expressions reveal useful connections between the functions and their graphs.

For example, the next diagram shows graphs of the functions $f(x) = x^2 + 2x - 8$ and $g(x) = -x^2 + 5x$. The rules for those functions can also be expressed as $f(x) = (x + 4)(x - 2)$ and $g(x) = -x(x - 5)$, forms that reveal the x-intercepts of each graph.

As you work on the problems of this investigation, look for answers to these questions:

What reasoning can be used to expand products of linear factors into equivalent standard form?

How can standard-form quadratic expressions be written as products of linear factors?

1 The next diagram illustrates a visual strategy for finding products of linear expressions.

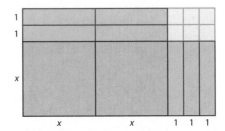

a. How does the diagram show that $(x + 2)(2x + 3) = 2x^2 + 7x + 6$?

b. What similar diagram would help to find the expanded form of $(x + 3)(x + 1)$, and what is that expanded form?

The focus of this investigation is to develop students' abilities to recognize patterns associated with symbolic forms in order to be able to multiply simple linear expressions and factor quadratic expressions.

1
   a. The figure is a rectangle with height $x + 2$ and base $2x + 3$, so its area is $(x + 2)(2x + 3)$. Looking at the sub-rectangles that make up the larger figure, we see two squares with area x^2, seven rectangles with area x, and six unit squares.

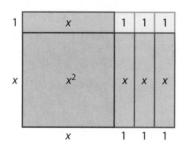

   b. The product $(x + 3)(x + 1) = x^2 + 4x + 3$ is illustrated by the following diagram:

Unit 5

2 In earlier work with quadratic expressions like $-3x(4x - 5)$, you have seen how the distributive property can be applied to write the equivalent form $-12x^2 + 15x$. A group of students at Spring Valley High School claimed that by using the distributive property twice, they could expand other factored quadratic expressions. Check the steps in their example below and then apply similar reasoning to expand the expressions in Parts a–f.

$$(x + 5)(x - 7) = (x + 5)x - (x + 5)7$$
$$= (x^2 + 5x) - (7x + 35)$$
$$= x^2 - 2x - 35$$

   a. $(x + 5)(x + 6)$ **b.** $(x - 3)(x + 9)$

   c. $(x + 10)(x - 10)$ **d.** $(x - 5)(x + 1)$

   e. $(x + a)(x + b)$ **f.** $(x + 7)(2x + 3)$

3 Look back at your work in Problem 2. Compare the standard-form results to their equivalent factored forms in search of a pattern that you can use as a shortcut in expanding such products. Describe in words the pattern that can be used to produce the expanded forms.

4 The next six expressions have a special form $(x + a)^2$ in which both linear factors are the same. They are called *perfect squares*. Find an equivalent expanded form for each expression. Remember: $(x + a)^2 = (x + a)(x + a)$.

   a. $(x + 5)^2$ **b.** $(x - 3)^2$

   c. $(x + 7)^2$ **d.** $(x - 4)^2$

   e. $(x + a)^2$ **f.** $(3x + 2)^2$

5 Compare the standard-form results to their equivalent factored forms in Problem 4. Find a pattern that you can use as a shortcut in expanding such perfect squares. Describe in words the pattern that can be used to produce the expanded form.

6 Write each of these quadratic expressions in equivalent expanded form.

   a. $(x + 6)(x - 6)$ **b.** $(x + 6)(x - 3)$

   c. $(2x + 5)(2x - 5)$ **d.** $(x - 2.5)(x + 2.5)$

   e. $(8 - x)(8 + x)$ **f.** $(x - a)(x + a)$

7 Look back at your work in Problem 6. Compare the standard-form results to their equivalent factored forms to find a pattern that you can use as a shortcut in expanding products like those in Part a and Parts c–f. Describe the pattern in words.

Factoring Quadratic Expressions In many problems that involve quadratic functions, the function rule occurs naturally in standard form $f(x) = ax^2 + bx + c$. In those cases, it is often helpful to rewrite the rule in equivalent factored form to find the x-intercepts of the graph and then the maximum or minimum point.

2   **a.** $x^2 + 11x + 30$ **b.** $x^2 + 6x - 27$ **c.** $x^2 - 100$
      d. $x^2 - 4x - 5$ **e.** $x^2 + (a + b)x + ab$ **f.** $2x^2 + 17x + 21$

INSTRUCTIONAL NOTE
By focusing students on the distributive property (rather than FOIL), students will be better able to generalize when multiplying polynomials with more than two terms.

3   Using the distributive property twice gives four product terms. Combining like terms and rearranging order of terms will, in general, produce a quadratic expression in the form $ax^2 + bx + c$. When the starting product is in the form $(x + m)(x + n)$, the coefficient of x^2 is 1, the coefficient of x is $(m + n)$, and the constant term is mn.

4   **POSSIBLE MISCONCEPTION** For $a \neq 0$, $(x + a)^2 \neq x^2 + a^2$, this may take a number of reminders. Rather than encouraging memorization of the "shortcut" $(x + a)^2 = x^2 + 2ax + a^2$, it may be more effective to ask students to think about the meaning of a power of two found in the expression (i.e., that $(x + a)^2 = (x + a)(x + a)$). Then ask them to visualize the square formed by sides of length $a + x$ to remind them of the correct result.

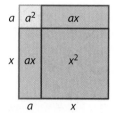

      a. $x^2 + 10x + 25$ **b.** $x^2 - 6x + 9$ **c.** $x^2 + 14x + 49$
      d. $x^2 - 8x + 16$ **e.** $x^2 + 2ax + a^2$ **f.** $9x^2 + 12x + 4$

5   One pattern is to square the first term, multiply the first and last term (considering subtraction signs as negative signs) and double the result, and then square the last term.

6   **a.** $x^2 - 36$ **b.** $x^2 + 3x - 18$ **c.** $4x^2 - 25$
      d. $x^2 - 6.25$ **e.** $-x^2 + 64$ **f.** $x^2 - a^2$

7   In five of the six examples, the products have a special form where the factors are the sum and difference of the same two numbers. The result in each of those cases is the difference of the squares of the two numbers.

Unit 5

For example, the height of a gymnast's bounce above a trampoline is a function of time after the takeoff bounce. The function might have rule:

$$h(t) = -16t^2 + 24t$$
$$= -8t(2t - 3)$$

This information makes it easy to find the time when the gymnast hits the trampoline surface again and when she reaches her maximum height.

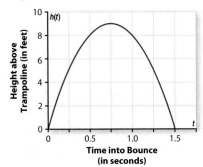

$h(t) = 0$ when $-8t(2t - 3) = 0$
　　　　when $-8t = 0$ or when $2t - 3 = 0$
　　　　when $t = 0$ or when $t = 1.5$

Maximum value of $h(t)$ is $h(0.75)$ or 9.

In general, it is more difficult to write a quadratic expression like $ax^2 + bx + c$ in equivalent factored form than to expand a product of linear factors into equivalent standard form. In fact, it is not always possible to write a factored form for given standard-form quadratic expressions (using only integers as coefficients and constant terms in the factors).

8 To find a factored form for a quadratic expression like $x^2 + 5x + 6$, you have to think backward through the reasoning used to expand products of linear factors.

Suppose that $(x + m)(x + n) = x^2 + 5x + 6$.

a. How is the number 6 related to the integers m and n in the factored form?

b. How is the number 5 related to the integers m and n in the factored form?

c. What is a factored form for $x^2 + 5x + 6$?

9 Find equivalent factored forms for each of these standard-form quadratic expressions.

a. $x^2 + 7x + 6$　　　　　　**b.** $x^2 + 7x + 12$

c. $x^2 + 8x + 12$　　　　　　**d.** $x^2 + 13x + 12$

e. $x^2 + 10x + 24$　　　　　　**f.** $x^2 + 11x + 24$

g. $x^2 + 9x + 8$　　　　　　**h.** $x^2 + 6x$

i. $x^2 + 9x + 18$　　　　　　**j.** $3x^2 + 18x + 24$

What general guidelines do you see for factoring expressions like these?

8   **a.** $mn = 6$

     b. $m + n = 5$

     c. $(x + 2)(x + 3)$

9   **a.** $(x + 1)(x + 6)$ **b.** $(x + 3)(x + 4)$ **c.** $(x + 2)(x + 6)$

     d. $(x + 1)(x + 12)$ **e.** $(x + 4)(x + 6)$ **f.** $(x + 3)(x + 8)$

     g. $(x + 1)(x + 8)$ **h.** $x(x + 6)$ **i.** $(x + 3)(x + 6)$

     j. $3(x + 2)(x + 4)$ or

        $(3x + 6)(x + 4)$ or

        $(x + 2)(3x + 12)$

In general, to factor expressions like these, find two factors with constant terms whose product is equal to the constant term of the expression and whose sum is equal to the coefficient of x.

10 When a quadratic expression involves differences, finding possible factors requires thinking about products and sums involving negative numbers. Write these expressions in equivalent forms as products of linear expressions.

a. $x^2 - 7x + 12$ **b.** $x^2 + 5x - 6$

c. $x^2 - 8x + 12$ **d.** $x^2 - x - 12$

e. $x^2 - 10x + 24$ **f.** $x^2 + 10x - 24$

g. $x^2 - 9x + 8$ **h.** $x^2 - 4x$

i. $x^2 - 7x - 18$ **j.** $2x^2 + 13x - 7$

What general guidelines do you see for factoring expressions like these?

11 The examples here involve some of the special cases you studied in the practice of expanding products. Where possible, write each given expression as the product of linear expressions.

a. $x^2 - 9$ **b.** $x^2 - 81$

c. $x^2 + 16$ **d.** $x^2 + 10x + 25$

e. $x^2 - 6x + 9$ **f.** $x^2 + 16x + 64$

g. $4x^2 - 49$ **h.** $9x^2 + 6x + 1$

What general guidelines do you see for factoring expressions like these? The two special forms are called *difference of squares* and *perfect square* quadratic expressions.

Using Computer Algebra Tools When the factoring task involves an expression like $-10x^2 + 240x - 950$, things get more challenging. Fortunately, what *is* known about factoring quadratic expressions has been converted into routines for computer algebra systems. Thus, some simple commands will produce the desired factored forms and the insight that comes with them.

For example, the next screen display shows how a CAS would produce a factored form of $-10x^2 + 240x - 950$.

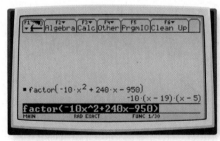

12 Use a computer algebra system to write each expression in equivalent form as products of linear factors. Then use your own reasoning to check the accuracy of the CAS results.

a. $x^2 + 2x - 24$ **b.** $x^2 - 6x + 5$

c. $-x^2 + 8x - 15$ **d.** $2x^2 - 7x - 4$

e. $2x^2 + 15x + 18$ **f.** $3x^2 - 7x - 6$

g. $-3x^2 + 8x$ **h.** $5x + 3x^2$

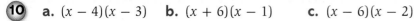

10 **a.** $(x - 4)(x - 3)$ **b.** $(x + 6)(x - 1)$ **c.** $(x - 6)(x - 2)$
d. $(x + 3)(x - 4)$ **e.** $(x - 6)(x - 4)$ **f.** $(x + 12)(x - 2)$
g. $(x - 8)(x - 1)$ **h.** $x(x - 4)$ **i.** $(x + 2)(x - 9)$
j. $(2x - 1)(x + 7)$

In general, when the coefficient on the x^2 term is one, you find factors of the constant term that when added or subtracted form the correct coefficient for the x-term. If the coefficient on x^2 is not 1, then you look for factors of that term and factors of the constant term that provide the correct trinomial when the two linear terms are multiplied.

11 **INSTRUCTIONAL NOTE** While some students may pick up on these special cases rather quickly, others may be just as successful in treating them as "typical" factorable expressions. This might be accomplished with those in the $x^2 - a^2$ form, by rewriting (or rethinking) of the expression as $x^2 + 0x - a^2$.

a. $(x + 3)(x - 3)$ **b.** $(x + 9)(x - 9)$ **c.** Not possible
d. $(x + 5)^2$ **e.** $(x - 3)^2$ **f.** $(x + 8)^2$
g. $(2x + 7)(2x - 7)$ **h.** $(3x + 1)^2$

In general, the difference of squares (a two-term expression) can be factored into two linear terms that are formed from the square roots of the terms of the original expression. One linear term is an addition of two square roots and the other linear term is the subtraction of the square roots. A perfect square term can be recognized by noticing that the first and last terms of the trinomial are squares and that the linear term in standard form is the product of the square roots of the first and last terms doubled. When the coefficient on the x^2 term is 1, the middle term will be twice the square root of the constant term of the original expression if the trinomial is a perfect square.

INSTRUCTIONAL NOTE While the expressions in Problem 12 are each factorable without the use of a CAS, at this stage, students can be expected to range in their proficiency in factoring expressions like those in Parts d, e, and f. In other words, they should have a good grasp of the concept here but perhaps not full command of the mechanics. Review tasks in subsequent units will be provided.

> **TECHNOLOGY NOTE**
> The *CPMP-Tools* algebra software contains a CAS that students can use to check results.

12 **a.** $(x + 6)(x - 4)$ **b.** $(x - 1)(x - 5)$
c. $-(x - 5)(x - 3)$ **d.** $(2x + 1)(x - 4)$
e. $(2x + 3)(x + 6)$ **f.** $(3x + 2)(x - 3)$
g. $-x(3x - 8)$ **h.** $x(3x + 5)$

Summarize
the Mathematics

In this investigation, you discovered strategies for expanding and factoring expressions that represent quadratic functions.

a How do you go about expanding a product of two linear expressions like $(x + a)(x - b)$?

b What shortcut can be applied to expand products in the form $(x + a)^2$? In the form $(x + a)(x - a)$?

c How would your answers to Parts a and b change if the coefficients of x were numbers other than 1?

d How do you go about finding a factored form for quadratic expressions like $x^2 + bx + c$?

e How would you modify your strategy in Part d for quadratic expressions of the form $ax^2 + bx + c$?

Be prepared to explain your ideas and strategies to others in your class.

✔Check Your Understanding

Write the following expressions in equivalent expanded or factored forms.

a. $(x + 7)(x - 4)$

b. $(x - 5)(x + 5)$

c. $(x - 3)^2$

d. $x^2 - 100$

e. $x^2 + 9x + 20$

f. $x^2 + 3x - 10$

g. $x^2 + 7x$

h. $5x(x - 3)$

Investigation 4   Solving Quadratic Equations

In situations that involve quadratic functions, the interesting questions often require solving equations. For example,

When a pumpkin is dropped from a point 50 feet above the ground, it will hit the ground at the time t that satisfies the equation $50 - 16t^2 = 0$.

To find points where the main cable of a suspension bridge is 20 feet above the bridge surface, you might need to solve an equation like
$$0.02x^2 - x + 110 = 20.$$

You can always estimate solutions for these equations by scanning tables of (x, y) values or by tracing coordinates of points on function graphs. In some cases, you can get exact solutions by reasoning algebraically—without use of calculator tables or graphs. As you work on the problems of this investigation, look for answers to this question:

What strategies can be used to solve quadratic equations by factoring and the quadratic formula?

Summarize
the Mathematics

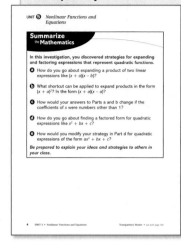

a Students will have a number of different strategies to expand such a product. One such method may involve the distributive property in which both terms in the first factor are multiplied by each of the terms of the second factor. Symbolically, $(x + a)(x - b) = x \cdot x - x \cdot b + a \cdot x - a \cdot b$ which is equal to $x^2 + (a - b)x - ab$.

b Products in the form $(x + a)^2$ can always be written $x^2 + 2ax + a^2$ and those in the form $(x + a)(x - a)$ can be written $x^2 - a^2$.

c If the coefficient of x in one of the factors is a number k other than 1, the expanded results become $(kx + a)(x - b) = kx^2 + (a - bk)x - ab$; $(kx + a)^2 = (kx)^2 + 2kax + a^2$; and $(kx - a)(kx + a) = (kx)^2 - a^2$, respectively.

d To go about finding a factored form for standard quadratic expressions like $x^2 + bx + c$, one looks for two numbers m and n such that $m + n = b$ and $mn = c$. Then, the factored form is $(x + m)(x + n)$.

e When the quadratic expression includes a coefficient a, not 1, the strategy becomes to find the factors for both the coefficient on the x^2 and the constant term that results in the correct middle (linear) term. This will likely require trying some linear factors and checking to see if they provide the trinomial expression when multiplied together. It is helpful to look for common factors of trinomials to reduce the possibilities for the trial and checking process.

> **MATH TOOLKIT** Write a summary of how you expand products and factor quadratic expressions that will help you recall how to apply these skills for other problems.

✓ Check Your Understanding

a. $x^2 + 3x - 28$

b. $x^2 - 25$

c. $x^2 - 6x + 9$

d. $(x + 10)(x - 10)$

e. $(x + 5)(x + 4)$

f. $(x + 5)(x - 2)$

g. $x(x + 7)$

h. $5x^2 - 15x$

> **PRACTICE** Additional practice of factoring and expanding quadratic expressions is built into Review tasks of later units. Some students will require additional practice over time to develop these skills.

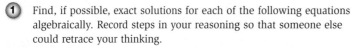

1 Find, if possible, exact solutions for each of the following equations algebraically. Record steps in your reasoning so that someone else could retrace your thinking.

   a. $5x^2 + 12 = 57$ **b.** $-5x^2 + 12 = -33$

   c. $3x^2 - 15 = 70$ **d.** $8 - 2x^2 = x^2 + 5$

   e. $7x^2 - 24 = 18 - 2x^2$ **f.** $x^2 + 4 = 2x^2 + 9$

   What general guidelines would you suggest for solving equations like these?

2 Solve the following equations algebraically. Record steps in your reasoning so that someone else could retrace your thinking.

   a. $x(5 - x) = 0$ **b.** $5x^2 + 15x = 0$

   c. $16x - 4x^2 = 0$ **d.** $3x + 5x^2 = -7x$

   What general guidelines would you suggest for solving equations like these?

3 Each of the following equations involves a quadratic expression that can be factored into a product of two linear expressions. Solve each equation and record steps in your reasoning so that someone else could retrace your thinking.

   a. $x^2 + 2x - 24 = 0$ **b.** $x^2 - 6x + 5 = 0$

   c. $-x^2 + 8x - 15 = 0$ **d.** $x^2 + 10x + 21 = 0$

   e. $2x^2 - 12x + 18 = 0$ **f.** $x^2 + 6x - 16 = 0$

When you know several strategies for solving different kinds of equations, the key step in working on any particular problem is matching your strategy to the equation form. Use what you have learned from work on Problems 1–3 to apply effective strategies for solving the quadratic equations in Problem 4.

4 Solve each of these equations by algebraic reasoning. Record steps in your reasoning so that someone else could retrace your thinking. Be prepared to explain how you analyzed each given problem to decide on a solution strategy.

   a. $x^2 + 6x + 5 = 0$ **b.** $6x + x^2 = 0$

   c. $x^2 + 12x + 20 = 0$ **d.** $7x + x^2 + 12 = 0$

   e. $9 = -7 + 4x^2$ **f.** $x^2 + 3x + 4 = 0$

   g. $2x^2 + 3x + 1 = 0$ **h.** $2x^2 - 5x = 12$

Investigation 4 — Solving Quadratic Equations

In this investigation, students use their factoring knowledge and apply the quadratic formula to solve quadratic equations. They also connect the possible number of solutions to the graph and the quadratic formula and recognize the information provided by the two parts of the quadratic formula.

The focus question for this investigation is on the strategies to solve quadratic equations. As students work on the investigation, help them continue to develop symbol sense to make choices for strategies more transparent. Students should recognize that the three types of quadratic equations they are solving take the following forms:

$$ax^2 = 0,$$
$$ax^2 + bx = 0, \text{ and}$$
$$ax^2 + bx + c = 0$$

In Problems 1–4, students develop reasoning strategies for solving quadratic equations. They may need to recall the relationship between the graphs of quadratic functions and the factored forms of the equations from Investigation 2. They may also need to return to the trampoline bounce as a function of time context on page 338. In Problems 1–4, students should record their solution steps. Students should discuss their general solution guidelines for Problems 1 and 2. It is not necessary for them to write a response. Following Problem 2, conduct a class discussion of their strategies and advantages of selected strategies as appropriate.

COLLABORATION SKILL
Take time to make sure everyone has correct solutions and understand the methods in this investigation.

(1)
a. $x = \pm 3$ **b.** $x = \pm 3$
c. $x = \pm \sqrt{\dfrac{85}{3}}$ **d.** $x = \pm 1$
e. $x = \pm \sqrt{\dfrac{14}{3}}$ **f.** No real solutions

(2)
a. $x = 0$ or $x = 5$ **b.** $x = 0$ or $x = -3$
c. $x = 0$ or $x = 4$ **d.** $x = 0$ or $x = -2$

(3) **INSTRUCTIONAL NOTE** Problem 3 Part e offers the opportunity for a class discussion of strategies used. The advantage of finding common factors should be discussed. Connections between finding common factors for forms such as $5x^2 + 15x$ in Problem 2 Part b and Problem 3 Part e will help students to be able to recognize instances where finding a common factor is valuable.

a. $x = -6$ or $x = 4$ **b.** $x = 1$ or $x = 5$
c. $x = 3$ or $x = 5$ **d.** $x = -3$ or $x = -7$
e. $x = 3$ **f.** $x = 2$ or $x = -8$

(4)
a. $x = -1$ or $x = -5$ **b.** $x = 0$ or $x = -6$
c. $x = -2$ or $x = -10$ **d.** $x = -3$ or $x = -4$
e. $x = 2$ or $x = -2$ **f.** No real solutions
g. $x = -\dfrac{1}{2}$ or $x = -1$ **h.** $x = -\dfrac{3}{2}$ or $x = 4$

Unit 5

⑤ In addition to expanding and factoring expressions, you can also use a computer algebra system to solve quadratic equations directly. The screen display below shows a CAS solution to the equation $2x^2 - 9x - 5 = 0$.

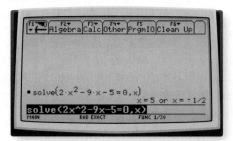

Use a calculator or computer algebra system to solve these equations.

a. $x^2 + 5x + 3 = 0$ **b.** $2x^2 - 5x - 12 = 0$

c. $-10x^2 + 240x - 950 = 0$ **d.** $x^2 - 6x + 10 = 0$

The Quadratic Formula Revisited In solving the equations of Problem 5, you saw how some equations that look fairly complex actually have simple whole number solutions, while equations that look quite simple end up with irrational number solutions or even no real number solutions at all.

When quadratic expressions involve fractions or decimals, mental factoring methods are not often easy to use. You will recall from *Core-Plus Mathematics* Course 1 that for those cases and for situations where you do not have access to a computer algebra system, there is a **quadratic formula** for finding solutions.

For any equation in the form $ax^2 + bx + c = 0$, the solutions are

$$x = \frac{-b}{2a} + \frac{\sqrt{b^2 - 4ac}}{2a} \text{ and } x = \frac{-b}{2a} - \frac{\sqrt{b^2 - 4ac}}{2a}.$$

To use the quadratic formula in any particular case, all you have to do is

Be sure that the equation is in the form prescribed by the formula.

Identify the values of a, b, and c.

Enter those values where they occur in the formula.

⑥ Test your understanding and skill with the quadratic formula by using it to solve the following equations. In each case:

- Give the values of a, b, and c that must be used to solve the equations.

- Evaluate $\frac{-b}{2a}$ and $\frac{\sqrt{b^2 - 4ac}}{2a}$.

- Evaluate $x = \frac{-b}{2a} + \frac{\sqrt{b^2 - 4ac}}{2a}$ and $x = \frac{-b}{2a} - \frac{\sqrt{b^2 - 4ac}}{2a}$.

5 **a.** $x = \dfrac{-5 + \sqrt{13}}{2}$ or $x = \dfrac{-5 - \sqrt{13}}{2}$

b. $x = 4$ or $x = -1.5$

c. $x = 19$ or $x = 5$

d. No real solutions

6 Parts a and b report the sequence of calculations involved in use of the quadratic formula. Parts c–h report only the solutions and the graphs that illustrate those solutions.

INSTRUCTIONAL NOTE
You might wish to have each student complete two or three of the parts in Problem 6 and then share their solutions and graphs with a partner who has done different equations.

a. • $a = 5$, $b = 3$, $c = -2$

• $\dfrac{-b}{2a} = \dfrac{-3}{10}$ and $\dfrac{\sqrt{b^2 - 4ac}}{2a} = \dfrac{7}{10}$

• $x = \dfrac{2}{5}$ or $x = -1$

• Check: $5(0.4)^2 + 3(0.4) - 2 = 0$
  $5(-1)^2 + 3(-1) - 2 = 0$

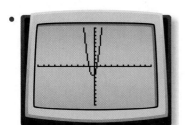

b. • $a = 1$, $b = -5$, $c = -6$

• $\dfrac{-b}{2a} = \dfrac{5}{2}$ and $\dfrac{\sqrt{b^2 - 4ac}}{2a} = \dfrac{7}{2}$

• $x = 6$ or $x = -1$

• Check: $(6)^2 - 5(6) - 6 = 0$
  $(-1)^2 - 5(-1) - 6 = 0$

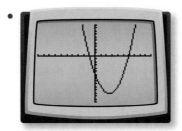

c. $x = 5$ or $x = 2$

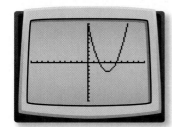

d. $x = 4$ or $x = -3$

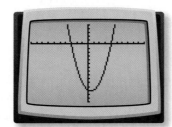

e. $x = -5$ or $x = 2$

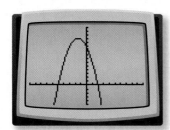

f. $x = 3$

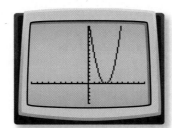

g. No real solutions

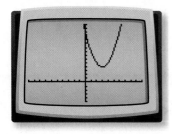

h. $x = -2$

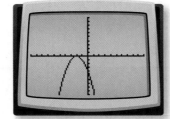

Unit 5

- Check that the solutions produced by the formula actually satisfy the equation.

- Graph the related quadratic function to see how the solutions appear as *x*-intercepts.

a. $5x^2 + 3x - 2 = 0$ **b.** $x^2 - 5x - 6 = 0$
c. $x^2 - 7x + 10 = 0$ **d.** $x^2 - x - 12 = 0$
e. $10 - x^2 - 3x = 0$ **f.** $2x^2 - 12x + 18 = 0$
g. $13 - 6x + x^2 = 0$ **h.** $-x^2 - 4x - 2 = 2$

7 Now look back at your work on Problem 6 in search of connections between the quadratic formula calculations and the graphs of the corresponding function rules.

For a quadratic function with rule in the form $f(x) = ax^2 + bx + c$:

a. What information about the graph is provided by $\frac{-b}{2a} + \frac{\sqrt{b^2 - 4ac}}{2a}$ and $\frac{-b}{2a} - \frac{\sqrt{b^2 - 4ac}}{2a}$?

b. What information about the graph is provided by the expression $\frac{-b}{2a}$?

c. What information about the graph is provided by the expression $\frac{\sqrt{b^2 - 4ac}}{2a}$?

Solution Possibilities In solving equations like $ax^2 + bx + c = 0$ with the quadratic formula, the key steps are evaluating $\frac{-b}{2a}$ and $\frac{\sqrt{b^2 - 4ac}}{2a}$.

Even if the coefficients *a* and *b* and the constant term *c* are integers, the formula can produce solutions that are not integers.

8 Use the quadratic formula to check each of the following claims about equations and solutions.

a. The solutions of $x^2 + 5x - 6 = 0$ are *integers* 6 and -1.

b. The solutions of $6x^2 + x - 2 = 0$ are *rational numbers* $\frac{1}{2}$ and $\frac{-2}{3}$.

c. The solutions of $x^2 - 6x + 4 = 0$ are *irrational numbers* $3 + \sqrt{5}$ and $3 - \sqrt{5}$.

d. The equation $x^2 + 5x + 7 = 0$ has no *real number* solutions.

9 Study the results of your work in Problem 8 to find answers to the questions below.

a. What part of the quadratic formula calculations shows whether there will be 2, 1, or 0 real number solutions? How is that information revealed by the calculations?

b. What part of the quadratic formula calculations shows whether the solutions will be rational or irrational numbers? How is that information revealed by the calculations?

7 **a.** The solutions provided by the quadratic formula tell the x-coordinates of the points where the graph of the corresponding quadratic function intersect the x-axis.

NOTE The solution to Problem 6 is on page T342.

   b. $\dfrac{-b}{2a}$ is the x-coordinate for the symmetry line and the maximum/minimum point.

   c. $\dfrac{\sqrt{b^2 - 4ac}}{2a}$ is the distance from the symmetry line along the x-axis to the x-intercepts.

8 **INSTRUCTIONAL NOTE** The proposed solutions for given quadratic equations could be checked by simply substituting them into the given equations to see whether they work. However, the aim of this problem is to give students further practice in use of the quadratic formula and to provide material for reflection in Problem 9 on the number of solutions possible and how one detects the occurrence of the different possibilities. Thus, you want to have students go through the work of using the quadratic formula on these four equations. You may consider having students leave answers in radical form to help them focus on the discriminant to see the connection between its value and the number of solutions.

INSTRUCTIONAL NOTE Students should complete just-in-time Review Task 42 before doing Problem 8.

   a. The proposed solutions are not correct. In fact, the correct solutions are -6 and 1.

   b. The proposed solutions are correct.

   c. The proposed solutions are correct.

   d. The proposed solution is correct.

9 **a–b.** Both answers are provided by examining the *discriminant* term $b^2 - 4ac$. It indicates no real number solutions when it is negative, one real number solution when it is zero, and two real number solutions when it is positive. The solutions will be irrational numbers if and only if the discriminant is not a perfect square integer.

Unit 5

Summarize
the Mathematics

In this investigation, you developed strategies for solving quadratic equations by algebraic reasoning without the aid of calculator or computer tables, graphs, or symbol manipulation programs.

a How can you solve quadratic equations like $ax^2 + b = c$ using algebraic reasoning?

b How can you solve equations like $ax^2 + bx = 0$ using algebraic reasoning?

c How can you solve equations like $ax^2 + bx + c = 0$ when the expression $ax^2 + bx + c$ can be written in equivalent form as the product of two linear expressions?

d In what situations does it make sense to use the quadratic formula to solve an equation?

e How does the quadratic formula show whether a given quadratic equation will have 2, 1, or 0 real number solutions? How will this information appear in a graph and in the calculations leading to the solutions?

Be prepared to share your strategies and thinking with the class.

✓ Check Your Understanding

Solve these equations algebraically—without the quadratic formula, if possible. Show your reasoning in each case.

a. $4x^2 + 7 = 31$

b. $8x^2 + 24x = 0$

c. $x^2 + 15x - 16 = 0$

d. $2x^2 + x = -1$

e. $3x^2 - 10x + 12 = 9$

Be sure to probe to see if students connect the graphical meaning. This is a WOW moment, and it really helps students by making the quadratic formula come alive and have meaning. This idea also comes up in the Looking Back lesson.

Summarize
the Mathematics

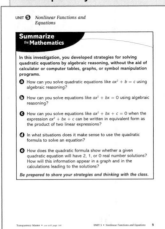
(a) To solve quadratic equations like $ax^2 + b = c$ by reasoning algebraically, one would first subtract b from both sides of the equation. Then, both sides of the equation would be divided by a. Finally, the square root of each side is taken. It is important to remember that x is equal to $+\sqrt{\dfrac{c-b}{a}}$ or $-\sqrt{\dfrac{c-b}{a}}$.

(b) To solve equations like $ax^2 + bx = 0$ by reasoning without use of a calculator, one would first factor an x from both terms $x(ax + b) = 0$. Then, both of the new factors would be set equal to zero and each of these new equations would be solved for x. If a and b have a common factor, that number can also be factored from both terms.

(c) To solve equations like $ax^2 + bx + c = 0$ when the expression $ax^2 + bx + c$ can be written in equivalent form as the product of two linear expressions, one should set each of the factors (in the new factored expression) equal to zero and solve the two new equations for x. To make this factoring more manageable, it is helpful to first look for common factors for a, b, and c.

(d) Student responses will vary, but many will agree that if the factored form is not quickly apparent or if it is clear that the solutions will be non-integer, then the quadratic formula would be a wise choice.

(e) $b^2 - 4ac$ indicates two real number solutions when it is positive, one real number solution when it is zero, and no real number solutions when it is negative. Quadratic equations of the form $ax^2 + bx + c = 0$ can be solved by analyzing the quadratic function $y = ax^2 + bx + c$. Solving for y values of zero is like finding the x values for the x-intercepts. So, when there are two real number solutions, the graph of the function intersects the x-axis twice. When there is one real number solution, the graph touches the x-axis once. This means that the maximum or minimum point is the x-intercept. When there are no real number solutions, the graph is either above or below the x-axis.

MATH TOOLKIT Record the quadratic formula and an example of its use. Explain what the $\dfrac{-b}{2a}$ and the value of $\dfrac{\sqrt{b^2 - 4ac}}{2a}$ tell about the solutions to the equation $ax^2 + bx + c = 0$ and the graph of the corresponding function $y = \ldots$.

COLLABORATION PROMPT I made sure everyone had correct solutions and understood by $\ldots$.

✔Check Your Understanding

Students should record their reasoning in each case.

a. $x = \sqrt{6}$ or $x - \sqrt{6}$
b. $x = 0$ or $x = -3$
c. $x = 1$ or $x = -16$
d. No real solutions
e. $x = 3$ or $x = \dfrac{1}{3}$

Applications

1 Consider $I(p) = p(50 - p)$, which gives the expected income in dollars from a bungee jump attraction when the ticket price is p dollars.

 a. Is I a function of p? Explain why or why not.

 b. What does $I(10) = 400$ tell about the bungee attraction?

 c. What are the theoretical domain and range of the function?

 d. What is a practical domain and range of the function in this context?

 e. How does a graph of the function $I(p)$ help determine both the theoretical and practical domains and ranges?

2 Examine the following tables to determine which show y as a function of x. For each table that is not a function, explain why not.

 a.

x	1	2	3	4	5	6	7	8	9
y	3	5	7	9	11	13	15	17	19

 b.

x	1	2	3	4	5	6	7	8	9
y	3	5	7	9	11	9	7	5	3

 c.

x	9	4	1	0	1	4	9	16	25
y	−3	−2	−1	0	1	2	3	4	3

 d.

x	1	2	3	4	5	4	3	2	1
y	3	5	7	9	11	9	7	5	3

3 Examine the following graphs to determine which show y as a function of x. For each graph that is not a function, explain why not.

 a.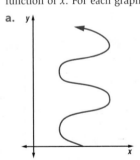

 b.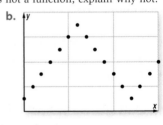

Applications

1 **a.** *I* is a function of *p* since for every set price, there is only one estimated income for the bungee jump attraction.

b. $I(10) = 400$ indicates that when the ticket price is set at $10, the estimated income for the attraction is $400.

c. The theoretical domain is all real numbers. The theoretical range is all real numbers less than or equal to 625. (At this stage, students may find the maximum value graphically.)

d. A sensible practical domain would be $0 \leq p \leq 50$. The practical range corresponding to that domain is $0 \leq I \leq 625$.

e. The theoretical domain and range can be determined by scanning a table of values or examining the graph of the function (a concave-down parabola with maximum at $(25, 625)$). The practical domain can be ascertained in the same way, looking only at the values when both the price and income are positive.

2 **a.** Yes, the relationship in the table is a function.

b. Yes, the relationship in the table is a function.

c. No, the relationship in the table is not a function because the numbers 1, 4, and 9 each have two different *y* values associated with them in the table.

d. Yes, the relationship in the table is a function. (Even though there are repeated (x, y) pairs such as $(3, 7)$, there are no different *y* values for any one *x* value.)

3 **a.** No, because several *x* values have more than one corresponding *y* value.

b. Yes, the 13 *x* values each have only one corresponding *y* value on the plot.

c.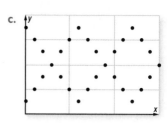

d.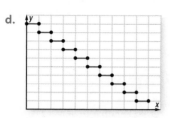

(4) If $h(t)$ represents height (in feet above the ground) of a skydiver t seconds into a drop, what do each of the following statements tell about the diver's flight?

a. $h(0) = 10,000$

b. $h(25) = 7,500$

c. $h(10) - h(5) = -2,500$

(5) The Zelden Athletic Shoe Company estimates that its production costs (per pair of shoes made) for a new model endorsed by a star athlete will be a function of the number of pairs of shoes that it makes. The rule relating cost to number of pairs of shoes is $c(x) = 29 + \frac{25,000,000}{x}$. Calculate and explain the meaning of:

a. $c(1)$ **b.** $c(1,000,000)$

c. $c(2,500,000)$ **d.** The value of x for which $c(x) = 40$.

(6) Describe the theoretical domains and ranges for the following functions. That is, explain the values of x that can be used as inputs and the values of y that can occur as outputs.

a. $f(x) = 5 + 3x$ **b.** $g(x) = x^2 + 4$ **c.** $h(x) = 1.5^x$

d. $j(x) = 3\sqrt{x}$ **e.** $k(x) = -x^2 + 2$ **f.** $m(x) = \frac{3}{x}$

(7) The reflectors in flashlights, like the headlamp model below, are often parabolic in shape so that the bulb sends maximum light forward. In one such headlamp, the reflectors have a diameter of 10 centimeters and are 5 centimeters deep.

c. No, because many of the x values have two different corresponding y values, as indicated by points in the plot.

d. No, because values at grid units each have two corresponding y values.

4 a. $h(0) = 10{,}000$ means that the diver left the plane at a height of 10,000 feet above ground.

b. $h(25) = 7{,}500$ means that after 25 seconds, the diver had reached a height of 7,500 feet.

c. $h(10) - h(5) = -2{,}500$ means that between 5 and 10 seconds, the diver fell 2,500 feet or became 2,500 feet closer to the ground.

5 a. $c(1) = 25{,}000{,}029$ means that if the company makes only 1 pair of shoes, its production cost per pair will be \$25,000,029.

b. $c(1{,}000{,}000) = 54$ means that if the company makes 1 million pairs of shoes, its production cost per pair will be \$54.

c. $c(2{,}500{,}000) = 39$ means that if the company makes 2.5 million pairs of shoes, its production cost per pair will be \$39.

d. $c(x) = 40$ when $x \approx 2{,}272{,}727$ which means that if the company makes 2,272,727 pairs of shoes, the production cost per pair will average \$40.

6 a. Both domain and range are all real numbers.

b. Domain is all real numbers and range is all real numbers greater than or equal to 4.

c. Domain is all real numbers and range is all positive real numbers.

d. Both domain and range are all non-negative real numbers.

e. Domain is all real numbers and range is all real numbers less than or equal to 2.

f. Both domain and range are all nonzero real numbers.

Find rules for three different quadratic functions that will each give a graph in the parabolic shape required for the headlamp reflector. Design the three function rules so that their graphs look like those in the following diagrams.

a. Open up with vertex below x-axis

b. Open up with vertex on x-axis

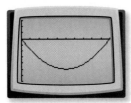

c. Open down with vertex above x-axis

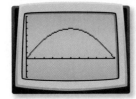

(8) The dish antennas used to receive satellite television signals vary in size but are all in the shape of parabolas. Suppose that you were asked to design such a parabolic dish that had a diameter of 4 feet and a depth of 1 foot.

a. Write the rule for a quadratic function with graph that has x-intercepts at $(0, 0)$ and $(4, 0)$ and minimum point at $(2, -1)$.

b. Write the rule for a quadratic function with graph that has x-intercepts at $(0, 0)$ and $(4, 0)$ and maximum point at $(2, 1)$.

LESSON 1 • Quadratic Functions, Expressions, and Equations   **347**

7   **a.** $f(x) = 0.2x(x - 10)$

       b. $f(x) = 0.2x(x - 10) + 5$

       c. $f(x) = -0.2x(x - 10)$

8   **a.** $f(x) = 0.25x(x - 4)$

       b. $f(x) = -0.25x(x - 4)$

Unit 5

9 Find coordinates of x-intercepts, y-intercept, and maximum or minimum points on the graphs of these quadratic functions. Show how the answers can be obtained by reasoning with the symbolic forms. Think strategically about when and how your answers for one part can help you with the next part.

   a. $f(x) = x(7 - x)$ **b.** $f(x) = -x(7 - x)$

   c. $f(x) = (x - 3)(x + 5)$ **d.** $f(x) = -(x - 3)(x + 5)$

   e. $f(x) = (x - 3)(x - 8)$ **f.** $f(x) = -(x - 3)(x - 8)$

   g. $f(x) = 2(x - 3)(x - 8)$ **h.** $f(x) = -2(x - 3)(x - 8)$

10 Write rules for quadratic functions with graphs that meet these conditions:

   a. x-intercepts at $(0, 0)$ and $(6, 0)$ with graph opening upward

   b. x-intercepts at $(-2, 0)$ and $(6, 0)$ with graph opening upward

   c. x-intercepts at $(-4, 0)$ and $(-6, 0)$ with graph opening downward

   d. x-intercepts at $(2, 0)$ and $(6, 0)$ with minimum point at $(4, -8)$

   e. x-intercepts at $(2, 0)$ and $(6, 0)$ with maximum point at $(4, 2)$

   f. x-intercepts at $(-2, 0)$ and $(6, 0)$ with y-intercept at $(0, -60)$

11 Write these products in equivalent $ax^2 + bx + c$ form.

   a. $(x + 7)(x - 3)$ **b.** $(x - 7)(x + 3)$

   c. $(x - 7)(x - 3)$ **d.** $(x + 3)(x - 3)$

   e. $(3 + x)(x - 3)$ **f.** $(x + 7)(x + 7)$

   g. $(2x + 7)(2x - 7)$ **h.** $(2x + 7)^2$

   i. $(5x - 3)(4 + 2x)$

12 Write these quadratic expressions in equivalent form as products of linear factors, where possible.

   a. $x^2 + 7x + 10$ **b.** $x^2 - 7x + 10$

   c. $x^2 + 4x - 12$ **d.** $x^2 - 64$

   e. $x^2 + 6x + 9$ **f.** $64 - x^2$

   g. $x^2 - 9x + 20$ **h.** $2x^2 - 8$

13 Solve these quadratic equations by factoring, where possible.

   a. $x^2 + 7x + 10 = 0$ **b.** $x^2 - 7x + 10 = 0$

   c. $x^2 + 4x - 10 = 2$ **d.** $x^2 - 64 = 0$

   e. $x^2 + 6x - 9 = 0$ **f.** $x^2 - 9x + 20 = 20$

   g. $2x^2 - 10x = 0$ **h.** $x^2 - 15x + 50 = 0$

14 Solve these quadratic equations by use of the quadratic formula.

   a. $2x^2 - 10x - 48 = 0$ **b.** $2x^2 - x + 8 = 0$

   c. $6x^2 + 7x - 10 = -5$ **d.** $3x^2 - 10x + 7 = 0$

   e. $4x^2 + 12x + 9 = 0$ **f.** $-2x^2 + 8x - 3 = 2$

9 **INSTRUCTIONAL NOTE** The following is a list only of the key coordinates; students should be able to communicate how to obtain these without the use of a calculator.

   a. x-intercepts: $(0, 0)$, $(7, 0)$; y-intercept: $(0, 0)$; maximum at $(3.5, 12.25)$

   b. x-intercepts: $(0, 0)$, $(7, 0)$; y-intercept: $(0, 0)$; minimum at $(3.5, -12.25)$

   c. x-intercepts: $(3, 0)$, $(-5, 0)$; y-intercept: $(0, -15)$; minimum at $(-1, -16)$

   d. x-intercepts: $(3, 0)$, $(-5, 0)$; y-intercept: $(0, 15)$; maximum at $(-1, 16)$

   e. x-intercepts: $(3, 0)$, $(8, 0)$; y-intercept: $(0, 24)$; minimum at $(5.5, -6.25)$

   f. x-intercepts: $(3, 0)$, $(8, 0)$; y-intercept: $(0, -24)$; maximum at $(5.5, 6.25)$

   g. x-intercepts: $(3, 0)$, $(8, 0)$; y-intercept: $(0, 48)$; minimum at $(5.5, -12.5)$

   h. x-intercepts: $(3, 0)$, $(8, 0)$; y-intercept: $(0, -48)$; minimum at $(5.5, 12.5)$

10   **a.** $y = ax(x - 6)$, where a is any positive number

   b. $y = a(x + 2)(x - 6)$, where a is any positive number

   c. $y = -a(x + 4)(x + 6)$, where a is any positive number

   d. $y = 2(x - 2)(x - 6)$

   e. $y = -\frac{1}{2}(x - 2)(x - 6)$

   f. $y = 5(x + 2)(x - 6)$

11   **a.** $(x + 7)(x - 3) = x^2 + 4x - 21$ **b.** $(x - 7)(x + 3) = x^2 - 4x - 21$

   c. $(x - 7)(x - 3) = x^2 - 10x + 21$ **d.** $(x + 3)(x - 3) = x^2 - 9$

   e. $(3 + x)(x - 3) = x^2 - 9$ **f.** $(x + 7)(x + 7) = x^2 + 14x + 49$

   g. $(2x + 7)(2x - 7) = 4x^2 - 49$ **h.** $(2x + 7)^2 = 4x^2 + 28x + 49$

   i. $(5x - 3)(4 + 2x) = 10x^2 + 14x - 12$

12   **a.** $x^2 + 7x + 10 = (x + 2)(x + 5)$ **b.** $x^2 - 7x + 10 = (x - 2)(x - 5)$

   c. $x^2 + 4x - 12 = (x + 6)(x - 2)$ **d.** $x^2 - 64 = (x + 8)(x - 8)$

   e. $x^2 + 6x + 9 = (x + 3)^2$ **f.** $64 - x^2 = (8 - x)(8 + x)$

   g. $x^2 - 9x + 20 = (x - 5)(x - 4)$ **h.** $2x^2 - 8 = 2(x - 2)(x + 2)$ or $(2x - 4)(x + 2)$ or $(x - 2)(2x + 4)$

13 Students should be able to factor all parts except Part e.

   a. $x = -2$ or $x = -5$ **b.** $x = 2$ or $x = 5$

   c. $x = 2$ or $x = -6$ **d.** $x = 8$ or $x = -8$

   e. $x = -3 \pm 3\sqrt{2}$ **f.** $x = 0$ or $x = 9$

   g. $x = 0$ or $x = 5$ **h.** $x = 5$ or $x = 10$

14   **a.** $x = -3$ or $x = 8$ **b.** No real solutions

   c. $x = \frac{1}{2}$ or $x = -1\frac{2}{3}$ **d.** $x = 1$ or $x = 2\frac{1}{3}$

   e. $x = -1.5$ **f.** $x = 2 \pm \dfrac{\sqrt{6}}{2}$

15 For each part, write a quadratic equation that has the indicated solutions.

a. $x = 5$ and $x = -2$ b. $x = -5$ and $x = -2$

c. $x = 0.5$ and $x = \frac{2}{3}$ d. $x = 1$ and $x = \frac{1}{2}$

Connections

16 The graphs below illustrate three different relationships between variables. Match each graph with the description in Parts a–c it seems most likely to represent. In each case, decide whether the graph shows y as a function of x.

a. Age (in years) and height (in centimeters) for a group of 20 young people of various ages

b. Age (in years) and IQ for the same group of 20 young people

c. Age (in years) and average height (in centimeters) for young people of various ages

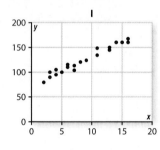

I

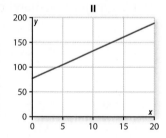

II

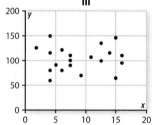

III

17 The transformations you studied in Unit 3, *Coordinate Methods*, are geometric functions. Under a transformation, each preimage point is paired with exactly one image point. You can use function notation when describing these transformations.

a. Consider $T(x, y) = (x + 5, y - 12)$.

i. Find $T(1, 1)$.

ii. Find $T(-20, 15)$.

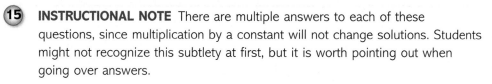

15 **INSTRUCTIONAL NOTE** There are multiple answers to each of these questions, since multiplication by a constant will not change solutions. Students might not recognize this subtlety at first, but it is worth pointing out when going over answers.

a. $x = 5$ and $x = -2$; $k(x - 5)(x + 2) = 0$

b. $x = -5$ and $x = -2$; $k(x + 5)(x + 2) = 0$

c. $x = 0.5$ and $x = \frac{2}{3}$; $k(2x - 1)(3x - 2) = 0$

d. $x = 1$ and $x = \frac{1}{2}$; $k(x - 1)(2x - 1) = 0$

Connections

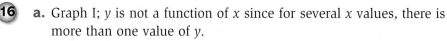

16 **a.** Graph I; y is not a function of x since for several x values, there is more than one value of y.

b. Graph III; y is not a function of x since for several x values, there is more than one value of y.

c. Graph II; y is a function of x since there is only one y value for every x value shown on the graph.

17 **a.** **i.** $(6, -11)$

      ii. $(-15, 3)$

Unit 5

iii. Find $T(0, 0)$.

iv. Find (x, y) so that $T(x, y) = (-32, 18)$.

v. What type of transformation is T?

b. Consider $M(x, y) = (y, x)$.

 i. Find $M(2, 2)$.

 ii. Find $M(16, -11)$.

 iii. Find $M(0, 0)$.

 iv. Find (x, y) so that $M(x, y) = (23, -30)$.

 v. What type of transformation is M?

c. Consider $S(x, y) = (8x, 8y)$.

 i. Find $S(5, 5)$.

 ii. Find $S(-12, 10)$.

 iii. Find $S(0, 0)$.

 iv. Find (x, y) so that $S(x, y) = (2, -6)$.

 v. What type of transformation is S?

18 When elementary school students first learn the standard algorithm for multiplication, they are often encouraged to record their work for a calculation like 65×42 in a form like this:

$$
\begin{array}{r}
65 \\
\times\ 42 \\
\hline
10 \\
120 \\
200 \\
2,400 \\
\hline
2,730
\end{array}
$$

a. Expand the product $(60 + 5)(40 + 2)$ to show why that "beginner's" multiplication algorithm works.

b. Show how to calculate 73×57 using the "beginner's" multiplication algorithm and how expansion of $(70 + 3)(50 + 7)$ explains why the steps work.

19 Use the algebraic principle that $(m - n)(m + n) = m^2 - n^2$ for any numbers m and n to explain these shortcuts for what seem to be complex arithmetic calculations.

a. $95 \times 105 = 10,000 - 25$ or $9,975$

b. $93 \times 107 = 10,000 - 49$ or $9,951$

c. $991 \times 1,009 = 1,000,000 - 81$ or $999,919$

    iii. $(5, -12)$

    iv. $(-37, 30)$

    v. Translation with $h = 5$ and $k = -12$

b. **i.** $(2, 2)$

    ii. $(-11, 16)$

    iii. $(0, 0)$

    iv. $(-30, 23)$

    v. Reflection across the line $y = x$

c. **i.** $(40, 40)$

    ii. $(-96, 80)$

    iii. $(0, 0)$

    iv. $\left(\dfrac{2}{8}, -\dfrac{6}{8}\right)$

    v. Size transformation centered at origin with magnitude 8

(18) **a.** $(60 + 5)(40 + 2) = 60 \cdot 40 + 60 \cdot 2 + 5 \cdot 40 + 5 \cdot 2$
$$= 2{,}400 + 120 + 200 + 10$$
$$= 2{,}730$$

b. $(70 + 3)(50 + 7) = 70(50) + 70(7) + 3(50) + 3(7)$ and

$$
\begin{array}{r}
57 \\
\times 73 \\
\hline
21 \\
150 \\
490 \\
3500 \\
\hline
4161 \\
\end{array}
$$

(19) **a.** Explanations should incorporate the expression $(100 - 5)(100 + 5)$.

b. Explanations should include the expression $(100 - 7)(100 + 7)$ which leads to $10{,}000 - 49 = 9{,}951$.

c. Explanations should use the expression $(1{,}000 - 9)(1{,}000 + 9)$.

20 How can areas of regions in the diagram below be used to give a visual proof that $(x + q)(x + p) = x^2 + (q + p)x + qp$ for any positive numbers p and q?

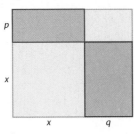

21 Consider matrices $M = \begin{bmatrix} 2 & 3 \\ 4 & 5 \end{bmatrix}$ and $N = \begin{bmatrix} 3 & 4 \\ 2 & 5 \end{bmatrix}$.

a. Compare $7M + 7N$ and $7(M + N)$.

   i. Are the results equal?

   ii. Which expression requires fewer calculations to evaluate?

b. Compare $M(M + N)$ and $M^2 + MN$.

   i. Are the results equal?

   ii. Which expression requires fewer calculations to evaluate?

22 In the *Coordinate Methods* unit, you learned that points on a circle with radius r and center (p, q) have coordinates that satisfy the equation $(x - p)^2 + (y - q)^2 = r^2$. In a precalculus textbook, the following equation was given as an equation of a circle:

$$x^2 + y^2 + 6x - 4y = 23$$

Rebecca believed she could reason as follows to determine the center and radius of the circle and then easily sketch it.

$x^2 + y^2 + 6x - 4y = 23$ is equivalent to $(x^2 + 6x) + (y^2 - 4y) = 23$, which is equivalent to $(x^2 + 6x + 9) + (y^2 - 4y + 4) = 23 + 9 + 4$, which is equivalent to $(x + 3)^2 + (y - 2)^2 = 36$. So, the circle has center at $(-3, 2)$ and radius 6.

a. Explain Rebecca's strategy and how it is related to your earlier work with recognizing the form of *perfect square* quadratic expressions that are the expanded form of expressions like $(x + a)^2$.

b. Sketch the circle in a coordinate plane.

c. Use similar reasoning to identify the center and radius of each circle below, and then sketch the circle in a coordinate plane.

   i. $x^2 + y^2 + 12x - 2y = -21$

   ii. $x^2 + y^2 + 8y = 9$

20
$$(x + p)(x + q) = px + pq + x^2 + qx$$
$$= x^2 + (p + q)x + pq$$

Algebraically, using the distributive property,

$$(x + p)(x + q) = x(x + q) + p(x + q)$$
$$= x^2 + qx + px + pq$$
$$= x^2 + (p + q)x + pq$$

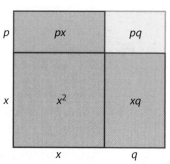

21 **a.** $7M + 7N = \begin{bmatrix} 35 & 49 \\ 42 & 70 \end{bmatrix}$ and $7(M + N) = \begin{bmatrix} 35 & 49 \\ 42 & 70 \end{bmatrix}$.

  i. The resulting matrices are the same.

  ii. The expression $7(M + N)$ when evaluated required fewer calculations.

b. $M(M + N) = \begin{bmatrix} 28 & 44 \\ 50 & 78 \end{bmatrix}$ and $M^2 + MN = \begin{bmatrix} 28 & 44 \\ 50 & 78 \end{bmatrix}$.

  i. The resulting matrices are the same.

  ii. Again, the $M(M + N)$ expression required fewer calculations.

22 **a.** Rebecca is "completing the square" or creating two perfect square quadratic expressions so she can factor them and end up with the standard form for the equation of a circle.

b.
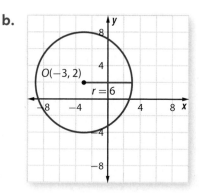

c. **i.** $(x^2 + 12x + 36) + (y^2 - 2y + 1) = -21 + 36 + 1$; $(x + 6)^2 + (y - 1)^2 = 16$

ii. $x^2 + y^2 + 8y + 16 = 9 + 16$
$x^2 + (y + 4)^2 = 25$

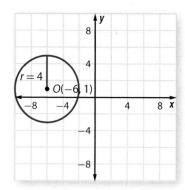

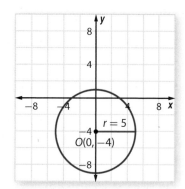

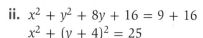

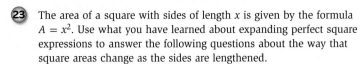

23 The area of a square with sides of length x is given by the formula $A = x^2$. Use what you have learned about expanding perfect square expressions to answer the following questions about the way that square areas change as the sides are lengthened.

a. Kei and Matsu claimed that if you increase the side lengths in a square from x to $x + 2$, the area will increase by $2^2 = 4$; if you increase side lengths to $x + 3$, the area will increase by $3^2 = 9$; and, in general, if you increase the side lengths to $x + k$, the area will increase by k^2. Are they right? Explain.

b. What algebraic argument would prove or disprove the conjecture by Kei and Matsu?

c. What visual proof would prove or disprove their conjecture?

24 Use the meaning of square root to help solve each equation.

a. $\sqrt{x - 4} = 10$

b. $\sqrt{3x - 5} = 4$

c. $\sqrt{x - 1} + 3 = x$

Reflections

25 When mathematics students first meet the function notation $f(x)$, they often assume that it means "f times x." Why do you suppose that is such a common difficulty, and what could you do to keep the special meaning of the notation clear?

26 What seems to be the difference between claiming that a relationship between variables x and y *is a function* and suggesting that y *depends on x*?

27 Explain the difference in meaning of these equations: $f(a) = 0$ and $f(0) = a$.

28 Consider the graph of $f(x) = (x - 3)(x + 4)$.

a. What are the x-intercepts of the graph?

b. Why does the graph of the function $g(x) = (x - 3)(x + 4) + 2$ have different x-intercepts than $f(x)$?

c. Why does the graph of the function $h(x) = 2(x - 3)(x + 4)$ have the same x-intercepts as $f(x)$?

29 Based on your earlier studies, you know that two points determine a line. Given the coordinates of the points, you can write an equation $y = ax + b$ for the line.

a. How many points do you think are needed to determine the equation of a parabola?

b. Does it make any difference which points you are given? Explain your thinking.

23 **a.** No, they are not correct. Students may use a specific square to provide a counterexample.

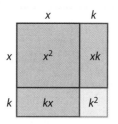

b. $(s + k)^2 = s^2 + 2sk + k^2$; so area increases by $(k^2 + 2sk)$

c. The sketch at the right suggests a visual disproof of their conjecture.

24 **a.** $x = 104$ **b.** $x = 7$ **c.** $x = 5$

INSTRUCTIONAL NOTE
Task 24 Part c provides an opportunity to discuss extraneous solutions.

Reflections

25 Student responses may vary but should include a statement about how parentheses around a number or expression often indicates multiplication by the number, variable, or expression adjacent to the quantity in parentheses. Students may suggest that when multiplication is to be indicated, all terms should be placed in parentheses.

26 The difference between claiming that *y is a function of x* and *y depends on x* is the difference between a term that has precise mathematical meaning and one that is used more casually in everyday discourse. The term "function" as it is used in mathematics implies a precisely determined relationship: given the value of one variable, there is exactly one well-defined value of the other. When there is simply a loosely defined relationship of dependence between the two variables, the correlation of values for the variables will not be as exact or as well defined.

27 $f(a) = 0$ implies that when a is the input, the value of the function is 0. The point $(a, 0)$ will be on the graph of the function and the function will have an x-intercept at a. The expression $f(0) = a$ implies that when 0 is the input, the value of the function is a. The point $(0, a)$ will be on the graph of the function, and the function will have a y-intercept at a.

28 **a.** $(3, 0)$ and $(-4, 0)$

b. The two functions have different x-intercepts because the graph of $g(x)$ is obtained by shifting the graph of $f(x)$ two units up. Therefore, a narrower part of the parabola crosses the x-axis, causing the x-intercepts to be closer together on $g(x)$ than on $f(x)$.

c. Since the graph of $h(x)$ is obtained by vertically "stretching" the graph of $f(x)$, points on the x-axis stay fixed while all other points shift away from the x-axis. Also, the product $2(x - 3)(x + 4)$ is zero exactly when the product $(x - 3)(x + 4)$ is zero.

29 **a–b.** Any three (non-collinear) points determine a parabola.

INSTRUCTIONAL NOTE
For Task 29, refer to Summarize the Mathematics page 335 and PMD for other ideas discussed earlier. You may want to have students choose any three points and find the resulting quadratic equation using matrices. See Extensions Task 17 in Lesson 3 of *Matrix Methods*.

30 When students are asked to expand quadratic expressions, there are some common errors.

   a. What do you think is the most common error in expanding $(x + a)^2$, and how would you help someone see the error and understand the correct expansion?

   b. What do you think is the most common error in expanding $(x + a)(x + b)$, and how would you help someone see the error and understand the correct expansion?

31 When you need to solve a quadratic equation, how do you decide whether to try factoring, to use the quadratic formula, to use a CAS, or to use a table or a graph of the related quadratic function?

32 When attempting to solve a quadratic equation of the form $x^2 + bx + c = 0$ by factoring, how do you approach the task of finding linear factors whose product is the given quadratic expression?

33 Two students, Brody and Lydia, were arguing about how to solve $(x + 3)(x + 1) = 24$. Brody figured that since $6 \cdot 4 = 24$, he could use the equations $x + 3 = 6$ and $x + 1 = 4$ to find the solution. Lydia insisted that his method will not always give him the right answer. What do you think about Brody's approach?

Extensions

34 In testing the effect of platform height on roll time for the *On a Roll* experiments from Unit 1, *Functions, Equations, and Systems*, it makes sense to use a single ramp length in all rolls. Suppose that a 10-foot ramp length was the choice.

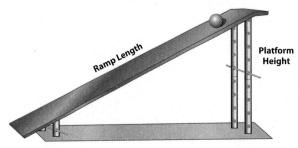

   a. What rule can be used to calculate the distance from the base of the platform to the end of the ramp for any platform height?

   i. Why does this rule describe a function relating distance from platform base to ramp end and platform height?

   ii. What is the practical domain of this function? What is the theoretical domain?

   iii. What is the practical range of this function? What is the theoretical range?

LESSON 1 • Quadratic Functions, Expressions, and Equations **353**

30 **a.** Beginning students most likely will expand $(x + a)^2$ as $x^2 + a^2$. They can avoid that error by writing $(x + a)^2$ as $(x + a)(x + a)$ and using the distributive property or by recalling an area model for representing the square.

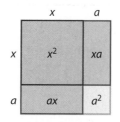

b. Beginning students most likely will expand $(x + a)(x + b)$ as $x^2 + ab$. They can avoid that error by remembering to use the distributive property or recalling an area model for representing the product of binomials.

31 Student preferences may vary. Students should include rationale for their preferences. They are likely to mention that they will use factoring if they can see quite quickly just how to factor the given quadratic expression. If not, they might turn to the quadratic formula, although it involves many sub-calculations that some students might find pitfalls to error. A CAS avoids those complications if it is handy and if the students are good at entering expressions.

Even if students do not readily mention using approximation by scanning tables or graphs, you should remind them that those strategies are available and that in such approaches to solving, you get some insight into the way the involved quadratic expression behaves near solution points—in applied problem solving that is a valuable insight because it tells how sensitive the solution is to small variations in problem conditions.

32 If the leading coefficient of the quadratic expression is 1, students will most likely look for numbers whose product is the constant term and whose sum is the coefficient of the x term.

33 Although Brody's approach works in this case, it will only be successful if a single value of x satisfies both equations. If his logic were to be based upon the fact that $4 \cdot 6 = 24$, there would have to be a single value of x which satisfies both $x + 3 = 4$ and $x + 1 = 6$. Solving the first equation, you get $x = 1$. Substituting that value into the second, you get $2 = 6$, which is clearly a false statement.

Extensions

34 **a.** Let h be platform height and let d be distance from the end of the ramp to the base of the platform.

Rule: $d = \sqrt{100 - h^2}$

   i. For any given platform height, there is exactly one corresponding distance from the end of the ramp to the base of the platform.

   ii. The practical domain is $0 \leq h \leq 10$. The theoretical domain is all real numbers between -10 and 10 (when $|h| > 10$, the quantity under the radical sign is negative and the square root is a complex number (that students have not yet learned about).

   iii. The practical range is $0 \leq d \leq 10$. The theoretical range is the same.

Unit 5

b. Use the function rule from Part a to produce a table showing how the distance from platform base to ramp end changes as the platform height increases from 0 to 10 feet in steps of 1 foot. Plot these (*height, distance*) values. Then add the function graph to your plot.

c. Use the function rule from Part a to write a rule giving ramp slope as a function of platform height.

   i. Use that rule to produce a table showing the slope of the ramp for platform heights from 0 to 10 feet in steps of 1 foot.

   ii. Plot these (*height, slope*) values. Add to your plot the function giving the slope for any platform height.

35 Consider the following functions.

$$f(x) = 3x^2 \qquad g(x) = -2x^3 \qquad h(x) = \frac{5}{x} \qquad k(x) = -\frac{4}{x^2}$$

a. Write sentences describing, in terms of direct and inverse variation, how each of the above functions vary with x.

b. What is the value of each function when $x = 1$? When $x = -1$? Express your answers using function notation.

c. When a function correspondence holds in both directions (when each value of x corresponds to exactly one value of the function, *and* each value of the function corresponds to exactly one value of x), we say that the function is **one-to-one**.

   i. Determine whether or not each of the above functions is one-to-one.

   ii. How could you tell by looking at a function rule that describes a direct or inverse variation whether the function is one-to-one?

   iii. How could you tell by looking at a graph of a function whether the function is one-to-one?

36 In the Course 1 *Patterns in Shape* unit, you used congruent triangles to prove that if the diagonals of a parallelogram are congruent, then the parallelogram is a rectangle. In this task, you will establish that result by algebraic reasoning with coordinates.

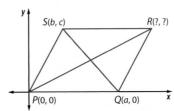

a. What must the coordinates of point R be if the quadrilateral is a parallelogram?

b. Write expressions for the length of diagonal $\overline{PR}$ and for the length of diagonal $\overline{QS}$.

c. Use the given fact $\overline{PR} \cong \overline{QS}$ and your expressions in Part b to write a convincing argument that $\square PQRS$ is a rectangle.

37 Solve $x^2 - x - 42 > 0$ by first factoring the quadratic expression.

b.

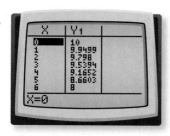 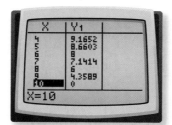 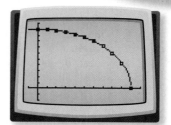

c. i. $s = \dfrac{h}{\sqrt{100 - h^2}}$, where s is the ramp slope

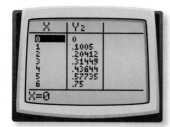 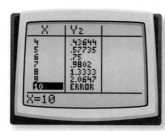

ii.

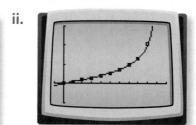

35

a. $f(x) = 3x^2$ shows f varying directly with the square of x with constant of proportionality 3.

$g(x) = -2x^3$ shows g varying directly with the cube of x with constant of proportionality -2.

$h(x) = \dfrac{5}{x}$ shows h varying inversely to x with constant of proportionality 5.

$k(x) = -\dfrac{4}{x^2}$ shows k varying inversely with the square of x with constant of proportionality -4.

b. $f(1) = 3$ and $f(-1) = 3$
$g(1) = -2$ and $g(-1) = 2$
$h(1) = 5$ and $h(-1) = -5$
$k(1) = -4$ and $k(-1) = -4$

c. i. The functions g and h are one-to-one; functions f and k are not.

ii. Direct or inverse variation functions that involve even powers of the independent variable are not one-to-one because x and $-x$ will always produce the same output values in the function. When an odd power is involved, the function is one-to-one.

iii. One can tell whether any function is one-to-one by inspecting the graph to see if there is any y value that corresponds to two or more x values. Problems will occur if a horizontal line cuts the graph in two or more distinct points, indicating that two different x values have the same corresponding y value. If not, then the function is one-to-one.

> **NOTE** The solutions to Tasks 36 and 37 are on page T355.

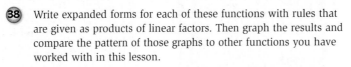

38 Write expanded forms for each of these functions with rules that are given as products of linear factors. Then graph the results and compare the pattern of those graphs to other functions you have worked with in this lesson.

a. $y = x(x - 1)(x - 2)$

b. $y = x(x + 3)(x - 3)$

c. $y = (x + 2)(x - 1)(x - 4)$

39 Consider line segments of lengths $2m$, $m^2 - 1$, and $m^2 + 1$ where m is any positive integer greater than 1.

a. If $m = 3$, can a triangle be formed with the given lengths as sides? What about if $m = 5$? If $m = 10$?

b. For each triangle that could be formed in Part a, is the triangle a right triangle? Explain your reasoning.

c. Write a general argument that shows that for any positive integer $m > 1$, segments of lengths $2m$, $m^2 - 1$, and $m^2 + 1$ will form a triangle.

d. Show that for any positive integer $m > 1$, $(2m)^2 + (m^2 - 1)^2 = (m^2 + 1)^2$. What can you conclude about the triangles in Part c?

e. Develop a spreadsheet that can be used to make a list of *Pythagorean triples* (a, b, c)—three numbers that are lengths of the legs and hypotenuse of a right triangle. Then, in the same row that each triple appears in the spreadsheet, calculate $a^2 + b^2$ and c^2 to check your work.

40 Look back at your work for Extensions Task 39. If m and n are any two positive integers with $m > n$, will the three numbers $m^2 - n^2$, $2mn$, and $m^2 + n^2$ be a Pythagorean triple? Write a convincing argument justifying your answer.

41 Provide justifications for each step in the following proof that the quadratic formula will find any solutions for equations in the form $ax^2 + bx + c = 0$, $a \neq 0$.

If $ax^2 + bx + c = 0$:

then $a\left(x^2 + \frac{b}{a}x + \frac{c}{a}\right) = 0$; $\qquad\qquad$ (1)

then $x^2 + \frac{b}{a}x + \frac{c}{a} = 0$; $\qquad\qquad$ (2)

then $x^2 + \frac{b}{a}x = \frac{-c}{a}$; $\qquad\qquad$ (3)

then $x^2 + \frac{b}{a}x + \frac{b^2}{4a^2} = \frac{-c}{a} + \frac{b^2}{4a^2}$; $\qquad$ (4)

then $\left(x + \frac{b}{2a}\right)^2 = \frac{b^2}{4a^2} + \frac{-c}{a}$; $\qquad$ (5)

then $\left(x + \frac{b}{2a}\right)^2 = \frac{b^2}{4a^2} + \frac{-4ac}{4a^2}$; $\qquad$ (6)

then $\left(x + \frac{b}{2a}\right)^2 = \frac{b^2 - 4ac}{4a^2}$; $\qquad\qquad$ (7)

then $x + \frac{b}{2a} = \frac{\sqrt{b^2 - 4ac}}{2a}$ or $x + \frac{b}{2a} = \frac{-\sqrt{b^2 - 4ac}}{2a}$. $\quad$ (8)

So, $x = \frac{-b}{2a} + \frac{\sqrt{b^2 - 4ac}}{2a}$ or $x = \frac{-b}{2a} - \frac{\sqrt{b^2 - 4ac}}{2a}$. $\quad$ (9)

LESSON 1 • Quadratic Functions, Expressions, and Equations **355**

36 **a.** $R(a + b, c)$

b. $PR = \sqrt{(a + b)^2 + c^2}$ and $QS = \sqrt{(a - b)^2 + c^2}$

c. If the two diagonals are congruent, then we know that

$$\sqrt{(a + b)^2 + c^2} = \sqrt{(a - b)^2 + c^2}$$

or $$(a + b)^2 + c^2 = (a - b)^2 + c^2$$

or $$a^2 + 2ab + b^2 + c^2 = a^2 - 2ab + b^2 + c^2$$

or $$2ab = -2ab$$

This can only be true when a or b is 0. In the given situation, the only possibility is $b = 0$. But this means that $S(0, c)$ and $R(a, c)$. Those facts imply that $\overline{SP}$ lies on the y-axis and R lies directly above Q, meaning that $\overline{RQ}$ is perpendicular to the x-axis also. Using the fact that opposite angles of any parallelogram are congruent, we conclude that the angles at S and R are also right angles and the figure $PQRS$ is a rectangle.

37 $(x - 7)(x + 6) > 0$ when both factors are positive or both factors are negative. That means $[(x > 7)$ and $(x > -6)]$ or $[(x < 7)$ and $(x < -6)]$. These conditions simplify to $x > 7$ or $x < -6$. Students will likely visualize the graph of $y = x^2 - x - 42$ and identify the x-intercepts from the factored form to arrive at the solution.

38 **INSTRUCTIONAL NOTE** Two main ideas students should get from their comparisons follow:

• Unlike quadratic functions, which either increase then decrease or decrease then increase, the functions above are increasing then decreasing then increasing again.

• These third-degree functions have 3 zeroes.

a. $y = x^3 - 3x^2 + 2x$ **b.** $y = x^3 - 9x$ **c.** $y = x^3 - 3x^2 - 6x + 8$

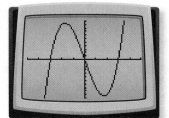 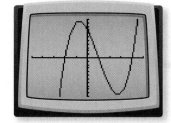

39 Consider line segments of lengths $2m$, $m^2 - 1$, and $m^2 + 1$ where m is any positive integer greater than 1.

a. In all three cases, since $2m + m^2 + 1 > m^2 - 1$ by the Triangle Inequality, a triangle can be formed.

m	$2m$	$m^2 - 1$	$m^2 + 1$
3	6	8	10
5	10	24	26
100	200	9,999	10,001

b. The converse of the Pythagorean Theorem implies that the triangles are right triangles: $(2m)^2 + (m^2 - 1)^2 = (m^2 + 1)^2$.

m	$(2m)^2$	$(m^2 - 1)^2$	$(m^2 + 1)^2$
3	36	64	100
5	100	576	676
100	40,000	99,980,001	100,020,001

c. One possible argument uses the following chain of reasoning:

$2m > 2$ (since $m > 1$)
So, $m^2 + 2m > m^2 + 2$ (add m^2 to both sides)
and $(2m) + (m^2 - 1) > m^2 + 1$. (subtract 1 from both sides)

This is true for all positive m, and, therefore, the original statement must be true for $m > 1$.

d. Show: $(2m)^2 + (m^2 - 1)^2 = (m^2 + 1)^2$

$(2m)^2 + (m^2 - 1)^2 = m^4 + 2m^2 + 1$ and $(m^2 + 1)^2 = m^4 + 2m^2 + 1$
So, $(2m)^2 + (m^2 - 1)^2 = (m^2 + 1)^2$ since they both equal the same expression.

Because the equality is true, the converse of the Pythagorean Theorem ensures that all triangles formed by segments whose lengths are determined by $2m$, $m^2 - 1$, and $m^2 + 1$ where m is any positive integer greater than 1 must be right triangles.

e. Student spreadsheets should define one column for the m values, one each for the different side lengths, and one for checking the results.

40 One possible line of reasoning would include the following statements of equality to show that any two numbers, m and n, would result in a Pythagorean triple as long as $m > n$:

$(m^2 - n^2)^2 + (2mn)^2 = m^4 - 2m^2n^2 + n^4 + 4m^2n^2 = m^4 + 2m^2n^2 + n^4$
and $(m^2 + n^2)^2 = m^4 + 2m^2n^2 + n^4 = m^4 + 2m^2n^2 + n^4$

Since both expressions are equal, the 3 numbers $m^2 - n^2$, $2mn$, and $m^2 + n^2$ are a Pythagorean Triple.

41 (1) Use the distributive property to factor out a.

(2) Product is zero only when at least one factor is zero. In this case, we assume that $a \neq 0$, so the other factor must be zero.

(3) Add $\frac{-c}{a}$ to both sides or use the general principle that $A + B = C$ implies that $A = C - B$.

(4) Add $\frac{b^2}{4a^2}$ to both sides (completing the square).

(5) Factor the left side and use the commutative property on the right side.

(6) Multiply the right term on the right side by $\frac{4a}{4a} = 1$.

(7) Add the fractions on the right side.

(8) Take the square root of both sides.

(9) Subtract $\frac{b}{2a}$ from both sides of both equations.

42 The diagram below shows two intersecting circles in a coordinate plane. One has radius 2 and is centered at the origin (0, 0). The other has radius 4 and is centered at the point (4, 0).

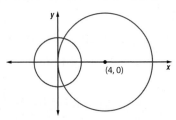

a. What is your best guess for the coordinates of points where the two circles intersect?

b. Write equations for the two circles.

c. To find the intersection points of the circles, you need to solve the system of equations from Part b. Adapt the *method of elimination* from your earlier work with systems of linear equations to solve this system of quadratic equations.

Review

43 You may recall that a number is rational if it can be written as a ratio of two integers. The decimal form of a rational number is either a terminating or a repeating decimal. Some examples of rational numbers are $\frac{2}{3}$, $1.\overline{256}$, -12, and 0. If a real number is not rational, it is irrational. Two examples of irrational numbers that you are familiar with are $\sqrt{2}$ and π. Classify each of the following numbers as rational or irrational.

a. $\sqrt{7}$

b. $\frac{136}{5}$

c. $\sqrt{250}$

d. $\sqrt{\frac{1}{9}}$

e. $(\sqrt{5})^2$

f. $-\frac{2\pi}{3\pi}$

g. $\sqrt{\frac{18}{4}}$

h. $\sqrt{0.81}$

44 Find matrix M such that $3M + \begin{bmatrix} -2 & 4 \\ 5 & -1 \end{bmatrix} = \begin{bmatrix} 1 & 19 \\ -1 & 8 \end{bmatrix}$.

45 Write each of these radical expressions in an equivalent form with the smallest possible positive integer under the radical sign.

a. $\sqrt{250}$

b. $\frac{\sqrt{24}}{2}$

c. $\sqrt{54}\sqrt{12}$

d. $\frac{\sqrt{100 - 4(16)}}{4}$

42 **a.** Students' guesses will vary.

b. Smaller circle: $x^2 + y^2 = 4$; larger circle: $(x - 4)^2 + y^2 = 16$

c. The coordinates of the intersection are $\left(\frac{1}{2}, \frac{\sqrt{15}}{2}\right)$ and $\left(\frac{1}{2}, -\frac{\sqrt{15}}{2}\right)$.

One way to find this solution is to use the equation of the first circle to find that $y^2 = 4 - x^2$; then *substitute* this relationship in the equation for the second circle to get the quadratic equation in x:

$$(x - 4)^2 + 4 - x^2 = 16.$$

By expanding and collecting like terms, one gets the linear equation

$$-8x + 20 = 16$$

which has solution $x = \frac{1}{2}$. Substituting that in either circle equation, one gets the required values of y.

Another solution strategy would be to subtract the first circle equation from the second to get the quadratic in x:

$$(x - 4)^2 - x^2 = 12.$$

This equation in fact simplifies to $-8x + 16 = 12$, giving the same x value as the other strategy, and thus the same y values.

Review

 Just in Time

43 **a.** Irrational   **b.** Rational

    c. Irrational   **d.** Rational

    e. Rational   **f.** Rational

    g. Irrational   **h.** Rational

44 $M = \begin{bmatrix} 1 & 5 \\ -2 & 3 \end{bmatrix}$

 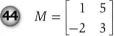 **Just in Time**

45 **a.** $5\sqrt{10}$ **b.** $\sqrt{6}$

    c. $18\sqrt{2}$ **d.** $\frac{3}{2}$

46 The graph below displays the average tuition costs for four-year and two-year public colleges by state. The equation of the regression line is $y = 0.365x + 400$.

2003–2004 College Costs

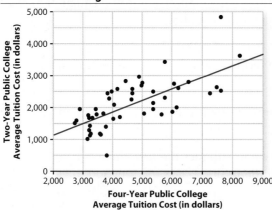

Source: nces.ed.gov/programs/digest/d04/tables/dt04_314.asp

a. Explain the meaning of the slope of the regression line.

b. Is the regression coefficient for this set of data positive or negative? Explain your reasoning.

c. In California, the average tuition at four-year public colleges is $3,785 and the average tuition cost at two-year public colleges is $485. Find the residual for this point.

47 Solve each of the following linear inequalities. Graph each solution on a number line.

a. $2x + 5 < 17$ **b.** $-2x + 5 < 17$

c. $8 - 5x \geq 43$ **d.** $7x + 3 > 4x - 9$

e. $\frac{x}{2} + 7 < 12$ **f.** $\frac{3x}{2} + 7 \leq 12$

48 Use rules of exponents to determine the value of x in each equation.

a. $(2^{30})^5 = 2^x$

b. $(30^x)(30^{16}) = 30^{64}$

c. $\frac{5^x}{5^{40}} = 5^{70}$

49 Express each of these relationships among variables in at least two equivalent forms.

a. y is inversely proportional to x with constant of proportionality 5.

b. z is directly proportional to x and inversely proportional to y with constant of proportionality -3.

46 **a.** The slope indicates that if the average four-year college tuition in one state is \$1 more than the average four-year college tuition in another state, then the average two-year college tuition will be \$0.365 more in the first state than in the second.

b. The regression coefficient will be positive since the slope of the regression line is positive.

c. The regression equation predicts a two-year college tuition of $0.365(3,785) + 400 = 1,781.53$. Since the actual average two-year college tuition is only \$485, the residual is $485 - 1,781.53 = -1,296.53$ dollars.

47 **INSTRUCTIONAL NOTE** The graphing portion of this task is included strictly as a review of middle school math content. The graphing of solutions to one- and two-variable inequalities and systems on a number line will be specifically addressed in Course 3, Unit 2, *Inequalities and Linear Programming*.

a. $x < 6$

b. $x > -6$

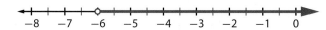

c. $x \leq -7$

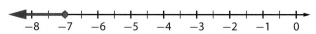

d. $x > -4$

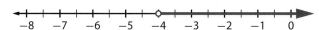

e. $x < 10$

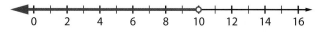

f. $x \leq \frac{10}{3}$

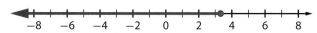

 Just in Time

48 **a.** $x = 150$

b. $x = 48$

c. $x = 110$

49 The following are two of the possibilities for each.

a. $y = \frac{5}{x}$; $xy = 5$

b. $z = \frac{-3x}{y}$; $zy = -3x$

50 The points $A(0, 0)$ and $B(4, 8)$ are two vertices of a triangle.

   a. If the coordinates of vertex C are $(-3, 6)$, is $\triangle ABC$ a right triangle? Explain your reasoning.

   b. If the coordinates of vertex D are $(5, -2)$, is $\triangle ABD$ an isosceles triangle? Explain your reasoning.

   c. Is the line with equation $y = -\frac{1}{2}x + 8$ the perpendicular bisector of $\overline{AB}$? Explain your reasoning.

51 Solve these proportions.

   a. $\frac{17}{x} = 25$

   b. $487 = \frac{x}{4.9}$

   c. $\frac{6 + x}{3} = \frac{9 + x}{5}$

52 Two octahedral dice with the numbers 1 through 8 on the sides are rolled. The sum of the numbers is found.

   a. What is the probability that the sum will be less than 3?

   b. What sum has the greatest probability of being rolled?

   c. What is the probability that the sum is an even number and less than 5?

50 **a.** No, △ABC is not a right triangle. One possible explanation follows:

The slope of $\overline{AB}$ is 2, the slope of $\overline{BC}$ is $\frac{2}{7}$, and the slope of $\overline{AC}$ is -2. Since no two consecutive sides have slopes whose product is equal to -1, no two consecutive sides are perpendicular; hence, the triangle does not have a right angle as one of its angles. Alternatively, students could use the distance formula and the converse of the Pythagorean Theorem.

b. No, △ABD is not isosceles. One possible explanation follows: $AB = \sqrt{80}$, $AD = \sqrt{29}$, $BD = \sqrt{101}$. Since all three sides have different lengths, △ABD is not isosceles.

c. No. One possible explanation follows:

The slope of $\overline{AB}$ is 2. Therefore, the line with equation $y = -\frac{1}{2}x + 8$ is perpendicular to $\overline{AB}$ since the product of their slopes is -1. However, the midpoint of $\overline{AB}$ is $(2, 4)$, but $(2, 4)$ does not lie on the line $y = -\frac{1}{2}x + 8$ since $4 \neq -\frac{1}{2}(2) + 8$.

51 **a.** $x = \frac{17}{25}$

b. $x = 2{,}386.3$

c. $x = -\frac{3}{2}$

52 **a.** $\frac{1}{64}$

b. 9; it has a probability of $\frac{8}{64} = \frac{1}{8}$.

c. $\frac{4}{64}$ or $\frac{1}{16}$

LESSON
2

Nonlinear Systems of Equations

Unit 5

When summer approaches, high school and college students start thinking about finding summer jobs. In some cities and towns, students can find work in shops, restaurants, and seasonal service jobs like lawn mowing, farm work, or lifeguarding. But often, there are not enough jobs to ensure that everyone who wants to work will be employed.

Want Ads — Help Wanted

Fast Food—Restaurant seeks summer help; cashiers, cooks, cleanup; 20 hours per week all shifts available. Call 555-5678.

Camp Staff—Playground supervisors and camp counselors age 15 or older. Good pay and lots of fresh air. Call 555-6543.

Natural Lawns—Summer Help needed. $7.50 per hour. No prior experience required. Call 24 hours 1-800-555-1589.

Child Care—Tiny Tots Day Care Center seeks summer help for child care positions. Hours 7-5 four days per week. References to Box Q.

To help students find summer work, both to earn money and to get work experience, many city and county governments have special summer jobs programs. Students are hired to do cleanup and construction jobs in parks or other community facilities. These programs usually have a fixed budget of funds available to pay the student workers.

LESSON 2 • Nonlinear Systems of Equations **359**

Nonlinear Systems of Equations

T he goal of this lesson is to develop understanding of numeric, graphic, and symbolic strategies for solving systems of equations involving the intersections of linear and inverse variation functions and intersections of linear and quadratic functions.

Lesson Objectives

- Write an equation or inequality to represent a question about a "real-life" situation involving a comparison between a linear function and either an inverse variation or quadratic function
- Estimate solutions to equations in the form $ax + b = \frac{k}{x}$ using tables or graphs and solve algebraically
- Estimate solutions to equations in the form $mx + d = ax^2 + bx + c$ using tables or graphs and solve algebraically

Think About This Situation

Suppose that the Kent County government sets aside $200,000 each summer for student salaries in a youth jobs program.

a What factors should planners of the jobs program consider when they set the pay that will be offered to each student worker?

b What factors should students consider when deciding whether or not to apply for the summer work program?

c What salary for 2 months of summer work would attract you to participate in such a program?

Solving the problems of this lesson will help you develop skill in answering questions like these that involve combinations of linear and nonlinear functions.

Investigation 1 — Supply and Demand

In planning the Kent County summer jobs program, county officials must consider the relationships between the pay offered for each student, the number of students who could be hired, and the number of students interested in the work opportunity. Analysis of these relationships involves work with systems of functions. As you complete this investigation, look for answers to this question:

> *What strategies are useful in solving problems that involve links between two functions—one a linear function and one an inverse variation function?*

The problem-solving process involves two major steps. First, you have to identify independent and dependent variables and the functions that relate those variables. Then you have to use the functions to answer questions about the variables.

1 Kent County has $200,000 to spend on student salaries.

    a. How many student workers can be hired if the county pays $2,000 per worker for a summer contract covering eight weeks? What if the county pays only $1,500 per worker? What if the county pays only $1,000 per worker?

    b. If the pay per worker is represented by p, what function $h(p)$ shows how the number of students who could be hired depends on the level of pay offered?

    c. Sketch a graph of the function $h(p)$ and write a brief description of the way $h(p)$ changes as p increases.

Think About This Situation

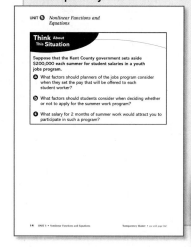

(a) Student responses will vary. Possible ideas might include the number of students available for work, the number of jobs available, the federal or state minimum wage, etc. Students may suggest that the pay rate might be higher for older or more experienced workers and for some types of jobs. (This type of variation in pay scales will not be addressed in this lesson.)

(b) Student responses will vary, though the potential salary is sure to be a concern. The number of hours to be worked and the type of work should also be considered.

(c) Depending on the students' work experiences, there will be a great range of answers to this question.

COLLABORATION SKILL
Take turns proposing ways to do the problem.

Investigation 1 — Supply and Demand

In this investigation, students solve equations that involve combinations of linear functions and inverse variation functions using tables, graphs, and symbolic reasoning and, potentially, the "solve" command of a CAS.

TECHNOLOGY NOTE
Students can use the CAS in *CPMP-Tools* to check their answers. A TI-89 technology tip for solving are located in the Course 1 Unit 1, *Unit 1 Resources Masters* page 40.

1 **a.** 100 workers can be hired at $2,000 per worker, 133 at $1,500 per worker, and 200 at $1,000 per worker.

   b. $h(p) = \dfrac{200,000}{p}$

   c. As p increases at a constant rate, the number of potential workers decreases at a decreasing rate.

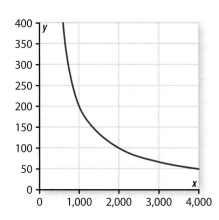

Unit 5

2 If the jobs program offers very low pay, then few students will be interested in the work opportunity. After doing a survey in one local high school, Kent County officials arrived at the following estimates of the relation between summer pay rate and number of students they can expect to apply for the jobs.

Summer Jobs Program

Pay Offered (in dollars)	500	1,000	1,500	2,000	2,500
Expected Applicants	55	100	155	210	255

   a. Does the pattern in the data table seem reasonable? Why or why not?

   b. What function $s(p)$ would be a good model of the relationship between the number of students who will apply for the jobs and the level of pay offered?

   c. Sketch a graph of $s(p)$ and write a brief description of what it shows about the way the number of job applicants changes as pay increases.

3 The decision to be made by Kent County summer jobs officials is how much pay to offer for the eight-week summer work contracts. Both the number of students who could be hired and the number of students who would be interested in the summer work depend on the pay rate p.

   a. Write equations and inequalities that match the following questions about the jobs program, and then estimate or find exact values for solutions.

      i. For what pay rate(s) will the number of students who can be hired equal the number of students who would be interested in the work?

      ii. For what pay rate(s) will the number of students who can be hired be less than the number of students who would be interested in the work?

      iii. For what pay rate(s) will the number of students who can be hired be greater than the number of students who would be interested in the work?

   b. When the head of the Kent County summer jobs program had to report to the county council about program plans, he wanted a visual aid to help in explaining the choice of a pay rate to be offered to student workers. Sketch a graph showing how both $h(p)$ and $s(p)$ depend on p and explain how the graph illustrates your answers to the questions in Part a.

Solving Equations in the Form $ax + b = \dfrac{k}{x}$ An equation like $0.1x = \dfrac{200,000}{x}$ can be solved by finding point(s) where graphs of the two functions, $y = 0.1x$ and $y = \dfrac{200,000}{x}$, intersect. The functions involved are representatives of two important function families—one in which the dependent variable is *linearly* related to the independent variable and one in which the dependent variable is *inversely* related to the independent variable.

2 **a.** Yes, the more money that is offered, the more applicants one would expect. Some students might suggest that the relationship increases at a larger constant rate or an increasing rate.

b. $s(p) = 0.1p$ models the relationship well.

c. The graph shows that for every increase of one in p, $s(p)$ will increase by 0.1. Perhaps a more logical representation in this case is that for every increase of $10 in the pay offered, Kent County should expect one more applicant.

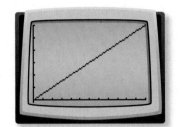

3 **a.** **i.** $\dfrac{200,000}{p} = 0.1p$; $p = \$1,414.21$

ii. $\dfrac{200,000}{p} < 0.1p$; $p > \$1,414.21$

iii. $\dfrac{200,000}{p} > 0.1p$; $p < \$1,414.21$

b. $h(p) = \dfrac{200,000}{p}$ and $s(p) = 0.1p$

The intersection point represents the case of the pay rate when the number of students who can be hired equals the number interested in work. The curve representing $y = \dfrac{200,000}{x}$, the number of students who can be hired, is above the line representing the number of students interested when $x \leq 1,414$ and below the line when $x \geq 1,415$ students.

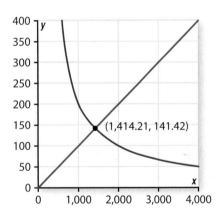

INVESTIGATION NOTE
Whether students solve using algebra, graphs, or a CAS, it is important to stress the meaning of the solution.

Unit 5

In Problems 4 and 5, use tables, graphs, and reasoning about equations to explore the solution possibilities for equations that seek intersection points of graphs for one linear function and one inverse variation function.

④ Consider first, equations in the form $ax = \dfrac{k}{x}$ where a and k are not zero.

   a. Use tables or graphs of functions to estimate solutions for the following equations. In each case, sketch a graph showing the two functions involved in the equation and give coordinates of point(s) that correspond to solutions of the equation.

   i. $1.5x = \dfrac{6}{x}$ **ii.** $-1.5x = \dfrac{6}{x}$

   iii. $-2x = \dfrac{-18}{x}$ **iv.** $2x = \dfrac{-18}{x}$

   b. Recall from work with multivariable relations that any statement in the form $a = \dfrac{b}{c}$ is equivalent to $ac = b$. Use this principle to find exact values of solutions to the equations in Part a by algebraic reasoning. Check your work using a CAS command like **solve(1.5*x*=6/*x*,*x*)**.

   c. Look at the results of your work in Parts a and b. In general, how many solutions can there be for an equation in the form $ax = \dfrac{k}{x}$? Illustrate your answer with sketches of graphs showing the different cases.

⑤ Now consider equations in the form $ax + b = \dfrac{k}{x}$, where a, b, and k are not zero.

   a. Estimate the solutions to the following equations using tables or graphs of values for the related functions. In each case, sketch a graph showing the two functions involved in the equation and give coordinates of point(s) that correspond to solutions of the equation.

   i. $x - 1 = \dfrac{6}{x}$ **ii.** $x - 6 = \dfrac{-9}{x}$

   iii. $-x + 10 = \dfrac{9}{x}$ **iv.** $-x + 1 = \dfrac{4}{x}$

   b. Use the principle that any statement in the form $a = \dfrac{b}{c}$ is equivalent to $ac = b$ to write the equations in equivalent form without fractions. Then find exact values of the solutions by algebraic reasoning. For example, when solving the first equation, you may want to start like this:

$$x - 1 = \dfrac{6}{x}$$
$$x(x - 1) = 6$$
$$x^2 - x = 6$$
$$x^2 - x - 6 = 0$$

   c. Look at the results of your work in Parts a and b. In general, how many solutions can there be for an equation in the form $ax + b = \dfrac{k}{x}$? Illustrate your answer with sketches showing the different cases.

4 **a.** **i.** $x = \pm 2$ **ii.** No solution

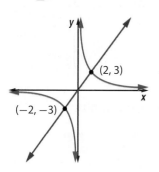   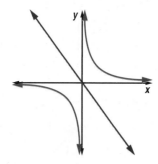

  iii. $x = \pm 3$ **iv.** No solution

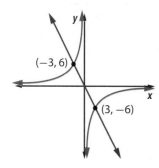   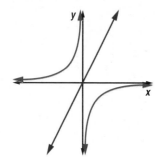

b. **i.** $1.5x = \dfrac{6}{x}$ is equivalent to $1.5x^2 = 6$. So, $x^2 = 4$, or $x = \pm 2$.

  ii. $-1.5x = \dfrac{6}{x}$ is equivalent to $-1.5x^2 = 6$. So, $x^2 = -4$. Therefore, there is no solution.

  iii. $-2x = \dfrac{-18}{x}$ is equivalent to $-2x^2 = -18$. So, $x^2 = 9$, or $x = \pm 3$.

  iv. $2x = \dfrac{-18}{x}$ is equivalent to $2x^2 = -18$. So, $x^2 = -9$. Therefore, there is no solution.

c. Either 2 solutions or 0 solutions can be found. The graphs below demonstrate both cases, respectively. (Since the line $y = ax$ contains the origin, it will never be tangent to the inverse variation function.)

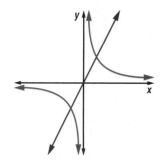   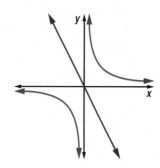

Unit 5

5 **a.** **i.** $x = -2$ or $x = 3$ **ii.** $x = 3$

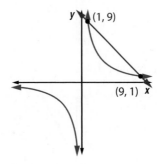

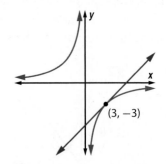

iii. $x = 1$ or $x = 9$ **iv.** No solution

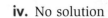

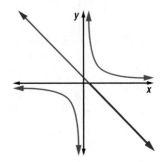

b. **i.** $x^2 - x - 6 = 0$
$(x - 3)(x + 2) = 0$
$x = 3$ or $x = -2$

ii. $x - 6 = \dfrac{-9}{x}$
$x^2 - 6x = -9$
$x^2 - 6x + 9 = 0$
$(x - 3)^2 = 0$
$x = 3$

iii. $-x + 10 = \dfrac{9}{x}$
$-x^2 + 10x = 9$
$x^2 - 10x + 9 = 0$
$(x - 9)(x - 1) = 0$
$x = 9$ or $x = 1$

iv. $-x + 1 = \dfrac{4}{x}$
$-x^2 + x = 4$
$x^2 - x + 4 = 0$
No solution

c. 0, 1, or 2 solutions can be found. The graphs below represent each case, respectively.

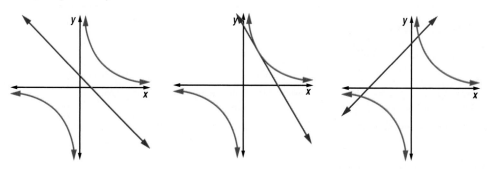

Summary

While discussing student strategies for solving a system of equations in Part a, be sure that students are indicating final solutions of ordered pairs that correspond to intersection points on the graph. When discussing Part c, students should recognize that when solving equations in one variable by using the two functions corresponding to each side of the equation, the solution(s) are only x values. Using this approach and examining the tables and graphs may influence some students to think of the ordered pair as the solution. To make this issue explicit, you might ask a question similar to:

> *"How do you know whether or not your solution should be*
> *an ordered pair (x, y) or only related x values?"*

Summarize the Mathematics

In this investigation, you developed strategies for solving problems that involve both a linear function and an inverse variation function.

a What strategy would you use to solve a system of equations of the form $y = ax + b$ and $y = \frac{k}{x}$?

b What are the possible numbers of solutions for equations in the form $ax = \frac{k}{x}$? How about equations like $ax + b = \frac{k}{x}$? How are these equations related to quadratic equations?

c How can you estimate the solutions to equations like those in Part b by inspecting tables and graphs of functions? What will graphs look like in each solution case?

d How can you calculate exact values of the solutions for such equations by reasoning with the symbolic expressions involved? By using a computer algebra system *solve* command?

Be prepared to explain your ideas to the class.

✓ Check Your Understanding

Each year, the Wheaton Boys and Girls Club sells fresh Christmas trees in December to raise money for sports equipment. They have $2,400 to use to buy trees for their lot; so the number of trees they can buy depends on the purchase price per tree p, according to the function $n(p) = \frac{2,400}{p}$.

Experience has shown that (allowing for profit on each tree sold) the number of trees that customers will purchase also depends on p with function $c(p) = 300 - 6p$.

a. Write equations and inequalities that match the following questions about prospects of the tree sale and then estimate solutions.

   i. For what price per tree will the number of trees that can be bought equal the number of trees that will be sold?

   ii. For what price per tree will the number of trees that can be bought be greater than the number of trees that will be sold?

   iii. For what price per tree will the number of trees that can be bought be less than the number of trees that will be sold?

b. Sketch graphs showing how the supply and demand functions $n(p)$ and $c(p)$ depend on price per tree and explain how the graphs illustrate your answers to the questions of Part a.

Summarize
the Mathematics

Teaching Resources

Transparency Master 15.

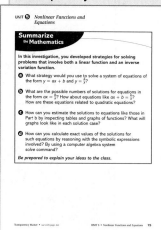

(a) A solution could be estimated by using graphs or tables to find the common point(s) of the two functions. To solve the system of equations symbolically, set $ax + b = \frac{k}{x}$ and solve this equation for x. Then substitute the x value(s) into $y = ax + b$ or $y = \frac{k}{x}$ to find the corresponding y values. Then check the (x, y) solution(s).

(b) Either 2 solutions or 0 solutions can be found for $ax = \frac{k}{x}$. 0, 1, or 2 solutions can be found for $ax + b = \frac{k}{x}$. Both cases can be transformed into equivalent equations in familiar quadratic forms.

(c) To use tables or graphs, each side of the equations should be treated as a separate function. Then, input and output values for these functions can be viewed in a table. Solutions occur when output values are equal for the same input values. When using graphs to estimate, one can use the TRACE feature of a graphing calculator or other means to estimate the x-coordinates of the points where the graphs intersect.

Graphs representing $ax = \frac{k}{x}$ are as follows:

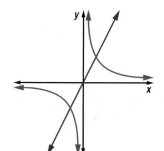
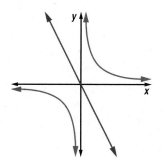

For $ax + b = \frac{k}{x}$:

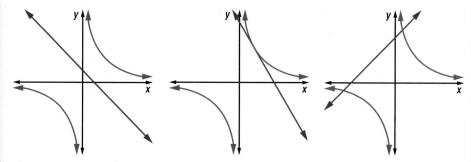

(d) The first case presents equations that are not difficult to solve using symbolic reasoning. For those students adept at solving proportions, an additional step of taking the square root is all that is needed. In the second case, a more complex quadratic equation results. To solve, you could rewrite the equation in the form $ax^2 + bx + c = 0$ and use the quadratic formula or factoring to find solutions. (This will be reviewed in more depth in the next investigation.) To solve using a CAS, students could create entries such as **solve(a*x=k/x,x)** or **solve(a*x+b=k/x,x)**.

MATH TOOLKIT What strategies are useful in solving problems that involve links between two functions—one a linear function and one an inverse variation function? Provide an example that has two solutions.

COLLABORATION PROMPT On a scale of 1 to 5, with 5 being the best, we rate the effectiveness of our taking turns suggesting methods to do problems as _____ (number) because … .

NOTE The solutions to the Check Your Understanding are on page T364.

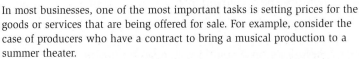

Making More by Charging Less

In your work on the problems of Investigation 1, you developed strategies for solving equations involving linear and inverse variation functions. As you work on the problems in this investigation, look for answers to this question:

What strategies are effective in solving equations that relate linear and quadratic functions?

In most businesses, one of the most important tasks is setting prices for the goods or services that are being offered for sale. For example, consider the case of producers who have a contract to bring a musical production to a summer theater.

They have to estimate costs of putting on the show, income from ticket sales and concessions, and the profit that can be made. Values of these variables depend on the number of tickets sold and the prices charged for tickets.

 Data from a market survey suggest the following relationship between ticket price and number of tickets sold.

Relationship between Ticket Price and Ticket Sales

Price (in dollars)	5	10	15	20	30	40
Tickets Sold	2,300	2,000	1,700	1,500	1,050	500

a. After plotting the data and experimenting to find a function model for the pattern, the business planners proposed the function $s(p) = 2,500 - 50p$ for this demand pattern.

   i. What do p and $s(p)$ represent in that function?

   ii. Is that function reasonable? Can you produce a better model?

b. What do the numbers 2,500 and -50 tell about the way ticket sales depend on ticket price?

 Based on the relationship between ticket price and number of tickets sold, the show planners figured that income could be predicted from ticket price, as well. They reasoned that since income is equal to the product of price per ticket and number of tickets sold, $I(p) = p(2,500 - 50p)$.

a. Test this function rule by calculating the predicted income from ticket sales in two ways.

   i. First, use the data in Problem 1 to estimate income if the ticket price is set at $10, $20, and $40.

   ii. Then use the function to calculate predicted ticket income for the same ticket prices.

Check Your Understanding

a. i. $\dfrac{2{,}400}{p} = 300 - 6p$; $p = 10$ or $p = 40$

ii. $\dfrac{2{,}400}{p} > 300 - 6p$; $p < 10$ or $p > 40$

iii. $\dfrac{2{,}400}{p} < 300 - 6p$; $10 < p < 40$

b. The graph below shows the two graphs, the linear, number of customers (or demand), function and the inverse variation, number of trees available (or supply), function. Their intersection points indicate the prices where supply equals demand. When the linear graph is "above" the inverse variation graph, demand exceeds supply, and when the inverse variation graph is "above" the linear graph, supply exceeds demand.

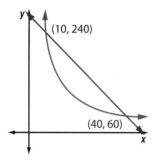

Investigation 2 Making More by Charging Less

In this investigation, students solve equations that involve combinations of linear functions and quadratic functions using tables, graphs, and symbolic reasoning and, potentially, the "solve" command of a CAS.

1 **a.** This fits reasonably well: p represents the ticket price, $s(p)$ represents the projected number of tickets sold. Using 2,508 instead of 2,500 is actually a slightly better fit with the given data.

b. The 2,500 may indicate the capacity of the theatre or that if the tickets were given away for free that 2,500 people would take tickets.
The -50 indicates that according to the function, for every \$1 increase in ticket price, 50 fewer people will buy tickets for the show.

2 **a.** i. (*Price, Income*): (10, 20,000), (20, 30,000), and (40, 20,000)

ii. (*Price, Income*): (10, 20,000), (20, 30,000), and (40, 20,000)

b. Sarrem proposed the function $I(p) = 2{,}500p - 50p^2$ for predicting income from ticket price. Is this equivalent to $I(p) = p(2{,}500 - 50p)$? Why or why not?

③ The next step in making business plans for the production was to estimate operating costs. Some costs were fixed (for example, pay for the cast and rent of the theater), but other costs would depend on the number of tickets sold s (for example, number of ushers and ticket takers needed). After estimating all of the possible operating costs, the function $c(s) = 17{,}500 + 2s$ was proposed.

a. According to that rule, what are the fixed operating costs and the costs per customer?

b. To show how operating costs depend on ticket price, Daniel proposed the function $c(p) = 17{,}500 + 2(2{,}500 - 50p)$. Is this rule correct? Why or why not?

c. Minta suggested that the expression $17{,}500 + 2(2{,}500 - 50p)$ in Part b could be simplified to $22{,}500 - 100p$. Is that correct? Why or why not?

④ The crucial step in business planning came next—finding out the way that ticket price would affect profit. The following graph shows how income and operating cost depend on ticket price and how they are related to each other.

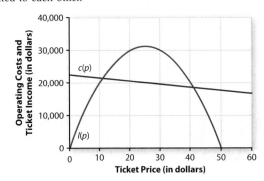

a. Use the graph to estimate answers for the following questions, and explain how you arrive at each estimate.

   i. For what ticket price(s) will operating cost exceed income?

   ii. For what ticket price(s) will income exceed operating cost?

   iii. For what ticket price(s) will income equal operating cost?

b. Use expressions in the income and operating cost functions to write and solve an equation that helps in locating the *break-even* point(s)—the ticket prices for which income exactly equals operating cost.

b. Yes, the distributive property was used, which makes the two expressions equivalent. (Students may also compare graphs and tables of both functions to explore the equivalence.)

3   **a.** The fixed costs are $17,500. The cost per customer is $2.

     b. Yes, because the $2,500 - 50p$ expression can be substituted for s in the first proposed cost function.

     c. Yes, the distributive property can be used followed by a combining of like terms.

4   **a.**   **i.** Operating costs will exceed income when $p < 11$ or $p > 41$.

        ii. Income will exceed operating cost when $11 < p < 41$.

        iii. When $p \approx 41$ or $p \approx 11$, income will equal operating cost.

     b. $22,500 - 100p = 2,500p - 50p^2$

        $50p^2 - 2,600p + 22,500 = 0$

        $50(p^2 - 52p + 450) = 0$

$$p = \frac{52}{2} \pm \frac{\sqrt{904}}{2}$$

        $p \approx 26 \pm 15$

        The break-even points are around $11 and $41.

It is likely that the show producers want to do more than break even. They will probably seek maximum profit.

a. Use the income and operating cost functions to write a function showing how profit depends on ticket price. Write the function in two equivalent forms—one that shows the expressions for income and cost and another that is simplest for calculation of profit.

b. Use the profit function to estimate the maximum profit plan—the ticket price that will lead to maximum profit and the dollar profit that will be made at that price.

c. Use the results from Part b to calculate the number of tickets sold and the operating cost in the maximum profit situation.

Solving Equations of the Form $mx + d = ax^2 + bx + c$

The work you did in analyzing business prospects of the summer theater musical production illustrated ways that problems can require solving equations involving linear and quadratic functions. To work effectively in such situations, it helps to know the solution possibilities and how they will be expressed in graphs of the functions involved.

 Use your table and graph tools and what you know about linear and quadratic functions to explore solution possibilities for equations in the form $mx + d = ax^2 + bx + c$.

a. Sketch function graphs illustrating the possible number of solutions for equations involving linear and quadratic functions. Compare your graphs with those of others and resolve any differences.

b. Solve each of the following equations using factoring or the quadratic formula.

   i. $x^2 - x + 3 = 2x - 1$

   ii. $x^2 - 3x + 2 = x - 2$

   iii. $10x^2 - 28x - 39 = 2x + 1$

c. For each equation in Part b, sketch graphs of the linear and quadratic functions involved and explain how the graphs illustrate the solutions.

5 **a.** $F = (2{,}500p - 50p^2) - (22{,}500 - 100p)$
$F = -50p^2 + 2{,}600p - 22{,}500$

b. The maximum profit of \$11,300 will occur with the ticket price set at about \$26.

c. With the ticket price set at \$26, about 1,200 tickets will be sold with operating costs around \$19,900.

6 **a.** 0, 1, or 2 solutions can be found.

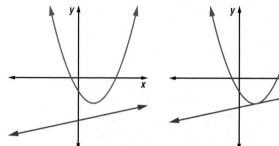

b. i. $x^2 - 3x + 4 = 0$

$x = \dfrac{3}{2} \pm \dfrac{\sqrt{9 - 16}}{2}$

No solution

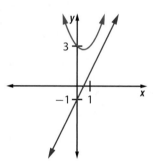

ii. $x^2 - 4x + 4 = 0$
$(x - 2)^2 = 0$
$x = 2$

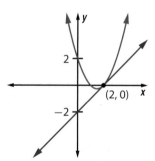

iii. $10x^2 - 30x - 40 = 0$
$10(x^2 - 3x - 4) = 0$
$10(x - 4)(x + 1) = 0$
$x \approx -1$ or $x \approx 4$

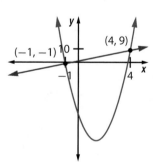

c. The solutions are the x-coordinates of the intersection points of the two graphs.

Summarize
the Mathematics

In this investigation, you developed strategies for solving problems that involve combinations of linear and quadratic functions.

a What strategy would you use to solve a system of equations of the form
$$y = mx + d \text{ and } y = ax^2 + bx + c?$$

b What are the possible numbers of solutions for equations in the form
$$mx + d = ax^2 + bx + c?$$

c How can you estimate the solutions for equations like those in Part b by inspecting tables and graphs of functions? What will graphs look like for the various solution possibilities?

d How can exact values of the solutions be found by reasoning with the symbolic expressions involved? By using a computer algebra system *solve* command?

Be prepared to explain your ideas to the class.

✓ Check Your Understanding

Solve each of these equations, sketch graphs showing the functions involved, and label points corresponding to solutions with their coordinates.

a. $x + 2 = x^2 + 3x - 6$

b. $-x + 2 = x^2 + x - 6$

c. $2x + 3 = 4 - x^2$

d. $2x^2 - x = 3x + 16$

Summarize
the Mathematics

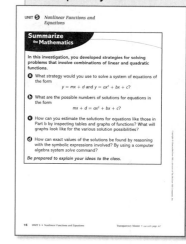
a A solution could be estimated by using graphs or tables to find the common point(s) of the two functions. To solve the system of equations symbolically, set $mx + d = ax^2 + bx + c$ and solve this equation for x. Then substitute the x value(s) into $y = mx + d$ or $y = ax^2 + bx + c$ to find the corresponding y values. Then check the (x, y) solution(s).

b It is possible that there could be 0, 1, or 2 solutions.

c To use tables or graphs, each side of the equations should be treated as a separate function. Then, input and output values for these functions can be viewed in a table. Solutions occur when output values are equal for the same input values. When using graphs to estimate, one can use the TRACE feature of a graphing calculator or other means to estimate the x-coordinates of the points where the graphs of the two functions intersect. See graphs in Problem 6.

d To solve, rewrite the equation in the form $ax^2 + bx + c = 0$. Then factor or use the quadratic formula to solve for x. Using the solve command in a computer algebra system, one could enter (using the equation in Problem 6 Part bii as an example) the following to solve the equation: $\mathbf{solve(x\text{\textasciicircum}2\text{-}3x\text{+}2\text{=}x\text{-}2,x)}$.

MATH TOOLKIT What strategies are effective in solving a system that consists of one linear and one quadratic function? Provide an example that has two solutions.

✓ Check Your Understanding

a.
$$x + 2 = x^2 + 3x - 6$$
$$0 = x^2 + 2x - 8$$
$$0 = (x + 4)(x - 2)$$
$$x = -4 \text{ or } x = 2$$

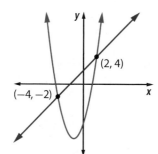

(2, 4)

(−4, −2)

b.
$$-x + 2 = x^2 + x - 6$$
$$0 = x^2 + 2x - 8$$
$$x = -4 \text{ or } x = 2$$

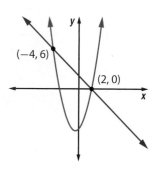

(−4, 6)

(2, 0)

c.
$$2x + 3 = 4 - x^2$$
$$x^2 + 2x - 1 = 0$$
$$x = -1 \pm \sqrt{2}$$

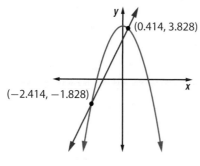

(0.414, 3.828)

(−2.414, −1.828)

d.
$$2x^2 - x = 3x + 16$$
$$2x^2 - 4x - 16 = 0$$
$$2(x^2 - 2x - 8) = 0$$
$$2(x - 4)(x + 2) = 0$$
$$x = -2 \text{ or } x = 4$$

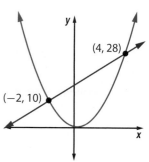

(4, 28)

(−2, 10)

Unit 5

On Your Own

Applications

1. The tenth-grade class officers at Columbus High School want to have a special event to welcome the incoming ninth-grade students. For $1,500, they can rent the Big Ten entertainment center for an evening. Their question is what to charge for tickets to the event so that income from ticket sales will be very close to the rental charge.

   a. Complete a table illustrating the pattern relating number of ticket sales n required to meet the "break-even" goal to the price charged p. Then write a rule relating n to p.

Price p (in dollars)	1	3	6	9	12	15
Tickets Sales Needed n	1,500	500				

   b. Study entries in the following table showing the class officers' ideas about how price charged p will affect number of students s who will buy tickets to the event. Then write a rule relating s to p.

Price p (in dollars)	0	3	6	9	12	15
Likely Ticket Sales s	600	540	480	420	360	300

   c. Write and solve an equation that will identify the ticket price(s) that will attract enough students for the event to meet its income goal. Illustrate your solution by a sketch of the graphs of the functions involved with key intersection points labeled by their coordinates.

2. When Coty was working on his Eagle Scout project, he figured he needed 60 hours of help from volunteer workers. He did some thinking to get an idea of how many workers he might need and how many volunteers he might be able to get.

   a. He began by assuming that each volunteer would work the same number of hours. In that case, what function $w(h)$ shows how the number of volunteer workers needed depends on the number of hours per worker h?

   b. Coty estimated that he could get 25 volunteers if each had to work only 3 hours and only 15 volunteers if each had to work 5 hours. What linear function $v(h)$ matches these assumptions about the relationship between the number of volunteers and the number of hours per worker h?

   c. Write and solve an equation that will help in finding the number of hours per worker and number of workers that Coty needs. Illustrate your solution by a sketch of the graphs of the functions involved with coordinate labels on key points.

Applications

(1) **a.** Table values are below. The rule is $n = \dfrac{1{,}500}{p}$.

Price p (in dollars)	1	3	6	9	12	15
Ticket Sales Needed n	1,500	500	250	166.67	125	100

b. $s = 600 - 20p$

c. $\dfrac{1{,}500}{p} = 600 - 20p$; $p \approx 27.25$ or $p \approx 2.75$

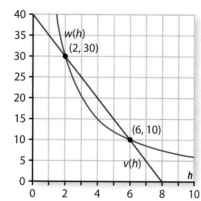

Key intersection points are approximately (2.75, 545) and (27.25, 55).

(2) **a.** $w(h) = \dfrac{60}{h}$

b. $v(h) = -5h + 40$

c. $\dfrac{60}{h} = -5h + 40$

$60 = -5h^2 + 40h$

$5h^2 - 40h + 60 = 0$

$5(h^2 - 8h + 12) = 0$

$(h - 6)(h - 2) = 0$

$h = 6$ or $h = 2$

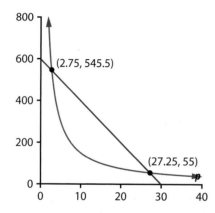

The solution is either 30 volunteers at 2 hours each or 10 volunteers at 6 hours each as shown on the graph.

(3) Use symbolic reasoning to find all solutions for these equations. Illustrate each solution by a sketch of the graphs of the functions involved, labeling key points with their coordinates.

a. $x + 5 = \frac{6}{x}$

b. $-0.5x = \frac{4}{x}$

c. $1.5x = \frac{24}{x}$

d. $10 - x = \frac{7}{x}$

(4) Use symbolic reasoning to find all solutions for the equation $\frac{4}{x} + 1 = 2 - x$. Illustrate the solution by a sketch of the graphs of the functions involved, labeling key points with their coordinates.

(5) In making business plans for a pizza sale fund-raiser, the Band Boosters at Roosevelt High School figured out how both sales income $I(n)$ and selling expenses $E(n)$ would probably depend on number of pizzas sold n. They predicted that $I(n) = -0.05n^2 + 20n$ and $E(n) = 5n + 250$.

a. Estimate value(s) of n for which $I(n) = E(n)$ and explain what the solution(s) of that equation tell about prospects of the pizza sale fund-raiser. Illustrate your answer with a sketch of the graphs of the two functions involved, labeling key points with their coordinates.

b. Write a rule that gives predicted profit $P(n)$ as a function of number of pizzas sold and use that function to estimate the number of pizza sales necessary for the fund-raiser to break even. Illustrate your answer with a sketch of the graph of the profit function, labeling key points with their coordinates.

c. Use the profit function to estimate the maximum profit possible from this fund-raiser. Then find number of pizzas sold, income, and expenses associated with that maximum profit situation.

(6) The stopping distance d in feet for a car traveling at a speed of s miles per hour depends on car and road conditions. Here are two possible stopping distance formulas: $d = 3s$ and $d = 0.05s^2 + s$.

a. Write and solve an equation to answer the question, "For what speed(s) do the two functions predict the same stopping distance?" Illustrate your answer with a sketch of the graphs of the two functions, labeling key point(s) with their coordinates.

b. In what ways are the patterns of change in stopping distance predicted by the two functions as speed increases similar and in what ways are they different? How do the function graphs illustrate the patterns you notice?

3 Students should solve symbolically and sketch graphs labeling intersection points.

a. $x = -6$ or $x = 1$

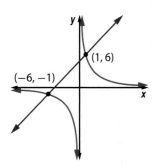

b. No solution

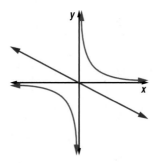

c. $x = -4$ or $x = 4$

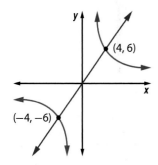

d. $x = 5 \pm 3\sqrt{2}$ ($x \approx 0.757$ or $x \approx 9.243$)

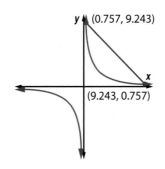

4 No real solution exists. The equation can be rewritten as $x^2 - x + 4 = 0$ which has no real solutions.

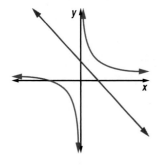

Unit 5

5 Approximate answers are provided below. Students can label their graphs with solutions rounded to integers.

a. $n \approx 282.29$ or $n \approx 17.71$. If the Boosters sell 282 pizzas or 18 pizzas, their income and expenses will be (approximately) equal.

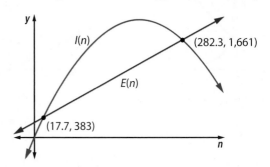

b. Profit: $P(n) = I(n) - E(n) = (-0.05n^2 + 20n) - (5n + 250) = -0.05n^2 + 15n - 250.$ $n \approx 17.71$ or $n \approx 282.29$

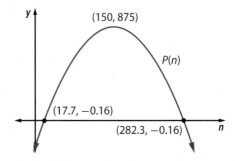

c. The maximum profit is around \$875. This would occur when 150 pizzas are sold and would result in an income of \$1,875 and expenses of \$1,000. See the graph in Part b.

6 **a.** $3s = 0.05s^2 + s;$ $s = 0$ or $s = 40$

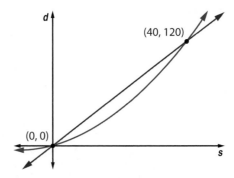

b. They are similar in that for speeds greater than zero, both graphs are increasing. However, the second function $(d = 0.05s^2 + s)$ is increasing at an increasing rate while the first $(d = 3s)$ increases at a constant rate. The graphs illustrate the patterns since one function is linear (increasing at a constant rate) and the other is quadratic (increasing at an increasing rate).

Teacher Notes

7 Use symbolic reasoning to find all solutions for these equations. Illustrate each solution by a sketch of the graphs of the functions involved, labeling key points with their coordinates.

   a. $2x = 2x^2 - 4x$

   b. $2x^2 - 4x = 4 - 2x$

   c. $x^2 - 4x - 5 = 2x + 2$

   d. $-3 - x = x^2 + 3x + 1$

8 Give specific examples of an equation involving one linear and one quadratic function that illustrate cases a–c described below. In each case, give a sketch showing how graphs of the two functions involved in the equation are related to each other. Explain how that relationship illustrates the number of solutions to the equation.

   a. Two distinct solutions

   b. Exactly one solution

   c. No solutions with real numbers

9 Find all points of intersection of graphs of the following linear functions with the circle $(x - 4)^2 + (y - 1)^2 = 10$.

   a. $y = 2$

   b. $y = x + 1$

   c. $y = -x - 3$

   d. $y = x$

10 Find all points of intersection of the graphs of the following pairs of functions.

   a. $y = x^2$ and $y = -4x^2 + 5$

   b. $y = x^2 + 6x$ and $y = 0.5x^2$

   c. $y = x^2 + 3x - 4$ and $y = -x^2 + x + 6$

Connections

11 In your early study of systems of linear equations, you found the intersection point of graphs for linear functions like $y = mx + n$ and $y = ax + b$. You found that you could solve such systems by setting $mx + n = ax + b$ and solving for x. You used a similar strategy in the investigations of this lesson to solve systems of equations like $y = mx + b$ and $y = \frac{k}{x}$ and like $y = mx + b$ and $y = ax^2 + bx + c$. Compare the solution possibilities for these three types of systems by answering Parts a–c.

   a. How many solutions can there be for a system of two linear equations with two variables? Draw sketches of graphs showing the different possibilities.

7 Students should solve by factoring. Solutions and corresponding graphs are shown below.

a. $x = 0$ or $x = 3$

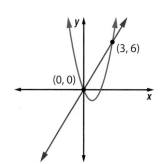

b. $x = -1$ or $x = 2$

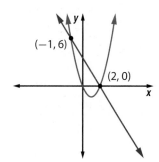

c. $x = -1$ or $x = 7$

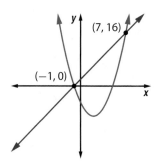

d. $x = -2$

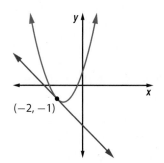

8 For each part, students should give an example of equations involving one linear and one quadratic function, sketch a graph illustrating the number of solutions to the equation, and explain how the sketch of the graphs relates to the solution of their specific one-variable equation.

a.

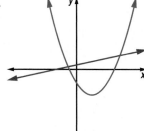

b.

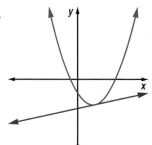

c.

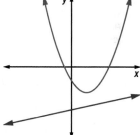

9 **a.** $(x - 4)^2 + (2 - 1)^2 = 10$

$x^2 - 8x + 17 = 10$

$x^2 - 8x + 7 = 0$

$(x - 7)(x - 1) = 0$

$x = 1$ or $x = 7$

Points of intersection: $(1, 2)$ and $(7, 2)$

b. $(x - 4)^2 + (x + 1 - 1)^2 = 10$

$2x^2 - 8x + 16 = 10$

$2(x^2 - 4x + 3) = 0$

$(x - 3)(x - 1) = 0$

$x = 1$ or $x = 3$

Points of intersection: $(1, 2)$ and $(3, 4)$

> **INSTRUCTIONAL NOTE**
> You may wish to have students sketch graphs of the circles and lines before solving symbolically so they can check the reasonableness of their points of intersections.

Unit 5

Unit 5

c. $(x - 4)^2 + (-x - 3 - 1)^2 = 10$

$x^2 - 8x + 16 + x^2 + 8x + 16 = 10$

$2x^2 + 22 = 0$

$x^2 = -11$

Points of intersection: none

d. $(x - 4)^2 + (x - 1)^2 = 10$

$x^2 - 8x + 16 + x^2 - 2x + 1 = 10$

$2x^2 - 10x + 17 = 10$

$2x^2 - 10x + 7 = 0$

$x = \dfrac{10}{4} \pm \dfrac{\sqrt{100 - 4(2)(7)}}{4}$

$x = \dfrac{5}{2} \pm \dfrac{\sqrt{11}}{2}$

Points of intersection: $\left(\dfrac{5}{2} - \dfrac{\sqrt{11}}{2}, \dfrac{5}{2} - \dfrac{\sqrt{11}}{2}\right)$ and $\left(\dfrac{5}{2} + \dfrac{\sqrt{11}}{2}, \dfrac{5}{2} + \dfrac{\sqrt{11}}{2}\right)$

10   a. $x^2 = -4x^2 + 5$

$5x^2 - 5 = 0$

$5(x^2 - 1) = 0$

$x = \pm 1$

Points of intersection: $(-1, 1)$ and $(1, 1)$

b. $x^2 + 6x = 0.5x^2$

$0.5x^2 + 6x = 0$

$x(0.5x + 6) = 0$

$x = 0$ or $x = -12$

Points of intersection: $(0, 0)$ and $(-12, 72)$

c. $x^2 + 3x - 16 = -x^2 + x + 6$

$2x^2 + 2x - 10 = 0$

$2(x^2 + x - 5) = 10$

$x = -\dfrac{1}{2} \pm \dfrac{\sqrt{21}}{2}$

$x \approx -2.79$ or 1.8

Points of intersection: $(-2.8, -4.6)$ and $(1.8, 4.6)$

Connections

11   a. There can be 0, 1, or an infinite number of solutions.

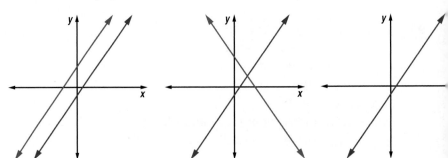

Teacher Notes

b. How many solutions can there be for a system like $y = mx + b$ and $y = \frac{k}{x}$? Draw sketches of graphs showing the different possibilities.

c. How many solutions can there be for a system like $y = mx + n$ and $y = ax^2 + bx + c$? Draw sketches of graphs illustrating the different possibilities.

12 In Investigation 2, the business planning for the summer theater production involved three different dependent variables: ticket sales income, operating costs, and profit; each related to the independent variable, ticket price. The following graphs show operating costs, ticket sales income, and profit all as functions of ticket price. Explain what each labeled point tells about the business situation and how you would find the coordinates of those points.

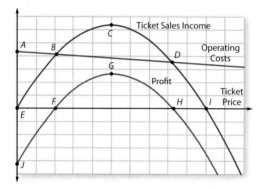

13 Analyze the systems of equations in Parts a–c, giving sketches of graphs for the functions involved to illustrate your answers. Then use the results and other examples you might explore to answer Part d.

a. Estimate solutions for the system $y = 2x + 1$ and $y = 2^x$.

b. Estimate solutions for the system $y = 2x - 1$ and $y = 2^x$.

c. Estimate solutions for the system $y = -2x$ and $y = 2^x$.

d. In general, how many solutions can there be for a system of equations like $y = mx + b$ and $y = a^x$?

14 In previous work with solving equations, you often found it useful to use two basic number properties to write relationships among variables in equivalent but more useful forms. The key ideas were:

$$a + b = c \text{ whenever } a = c - b \quad (1)$$
$$ab = c \text{ whenever } a = c \div b \ (b \neq 0) \quad (2)$$

Use these number properties to answer Parts a–c.

a. What quadratic equation has the same solution(s) as $4x = \frac{36}{x}$?

b. What quadratic equation has the same solution(s) as $5 - x = \frac{6}{x}$?

c. What equation in the form $ax^2 + bx + c = 0$ has the same solution as $x^2 + 9x + 7 = 3x - 1$?

b. There can be 0, 1, or 2 solutions.

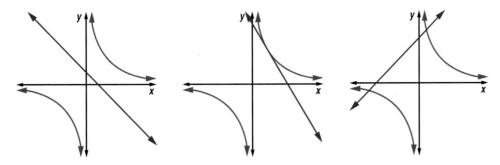

c. There can be 0, 1, or 2 solutions.

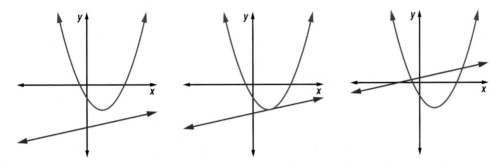

(12) Solution methods may vary.

A: Operation costs when tickets are free. Solve for operating costs when ticket price is 0.

B: First break-even point where *costs = income*. Use a table or graph to determine what ticket price will make *costs = income*. Reasoning symbolically, you would set the linear and quadratic function equal and solve for the ticket price *x*. The equal income and costs could be found by substituting *x* back into one of the functions.

C: Maximum income. Use the trace capability of a calculator to find the maximum point of the income graph. Symbolically, you could find the symmetry line $x = \frac{-b}{2a}$ from the quadratic expression for income and substitute that value in the function to find the vertical coordinate.

D: Second break-even point. (See description for point *B.*)

E: The amount of income you will have if the tickets are free. It is reasonable to expect the income function to be zero when $x = 0$ as shown on the graph. You could verify by substitution.

F: Break-even point where profit is zero; the ticket price generates just enough income to meet costs. Determine where the profit graph crosses the horizontal axis. You could factor, use the quadratic formula, or solve with tables or graphs.

G: Maximum profit. Use the trace capability of a calculator to find the maximum point of the profit graph. (See description for point *C.*)

H: Second break-even point where profit is zero. Determine where the profit graph crosses the horizontal axis. (See description for point *F.*)

I: Income is zero. Determine where the income graph crosses the horizontal axis. (See description for point *F.*)

J: Profit (actually loss) when ticket price is zero. Evaluate the profit equation when ticket price is zero, or use the trace capability of a calculator to determine where the profit graph crosses the *y*-axis.

Unit 5

13 **a.** $x \approx 0$ or $x \approx 2.66$

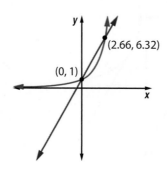

b. No solution

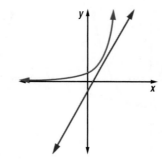

c. $x \approx -0.383$

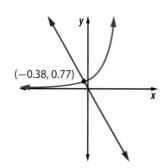

d. Since one equation is linear and one is exponential, it is possible that the graphs could intersect once, twice, or not at all. Therefore, the number of solutions is 1, 2, or 0.

14 **a.** $4x^2 = 36$, using property (2).

b. $5x - x^2 = 6$, using property (2).

c. $x^2 + 6x + 8 = 0$, using property (1) twice.

Teacher Notes

Reflections

15 What seems to be the difference between being asked to solve the system $y = mx + n$ and $y = \frac{k}{x}$ and being asked to solve the equation $mx + n = \frac{k}{x}$?

16 When two different students were asked to solve the equation $\frac{3}{x} = -\frac{2}{x}$, they came up with different answers.

Jim argued that there are no values of x that satisfy the equation. He sketched a graph of the two functions to support his claim.

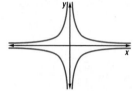

Linda gave the following "proof" that $x = 0$ is the solution.

$$\text{If } \frac{3}{x} = \frac{-2}{x}, \text{ then } \frac{x}{3} = \frac{x}{-2}$$
$$\text{then } \frac{x}{3} + \frac{x}{2} = 0$$
$$\text{then } \frac{5x}{6} = 0$$
$$\text{then } x = 0.$$

  a. Which student do you think is right—the student who used the graph or the student who used symbolic reasoning?

  b. What is the error in reasoning by the student who got the incorrect answer?

17 When you need to solve an equation in the form $f(x) = g(x)$, what are the values and limitations of using methods that involve:

  a. graphs of $f(x)$ and $g(x)$?

  b. tables of values for $f(x)$ and $g(x)$?

  c. reasoning that uses only the symbolic expressions for each function rule?

18 If you were asked to give advice on symbolic equation solving strategies to another student, what list of steps would you recommend to solve the following equations?

  a. $mx = \frac{k}{x}$

  b. $mx + n = \frac{k}{x}$

  c. $mx + n = ax^2 + bx + c$

Reflections

15 The first sentence asks for the values of x and y that solve the system. The second sentence asks for the values of x that solve the equation; y is not involved this time.

16 **a.** Jim, the student who used the graph, is correct.

b. In $\frac{3}{x} = \frac{-2}{x}$, x cannot be equal to zero. Linda assumed that she could rewrite $\frac{3}{x} = \frac{-2}{x}$ as $\frac{x}{3} = \frac{x}{-2}$ but ignored the initial condition that $x \neq 0$.

17 Student answers may vary, but here are some points to look for.

a. Values: The graphs allow approximate solutions. Graphs also give a visual representation of the number of solutions by showing where the graphs intersect. It also shows how quickly the two functions diverge from intersection points. In applied problem solving, that indicates the importance of setting conditions so that the intersection point is accomplished (or the freedom to deviate from what seems to be the optimal condition without changing results too drastically).

Limitations: Sometimes it is difficult to tell whether two graphs intersect at one point or at two points, depending on the calculator viewing window. Also, you may not get exact solutions.

b. Values: Tables of values may reveal the common x value when two functions have the same y value.

Limitations: It may be more difficult to determine the number of solutions by using a table. Scrolling through the table to find points of intersection is time consuming. Points of intersection may be missed if the table is changing by inappropriate incremental values.

c. Values: The symbolic expressions will provide exact solutions.

Limitations: The calculations may be complex depending on the coefficients of the terms. It may be difficult to anticipate the number of solutions. A purely symbolic solution also does not indicate in any way how quickly the two functions diverge from their intersection point. In an applied problem, that means that one does not know how important it is to set conditions quite precisely or whether one has some flexibility that will not drastically affect results.

18 Students may suggest advice similar to the following:

a. Multiply both sides of the equation by x to get $mx^2 = k$.

Divide both sides by m to get $x^2 = \frac{k}{m}$.

Take the square root of both sides to get $x = \pm\sqrt{\frac{k}{m}}$.

One could also use the property that $ab = c$ is equivalent to $a = \frac{c}{b}$ repeatedly.

NOTE Solutions to Task 18 Parts b and c are on page T373.

Extensions

19 Shown below is a portion of the graph of the system of equations
$y = \frac{50}{x^2}$ and $y = x^2 - 5x$.

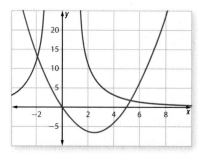

a. Make a copy of these graphs. If possible, color the graph of $y = \frac{50}{x^2}$ in yellow.

b. What connections between function rules and graphs allow you to match $y = \frac{50}{x^2}$ and $y = x^2 - 5x$ to their graphs?

c. On the *x*-axis, mark the points corresponding to solutions of the following equation and inequalities. If possible, use the colors suggested.

   i. in blue: $\frac{50}{x^2} = x^2 - 5x$

   ii. in red: $\frac{50}{x^2} > x^2 - 5x$

   iii. in green: $\frac{50}{x^2} < x^2 - 5x$

d. Find estimates of the solutions to the equation and inequalities in Part c.

e. How could you convince someone that your solutions are correct?

20 Determine the possible numbers of solutions (x, y) for each of these kinds of systems of equations. In each case, illustrate your answers by sketching graphs for pairs of functions that illustrate the possibilities.

a. $y = \frac{p}{x}$ and $y = \frac{q}{x}$

b. $y = \frac{k}{x}$ and $y = ax^2 + bx + c$

c. $y = ax^2 + c$ and $y = dx^2$

d. $y = \frac{k}{x^2}$ and $y = ax^2 + bx + c$

b. Multiply both sides by x to get $mx^2 + nx = k$.

Subtract k from both sides to get $mx^2 + nx - k = 0$.

Use the quadratic formula or factoring to solve for x.

Alternatively, one could use the properties that $ab = c$ is equivalent to $a = \frac{c}{b}$ and $a + b = c$ is equivalent to $a = c - b$ repeatedly before solving the standard-form quadratic in one of several available ways.

c. Subtract mx from both sides.

Subtract n from both sides.

Use the quadratic formula or factoring to solve for x.

Extensions

 a. The function $y = \dfrac{50}{x^2}$ is colored yellow.

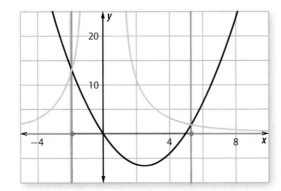

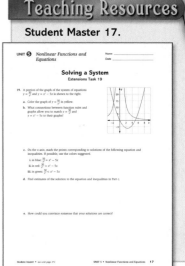

Teaching Resources

Student Master 17.

b. The graph of $y = \dfrac{50}{x^2}$ will have the x- and y-axes as asymptotes. The graph of $y = x^2 - 5x$ is U-shaped and opens upward because the equation has a positive x^2 term. Some students may also note that the graph of $y = x^2 - 5x$ should have a y-intercept of $(0, 0)$ and x-intercepts of $(0, 0)$ and $(5, 0)$.

c. See graph in Part a.

   i. Blue marks the solution of $\dfrac{50}{x^2} = x^2 - 5x$.

   ii. Red marks the solution of $\dfrac{50}{x^2} > x^2 - 5x$. (Students may indicate that $x = 0$ is not a part of this solution since one of the equations is not defined there.)

   iii. Green marks the solution of $\dfrac{50}{x^2} < x^2 - 5x$.

d. **i.** $x \approx -1.9$ and $x \approx 5.3$

   ii. $-1.9 < x < 5.3$ (except $x = 0$ where $y = \dfrac{50}{x^2}$ is not defined)

   iii. $x < -1.9$ and $x > 5.3$

e. The solutions could be verified informally by using the calculator TRACE function, a table of values, or by substituting values into the symbolic representation of the equation and inequalities.

20 **a.** There are either no solutions (if $p \neq q$) or infinitely many solutions (if $p = q$).

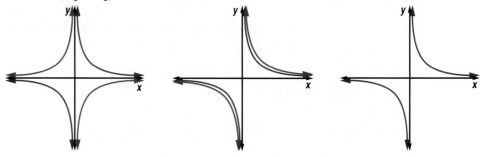

b. There is a possibility of 1, 2, or 3 solutions.

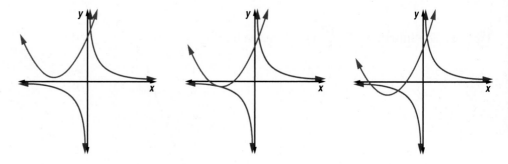

c. If $c \neq 0$, there is a possibility of 0 or 2 solutions. If $c = 0$, then there also can be 1 or infinitely many solutions.

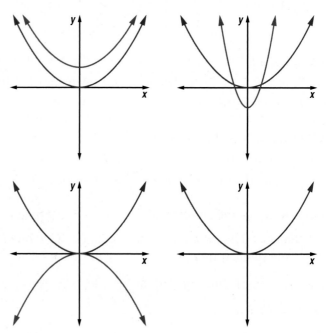

d. There is a possibility of 0, 1, 2, 3, or 4 solutions. (If students limit their thinking to cases of $a > 0$, they will indicate only the possibility of 2 solutions.)

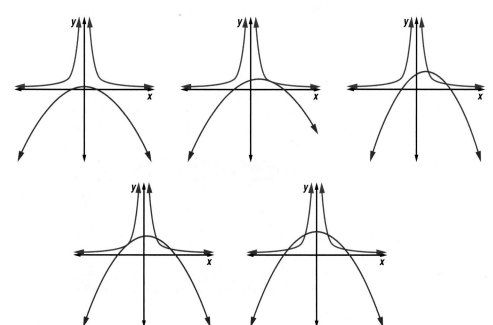

21 Determine the possible numbers of solutions (x, y) for each of these kinds of systems of equations. In each case, illustrate your answers by sketching graphs for pairs of functions that illustrate the possibilities.

a. $y = ax^2 + bx + c$ and $y = p^x$ ($p > 0$ and $p \neq 1$)

b. $y = \frac{k}{x}$ and $y = p^x$ ($p > 0$ and $p \neq 1$)

22 Jackie has found a spreadsheet to be a useful tool in her work in previous units. To explore how a spreadsheet might be used as a tool for estimating solutions to nonlinear systems, she created a spreadsheet to help solve $x - 2 = \frac{24}{x}$. The spreadsheet gave results starting like this:

Nonlinear Systems.xls			
	A	B	C	D
1	0	−2	error	
2	1	−1	24	
3	2	⋮	⋮	
4	3			
5	4			
6	⋮			

a. How could you produce such a spreadsheet table to check for solutions from $x = 0$ to $x = 10$ by entering only one number, formulas in 3 cells, and several fill-down or fill-across commands?

b. How could the spreadsheet be modified so that the search began at $x = 0$ and checked as x increased in steps of 0.5 at a time?

c. How could the spreadsheet be modified so that it would help to find solutions to the equation $4x - 3 = x^2 - 2x + 2$?

23 When Tanya and Mike were 15 years old, they had summer jobs. Tanya saved $500 from her earnings, and Mike saved $600 from his earnings.

- Tanya decided to keep her money at home but to add $10 per month from what she earned doing lawn mowing, snow shoveling, and other errands for neighbors.

- Mike decided to invest his savings in a bank account that paid interest at an annual rate of 6% compounded monthly (0.5% monthly interest).

a. What were the values of Tanya's and Mike's savings after 1 month? 2 months?

b. What rules give the values (V_T and V_M) of their savings after m months?

c. At what time (if any), did Tanya's savings grow to become greater than Mike's savings?

d. Illustrate your answer to Part c by sketching graphs of the functions in Part b and by labeling coordinates of key points.

e. How would your answer to Part c change if Tanya decided to save only $5 per month? If Mike was able to invest his savings at a 9% annual interest rate compounded monthly?

21 **a.** There is a possibility of 0, 1, 2, or 3 solutions.

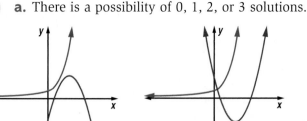

b. There is a possibility of either 0, 1, or 2 solutions. An example of two solutions that is difficult to see on a graph is $y = \frac{-1}{x}$ and $y = 1.1^x$. The solutions are $(-1.112, 0.899)$ and $(-38.232, 0.2616)$.

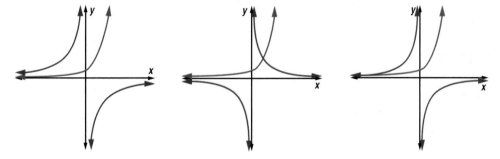

22 **a.** One could enter a 0 in cell **A1** and then create column **A** by entering the formula "=A1+1" into cell **A2** and then using the fill down command. In cell **B1**, the formula "=A1-2" representing $x - 2$ and using the fill down command would give the desired results for column **B**. In cell **C1**, the formula "=24/A1" representing $\frac{24}{x}$ and using the fill down command would give the desired results for column **C**.

b. Instead of entering "=A1+1" into cell **A2**, enter "=A1+0.5" and use the fill down command.

c. In cell **B1**, entering the formula "=4*A1-3" and using fill down would give the new results for column **B**. In cell **C1**, entering the formula "=A1^2-2*A1+2" and using fill down would give the new results for column **C**.

23 **a.** Tanya will have $510 after 1 month and $520 after 2 months. Mike will have $603 after 1 month and $606.02 after 2 months.

b. $V_T = 500 + 10m$; $V_M = 600(1.005^m)$

c. At 15 months, Tanya's account will be greater; but by 408 months, Mike will "regain the lead."

d. As shown at the right, Tanya's function is the linear graph $y = 500 + 10m$ and Mike's is the exponential $y = 600(1.005^m)$. One can see that Tanya's account value is greater at 15 months.

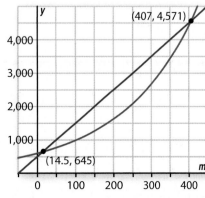

NOTE The solution to Task 23 Part e is on page T375.

Unit 5

Unit 5

24 Throughout this lesson, you have been solving systems of equations. In practical problems, it is common to encounter situations in which one or more of the constraints in a system involve inequalities like $y \leq 4x^2$.

Use what you have learned in this lesson as well as what you know about inequalities and graphing to solve the following systems of inequalities. The task is to find all points with coordinates satisfying both inequality conditions. Express your answer with a graph on which solutions are indicated by shading regions of the coordinate plane. (*Hint*: It might help to start with CAS graphs of each system of inequalities.)

a. $y \geq x^2 + 2x - 15$ and $y \leq -x^2 - 1$

b. $y \geq x^2 + x - 6$ and $y \leq 2x + 4$

c. $y \geq x^2$ and $y \leq \frac{5}{x}$

d. How could you convince someone that your solutions to the inequality systems are correct?

Review

25 Find rules for the linear functions with graphs meeting the following conditions. Then draw each graph on a coordinate system.

a. Slope of -3.5 and y-intercept at $(0, 2)$

b. Slope of 2.5 and containing the point $(2, 3)$

c. Containing the points $(-1, 2)$ and $(2, -3)$

26 Rewrite each rule in the requested equivalent form.

a. If $y = 4xz$, express x as a function of y and z.

b. If $z = 4x + 2y$, express y as a function of x and z.

c. If $z = \frac{x}{y + 2}$, express x as a function of y and z.

27 When owners of A-1 Auto Parts looked for a new delivery truck, they found a small pickup model they liked and got the following offers of lease payment plans from the dealer:

Plan A They could make a down payment of $3,500 and then monthly payments of $250.

Plan B They could make a down payment of only $1,500 and then monthly payments of $330.

They had to make a choice between a higher down payment with lower monthly payments or a lower down payment with higher monthly payments.

a. Write rules giving total lease payment as a function of the number of months in the lease for each plan. Use P_A for total amount paid under lease Plan A, P_B for total amount paid under lease Plan B, and m for the number of months in the lease.

e. For the system $V_T = 500 + 5m$ and $V_M = 600(1.005^m)$, Tanya's savings is greater than Mike's from about 70.9 to 133.3 months. For the system $V_T = 500 + 10m$ and $V_M = 600(1.0075^m)$, Tanya's savings is greater than Mike's from about 19.3 to 179.6 months.

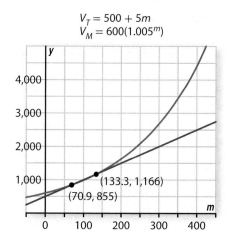
$V_T = 500 + 5m$
$V_M = 600(1.005^m)$

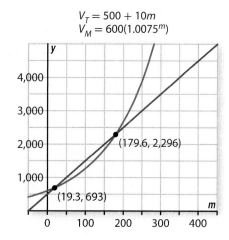
$V_T = 500 + 10m$
$V_M = 600(1.0075^m)$

24 **INSTRUCTIONAL NOTE** When using graphs to help identify solutions for systems of inequalities, you can either shade the solution areas or shade the nonsolution areas. Students have little experience solving systems of inequalities, so they may approach this task by finding the solutions for the first inequality and then identifying which of those solutions also qualify as solutions for the second inequality. Alternatively, students might use a CAS to graph these systems of inequalities as shown in Part c.

a. $y \geq x^2 + 2x - 15$ and $y \leq -x^2 - 1$ **b.** $y \geq x^2 + x - 6$ and $y \leq 2x + 4$

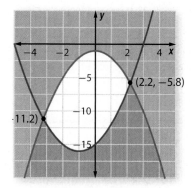

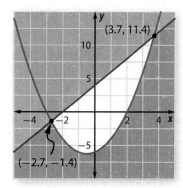

NOTE Solutions to Problems 25–27a are on page T376.

c. The *CPMP-Tools* CAS screen at the right shows the solution by shading the solution to each inequality with the overlap indicating the solutions to both inequalities. Note that for $y = \dfrac{5}{x}$, you must consider above and below the graph and also both sides of the discontinuity at $x = 0$.

d. Convincing might be possible by testing points in the different regions formed by the graphs to check if both inequalities hold true.

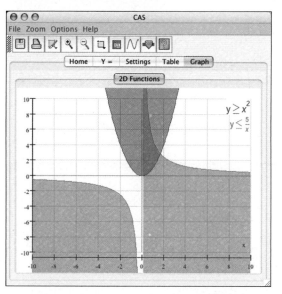

    b. Write and solve equations or inequalities that answer these questions about the two lease plans.

        i. For what lease lengths will Plan A be cheaper than Plan B?

        ii. For what lease lengths will Plan A be more expensive than Plan B?

        iii. For what lease length(s) will Plans A and B have the same cost to A-1 Auto Parts?

    c. Explain how the answers to the questions in Part b could be found using graphs of P_A and P_B.

28 A fuel storage tank is in the shape of a cylinder. The cylinder has a height of 32 feet and the circumference of the base is 135 feet.

    a. What is the radius of the base of the tank?

    b. How much fuel will the tank hold?

    c. A freighter that delivers fuel can pump the fuel into the tank at 250 gallons per minute. If 1 gallon is equal to 0.134 cubic feet, how long will it take to fill the tank if it is currently empty?

29 Writing numbers in scientific notation is a compact way to represent very large or very small numbers. It can also make multiplying and dividing very large or very small numbers easier.

    a. Place the following numbers in order from smallest to largest.

$$321.56 \times 10^4 \qquad 0.00329 \qquad 123{,}537{,}821$$
$$6.2 \times 10^{-5} \qquad 2.1 \times 10^5 \qquad 3.1 \times 10^{-2}$$

    b. Rewrite each number in scientific notation and evaluate each product without using your calculator. Then represent the product using scientific notation.

        i. $(300{,}000{,}000)(5{,}000{,}000)$

        ii. $(0.00000006)(3{,}000)$

        iii. $(0.00000012)(0.000005)$

    c. Rewrite each number in scientific notation and evaluate each product without using your calculator. Then represent the quotient using scientific notation.

        i. $\dfrac{12{,}000{,}000{,}000}{6{,}000{,}000}$

        ii. $\dfrac{0.000000012}{0.00024}$

        iii. $\dfrac{0.00072}{8{,}000{,}000}$

Review

25   **a.** $y = -3.5x + 2$ **b.** $y = 2.5x - 2$ **c.** $y = -\frac{5}{3}x + \frac{1}{3}$ or $y = -\frac{5x - 1}{3}$

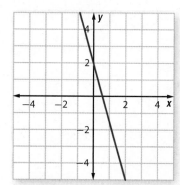 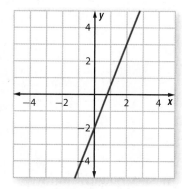 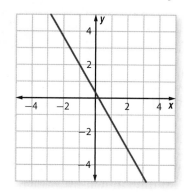

26   **a.** $x = \dfrac{y}{4z}$

     b. $y = \dfrac{z - 4x}{2}$

     c. $x = z(y + 2)$

27   **a.** $P_A = 3{,}500 + 250m$
           $P_B = 1{,}500 + 330m$

     b.   **i.** $3{,}500 + 250m < 1{,}500 + 330m$; when the number of months is greater than 25.

        ii. $3{,}500 + 250m > 1{,}500 + 330m$; when the number of months is less than 25.

       iii. $3{,}500 + 250m = 1{,}500 + 330m$; when the number of months is 25.

     c. You could answer the equality question by graphing both linear functions and finding the m value for the point of intersection. The inequality questions can be answered by finding the m values where the line for P_A is below the line for P_B and where the line for P_B is below the line for P_A, respectively.

28   **a.** The radius is $\dfrac{135}{2\pi} \approx 21.49$ feet.

     b. The tank will hold $\pi(21.49)^2(32) \approx 46{,}427$ ft^3 of fuel.

     c. Since $46{,}427$ ft$^3 \approx 346{,}470$ gallons, it will take $\dfrac{346{,}470}{250} \approx 1{,}386$ minutes or about 23 hours to fill the tank.

29   **a.** 6.2×10^{-5}; 0.00329; 3.1×10^{-2}; 2.1×10^5; 321.56×10^4; $123{,}537{,}821$

     b.   **i.** $(3 \times 10^8)(5 \times 10^6) = 15 \times 10^{14} = 1.5 \times 10^{15}$

        ii. $(6 \times 10^{-8})(3 \times 10^3) = 18 \times 10^{-5} = 1.8 \times 10^{-4}$

       iii. $(1.2 \times 10^{-7})(5 \times 10^{-6}) = 6 \times 10^{-13}$

     c.   **i.** $\dfrac{1.2 \times 10^{10}}{6 \times 10^6} = 0.2 \times 10^4 = 2 \times 10^3$

        ii. $\dfrac{1.2 \times 10^{-8}}{2.4 \times 10^{-4}} = 0.5 \times 10^{-4} = 5 \times 10^{-5}$

       iii. $\dfrac{7.2 \times 10^{-4}}{8 \times 10^6} = 0.9 \times 10^{-10} = 9 \times 10^{-11}$

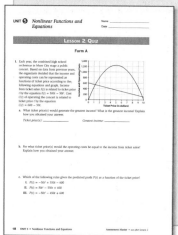
INSTRUCTIONAL NOTE
Task 29 provides an opportunity to discuss the value of using scientific notation for computation.

LESSON 3

Common Logarithms *and* Exponential Equations

Have you ever had someone tell you that you were speaking too loudly (or too softly) or that the volume on a television was turned up too high (or down too low)? While sensitivity to noise can vary from person to person, in general, people can hear sounds over an incredible range of loudness.

Sound intensity is measured in physical units of watts per square centimeter. But the loudness is typically reported in units called decibels. The next table shows intensity values for a variety of familiar sounds and the related number of decibels—as measured at common distances from the sources.

Common Logarithms and Exponential Equations

The goal of this lesson is to begin to develop understanding of common logarithms and how they relate to and can help in solving exponential equations.

It is extremely important that this is viewed as strictly an introduction to an algebraic view of logarithms. The development of the traditional "rules of logarithms" and how they can be used in solving logarithmic equations and rewriting logarithmic expressions will be presented in the Course 3 unit *Inverse Functions*. Natural logarithms will be studied in the Course 4 unit *Exponential Functions, Logarithms, and Data Modeling*.

Lesson Objectives

- Recognize what is meant by "taking the common logarithm" of a real number
- Be able to rewrite any real number as a power of 10 by finding common logarithms
- Use common logarithms to solve exponential equations, both in and out of context

Sound Intensity (in watts/cm^2)	Noise Source	Relative Intensity (in decibels)
10^3	Military rifle	150
10^2	Jet plane (30 meters away)	140
10^1	[Level at which sound is painful]	130
10^0	Amplified rock music	120
10^{-1}	Power tools	110
10^{-2}	Noisy kitchen	100
10^{-3}	Heavy traffic	90
10^{-4}	Traffic noise in a small car	80
10^{-5}	Vacuum cleaner	70
10^{-6}	Normal conversation	60
10^{-7}	Average home	50
10^{-8}	Quiet conversation	40
10^{-9}	Soft whisper	30
10^{-10}	Quiet living room	20
10^{-11}	Quiet recording studio	10
10^{-12}	[Barely audible]	0

Source: *Real-Life Math: Everyday Use of Mathematical Concepts*, Evan Glazer and John McConnell, 2002.

Think About This Situation

Study the sound intensity values, sources, and decibel ratings given in the table.

a Are the intensity and decibel numbers in the order of loudness that you would expect for the different familiar sources?

b What pattern do you see relating the sound intensity values (watts/cm^2) and the decibel numbers?

In this lesson, you will learn about *logarithms*—the mathematical idea used to express sound intensity in decibels and to solve a variety of problems related to exponential functions and equations.

 **How Loud is Too Loud?**

Your analysis of the sound intensity data might have suggested several different algorithms for converting watts per square centimeter into decibels. For example,

if the intensity of a sound is $10^x \dfrac{\text{watts}}{\text{cm}^2}$,

its loudness in decibels is $10x + 120$.

Think About This Situation

(a) Student responses will vary. However, students should agree that whispers should have a low decibel rating and a jet engine should have a high decibel rating.

(b) Student responses will vary, though students should see that for every increase of 1 in the exponent of the sound intensity, there is a corresponding increase of 10 in the relative intensity of the sound. Some students may develop a rule with the exponent of the sound intensity values serving as a variable. While this insight would lead to rich discussion, it is not vital at this stage that all are able to come up with such a rule.

Investigation 1 — How Loud is Too Loud?

In this investigation, students will express positive numbers as powers of ten and be introduced to the concept of the common logarithm.

COLLABORATION SKILL
Ask questions when I am not sure I understand.

Launch

The introduction to this investigation is critical to set up the work and to motivate the need to write a positive number as a power of 10. Students will need to use the decibel expression $10x + 120$ in Problem 3. Do not help students write 3.45 and 0.0023 as powers of 10 at this time. Since the concept of logarithms is difficult for students, look for opportunities to refer students to the definition and help them recognize that log c, where $c > 0$, is a real number. In Problem 1 Part e, some students may write -0.001 as -10^{-3}. It would be a good idea to discuss the difference between the results of Parts e and g, whose values are negative and *not* possible to write as a power of 10, and the results of Parts d and i, whose values are positive, but written as negative powers of 10. It would also be appropriate to save such a discussion until after Problem 3.

Unit 5

The key to discovery of this conversion rule is the fact that all sound intensities were written as powers of 10. What would you have done if the sound intensity readings had been written as numbers like $3.45 \frac{\text{watts}}{\text{cm}^2}$ or $0.0023 \frac{\text{watts}}{\text{cm}^2}$?

As you work on problems of this investigation, look for an answer to this question:

How can any positive number be expressed as a power of 10?

 1 Express each of the numbers in Parts a–i as accurately as possible as a power of 10. You can find exact values for some of the required exponents by thinking about the meanings of positive and negative exponents. Others might require some calculator exploration of ordered pairs that satisfy the exponential equation $y = 10^x$.

    a. 100   **b.** 10,000   **c.** 1,000,000

    d. 0.01   **e.** −0.001   **f.** 3.45

    g. −34.5   **h.** 345   **i.** 0.0023

2 Suppose that the sound intensity of a screaming baby was measured as $9.5 \frac{\text{watts}}{\text{cm}^2}$. To calculate the equivalent intensity in decibels, 9.5 must be written as 10^x for some value of x.

    a. Between which two integers does it make sense to look for values of the required exponent? How do you know?

    b. Which of the two integer values in Part a is probably closer to the required power of 10?

    c. Estimate the required exponent to the nearest hundredth. Then use your estimate to calculate a decibel rating for the loudness of the baby's scream.

    d. Estimate the decibel rating for loudness of sound from a television set that registers intensity of $6.2 \frac{\text{watts}}{\text{cm}^2}$.

Common Logarithms As you probably discovered in your work on Problems 1 and 2, it is not easy to solve equations like $10^x = 9.5$ or $10^x = 0.0023$—even by estimation. To deal with this very important problem, mathematicians have developed procedures for finding exponents. If $10^x = y$, then x is called the **base 10 logarithm** of y.

This definition of base 10 or *common logarithm* is usually expressed in function-like notation:

$$\log_{10} a = b \text{ if and only if } 10^b = a.$$

$\log_{10} a$ is pronounced "log base 10 of a." Because base 10 logarithms are so commonly used, $\log_{10} a$ is often written simply as $\log a$. Most scientific calculators have a built-in log function () that automatically finds the required exponent values.

3 Use your calculator to find the following logarithms. Then compare the results with your work on Problem 1.

    a. log 100   **b.** log 10,000   **c.** log 1,000,000

    d. log 0.01   **e.** log (−0.001)   **f.** log 3.45

    g. log (−34.5)   **h.** log 345   **i.** log 0.0023

LESSON 3 • Common Logarithms and Exponential Equations **379**

1   **a.** 10^2 **b.** 10^4 **c.** 10^6

     d. 10^{-2} **e.** Not possible   **f.** $10^{0.54}$

     g. Not possible   **h.** $10^{2.54}$ **i.** $10^{-2.64}$

2   **a.** The sensible place to look for a value of x where $10^x = 9.5$ is true is for $0 < x < 1$ since, for $10^x = 9.5$, $1 < 10^x < 10$.

     b. The value of x is probably closer to 1 since 9.5 is much closer to $10 = 10^1$ than it is to $1 = 10^0$.

     c. The required exponent is approximately 0.98. The decibel rating is then $10(0.98) + 120 = 129.8$ dB.

     d. 6.2 can be expressed as $10^{0.79}$. Therefore, the decibel rating is $10(0.79) + 120 = 127.9$ dB.

3   **INSTRUCTIONAL NOTE** The idea that there can be logarithms of bases other than 10 is not directly addressed here, though some students may ask about non-10 bases. Depending on the student comfort level, you may wish to briefly discuss what values of some base 2 or base 5 logarithmic expressions are.

     a. 2   **b.** 4   **c.** 6

     d. −2   **e.** Not possible   **f.** 0.54

     g. Not possible   **h.** 2.54   **i.** −2.64

(4) What do your results from Problem 3 (especially Parts e and g) suggest about the kinds of numbers that have logarithms? See if you can explain your answer by using the connection between logarithms and the exponential function $y = 10^x$.

(5) Logarithms can be used to calculate the decibel rating of sounds, when the intensity is measured in $\frac{\text{watts}}{\text{cm}^2}$.

  a. Use the logarithm feature of your calculator to rewrite 9.5 as a power of 10. That is, find x so that $9.5 = 10^x$.

  b. Recall that if the intensity of a sound is $10^x \frac{\text{watts}}{\text{cm}^2}$, then the expression $10x + 120$ can be used to convert the sound's intensity to decibels. Use your result from Part a to find the decibel rating of the crying baby in Problem 2.

(6) Assume the intensity of a sound $I = 10^x \frac{\text{watts}}{\text{cm}^2}$.

  a. Explain why $x = \log I$.

  b. Rewrite the expression for converting sound intensity readings to decibel numbers using $\log I$.

(7) Use your conversion expression from Problem 6 to find the decibel rating of the television set in Problem 2 Part d.

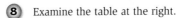

Why Do They Taste Different? You may recall from your study of science that the acidity of a substance is described by its pH rating—*the lower its pH, the more acidic a substance is*. The acidity depends on the hydrogen ion concentration in the substance (in moles per liter). Some sample hydrogen ion concentrations are given below. Since those hydrogen ion concentrations are generally very small numbers, they are converted to the simpler pH scale for reporting.

(8) Examine the table at the right.

  a. Describe how hydrogen ion concentrations [H⁺] are converted into pH readings.

  b. Write an equation that makes use of logarithms expressing pH as a function of hydrogen ion concentration [H⁺].

Substance	[H⁺]	pH
Hand soap	10^{-10}	10
Egg white	10^{-9}	9
Sea water	10^{-8}	8
Pure water	10^{-7}	7
White bread	10^{-6}	6
Coffee	10^{-5}	5
Tomato juice	10^{-4}	4
Orange juice	10^{-3}	3

(9) Use the equation relating hydrogen ion concentration and pH reading to compare acidity of some familiar liquids.

  a. Complete a copy of the table at the right. Round results to the nearest tenth.

  b. Explain how your results tell which is more acidic—lemonade, apple juice, or milk.

Substance	[H⁺] Proportion	pH Reading
lemonade	0.00501	
apple juice	0.000794	
milk	0.000000355	

(4) A logarithm can only be taken for a positive number since 10^x will always be positive for any value of x.

(5) **a.** Since $\log 9.5 \approx 0.9777$, $9.5 = 10^{0.9777}$ and $x \approx 0.9777$.

b. Using Part a, the decibel rating for the crying baby would be $10(0.9777) + 120 = 129.777$ dB. (This answer should agree with the answer to Problem 2 Part c.)

(6) **a.** The definition of $\log_{10} a = b$ is that $10^b = a$, so $I = 10^x$ means $x = \log I$.

b. $10 \log I + 120$

(7) $10 \log 6.2 + 120 \approx 127.9$

(8) **INSTRUCTIONAL NOTE** This problem requires a thorough understanding of the definition of a logarithm. It is another opportunity for students to think hard about the definition and should not be glossed over.

a. pH is the opposite of the base 10 exponent of the hydrogen ion concentration.

b. $\text{pH} = -\log \text{H}^+$

(9) **a.** The completed table using $\text{pH} = -\log \text{H}^+$ follows:

Substance	[H^+] Proportion	pH Reading
lemonade	0.00501	2.3
apple juice	0.000794	3.1
milk	0.000000355	6.4

b. Lemonade, which has the lowest pH reading and the highest proportion of hydrogen ions, is the most acidic. Milk, which has the highest pH reading and the lowest proportion of hydrogen ions is the least acidic. Apple juice is in between the two but is more like lemon juice than milk.

EXTENSION This may lead to an assignment along the lines of "Find a household product whose pH level is stated on its label and figure out its hydrogen ion concentration." The products' acidity levels can be compared to each other as well as to the substances given on page 380. You could also decide to bring such substances and have students predict, then calculate, the acidity of the substances.

DIFFERENTIATION
For some students, it may be helpful to use a single letter such as A to represent the pH reading and H to represent [H^+].

Unit 5

Summarize the Mathematics

In work on the problems of this investigation, you learned how physical measurements of sound intensity and acidity of a chemical substance are converted into the more familiar decibel and pH numbers. You also learned how the *logarithm* function is used in those processes.

a How would you explain to someone who did not know about logarithms what the expression log y = x tells about the numbers x and y?

b What can be said about the value of log y in each case below? Give brief justifications of your answers.

   i. $0 < y < 1$
   ii. $1 < y < 10$
   iii. $10 < y < 100$
   iv. $100 < y < 1,000$

Be prepared to explain your ideas to the class.

✔Check Your Understanding

Use your understanding of the relationship between logarithms and exponents to help complete these tasks.

a. Find these common (base 10) logarithms without using a calculator.

   i. log 1,000   **ii.** log 0.001   **iii.** log $10^{3.2}$

b. Use the function $y = 10^x$, but not the logarithm key of your calculator, to estimate each of these logarithms to the nearest tenth. Explain how you arrived at your answers.

   i. log 75   **ii.** log 750   **iii.** log 7.5

c. If the intensity of sound from a drag race car is 125 watts per square centimeter, what is the decibel rating of the loudness for that sound?

Summarize
the Mathematics

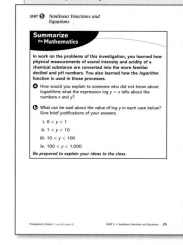

(a) log $y = x$ implies $10^x = y$. In casual language, "The logarithm of y is the exponent required to produce an outcome of y when the base is 10."

(b) Student explanations should indicate that they understand that log y represents the power to which 10 must be raised to obtain the values in the intervals. For example, when $1 < y < 10$, you think about what powers of 10 provide values between 1 and 10. Thus, $0 < \log y < 1$.

 i. log $y < 0$
 ii. $0 < \log y < 1$
 iii. $1 < \log y < 2$
 iv. $2 < \log y < 3$

✔Check Your Understanding

a. **i.** 3
 ii. -3
 iii. 3.2

b. Students might scan the table or trace the graph of $y = 10^x$ to find estimates for x when y is 75, 750, and 7.5.
 i. 1.9
 ii. 2.9
 iii. 0.9

c. $10(\log 125) + 120 \approx 10(2.1) + 120 \approx 141$ dB

Investigation 2 **Solving for Exponents**

Logarithms can be used to find exponents that solve equations like $10^x = 9.5$. For this reason, they are an invaluable tool in answering questions about exponential growth and decay. For example, the world population is currently about 6.2 billion and growing exponentially at a rate of about 1.14% per year. To find the time when this population is likely to double, you need to solve the equation

$$6.2(1.0114)^t = 12.4, \text{ or } (1.0114)^t = 2.$$

As you work on the problems of this investigation, look for ways to answer this question:

How can common logarithms help in finding
solutions of exponential equations?

 Use number sense and what you already know about logarithms to solve these equations.

a. $10^x = 1,000$
b. $10^{x+2} = 1,000$
c. $10^{3x+2} = 1,000$
d. $2(10)^x = 200$
e. $3(10)^{x+4} = 3,000$
f. $10^{2x} = 50$
g. $10^{3x+2} = 43$
h. $12(10)^{3x+2} = 120$
i. $3(10)^{x+4} + 7 = 28$

Unfortunately, many of the functions that you have used to model exponential growth and decay have not used 10 as the base. On the other hand, it is not too hard to transform any exponential expression in the form b^x into an equivalent expression with base 10. You will learn how to do this after future work with logarithms. The next three problems ask you to use what you already know about solving exponential equations with base 10 to solve several exponential growth problems.

 If a scientist counts 50 bacteria in an experimental culture and observes that one hour later the count is up to 100 bacteria, the function $P(t) = 50(10^{0.3t})$ provides an exponential growth model that matches these data points.

a. Explain how you can be sure that $P(0) = 50$.

b. Show that $P(1) \approx 100$.

c. Use the given function to estimate the time when the bacteria population would be expected to reach 1,000,000. Explain how to find this time in two ways—one by numerical or graphic estimation and the other by use of logarithms and algebraic reasoning.

In this investigation, students will use what they learned about logarithms in Investigation 1 to solve exponential equations. It is *not* necessary to supplement with the traditional logarithm rules (e.g., $\log x^m = m \log x$). These rules are introduced in the Course 3 unit, *Inverse Functions*. Students should be focusing on the definition of logarithms on page 378 to solve these problems (especially for Problem 1 Parts f, g, and i).

COMMON ERROR Students like to divide both sides by the base. For example, in Problem 1 Part f, $10^{2x} = 50$ becomes $2x = 5$. You may want to have students check this solution and focus on the meaning of $10^{2x} = 50$. You might ask, "About what power of 10 would result in 50?"

a. $x = 3$

b. $x + 2 = 3$, so $x = 1$.

c. $3x + 2 = 3$, so $3x = 1$ and $x = \frac{1}{3}$.

d. $10^x = 100$, so $x = 2$.

e. $10^{x + 4} = 1{,}000$, so $x + 4 = 3$ and $x = -1$.

f. $10^{2x} = 50$, so $2x = \log 50$, $2x \approx 1.7$ and $x \approx 0.85$.

g. $10^{3x + 2} = 43$, so $3x + 2 = \log 43$, $3x + 2 \approx 1.633$ and $x \approx -0.12$.

h. $12(10)^{3x + 2} = 120$, so $3x + 2 = \log 10$, $3x + 2 = 1$ and $x = -\frac{1}{3}$.

i. $3(10)^{x + 4} + 7 = 28$, so $x + 4 = \log 7$ and $x \approx -3.15$.

a. $P(0) = 50$ because $50(10^{0.3(0)}) = 50(10^0) = 50(1)$.

b. $P(1) = 50(10^{0.3(1)})$, so $P(1) = 50(10^{0.3})$ or $P(1) \approx 99.8$

c. $P(t) = 1{,}000{,}000$ when $t \approx 14.3$ hours. One can find this by scanning tables or graphs of the given population function or by algebraic reasoning to solve the equation $1{,}000{,}000 = 50(10^{0.3t})$ as shown below. Students are not expected to write the reasons supplied, but you can ask students to explain their reasoning.

> If $1{,}000{,}000 = 50(10^{0.3t})$
> Then $20{,}000 = 10^{0.3t}$ (divide by 50)
> $\log 20{,}000 = 0.3t$ (definition of a logarithm)
> $4.301 = 0.3t$ (evaluate $\log 20{,}000$)
> $14.337 \approx t$ (divide by 0.3)

INSTRUCTIONAL NOTE
Problem 1 Parts f, g, and i, Problem 2 Part c, and Problem 3 Part c will be challenging for students. Keep referring them back to the definition of a logarithm. See the investigation introduction.

Unit 5

3 The world population in 2005 was 6.2 billion and growing exponentially at a rate of 1.14% per year. The function $P(t) = 6.2(10^{0.005t})$ provides a good model for the population growth pattern.

a. Explain how you can be sure that $P(0) = 6.2$.

b. Show that $P(1) = 6.2 + 1.14\%(6.2)$.

c. Find the time when world population would be expected to reach 10 billion if growth continues at the same exponential rate. Explain how to find this time in two ways—one by numerical or graphic estimation and the other by use of logarithms and algebraic reasoning.

Summarize
the Mathematics

In work on the problems of this investigation, you learned how to use logarithms to solve equations related to exponential functions.

a How can logarithms be used to solve equations in the form $10^{mx + n} = c$?

b How can logarithms be used to solve scientific problems that lead to equations in the form $a(10^{mx}) = c$?

c How are the methods you described in Parts a and b related?

Be prepared to explain your ideas to the class.

✔Check Your Understanding

Use logarithms and other algebraic methods as needed to complete the following tasks.

a. Solve these equations.

  i. $5(10)^x = 450$

  ii. $4(10)^{2x} = 40$

  iii. $5(10)^{4x - 2} = 500$

  iv. $8x^2 + 3 = 35$

b. The population of the United States in 2006 was about 300 million and growing exponentially at a rate of about 0.7% per year. If that growth rate continues, the population of the country in year $2006 + t$ will be given by the function $P(t) = 300(10^{0.003t})$. According to that population model, when is the U.S. population predicted to reach 400 million? Check the reasonableness of your answer with a table or a graph of $P(t)$.

3. **a.** $P(0) = 6.2$ because $6.2(10^{0.005(0)}) = 6.2(10^0) = 6.2(1)$.

b. $P(1) = 6.2(10^{0.005(1)})$, so $P(1) = 6.2(10^{0.005})$ or $P(1) \approx 6.272$ which is approximately the same as $6.2 + 0.0114(6.2) = 6.287$. The difference is probably due to the rounding in the exponential parameter 0.005 which should more precisely be 0.004923.

c. $P(t) = 10$ when $t \approx 41$. One can find this by scanning tables or graphs of the given population function or by algebraic reasoning to solve the equation $10 = 6.2(10^{0.005t})$ resulting in $t \approx \dfrac{\log 1.6129}{0.005} \approx 41.5$.

Thus, the world population is predicted to reach 10 billion during the year 2046 if growth trends continue as at the present time.

Summarize
the Mathematics

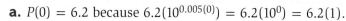
Teaching Resources

Transparency Master 26.

a. Use the definition of a logarithm to convert the equation to $\log c = mx + n$. Since $\log c$ is simply a number, solving for x is done as follows:

$$\log c = mx + n$$
$$\log c - n = mx \qquad \text{(subtract } n\text{)}$$
$$x = \frac{\log c - n}{m} \qquad \text{(divide by } m\text{)}$$

b. First, both sides of the equation can be divided by a to get $10^{mx} = \dfrac{c}{a}$. Then the definition of a logarithm is used to give the linear equation $mx = \log \dfrac{c}{a}$. This yields the solution $x = \dfrac{\log\left(\frac{c}{a}\right)}{m}$.

c. Solving $a(10^{mx}) = c$ is really only one step removed from solving $10^{mx + n} = c$. Solving $a(10^{mx}) = c$ for x can be considered as solving $a(10^{mx + n}) = c$ where $n = 0$. The generalized solution method is to rewrite the expression that contains 10 raised to a power (that includes the variable) so that it does not have a coefficient; that is, isolate $10^{mx + n}$ on one side of the equation with a number on the other side of the equation. Then rewrite the equation using the definition of a logarithm.

MATH TOOLKIT Provide examples of how to use logarithms to solve equations of the form $a(10^{mx + n}) = c$.

✓Check Your Understanding

a. **i.** $10^x = 90$, so $x = \log 90 \approx 1.95$.

ii. $10^{2x} = 10$, so $x = \dfrac{1}{2}$.

iii. $10^{4x - 2} = 100$, so $4x - 2 = 2$, and $x = 1$.

iv. $8x^2 = 32$, so $x^2 = 4$ and $x = \pm 2$.

b. Estimate answer: The population will reach 400 million in about 41.6 years, during the year 2047.

On Your Own

Applications

(1) Find the decibel ratings of these sounds.

    a. A passing subway train with sound intensity reading of $10^{-0.5} \frac{\text{watts}}{\text{cm}^2}$

    b. An excited crowd at a basketball game with sound intensity reading of $10^{1.25} \frac{\text{watts}}{\text{cm}^2}$

(2) Find these common (base 10) logarithms without using a calculator and explain your reasoning.

    a. log 100,000   **b.** log 0.001

    c. $\log(10^{4.75})$ **d.** log 1

(3) Find the decibel ratings of these sounds.

    a. A door slamming with sound intensity $89 \frac{\text{watts}}{\text{cm}^2}$

    b. A radio playing with sound intensity $0.005 \frac{\text{watts}}{\text{cm}^2}$

(4) Pure water has a pH of 7. Liquids with pH less than 7 are called acidic; those with pH greater than 7 are called alkaline. Typical seawater has pH about 8.5, soft drinks have pH about 3.1, and stomach gastric juices have pH about 1.7.

    a. Which of the three liquids are acidic and which are alkaline?

    b. Find the concentration of hydrogen ions in seawater, soft drinks, and gastric juices.

    c. Explain why it is correct to say that the concentration of hydrogen ions in gastric juices is about 25 times that of soft drinks.

    d. If a new soft drink has a hydrogen ion concentration that is one-fifth that of typical soft drinks, what is its pH?

(5) Use algebraic reasoning with logarithms to solve the following equations for x.

    a. $\log x = 2$

    b. $15 = 10^x$

    c. $5(10)^{2x} = 60$

    d. $10^{3x-1} = 100,000$

On Your Own

Applications

1 **a.** $I = 10(-0.5) + 120 = 115$ dB

    b. $I = 10(1.25) + 120 = 132.5$ dB

2 **a.** 5 dB because $10^5 = 100,000$.

    b. -3 dB because $10^{-3} = 0.001$.

    c. 4.75 dB because $10^{4.75} = 10^{4.75}$.

    d. 0 dB because $10^0 = 1$.

3 **a.** Since $\log 89 \approx 1.9$, $89 \approx 10^{1.9}$. So, the decibel rating is $10(1.9) + 120$, or 139.

    b. Since $\log 0.005 \approx -2.3$, $0.005 \approx 10^{-2.3}$. So, the decibel rating is $10(-2.3) + 120$, or 97.

4 **a.** Soft drinks and gastric juices are acidic. Seawater is alkaline.

> **NOTE** This task refers back to the table in Problem 8 on page 380 where students developed the formula $pH = -\log H^+$.

    b. Solving for H^+ using $pH = -\log H^+$ (or $-pH = \log H^+$) gives the following answers.

The hydrogen ion concentration in sea water is about $10^{-8.5} \approx 0.000000003$.

The hydrogen ion concentration in soft drinks is about $10^{-3.1} \approx 0.0008$.

The hydrogen ion concentration in gastric juices is about $10^{-1.7} \approx 0.02$.

    c. The hydrogen ion concentration of gastric juices is about 25 times the concentration of soft drinks since the approximate hydrogen ion concentration of gastric juices, 0.02, is 25 times the approximate hydrogen ion concentration of soft drinks, 0.0008.

    d. The hydrogen ion concentration of the new soft drink is $\frac{1}{5}(0.0008)$ or 0.00016. Since $\log 0.00016 \approx -3.8$, the number 0.00016 can be expressed as approximately $10^{-3.8}$. Therefore, the pH of the new soft drink is approximately 3.8.

5 **a.** $x = 100$

    b. $\log 15 = x$, so $x \approx 1.18$.

    c. $10^{2x} = 12$
$2x = \log 12$
$x \approx 0.54$

    d. $3x - 1 = 5$
$x = 2$

6 The Washington Nationals baseball team was purchased in 2006 for 450 million dollars. If the value of this investment grows at a rate of 5% compounded yearly, the purchase price of the team in year 2006 + t will be given by $V(t) = 450(10^{0.021t})$.

   a. Explain how you can be sure that this function gives the correct value of the investment in 2006.

   b. Use the function to estimate the value of the investment in 2010.

   c. Use logarithms and other algebraic reasoning to estimate the time when the value of the investment will be $1 billion ($1,000 million).

7 Suppose that the average rent for a two-bedroom apartment in Indianapolis is currently $750 per month and increasing at a rate of 8% per year. The function $R(t) = 750(10^{0.033t})$ provides a model for the pattern of expected increase in monthly rent after t more years.

   a. Explain how you know that $R(0) = 750$.

   b. Find the time when the average rent for a two-bedroom apartment will be $1,000 per month, if inflation continues at the current 8% rate. Show how to find that time in two ways—one by estimation using a table or graph of $R(t)$ and another using logarithms and algebraic reasoning.

8 If an athlete tries to improve his or her performance by taking an illegal drug, the amount of that drug in his or her blood will decline exponentially over time, but tests are quite sensitive to small amounts.
   For example, a 200 mg dose of a steroid might decay so that the amount remaining after t days is given by the rule $s(t) = 200(10^{-0.046t})$.

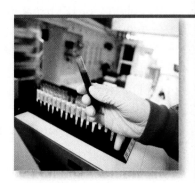

   a. Explain how you know that $s(0) = 200$.

   b. Estimate the time when only 5 mg of the steroid remains active in the athlete's blood. Show how to find that time in two ways—one by estimation using a table or graph of $s(t)$ and another using logarithms and algebraic reasoning.

9 Suppose that 500 mg of a medicine enters a hospital patient's bloodstream at noon and decays exponentially at a rate of 15% per hour.

   a. Use the exponential function $D(t) = 500(10^{-0.07t})$ to predict the amount of medicine active in the patient's blood at a time 5 hours later, where t is time in hours.

   b. Find the time when only 5% (25 mg) of the original amount of medicine will be active in the patient's body. Show how to find that time in two ways—one by estimation using a table or graph of $D(t)$ and another using logarithms and algebraic reasoning.

LESSON 3 • Common Logarithms and Exponential Equations   **385**

(6) **a.** $V(0) = 450(10^{0.021(0)}) = 450(10^0) = 450$ because $10^0 = 1$.

b. $V(4) = 450(10^{0.021(4)})$, so $V(4) = 546.02$

c. $1{,}000 = 450(10^{0.021t})$ when $t = 16.5$ or 6 months into the year 2022.

(7) **a.** $R(0) = 750(10^{0.033(0)}) = 750(10^0) = 750$ because $10^0 = 1$.

b. $1{,}000 = 750(10^{0.033t})$ when $t \approx 4$ years. This value can be estimated by scanning a table or graph of the function $R(t) = 750(10^{0.033t})$ to find values of t when $s(t) = 1{,}000$ or by reasoning algebraically.

$$\text{If } 1{,}000 = 750(10^{0.033t}),$$
$$\text{Then } 1.33 = 10^{0.033t}.$$
$$\log 1.33 = 0.033t$$
$$3.75 \approx t$$

(8) **a.** $s(0) = 200(10^{-0.046(0)}) = 200(10^0)$. Thus, because $10^0 = 1$, $s(0) = 200$.

b. $5 = 200(10^{-0.046t})$ when $t \approx 35$ days. This value can be estimated by scanning a table or graph of the function $s(t) = 200(10^{-0.046t})$ to find values of t when $s(t) = 5$ or by reasoning algebraically.

$$\text{If } 5 = 200(10^{-0.046t}),$$
$$\text{Then } 0.025 = 10^{-0.046t}.$$
$$\log 0.025 = -0.046t$$
$$34.8 \approx t$$

(9) **a.** $D(5) = 500(10^{-0.07(5)}) = 500(10^{-0.35}) \approx 223$. So, only about 223 mg of the drug remain active 5 hours after the initial injection.

b. 5% of 500 is 25, so we need to find t when $25 = 500(10^{-0.07t})$. This occurs when $t \approx 18$ hours. This value can be estimated by scanning a table or graph of the function $D(t) = 500(10^{-0.07t})$ to find values of t when $D(t) = 500$ or by reasoning algebraically.

$$\text{If } 25 = 500(10^{-0.07t}),$$
$$\text{Then } 0.05 = 10^{-0.07t}.$$
$$\log 0.05 = -0.07t$$
$$18.6 \approx t$$

10 The magnitude of an earthquake is often reported using the Richter scale. This rating depends on the amount of displacement recorded by a seismogram and the distance from the epicenter of the earthquake to the device. The table below gives the Richter scale ratings for measurements at a distance of 100 km from the epicenter of an earthquake.

Seismogram Displacement (in meters)	10^{-6}	10^{-5}	10^{-4}	10^{-3}	10^{-2}	10^{-1}	10^0	10^1	10^2
Richter Scale Rating	1	2	3	4	5	6	7	8	9

a. Write a function $R(x)$ which gives the Richter scale rating for an earthquake based upon the displacement x in meters of a seismograph located 100 km away from the epicenter.

b. A scientist noticed a displacement of 0.054 meters on a seismogram located 100 km from the epicenter of an earthquake.

  i. Between what two whole numbers did the Richter scale rating of this quake fall and how do you know from inspecting the table of sample Richter scale values?

  ii. What was the precise Richter scale rating of the earthquake?

c. The earthquake that caused the Indian Ocean Tsunami in December of 2004 reportedly measured 9.15 on the Richter scale. What displacement would be recorded on a seismograph on Simeulue Island, approximately 100 km away from the epicenter? (Source: en.wikipedia.org/wiki/2004_Indian_Ocean_earthquake)

11 When archaeologists discover remains of an ancient civilization, they use a technique called *carbon dating* to estimate the time when the person or animal died or when the artifact was made from living material.

The amount of radioactive Carbon-14 in such an artifact decreases exponentially according to the function $C(t) = 100(10^{-0.00005255t})$, where t is time in years and $C(t)$ is the percent of the Carbon-14 present in the artifact when it was last living material.

a. What is the half-life of Carbon-14, the time when only 50% remains from an original amount?

b. Suppose that a skeleton is discovered that has only 10% of the Carbon-14 that one finds in living animals. When was that skeleton part of a living animal?

10 **a.** $R(x) = \log x + 7$

b. **i.** The displacement of 0.054 lies between 10^{-1} (0.1) and 10^{-2} (0.01) and the table says that the Richter scale reading for such numbers will be between 5 and 6.

  ii. Since $\log 0.054 \approx -1.27$, $\log 0.054 + 7 \approx 5.7$.

c. $9.15 = \log x + 7$
  $2.15 = \log x$
  $x = 10^{2.15}$
  $x \approx 141.25$ meters

> **INSTRUCTIONAL NOTE**
> This task challenges students. Encourage them to focus on how the Richter scale rating relates to the exponent in the seismogram displacement.

11 **a.** $50 = 100(10^{-0.00005255t})$ when $t \approx 5{,}728$ years.

b. $10 = 100(10^{-0.00005255t})$ when $t \approx 19{,}029$ years.

Unit 5

Connections

(12) A large number like 2364700 is written in scientific notation as 2.3647×10^6 and a small number like 0.000045382 as 4.5382×10^{-5}.

   a. Write each of the following numbers in scientific notation with five significant digits (rounding appropriately where necessary to meet this condition).

   i. 47265   **ii.** 584.73

   iii. 97485302   **iv.** 0.002351

   b. Suppose that the only calculator you had was one that could multiply and divide numbers between 1 and 10 (including decimals) but no others. Explain how you could still use this calculator to find these products and quotient.

   i. 584.73×97485302 **ii.** 47265×0.002351

   iii. $47265 \div 584.73$

(13) Consider the function $y = \log x$. Study tables and graphs of the function to develop answers for these questions about its properties.

   a. What seem to be the domain and range of $\log x$?

   b. How does the relationship of logarithms and exponents explain your answer to Part a?

   c. How does the pattern of change in $\log x$ over its domain compare with the patterns of change for these functions over the same domain?

   i. $y = x$ **ii.** $y = \frac{1}{x}$

   iii. $y = x^2$ **iv.** $y = 2^x$

(14) Solve the following exponential equations and then explain how the strategies used are similar to what you use in solving linear equations.

   a. $10^{x+2} = 100{,}000$

   b. $10^{3x+2} = 10{,}000$

   c. $5(10^{3x+2}) + 6 = 506$

(15) The time it takes a computer program to run increases as the number of inputs increases. Three different companies wrote three different programs, A, B, and C, to compute the same information. The time, in milliseconds, it takes to run each of the programs when given n inputs is given by the three functions below:

   $A(n) = 10{,}000 + 2 \log n$
   $B(n) = 100 + 4n^2$
   $C(n) = (0.00003)(10^n)$

   a. Which program, A, B, or C, takes the least amount of time for 1 input?

   b. Which program is most efficient for 300 inputs?

   c. Which program is most efficient for 100,000 inputs?

   d. Which program would you market to home users? What about business users? Explain your reasoning.

LESSON 3 • Common Logarithms and Exponential Equations **387**

Connections

12 a. **i.** 4.7265×10^4 **ii.** 5.8473×10^2 **iii.** 9.7485×10^7 **iv.** 2.351×10^{-3}

     b. **i.** $584.73 \times 97485302 = (5.8473 \times 10^2) \times (9.7485 \times 10^7)$
                    $= (5.8473) \times (9.7485) \times 10^9 \approx 5.7 \times 10^{10}$

           ii. $47{,}265 \times 0.002351 = (4.7265 \times 10^4) \times (2.351 \times 10^{-3})$
                    $= (4.7265 \times 2.351) \times 10^1 \approx 1.11 \times 10^2$

           iii. $47{,}265 \div 584.73 = (4.7265 \times 10^4) \div (5.8473 \times 10^2)$
                    $= (4.7265 \div 5.8473) \times 10^2 = 8.0832 \times 10^1$

13 a. Domain: all positive numbers; range: all numbers

     b. Since one can think of logarithms as exponents, any real number can be a logarithm (range of the log function is all real numbers) but one can only find logarithms for positive numbers (domain of the log function is the positive real numbers).

     c. **i.** The function $\log x$ increases much more rapidly than $y = x$ when $0 < x < 1$ but then begins to increase at a much slower rate than $y = x$ for the rest of its domain.

           ii. The function $\log x$ increases throughout its domain while the function $y = \dfrac{1}{x}$ decreases throughout its domain. There is a kind of similar pattern in the shapes of the two graphs in that $y = \dfrac{1}{x}$ decreases rapidly for small positive x and then decreases at a very slow rate thereafter.

           iii. The function $y = x^2$ increases at an increasing rate over the domain of $\log x$, giving a graph that is concave up, while the graph of $\log x$ is concave down, indicating a function that is increasing at a decreasing rate.

           iv. The function $y = 2^x$ increases at an increasing rate over the domain of $\log x$, giving another graph that is concave up.

14 a. $x = 3$ since $x + 2 = 5$.   **b.** $x = \dfrac{2}{3}$ since $3x + 2 = 4$.

     c. $x = 0$ since $3x + 2 = 2$.

In all three cases, the idea is to isolate x on one side of the equation by algebraic operations that are similar to what one does to solve linear equations. Then one uses logs to remove the base 10 and proceeds as in solving linear equations to find x.

15 a. $A(1) = 10{,}000$, $B(1) = 104$, $C(1) = 0.0003$
       Program C would take the least amount of time for 1 input.

     b. $A(300) \approx 10{,}004.95$, $B(300) = 360{,}100$, $C(300) = 3 \times 10^{295}$
       Program A would take the least amount of time for 300 inputs.

     c. $A(100{,}000) = 10{,}010$, $B(100{,}000) = 40{,}000{,}000{,}100$,
       $C(100{,}000) = 3 \times 10^{99{,}995}$
       Program A would take the least amount of time for 100,000 inputs.

     d. Program C should be marketed for home users because it is more efficient for smaller input values. Program A should be marketed to business users because it is most efficient for large input values.

Reflections

16 Explain what is meant by the equation $\log a = b$. Then use your explanation to show why the following statements are true.

  a. $\log 1 = 0$

  b. $\log 10 = 1$

  c. $\log 10^x = x$

17 You are familiar with *linear scales* such as on a ruler or map. On these scales, the *difference* between equally-spaced scale points is a constant.

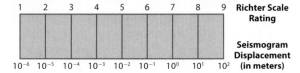

A Richter scale (see Applications Task 10) is an example of a *logarithmic scale*.

1	2	3	4	5	6	7	8	9	**Richter Scale Rating**

Seismogram Displacement

10^{-6} 10^{-5} 10^{-4} 10^{-3} 10^{-2} 10^{-1} 10^{0} 10^{1} 10^{2} **(in meters)**

What is constant in the case of equally-spaced scale points on a logarithmic scale?

18 Study a graph of $y = \log x$ for $0 < x \le 10{,}000$ and explain how the result justifies inclusion of logarithms in a unit on *nonlinear* functions.

19 With the introduction of logarithmic functions, you are now able to solve exponential equations using exact algebraic reasoning or a CAS, in addition to numeric and graphic estimation. Which method(s) do you prefer for solving equations like the following? Be prepared to explain your choice in each case.

  a. $100 = 4.5x - 885$

  b. $x^2 + x - 2 = 0$

  c. $3x^2 + 7x - 2 = 0$

  d. $5(10^x) = 500$

Reflections

16 The equation $\log a = b$ implies that $10^b = a$.

    a. $\log 1 = 0$ because $10^0 = 1$.

    b. $\log 10 = 1$ because $10^1 = 10$.

    c. $\log 10^x = x$ because $10^x = 10^x$ for all real numbers.

17 The constant is a product of 10 for logarithmic scales.

18 The graph of $\log x$ is asymptotic to the y-axis and rises rapidly for $0 < x < 1$ but then the curve bends concave down and settles into a pattern of increase that will actually look rather linear thereafter.

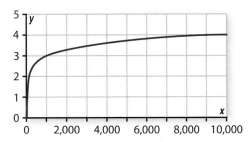

19 Student answers about their preferred style of solving various kinds of equations are likely to vary. As a general rule, they will probably say that they prefer algebraic methods (by hand) only when the required steps involve fairly simply arithmetic or obvious factoring (in the case of quadratics). Numerical and graphic approximation methods work in situations where no formal procedure is available. Use of a CAS is also advisable when the required procedure is not evident, but an exact answer is desirable.

Extensions

20 Suppose that n is a positive integer.

   a. If $0 < \log n < 1$, what can you say about n?

   b. If $5 < \log n < 6$, what can you say about n?

   c. If $p < \log n < p + 1$, where p is a positive integer, what can you say about n?

21 When you go to the movies, the number of frames that are displayed per second affects the "smoothness" of the perceived motion on the screen. If the frames are displayed slowly, our minds perceive the images as separate pictures rather than fluid motion. However, as the frequency of the images increases, the perceived gap between the images decreases and the motion appears fluid. The frequency f at which we stop seeing a flickering image and start perceiving motion is given by the equation $f = K \log S$, where K is a constant and S is the brightness of the image being projected.

   a. S is inversely proportional to the square of the observer's distance from the screen. What would be the effect on f if the distance to the screen were cut in half? What if the distance to the screen were doubled?

   b. If the image is being projected at a slow frequency and you perceive a flicker, where should you move in the theater: closer to the screen or closer to the rear?

   c. Suppose the show is sold out, and you cannot move your seat. What could you do to reduce the flickering of the image on-screen?

22 Recall that a prime number n is an integer greater than 1 that has only 1 and n as divisors. The first eight primes are 2, 3, 5, 7, 11, 13, 17, and 19. Mathematicians have proved that the number of primes less than or equal to n is approximated by $\frac{0.4343n}{\log n}$, quite an accomplishment since the primes appear irregularly among the natural numbers.

   a. Count the actual number of primes less than or equal to n to complete the table below. Plot the (n, *number of primes* $\leq n$) data.

n	10	25	40	55	70	85	100	115	130	145
Number of primes $\leq n$	4			16	19	23	25	30	31	34

   b. Graph $P(n) = \frac{0.4343n}{\log n}$, $0 < n \leq 150$. How well does this function model the counts in Part a?

   c. Use the function $P(n)$ to estimate the number of primes less than or equal to 1,000; less than or equal to 100,000; less than or equal to 1,000,000; less than or equal to 10^{18}.

   d. Using the function $P(n)$, about what percent of the numbers up to 10^6 are prime? Up to 10^{18}?

Extensions

20 **a.** $1 < n < 10$

b. $100,000 < n < 1,000,000$ or equivalently $10^5 < n < 10^6$

c. $10^p < n < 10^{p+1}$

21 **a.** When the distance decreases, the brightness increases and the frequency at which motion is perceived increases. (Derivation of this specific quantitative change in f requires using properties of logarithms not yet introduced.) If the distance is cut in half, the brightness will change by a factor of 4 and the frequency will increase by $K \log 4$. If the distance is doubled, the brightness will change by a factor of $\frac{1}{4}$ and f will decrease by $K \log 4$.

b. Since you cannot change the frequency at which the movie is displayed, you want to change your value of f to a lower number. This can be accomplished by decreasing the brightness through increasing the distance to the image. This can be accomplished by moving away from the screen.

c. If you cannot move your seat, you should decrease the brightness of the image. This can be accomplished by wearing sunglasses.

22 **a.**

n	10	25	40	55	70	85	100	115	130	145
Number of primes $\leq n$	4	9	12	16	19	23	25	30	31	34

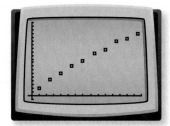 

b. As seen on the graph, the function $P(n)$ seems to give a low estimate for most of the data points.

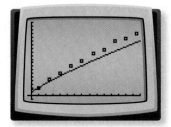

c. $P(1,000) \approx 145$
$P(100,000) \approx 8,686$
$P(1,000,000) \approx 72,383$
$P(10^{18}) \approx 2.4 \times 10^{16}$

d. $\dfrac{72,383}{1,000,000} \approx 7.2\%$ of the numbers less than 10^6 are prime and

$\dfrac{2.4 \times 10^{16}}{10^{18}} \approx$ approximately 2.4% of the numbers less than 10^{18} are prime.

23 Use base 10 logarithms to solve each of these equations for k.

  a. $10^k = 2$ **b.** $10^k = 5$ **c.** $10^k = 1.0114$

24 Use your results from Task 23 and what you know about properties of exponents to show how each of these exponential expressions can be written in equivalent form as $(10^k)^x$ and then 10^{kx}.

  a. 2^x **b.** 5^x **c.** 1.0114^t

25 Use your results from Task 24 and the ideas you developed in Investigation 2 to solve these exponential equations. Then check each solution and be prepared to explain your solution strategy.

  a. $2^x = 3.5$ **b.** $5(2^x) = 35$
  c. $5(2^x) + 20 = 125$ **d.** $5^x = 48$
  e. $3(5^x) + 12 = 60$ **f.** $300(5^x) = 60$

26 Use symbolic reasoning to solve the following equations for x.

  a. $\log(10^x) = 4$ **b.** $2^{2x+2} = 8^{x+2}$

27 The close connection between logarithm and exponential functions is used often by statisticians as they analyze patterns in data where the numbers range from very small to very large values. For example, the following table shows values that might occur as a bacteria population grows according to the exponential function $P(t) = 50(2^t)$:

Time t (in hours)	0	1	2	3	4	5	6	7	8
Population $P(t)$	50	100	200	400	800	1,600	3,200	6,400	12,800

  a. Complete another row of the table with values log (*population*) and identify the familiar function pattern illustrated by values in that row.

  b. Use your calculator to find log 2 and see how that value relates to the pattern you found in the log $P(t)$ row of the data table.

  c. Suppose that you had a different set of experimental data that you suspected was an example of exponential growth or decay, and you produced a similar "third row" with values equal to the logarithms of the population data. How could you use the pattern in that "third row" to figure out the actual rule for the exponential growth or decay model?

Review

28 How are the shape and location of the graph for an exponential function $f(x) = a(b^x)$ related to the values of a and b with $a, b > 0$ and $b \neq 1$?

23   **a.** $k = \log 2 \approx 0.301$ **b.** $k = \log 5 \approx 0.699$ **c.** $k = \log 1.0114 \approx 0.0049$

24   **a.** Since $10^{\log 2} = 2$, $2^x = 10^{(\log 2)x}$.   **b.** Since $10^{\log 5} = 5$, $5^x = 10^{(\log 5)x}$.

    c. Since $10^{\log 1.0114} = 1.0114$, $1.0114^x = 10^{(\log 1.0114)x}$.

25   **a.** $2^x = 3.5$ is equivalent to $10^{(\log 2)x} = 3.5$ which implies that

    $(\log 2)x = \log 3.5$, or $x = \dfrac{\log 3.5}{\log 2}$. This has numerical value of $x \approx 1.8$.

    Substituting back in the original equation, we get $2^{1.8} \approx 3.48$.

    b. $x = \dfrac{\log 7}{\log 2}$, or $x \approx 2.8$ **c.** $x = \dfrac{\log 21}{\log 2}$, or $x \approx 4.4$

    d. $x = \dfrac{\log 48}{\log 5}$, or $x \approx 2.4$ **e.** $x = \dfrac{\log 16}{\log 5}$, or $x \approx 1.7$

    f. $x = \dfrac{\log 0.2}{\log 5}$, or $x = -1$

26   **a.** By definition of logarithms, $\log(10^x) = 4$ implies that $x = 4$.

    b. Since $8 = 2^3$, the equation can be rewritten as $2^{2x + 2} = 2^{3x + 6}$ which is true when $2x + 2 = 3x + 6$, or when $x = -4$.

27   **a.** The extended table will look like this:

Time t (in hours)	0	1	2	3	4	5	6	7	8
Population $P(t)$	50	100	200	400	800	1,600	3,200	6,400	12,800
log (*population*)	1.7	2.0	2.3	2.6	2.9	3.2	3.5	3.8	4.1

    The table values for log (*population*) increase in a linear pattern with increments of 0.3 as the time increases in increments of 1 and the population doubles. The equation is log (*population*) $= 1.7 + 0.3t$

    b. $\log 2 \approx 0.3$, so the pattern suggests that log (*population*) $=$ $\log 50 + \log(2)t$. The actual population function is $P(t) = 50(2^t)$.

    c. The pattern observed in this particular well-behaved exponential growth situation suggests that if one finds a linear pattern in the log (*population*) data that obey the equation $y = a + bt$, then the actual population function will have rule $P(t) = 10^a(10^b)^t$ because if $P(t) = c(d^t)$, then $a = \log c$ and $b = \log d$.

Review

 Just in Time

28   All exponential function graphs have a domain of all real numbers and a range of real numbers greater than zero. They also all have a y-intercept of a. However, whether the function is increasing or decreasing and steepness of the graph are related to the base.

    For bases greater than 1, as the base gets larger, the graph approaches infinity more steeply on the right-hand side of the graph and approaches 0 more quickly on the left-hand side of the graph.

    For bases less than 1, the graph approaches infinity on the left-hand side and approaches zero on the right-hand side. As the base approaches zero, the graph becomes more steep on the left-hand side and approaches zero more quickly on the right.

Recall that the volume V of a cone can be found using the formula $V = \frac{1}{3}\pi r^2 h$, where r is the radius of the base and h is the height of the cone.

 a. What is the radius of a cone that has a volume of 400 cm³ and a height of 5 cm?

 b. Rewrite the formula so that it expresses h as a function of V and r.

 c. Rewrite the formula so that it expresses r as a function of V and h.

 d. How does the height of a cone change if the volume of the cone is constant but the radius increases?

30 Use algebraic reasoning to solve these equations.

 a. $7x^2 + 23 = 100$

 b. $x^2 + 13x + 42 = 0$

 c. $7x^2 + 23x = 0$

 d. $5(x - 8) + 12 = 4 - 7x$

31 Consider the coordinate grid at the right. Describe in words a transformation or composite of transformations that will map the first triangle onto the second. Then provide a coordinate rule for the mapping.

 a. $\triangle A$ onto $\triangle B$

 b. $\triangle A$ onto $\triangle C$

 c. $\triangle A$ onto $\triangle D$

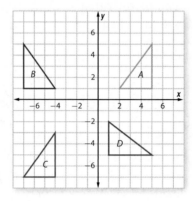

32 For each of the tables of values below:

 • Decide if the relationship between x and y can be represented by a linear, exponential, or quadratic function.

 • Find an appropriate function rule for the relationship.

 • Use your rule to find the y value that corresponds to an x value of 10.

a.

x	−2	−1	0	1	2	3	4	5
y	12	5	0	−3	−4	−3	0	5

b.

x	−2	−1	0	1	2	3	4	5
y	1	2.5	4	5.5	7	8.5	10	11.5

c.

x	−2	−1	0	1	2	3	4	5
y	1	2	4	8	16	32	64	128

LESSON 3 • Common Logarithms and Exponential Equations **391**

29
  a. $r \approx 8.74$ cm

$$400 = \frac{1}{3}\pi r^2 \cdot 5$$

$$400 = \frac{5\pi}{3} r^2$$

$$r = \sqrt{\frac{1{,}200}{5\pi}} \approx 8.74 \text{ cm}$$

  b. $h = \dfrac{3V}{\pi r^2}$

  c. $r = \sqrt{\dfrac{3V}{\pi h}}$

  d. The height decreases at a decreasing rate. (The height is inversely proportional to the square of the radius.)

30
  a. $x = \pm\sqrt{11}$

  b. $x = -6$ and $x = -7$

  c. $x = 0$ and $x = -\dfrac{23}{7}$

  d. $x = \dfrac{8}{3}$

31
There are many possible combinations of reflection, rotation, and translation that will accomplish each required motion. We provide solutions that use only reflections across the axes, rotations of 90°, and various translations.

  a. Reflect $\triangle A$ across the y-axis, then translate 2 units left.
$(x, y) \rightarrow (-x - 2, y)$

  b. Translate $\triangle A$ 9 units to the left and down 8 units.
$(x, y) \rightarrow (x - 9, y - 8)$

  c. Rotate $\triangle A$ 90° clockwise about the origin. $(x, y) \rightarrow (y, -x)$

32
  a. Quadratic; $y = x(x - 4)$; when $x = 10$, $y = 60$.

  b. Linear; $y = 1.5x + 4$; when $x = 10$, $y = 19$.

  c. Exponential; $y = 4(2^x)$; when $x = 10$, $y = 4{,}096$.

The table below provides information about the employees at Rosie's Grill. Fill in the remaining parts of the table.

	Full Time	Part Time	Total
Men	2		20
Women		20	
Total			45

Suppose that an employee is chosen at random. Find the probability of each event.

a. The employee is a full-time employee.

b. The employee is a man.

c. The employee is a man and a full-time employee.

d. The employee is a man or is a full-time employee.

34 The diagram below indicates the sidewalks and buildings in one apartment complex. Jamie is responsible for shoveling the sidewalks whenever it snows.

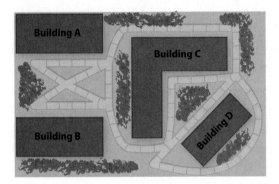

a. Draw a vertex-edge graph that represents this situation. Be sure to identify what the vertices and edges of your graph represent.

b. Explain how you know this graph has an Euler circuit. Then find one circuit.

c. Is the circuit you found in Part b the only Euler circuit for your graph? Explain your reasoning.

33

	Full Time	Part Time	Total
Men	2	18	20
Women	5	20	25
Total	7	38	45

a. $P(\text{full time}) = \dfrac{7}{45}$

b. $P(\text{man}) = \dfrac{20}{45}$

c. $P(\text{man and full time}) = \dfrac{2}{45}$

d. $P(\text{man or full time}) = \dfrac{25}{45}$

34 **INSTRUCTIONAL NOTE** Students will likely have a variety of correct vertex-edge graphs to represent the sidewalk-shoveling task. Vertices could represent only sidewalk intersections that have more than one possible exit, as the one shown below on the right. (See Course 1, Unit 4, page 241.)

a.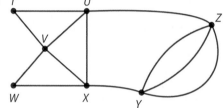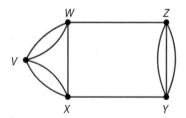

b. Since all the vertices have even degree, the graph has an Euler circuit. Circuits will vary depending on student graphs.

c. There are many possible circuits. You could start at a different location or traverse the edges in a different order.

Looking Back

The lessons in this unit involved many different situations in which quantitative variables were related to each other by linear, quadratic, and inverse variation functions. You also studied *logarithms*, a useful tool in solving problems related to exponential growth and decay. And you learned how to express information and questions about any function using the standard function notation $f(x)$.

As a result of your work on problems in the lessons of this unit, you should be able to better recognize situations in which each type of function is useful. You should also have an extended set of strategies for reasoning about the symbolic expressions and equations that represent those functions and the questions that arise in dealing with them. In particular, you should be more able to write quadratic expressions in useful equivalent forms by expanding products and factoring standard-form expressions. You should be able to solve quadratic equations by using the quadratic formula and by factoring where appropriate. You should also be able to use a variety of strategies to solve systems of equations involving a linear function and an inverse variation function or a linear function and a quadratic function. You should have a beginning understanding of ways to use logarithms to solve equations that involve exponential expressions.

The tasks in this final lesson will help you review and organize your knowledge of nonlinear functions and equations.

Looking Back

There are no corresponding teacher's notes for this student page.

(1) Business Economics In stores that sell athletic shoes of various kinds, the cost of doing business includes fixed expenses (like rent and pay for employees) and variable expenses (like payments for shoes bought from manufacturers). Operating costs of any store will be a function of those two main factors.

The typical American now owns two or three pairs of athletic shoes, which range in price from a $20 pair of old-fashioned sneakers at a discount store to $135 for top-of-the-line basketball shoes. One big seller has been Nike's Air Pegasus, which, like nearly all athletic shoes, is manufactured by suppliers in Asia. This accounting is based on a sale at an outlet of a large national retailer.

—By Steven Pearlstein

Production labor	$2.75
Materials	9.00
Rent, equipment	3.00
Supplier's operating profit	1.75
Duties	3.00
Shipping	.50
Cost to Nike	**$20.00**
Research/development	$.25
Promotion/advertising	4.00
Sales, distribution, administration	5.00
Nike's operating profit	6.25
Cost to retailer	**$35.50**
Rent	$9.00
Personnel	9.50
Other	7.00
Retailer's operating profit	9.00
COST TO CONSUMER	**$70.00**

Sources: Nike Inc., Reebok International Inc., The Finish Line Inc., Just for Feet Inc., Melville Corp., U.S. Customs Service, Atlantic Footwear Assn., industry consultants and executives, *The Washington Post*

Suppose that at *All Sport Shoes*, the manager estimates the monthly operating cost for the store (in dollars) as a function of the number of pairs of shoes that the store purchases from its suppliers. The rule for that function is $C(x) = 17,500 + 35x$.

a. Calculate and explain the meaning of each of the following:

   i. $C(100)$

   ii. $C(250)$

   iii. $C(0)$

b. What do the numbers 17,500 and 35 tell about the relation between the number of pairs of shoes purchased from the manufacturer and the total cost of doing business at the store for one month?

c. What value of x satisfies $C(x) = 24,500$? What does that value tell about the store's monthly business costs?

d. What table and graph patterns do you expect for this cost function?

e. What is the practical domain of the cost function? What is the practical range?

f. What is the theoretical domain of the function? What is the theoretical range?

a. **i.** $C(100) = 21{,}000$, which means that if 100 pairs of shoes are bought, the monthly operating cost is $21,000.

   ii. $C(250) = 26{,}250$, which means that if 250 pairs of shoes are bought, the monthly operating cost is $26,250.

   iii. $C(0) = 17{,}500$, which means that if 0 pairs of shoes are bought, the monthly operating cost is $17,500.

b. The fixed costs each month are $17,500, and 35 represents the operating cost for each pair of shoes bought.

c. $C(200) = 24{,}500$, which tells you that when 200 pairs of shoes are bought, the monthly operating cost is $24,500.

d. You would expect the change in a table of values to be constant. For each additional pair of shoes bought, there is a $35 increase in operating cost. In the table, each 1-unit increase in x corresponds to a 35-unit increase in y. The graph would be a straight line with slope of 35 and y-intercept of 17,500.

e. Since x represents the number of pairs of shoes bought, only non-negative integer values make sense as domain values. Considering the specific model, the realistic range values $C(x)$ are numbers greater than or equal to 17,500.

f. Both the theoretical domain and range are all real numbers.

(2) Developers of Waldo's World amusement park along Interstate I-75 wanted to install a large, illuminated sign that could be seen from a distance. A design firm suggested using a "W" logo made up of parabolas like the graphs below.

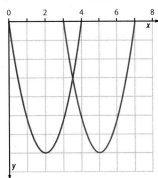

a. What functions will give parabolic graphs with the indicated x-intercepts? Write the function rules in two forms—one using a standard $ax^2 + bx + c$ expression and the other using an expression that is the product of two linear factors.

b. What are the minimum points of the graphs of the functions you defined in Part a?

c. If you wanted a W that was the same width as that shown but with minimum points along the line $y = -12$, what adjustment of your function rules in Part a would do the job?

(3) The design firm explored a second option using the functions $f(x) = x^2 - 6x$ and $g(x) = x^2 + 2x - 8$ to make the W appear somewhat taller and thinner.

a. Write each of these functions using equivalent factored forms of the expressions $x^2 - 6x$ and $x^2 + 2x - 8$.

b. Use the factored forms to locate the x-intercepts and minimum points of each function graph.

c. Will the new W appear somewhat taller and thinner than that in Task 2? Explain your answer.

(4) Write each of these quadratic expressions in equivalent expanded or factored form.

a. $(x + 3)(x - 7)$ b. $(x - 6)(x + 6)$

c. $(2x + 3)^2$ d. $x^2 + 8x + 7$

e. $x^2 - 144$ f. $3x^2 + 12x$

(5) Solve each of these equations in two ways—by factoring and by use of the quadratic formula. Explain how the number of solutions in each case is shown in the factored form of the quadratic expression and in the results of using the quadratic formula.

a. $x^2 - 5x + 4 = 0$ b. $x^2 - 6x + 9 = 0$

c. $x^2 + 11x + 10 = 0$ d. $3x^2 - 3x - 18 = 0$

2 **a.** The two functions that make up the logo will have the general forms $f(x) = ax(x - 4)$ and $g(x) = b(x - 3)(x - 7)$.

   b. The minimum y values will depend on values of the parameters a and b chosen by each student. However, the x-coordinates of those minimum points must be 2 and 5, respectively.

   c. Both parameters a and b should be 3 in order to make the minimum values of y equal to -12.

3 **a.** $f(x) = x(x - 6)$ and $g(x) = (x + 4)(x - 2)$

   b. The x-intercepts for $f(x)$ are at $(0, 0)$ and $(6, 0)$, with minimum $(3, -9)$. The x-intercepts for $g(x)$ are at $(-4, 0)$ and $(2, 0)$, with minimum $(-1, -9)$.

   c. These graphs will give a wider and shorter W.

4 **a.** $(x + 3)(x - 7) = x^2 - 4x - 21$ **b.** $(x - 6)(x + 6) = x^2 - 36$
   c. $(2x + 3)^2 = 4x^2 + 12x + 9$ **d.** $x^2 + 8x + 7 = (x + 1)(x + 7)$
   e. $x^2 - 144 = (x - 12)(x + 12)$ **f.** $3x^2 + 12x = 3x(x + 4)$

5 **a.** $x^2 - 5x + 4 = 0$ The 2 solutions are shown in the factored
      $(x - 4)(x - 1) = 0$ form by the 2 linear factors and shown in
      $x = 1$ or $x = 4$ the quadratic formula by $b^2 - 4ac = 9$.
                                     Since $\sqrt{9} = \pm 3$, there are 2 solutions.

   b. $x^2 - 6x + 9 = 0$ The 1 solution is shown in the factored
      $(x - 3)^2 = 0$ form by 1 linear factor and in the quadratic
      $x = 3$ formula by $b^2 - 4ac = 0$.

   c. $x^2 + 11x + 10 = 0$ The 2 solutions are shown in the factored
      $(x + 10)(x + 1) = 0$ form by the 2 linear factors and shown in
      $x = -10$ or $x = -1$ the quadratic formula by $b^2 - 4ac = 81$.
                                     Since $\sqrt{81} = \pm 9$, there are 2 solutions.

   d. $3x^2 - 3x - 18 = 0$ The 2 solutions are shown in the factored
      $3(x^2 - x - 6) = 0$ form by the 2 linear factors and shown in
      $3(x - 3)(x + 2) = 0$ the quadratic formula by $b^2 - 4ac = 225$.
      $x = 3$ or $x = -2$ Again, since $b^2 - 4ac > 0$, there are
                                     2 solutions.

6 Consider a quadratic function $f(x) = ax^2 + bx + c$.

   a. Explain the relationship between the graph of $f(x)$ and the values $\frac{-b}{2a}$ and $\frac{\sqrt{b^2 - 4ac}}{2a}$.

   b. Suppose the quadratic expression $ax^2 + bx + c$ can be written in factored form $(ax - m)(x + n)$. Explain what the linear factors tell about the graph of $f(x)$.

7 The three key variables in any type of racing are *distance*, *speed*, and *time*.

   a. If a runner covers 400 meters in 50 seconds, what is the runner's average speed? What if it takes the runner 60 seconds to cover the same distance? Write a rule that expresses average speed s as a function of distance d and time t.

   b. If a NASCAR driver plans to complete a race of 240 miles at an average speed of 150 miles per hour, how long will the race take? What if the average speed is 180 miles per hour? Write a rule that expresses race time t as a function of distance d and average speed s.

   c. If a participant in a triathlon swims at an average speed of 1.2 meters per second for 40 minutes, how much distance will be covered? What if the average speed drops to 0.9 meters per second and the time increases to 50 minutes? Write a rule that expresses distance d as a function of average speed s and time t.

   d. When Dakota was training for a long-distance race, she made some calculations about time and average speed.

   i. If the race is 24 miles long, how does race time t in hours depend on average speed s in miles per hour?

   ii. Dakota believes that her endurance depends on how fast she runs according to the function $t = 10 - s$. The faster she runs, the shorter the time she can actually keep going. How long can she run at an average speed of 4 miles per hour? How long at an average speed of 8 miles per hour?

   iii. At what speeds can Dakota run that will allow her to run long enough to complete the 24-mile race? Sketch a graph of "endurance time as a function of speed" and "required running time as a function of speed" to illustrate your answer.

8 As is the case with all businesses, the owners of Waldo's World need to make many decisions, including prices to charge for admission to the park.

6 **a.** $\frac{-b}{2a}$ is the x value of the minimum/maximum point on the graph.

$x = \frac{-b}{2a}$ represents the vertical symmetry line of the graph.

$\frac{\sqrt{b^2 - 4ac}}{2a}$ represents the distance away from $\frac{-b}{2a}$ along the x-axis, at which the x-intercepts may occur.

b. The graph of $f(x)$ will intersect the x-axis when $ax - m = 0$ and when $x + n = 0$. For this function, the x-intercepts are found at $x = \frac{m}{a}$ and $x = -n$.

7 **a.** 8 meters/second;

approximately 6.67 meters/second;

$s = \frac{d}{t}$ represents speed as a function of distance and time.

b. 1.6 hours;

approximately 1.33 hours;

$t = \frac{d}{s}$ represents time as a function of distance and speed.

c. 2,880 meters;

2,700 meters;

$d = st$ represents distance as a function of speed and time.

d. i. $t = \frac{24}{s}$ represents the relationship between race time and average speed. As the average speed increases, the race time will go down; as the average speed decreases, the race time will increase.

ii. 6 hours; 2 hours

iii. The answer involves solving:

$$10 - s = \frac{24}{s}$$
$$10s - s^2 = 24$$
$$s^2 - 10s + 24 = 0$$
$$(s - 6)(s - 4) = 0$$
$$s = 6 \text{ or } s = 4$$

At either 6 mph or 4 mph, Dakota could run long enough to finish the 24-mile race. Alternatively, students might find the x-coordinate for the intersection points of $y = 10 - x$ and $y = \frac{24}{x}$ as shown below.

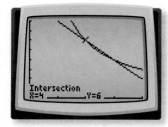  

Unit 5

Market research suggested that the income from admissions I in thousands of dollars would depend on the admission price charged x in dollars according to the rule $I(x) = -0.6x^2 + 28x$. Operating costs C were projected as a function of the admission price charged x according to the rule $C(x) = 250 - 2x$. The owners begin their analysis of profit prospects by first determining the admission price(s) for which income would exceed operating costs.

a. Use algebraic reasoning to determine admission price(s) for which income exceeds operating costs. Illustrate your answer by a sketch of the graphs of the functions involved with key points labeled with their coordinates.

b. Use algebraic reasoning to find the maximum profit possible for Waldo's World under the given assumptions. What ticket price should be charged to maximize profit?

9 Sketch graphs illustrating the number of solution possibilities for systems that link variables with conditions that are given by:

a. two linear equations with two variables.

b. one linear function and one inverse variation function.

c. one linear function and one quadratic function.

10 Evaluate each of these expressions. Give exact values where possible and estimates accurate to two decimal places otherwise.

a. log 10,000
b. log 0.0001
c. $\log (10^{3.72})$
d. $\log (10^{-3.72})$
e. $5 \log (10^7) - 8$
f. log 372

11 Many scientific and business calculations require high degrees of accuracy. So, there is value in not rounding computational results until the end of work on a problem. Early estimates can introduce errors that compound to produce final results that are not accurate enough. When the problem involves exponential expressions, logarithms can be helpful in this regard.

a. Solve the equation $10^{3x+5} = 100$ algebraically.

b. Write the solution for the equation $10^{3x+5} = 25$ as an expression involving $\log_{10} 25$.

c. Write a formula for the solution to any equation in the form $10^{ax+b} = c$.

8 **a.** $-0.6x^2 + 28x = 250 - 2x$
$-0.6x^2 + 30x - 250 = 0$

$$x = \frac{-30}{-1.2} \pm \frac{\sqrt{30^2 - 4(-0.6)(-250)}}{-1.2} = 25 \pm \frac{\sqrt{300}}{-1.2} \approx 39.43 \text{ and } 10.57$$

Income exceeds costs when the price charged for tickets is greater than $10.57 and less than $39.43.

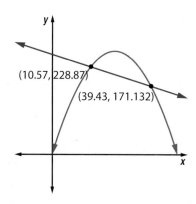

(10.57, 228.87)

(39.43, 171.132)

b. $P(x) = I(x) - C(x)$
$P(x) = -0.6x^2 + 28x - (250 - 2x)$
$P(x) = -0.6x^2 + 30x - 250$
To find the x-coordinate for the maximum profit, you can average the
ticket price limits above or just use $\frac{-b}{2a} = 25$. The maximum profit is
$P(25) = 125$ thousand dollars.

9 **a.** It is possible to have 0, 1, or infinitely many solutions.

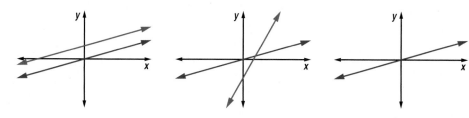

b. It is possible to have 0, 1, or 2 solutions.

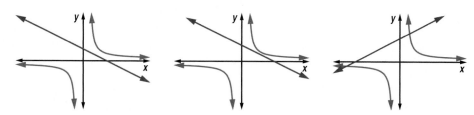

c. It is possible to have 0, 1, or 2 solutions.

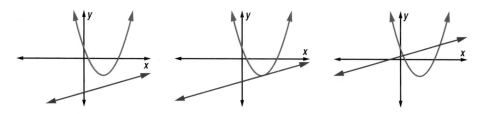

Unit 5

INSTRUCTIONAL NOTE
Students should be able to
answer Parts a, b, and e
without technology.

Unit 5

10 **a.** 4   **b.** −4

c. 3.72   **d.** −3.72

e. 27   **f.** 2.57

11 **a.** The equation can be converted to $3x + 5 = \log 100$ before solving.

$$3x + 5 = 2$$
$$3x = -3$$
$$x = -1$$

b. $x = \dfrac{\log 25 - 5}{3}$

c. $x = \dfrac{\log c - b}{a}$

Teacher Notes

Summarize
the Mathematics

In this unit, you investigated a variety of situations in which linear, quadratic, and inverse variation functions described relationships between variables. You further developed algebraic skills that are useful in writing the expressions for functions in equivalent forms, and you learned how to use logarithms to solve problems involving exponential functions.

a If two variables x and y are related by a function so that $y = f(x)$, what information about the relationship is expressed by statements in the form $f(a) = b$?

b How can knowledge of the x- and y-intercepts of graphs be used to write rules for quadratic functions?

c How do you find the expanded forms of expressions in the following forms?

    i. $(x + a)(x + b)$
    ii. $(x + a)^2$
    iii. $(x + a)(x - a)$

d What strategies do you use to write an expression like $x^2 + mx + n$ in equivalent form as a product of linear factors?

e What are the key steps in solving a quadratic equation:

    i. by factoring?
    ii. by use of the quadratic formula?

How do you decide which of these strategies is most likely to be effective in a particular case?

f What are the number of solution possibilities and solution strategies for systems of equations like:

    i. $f(x) = ax + b$ and $g(x) = \frac{k}{x}$?
    ii. $f(x) = ax + b$ and $h(x) = ax^2 + bx + c$?

g What does it mean to say "$\log b = a$"?

h How can the equation $y = 10^x$ be expressed in equivalent form using common logarithms?

Be prepared to explain your ideas and methods to the class.

✓ Check Your Understanding

Write, in outline form, a summary of the important mathematical concepts and methods developed in this unit. Organize your summary so that it can be used as a quick reference in future units and courses.

Summarize
the Mathematics

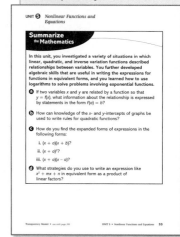

(a) When the value a is used as an input for the function (substitute it for x), the output is b. Also, the point (a, b) lies on the graph of the function.

(b) One possible response: If the x-intercepts are known, the function can be set up in the form $f(x) = a(x - p)(x - q)$, where p and q are the x-coordinates of the x-intercepts. If the y-intercept is known, then the coordinates for the y-intercept can be substituted for the $(x, f(x))$ coordinates in the function. This will result in an equation with a as the only variable. Solving this for a will provide the last piece of information needed to define the function.

(c) Students may have a number of strategies, ranging from memorization of the pattern to repeated use of the distributive property. Student strategies should be discussed for accuracy and possibly efficiency. Regardless of the chosen strategies, the following expressions should result:

  i. $(x + a)(x + b) = x^2 + (a + b)x + ab$

 ii. $(x + a)^2 = x^2 + 2ax + a^2$

iii. $(x + a)(x - a) = x^2 - a^2$

(d) Student strategies should include: (a) finding pairs of numbers, j and k, such that $j + k = m$ and $jk = n$ and (b) rewriting the original quadratic expression in the form $(x + j)(x + k)$.

(e) **i.** Factoring: To solve equations like $ax^2 + bx = 0$ by reasoning without use of a calculator, one would first factor an x from both terms, $x(ax + b) = 0$. Then, both of the new factors would be set equal to zero, and each of these new equations would be solved for x.

   To solve equations like $ax^2 + bx + c = 0$ when the expression $ax^2 + bx + c$ can be written in equivalent form as the product of two linear expressions, one should set each of the factors (in the new factored expression) equal to zero and solve the new equations for x. One should look for a common factor of the three terms to simplify factoring.

  ii. Using the quadratic formula: The first step, if necessary, is to arrange the equation so that it is in the form $ax^2 + bx + c = 0$ or at least arranged in such a form where the a, b, and c values can be determined where a is the x^2 coefficient, b is the linear coefficient, and c is the constant term. Once these a, b, and c values are determined, x value solutions can be found by substituting the a, b, and c values into the quadratic formula:

$$x = \frac{-b}{2a} \pm \frac{\sqrt{b^2 - 4ac}}{2a}$$

Student responses will vary as to which strategy is more effective in a particular case. They may talk about whether a linear pair of factors is easily visible. If factors are not readily visible, they may go to the quadratic formula. Some may use $b^2 - 4ac$ to determine whether a factored expression is worth seeking.

(f) Solution possibilities:

  i. 0, 1, or 2 solutions can be found.

  ii. 0, 1, or 2 solutions can be found.

Solution strategies:

In both cases, the input and output values for these functions can be viewed in a table. Solutions occur when output values for both functions are equal for equal input values.

When using graphs to estimate, one can use the TRACE feature of a graphing calculator or other means of estimating where the graphs of the two functions intersect.

Algebraically, the two input expressions should be set equal. Then rewrite the equation in the form $ax^2 + bx + c = 0$. Finally, factoring or the quadratic formula can be used to find solutions for x. The corresponding y values can be found by substituting each x value in one of the original functions.

(g) Saying "$\log b = a$" is the same as saying "$10^a = b$."

(h) $y = 10^x$ can also be expressed as $\log y = x$.

✓Check Your Understanding

You may wish to have students use the Teaching Master, *Nonlinear Functions and Equations* Unit Summary, to help them organize the information. Above all, this should be something that is useful to the individual student.

Practicing for Standardized Tests

Each Practicing for Standardized Tests master presents 10 questions in the multiple-choice format of test items similar to how they often appear in standardized tests. Answers are provided below.

Answers to Practice Set 5

1. (b) **2.** (c) **3.** (b) **4.** (e) **5.** (d)
6. (e) **7.** (b) **8.** (d) **9.** (c) **10.** (d)

Assessment Masters 39–56.

Student Masters 57–58.

UNIT
6

NETWORK OPTIMIZATION

Optimization is the process of finding the best. This process is important throughout mathematics and in everyday life. Everywhere you look, you'll see people trying to get the best, whether it's the best deal on a new purchase, the best job, the highest score in a game, or even something as ordinary as the best route from home to school. In your previous study of mathematics, you have often tried to optimize, for example, by finding the best-fitting line for a scatterplot of data, the maximum area of a shape with fixed perimeter, the highest point on the graph of a quadratic function, or the fewest number of colors needed to color the vertices of a graph.

In this unit of *Core-Plus Mathematics*, you will study optimization in the context of networks. For example, you might want to find an optimum road network or an optimum telecommunications network. To help solve network, optimization problems, you will use vertex-edge graphs. The necessary concepts and skills for solving the optimization problems in this unit are developed in two lessons.

Lessons

1 *Optimum Spanning Networks*

Use minimum spanning trees and Hamilton circuits to help find optimum networks that span (reach) all the vertices in a vertex-edge graph.

2 *Scheduling Projects Using Critical Paths*

Use critical path analysis to optimally schedule large projects that are comprised of many smaller tasks, like a building construction project.

NETWORK OPTIMIZATION

Unit Overview

In this unit of *Core-Plus Mathematics*, students continue their study of vertex-edge graphs. Vertex-edge graphs are also known simply as *graphs*, particularly in college courses, or as networks. The formal study of vertex-edge graphs is called graph theory. In the *Vertex-Edge Graphs* unit in Course 1, students learned about Euler paths, adjacency matrices for graphs, and vertex coloring. In *Matrix Methods*, they encountered digraphs and learned more about adjacency matrices. In *Network Optimization*, students will study several more fundamental topics in graph theory—minimum spanning trees, Hamilton paths, the Traveling Salesperson Problem (TSP), and project scheduling using critical paths (also called the Program Evaluation and Review Technique, PERT, or the Critical Path Method, CPM).

Vertex-edge graphs are part of geometry since they are geometric diagrams consisting of vertices and edges; although in contrast to most high school geometry, size and shape are not essential features of these geometric objects. Rather, it is the connections among vertices as shown by the edges that is essential. Vertex-edge graphs are also part of discrete mathematics, which includes vertex-edge graphs, iteration and recursion, combinatorics, and the mathematics of democratic decision making and information processing.

The study of discrete mathematics helps develop three important general skills: mathematical modeling, algorithmic problem solving, and optimization. This unit continues the development of all three of these skills with an emphasis on optimizing networks. Students will refine their optimization skills as they find *minimum* spanning trees, *shortest* Hamilton circuits, and *longest* paths that determine *earliest* finish time for large projects. They will further develop the skill of algorithmic problem solving as they carefully design, use, and analyze algorithms for optimizing networks. And they gain more experience with mathematical modeling as they model and solve problems using vertex-edge graphs.

This unit presents concepts and problems that most students find interesting, engaging, relevant, and sensible. Students who may have been struggling with previous material often find success in *Network Optimization*. Teachers report that, besides learning important new mathematics, students often leave the unit with a feeling of success and the impetus to tackle the remaining units of the year.

- Understand and apply minimum spanning trees, Hamilton circuits, the Traveling Salesperson Problem, and critical paths (including ideas from the Critical Path Method, CPM, which is also called the Program Evaluation and Review Technique, PERT)
- Further develop skill in mathematical modeling by modeling and solving problems with vertex-edge graphs
- Further develop skill in algorithmic problem solving by designing, using, and analyzing systematic procedures for solving problems involving vertex-edge graphs
- Further develop the ability to recognize, formulate, and solve optimization problems, particularly network optimization problems

CPMP-Tools

In this unit, some problems offer students an opportunity to use vertex-edge graph software to investigate concepts and methods and solve problems. *CPMP-Tools* is customized software provided with the *Core-Plus Mathematics* program that includes vertex-edge graph software. Go to the Discrete Math menu and choose *Vertex-Edge Graph* for certain applications.

Problems in which this software can be used are:

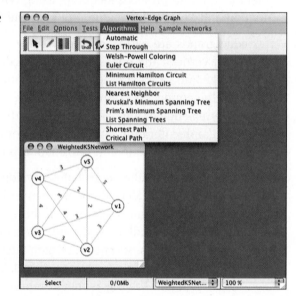

Lesson 1—Investigation 1, Problem 12 (p. 405); Investigation 2, Problem 6 (p. 409); Investigation 3, Problem 4 (p. 413); Extensions Task 20 (pp. 427–428)

Lesson 2—Investigation 2, Problem 7 (p. 441); Extensions Task 20 (p. 450)

Also, the software provides preloaded copies of the following graphs in the Sample Graphs menu: computer graph (p. 405), nearest-neighbor test graph (p. 405), connected weighted graph (pp. 405 and 428), sprinkler system graph (p. 409), brute-force K5 test graph (p. 409), Johnson County graph (p. 414), Orefield Graphs I and II (p. 418), complete graph (p. 430), complete bipartite graph (p. 430), and feasibility study graph (p. 441).

In addition, the *CPMP-Tools* geometry software can be used with Extensions Task 21 (pp. 428–429). Suggestions to integrate these software tools are included in the student text and teaching notes at point of use.

Additional References

The following references may be useful if you would like more information about vertex-edge graphs. If you choose to use videos with your students, carefully consider the content of each video. It is important to keep the investigative nature of this unit intact. Some videos present the main point of the investigation and so should be shown after, not before, the investigation. However, pieces of some videos may serve well as part of a lesson launch.

- Consortium for Mathematics and Its Applications (COMAP). *For All Practical Purposes: Introduction to Contemporary Mathematics*, 6th Edition. W. H. Freeman, 2002.

- COMAP. *For All Practical Purposes Video Series*. Annenberg Media, 1988.

- COMAP. *Geometry: New Tools for New Technologies*–Video. Lexington, MA: COMAP, 1992.

- Cozzens and Porter. *Problem Solving Using Graphs*, HiMAP Module 6. Lexington, MA: COMAP, 1987.

- Crisler, Nancy and Gary Froelich. *Discrete Mathematics Through Applications*, 3rd Edition. W. H. Freeman, 2006.

- Dossey, John, A., Albert D. Otto, Lawrence E. Spence, Charles Vanden Eynden. *Discrete Mathematics*, 4th Edition. Addison-Wesley, 2002.

- Hart, Eric, Margaret Kenney, Valerie DeBellis, and Joseph Rosenstein. *Navigating Through Discrete Mathematics in Grades 6-12*. National Council of Teachers of Mathematics, 2007.

- Kenney, Margaret and Christian Hirsch (eds.). *Discrete Mathematics Across the Curriculum, K–12*. Reston, VA: National Council of Teachers of Mathematics, 1991 NCTM Yearbook, 1991.

- Ore, Oystein. *Graphs and Their Uses* (revised and updated by Robin Wilson). Washington, D.C.: Mathematical Association of America, New Mathematical Library 34, 1990.

- Rosenstein, Joseph, Deborah Franzblau, and Fred Roberts (Eds.). *Discrete Mathematics in the Schools*. American Mathematical Society and National Council of Teachers of Mathematics, 1997.

- Sunburst. *Patterns: Networks, Paths, and Knots*–Video. Sunburst, 1993.

- Tannenbaum Peter. *Excursions in Modern Mathematics*, 6th edition. Englewood Cliffs, NJ: Prentice-Hall, 2007.

- Wilson, Robin and John Watkins. *Graphs: An Introductory Approach*. New York: John Wiley and Sons, 1990.

Additional Resources

In Lesson 1, Investigation 2 students consider the *Traveler's Dodecahedron* game as one example of a Hamilton circuit.

(1) Many polyhedra permit Hamilton circuits in addition to the dodecahedron used in Hamilton's game. For example, all the Platonic solids (regular polyhedra) permit Hamilton circuits.
See MathWorld (mathworld.wolfram.com/IcosianGame.html) for more details. Also, see Connections Task 13.

(2) Artists have created sculptures based on Hamilton circuits on a dodecahedron.
For example, see cs.berkeley.edu/ ~ sequin/SCULPTS/sequin.html.

Unit 6

Lesson Objectives	On Your Own Assignments*	Suggested Pacing	Materials
Lesson 1 Optimum Spanning Networks • Understand and apply minimum spanning trees, Hamilton circuits, and the Traveling Salesperson Problem (TSP) • Compare and contrast graph topics: TSP vs. minimum spanning trees, Hamilton vs. Euler circuits, matrices and graphs • Further develop skill in mathematical modeling, particularly modeling with vertex-edge graphs • Further develop skill in algorithmic problem solving, particularly designing, using, and analyzing algorithms for minimum spanning trees and the TSP • Further develop the ability to recognize, formulate, and solve optimization problems, particularly related to optimum spanning networks	**After Investigation 1:** A1, A2 or A3, choose two of C9–C11, R15, E20 or E21, Rv26, Rv27 **After Investigation 2:** A4, A5 or A6, C12, R16, R17, E22, Rv28, Rv29 **After Investigation 3:** A7, A8, C13 or C14, R18, R19, choose one of E23–E25, Rv30, Rv31	7 days (including assessment)	• Colored pencils • *CPMP-Tools* Discrete Math software • *CPMP-Tools* Geometry or other geometry software • Unit Resources
Lesson 2 Scheduling Projects using Critical Paths • Construct and interpret a project digraph • Determine earliest finish time for a project consisting of many tasks • Understand and apply critical paths and critical tasks in the context of project scheduling • Further develop skill in mathematical modeling, algorithmic problem solving, and optimization	**After Investigation 1:** C10–C12, E18, Rv22–Rv24 **After Investigation 2:** Choose three of A1–A6, A7, A8 or A9, choose 2 of R14–R17, E19, E20 or E21, Rv25, Rv26	3 days (including assessment)	• *CPMP-Tools* Discrete Math software • Unit Resources
Lesson 3 Looking Back • Review and synthesize the major objectives of the unit		3 days (including assessment)	• Unit Resources

* When choice is indicated, it is important to leave the choice to the student.

Note: It is best if Connections tasks are discussed as a whole class after they have been assigned as homework.

Think About This Situation, *page 401*

(Note: If students do not have ideas at this time, you may wish to look on the sitemap of a cell phone service to see if there is a vertex-edge graph of the network. An example of a fiber route for cell phones is shown on Web site: www.alltel.com/business/wholesale/index.html. The point here is to get some ideas on the table of various uses of networks, not to discuss different types of networks. The problems in the unit will expose students to networks for which spanning trees and circuits are useful.)

Teacher: There are many situations in which networks can be used for representation. Do you recall some of the situations in Course 1 where we used vertex-edge graphs? *(Allows students to offer contexts such as the locker-painting and radio-station problems.)* In this lesson, we will consider how to find networks that reach all the vertices in an optimum or best way. What kinds of situations in the communications industry might involve finding an optimum network?

Nancy: Phone lines to different places

Teacher: If you wanted to represent this with a vertex-edge graph, what would the vertices and edges represent?

Nancy: The vertices would be the phones or maybe equipment that joins a bunch of phone lines. The edges would be the phone cables.

Teacher: What would it mean to find an optimum phone-line network?

Keegen: To find the shortest way to connect all the phones so that you use less phone cable

Teacher: Okay. What kinds of situations in the transportation industry might involve finding an optimum network?

Maddy: My uncle is a truck driver for a company. He often needs to make many different deliveries. He talks about using certain routes to reach all of his delivery points. Since he can go home when he is done, he wants to finish quickly.

Sam: Remember the subway map we saw in last year's math class? That was a network.

Teacher: What might it mean to optimize a subway network?

Allison: Maybe it would mean having trains reaching all stations or having more trains at busy stations.

Teacher: What kinds of situations in manufacturing might involve finding optimum networks?

James: Maybe an assembly line is like a network. Like different parts of a car are made along one line and then joined with other lines later. Think about making the car doors and then adding them to the car body that was made on another line.

Teacher: What might "optimum" mean in your situation, James?

James: Maybe it could be related to having parts arrive at the same time—like fast. Then the parts could be made into one bigger thing before moving on.

Teacher: It seems that you are thinking of optimal as time—having parts arrive at the same time. Let's think now about some networks in your own life.

Kawan: Could our bus route to school be considered a network? The stops could be vertices and the roads edges.

Cynthia: Sure, how about our family tree? The diagram that I made for my social studies project in middle school looked something like this. *(She draws a tree diagram.)*

Teacher: Those do seem to be situations that can be modeled using vertex-edge graphs. In this unit, you will be learning about two important types of optimum spanning networks, both trees and circuits. You will also compare networks to the graphs you studied in Course 1.

Now take a look at the picture on page 401 of the computer lab. You know that in our computer lab, the computers are all connected to the hub in the room. In addition, we have hubs to which computers connect in the tech room. Each computer in teachers' rooms is connected directly or indirectly to the hub in the main office for recording attendance. To simplify this connection of computers, we are going to assume that we have 6 hubs in the school and consider the questions at the bottom of page 401. Ronald, please read the italic questions for us.

Unit 6

LESSON
1

Optimum Spanning Networks

Network optimization problems occur in many contexts. You can often represent these problems with *vertex-edge graphs* consisting of points (vertices) and line segments or arcs (edges) between some of the points. Sometimes when solving optimization problems related to vertex-edge graphs, you want to find a network that spans (reaches) all the vertices in the graph and is optimum in some way.

400 UNIT 6

Optimum Spanning Networks

In this lesson, students learn about two fundamental optimum spanning networks—minimum spanning trees and minimum spanning circuits. In Investigation 1, students investigate minimum spanning trees, which are trees that span (i.e., reach) all vertices of a weighted graph and have minimum total weight. In Investigation 2, students explore the Traveling Salesperson Problem (TSP). The goal in trying to solve the TSP is to find a circuit that visits each vertex exactly once (called a Hamilton circuit) and has minimum total weight. Because such a circuit spans (i.e., visits) all the vertices, it can be thought of as a minimum spanning circuit.

Lesson Objectives

- Understand and apply minimum spanning trees, Hamilton circuits, and the Traveling Salesperson Problem (TSP)
- Compare and contrast graph topics: TSP vs. minimum spanning trees, Hamilton vs. Euler circuits, matrices and graphs
- Further develop skill in mathematical modeling, particularly modeling with vertex-edge graphs
- Further develop skill in algorithmic problem solving, particularly designing, using, and analyzing algorithms for minimum spanning trees and the TSP
- Further develop the ability to recognize, formulate, and solve optimization problems, particularly related to optimum spanning networks

Lesson Launch

The goal of this brief discussion is for students to recognize the common occurrences of networks and the need to optimize those networks. As students respond to the questions in the TATS, you may wish to press them to be more descriptive about the situations—why they might want to find an optimum network and how they might find it.

Think About This Situation

Think about situations involving networks with which you are familiar and what it would mean to find an optimum or best network.

a What kinds of situations in the communications industry might involve finding an optimum network?

b What kinds of situations in the transportation industry might involve finding an optimum network?

c What kinds of situations in manufacturing might involve finding an optimum network?

d What kinds of situations in your own everyday life might involve finding an optimum network?

In this lesson, you will learn about two important types of *optimum spanning networks:* minimum spanning trees and minimum spanning circuits.

Investigation 1 — Minimum Spanning Trees

In this information age, it is important to find the best way to stay informed. You need to have the right information at the right time in order to make the best decisions and take the most effective action. One way to keep informed is through computer networks. Many places, including businesses, schools, and libraries, have computers linked together in networks so that information can be shared among many users. In fact, there is a common saying that "the network *is* the computer."

Suppose that a large school decides to create its own *intranet*, that is, a network of computers within the school. They will create the network by placing 6 *hubs* at different locations around the school, linking nearby computers to each hub, and then connecting all the hubs. Every hub does not need to be connected directly to every other hub, but they must all be connected in some way, directly or indirectly. The problem is to figure out how to connect all the hubs with the least amount of cable. As you work through the problems in this investigation, look for answers to the following questions:

> *How can you find a network that will connect all 6 hubs, directly or indirectly, using the minimum amount of cable?*

> *What are some properties of this network and of similar networks?*

LESSON 1 • Optimum Spanning Networks **401**

Think About This Situation

NOTE The PMD scenario is on page T399D.

(a)
- Finding an optimum cell phone network to maximize reception and route calls as quickly and cheaply as possible as in TV commercials advertising the largest network or the fewest dropped calls
- Finding an optimum computer network to use minimum wiring or to generate the fastest downloads as in peer-to-peer networks like BitTorrent and Gnutella

(b)
- Finding an optimum shipping network to ship packages as quickly as cheaply as possible
- Finding an optimum route for a multi-stop airline roundtrip

(c) Students' suggestions might include ideas related to assembly lines, getting parts to a central location from various plant divisions, or scheduling employees to work. A more specific example is finding the most efficient route for a robotic assembly machine on an automobile production line.

(d)
- Finding a cell phone company that provides the best calling network
- Finding an Internet music provider that provides the best network for buying music online
- Finding an optimum network of friends
- Finding an optimum route for a multi-stop airline roundtrip
- Finding an optimum route to visit all baseball stadiums in the U.S.

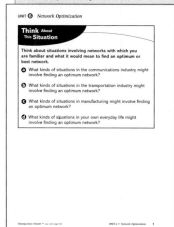

PROMOTING MATHEMATICAL DISCOURSE

Teaching Resources

Transparency Master 1.

Unit 6

Investigation 1 — Minimum Spanning Trees

Through investigating a problem about optimizing a computer network, students learn about minimum spanning trees. They explore a best-edge algorithm and a nearest-neighbor algorithm for finding a minimum spanning tree. A minimum spanning tree is a tree (a connected graph with no circuits) that spans (i.e., reaches) all the vertices of a weighted graph and has the least possible total weight.

You might show the following 30-minute video after this investigation as part of the closure and summary. (Showing the video before the investigation will impede students' exploration.) See For All Practical Purposes, Program 3: Trains, Planes, and Critical Paths, from Annenberg Media, produced by the Consortium for Mathematics and Its Applications (COMAP), 1988. There are three segments on this video; the second segment is on minimum spanning trees. You can purchase the video or view it online at www.learner.org/resources/series82.html.

COLLABORATION SKILL
Include every group member in discussions.

Computer Network Problem Because of the layout of the school, it is not possible to run cable directly between every pair of hubs. The matrix below shows which hubs can be linked directly, as well as how much cable is needed. The hubs are represented by letters and the distances are in meters.

Computer Network Matrix

$$
\begin{array}{c c c c c c c}
 & A & B & C & D & E & F \\
A & - & 45 & - & - & - & 15 \\
B & 45 & - & 40 & - & 40 & 55 \\
C & - & 40 & - & 15 & 25 & - \\
D & - & - & 15 & - & 30 & 55 \\
E & - & 40 & 25 & 30 & - & 45 \\
F & 15 & 55 & - & 55 & 45 & -
\end{array}
$$

1. Examine the computer network matrix.

   a. What does the "25" in the C row mean?

   b. Why is the A-B entry the same as the B-A entry?

   c. Why isn't there a B-B entry? Why isn't there a D-B entry?

   d. Why does it make sense that the matrix is symmetric about the main diagonal?

2. Draw a vertex-edge graph that represents the information in the matrix. Recall that when building a graph model, you must specify what the vertices and edges represent.

3. Use your graph to solve the computer network problem, as follows.

   a. Compare your graph to other students' graphs. Agree on a graph that best represents this problem situation. What do the vertices and edges represent?

   b. What is the least amount of wire needed to connect the hubs so that every hub is linked directly or indirectly to every other hub?

   c. Make a copy of the graph you agreed on in Part a and then darken the edges of a shortest network for this problem.

   d. Compare your shortest network and the minimum amount of cable needed to what other students found. Discuss and resolve any differences.

An Optimum Network An optimum network in this case is a shortest network. Think about how to find a shortest network and the properties of such a network.

4. Write step-by-step instructions for how to find a shortest network in a vertex-edge graph, like the shortest network you found in the computer networking problem. A set of step-by-step instructions like this is called an **algorithm**.

1 **a.** Twenty-five meters of cable are needed to connect the hubs at locations C and E.

b. The amount of cable needed to connect the hubs at locations A and B is the same as the amount needed to connect the hubs at locations B and A.

c. There is no number for the B-B entry because there is no need to connect the hub at location B to itself. The D-B entry is empty because, evidently, there is no way to connect the hubs at locations B and D.

d. The matrix is symmetric because the cable connects both A to B and B to A. In a similar manner, if you cannot connect two hubs, then the entries representing both orders of connection are empty.

INSTRUCTIONAL NOTE
Before beginning this first problem, be sure students understand that the hubs can be connected directly or indirectly, as discussed in the introduction.

2 Students might draw a variety of shapes and sizes of graphs. (They will compare and analyze graphs in Problem 3 below.)

3 **a.** The vertices represent hubs. The edges represent connections. The shape and size of the graphs are not important at all. It is only important that each graph accurately represents the information in the table.

b. 140 meters is the least amount of cable needed.

c. Following are two shortest networks. There are others.

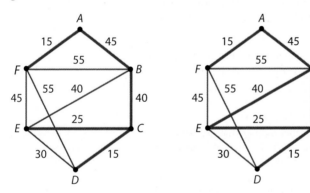

d. Students should see that there is just one minimum network length, but there may be different networks that have this minimum length.

4 It is important for students to try to write a systematic step-by-step description of their method. (Students may need to be reminded that guess-and-check is not an algorithm.)

INSTRUCTIONAL NOTE
A carefully written description is an *algorithm*. Students will compare their algorithms in the next problem, and they will explore a given algorithm in Problem 8.

Unit 6

(5) Exchange your algorithm for finding a shortest network with the algorithm written by another student or group of students.

a. Make a new copy of the graph. Carefully follow the steps in each other's algorithm for finding a shortest network. Compare results. Does each algorithm work? Is each algorithm written carefully enough so that anyone can follow the directions and find a shortest network?

b. Work together to refine the algorithms that work.

(6) Think about the properties of the shortest wiring networks you have been investigating. State whether each of the following statements is *true* or *false*. In each case, give a reason justifying your answer. Compare your answers to those of other students and resolve any differences.

Statement I   There is only one correct answer possible for the minimum amount of cable needed to connect all 6 hubs.

Statement II   There can be more than one shortest network for a given situation.

Statement III   There is more than one algorithm for finding a shortest network.

Statement IV   A shortest network must be all in one piece; that is, the network must be **connected**.

Statement V   All vertices must be joined by the network.

Statement VI   A shortest network cannot contain any circuits. (Recall that a **circuit** is a path that starts and ends at the same vertex and does not repeat any edges.)

(7) The type of shortest network that you have been studying is an important vertex-edge graph model, which can be described with some useful mathematical terms.

a. A connected graph that has no circuits is called a **tree**. Why does it make sense to call such a graph a *tree*?

b. A tree in a connected graph that reaches (that is, includes or connects) all the vertices in the graph is called a **spanning tree**. Why does it make sense to say that such a tree is *spanning*?

c. A graph with numbers on its edges is called a **weighted graph**. The numbers on the edges, whatever they represent, are called **weights**. The computer network graph that you have been working with is a weighted graph. What do the weights represent?

d. A **minimum spanning tree** in a weighted connected graph is a tree that has minimum total weight and *spans* the graph—that is, it includes every vertex. Explain why the shortest networks you have found in the computer network graph are minimum spanning trees.

(5) INSTRUCTIONAL NOTE You may wish to carry out this activity in a whole-group setting. For example, choose one student to go to the front of the class and be the "algorithm implementer." This student will act as a computer carrying out instructions to find a minimum spanning tree in the computer network graph. Then have another student or group of students read aloud their algorithm while the student at the front attempts to execute the instructions exactly as they are spoken without any extraneous judgment. The entire class should watch and analyze this. Then discuss whether the instructions were clear and whether they accomplished the goal. Refine the algorithm as necessary. Repeat with a different student up front and a different algorithm.

a–b. See student algorithms.

(6) All the statements are true, and all are important for the students to understand before they continue with this investigation.

The computer-network problem they have been working on should have elicited all these statements.

Statement I True. There is only one correct answer possible for the minimum amount of cable needed to connect all six hubs. There cannot be two different minimums.

Statement II True. There can be more than one shortest network for a given problem. The total lengths must be the same, but the edges might be different.

Statement III True. There is more than one algorithm for finding a shortest network. (Students should reflect back on their work from Problems 4 and 5 and should justify their responses with good reasoning.)

Statement IV True. A shortest network must be connected. It must be possible to get from any vertex (hub) to any other vertex (hub), directly or indirectly. (The definition of *connected* given here is intuitive and accurate. It just means that there are no isolated vertices or other separate pieces of the graph.)

Statement V True. All vertices (hubs) must be in the network. (Another way to say this, using the formal language introduced in Problem 7, is that the network *spans* all the vertices.)

Statement VI True. If there was a circuit, then there would be more than one way to move between vertices. This means there would be at least one unnecessary edge, which would make the network longer than it needs to be.

Unit 6

(7) **INSTRUCTIONAL NOTE** After defining "weight" in Problem 7, that term should be used almost always. However, it is fine to occasionally use more context-related language like "length." For example, the algorithm attributed to students in Problem 10 uses the term "shortest edge," rather than the more formal "edge of least weight." Be alert for correctness, but be flexible as long as the meaning is clear.

a. A tree in nature is all in one piece, i.e., connected. Also, the branches typically do not curve back into themselves and form loops, i.e., there are no circuits. Thus, a tree in nature has the same two essential properties as trees in mathematics.

b. It makes sense to say that the tree is "spanning" since it reaches, or spans, all the vertices. (You may wish to have students look up the verb "to span" in the dictionary and discuss why it is appropriate and meaningful in this context.)

c. The computer-network graph is an example of a weighted graph. The weights are distances.

d. The definition of *minimum spanning tree* includes properties discussed in Problem 6. In that problem, students should have concluded that shortest networks are connected (Part d), have no circuits (Part f), include all vertices (Part e), and have minimum length. That is, they are trees of minimum total weight that include all vertices. Thus, they are minimum spanning trees. The term *minimum spanning tree* will be used for the rest of the unit.

> **NOTE** Sometimes, to be more specific, a graph with numbers on the edges is called an edge-weighted graph.

Unit 6

Teacher Notes

More Algorithms As you may have concluded in Problem 6, there are several possible algorithms for finding a minimum spanning tree in a connected graph.

8 Study the algorithm below.

> **Step 1:** Draw all the vertices but no edges.
>
> **Step 2:** Add an edge with the smallest weight that will not create a circuit. If there is more than one such edge, choose any one. The edge you add does not have to be connected to previously-added edges, and you may use more than one edge of the same weight.
>
> **Step 3:** Repeat Step 2 until it is no longer possible to add an edge without creating a circuit.

a. Follow the steps of this algorithm to construct a minimum spanning tree for the computer network graph.

b. Explain why this algorithm could be called a *best-edge algorithm*.

c. Compare the minimum spanning tree you get using this best-edge algorithm to the one you found in Problem 3. How do the total weights of the minimum spanning trees compare?

9 Examine the graph below.

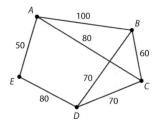

a. Use the best-edge algorithm from Problem 8 to find a minimum spanning tree for this graph. Calculate its total weight.

b. Explain why the algorithm can produce different minimum spanning trees.

c. Find all possible minimum spanning trees for the graph. Compare their total weights.

d. How is the best-edge algorithm similar to, or different from, the algorithms you produced in Problems 4 and 5?

10 Students in one class claimed that the following algorithm will produce a minimum spanning tree in a given graph.

> Step 1: Make a copy of the graph with the edges drawn lightly.
> Step 2: Choose a starting vertex.
> Step 3: For the vertex where you are, darken the shortest edge from that vertex that will not create a circuit. (If there is more than one such edge, choose any one.) Then move to the end vertex of that edge.
> Step 4: Repeat Step 3 until it is not possible to add another edge.

8 **a.** In addition to the two spanning trees shown by the colored edges in Problem 3 Part c, this algorithm can also produce either of the following trees.

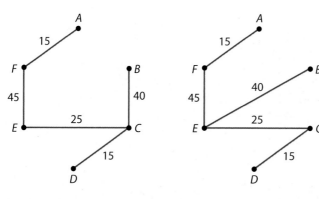

b. This algorithm could be called a best-edge algorithm because the minimum spanning tree is constructed by adding an edge of least possible weight (a "best edge") at each step.

c. The total weights of the two minimum spanning trees should be the same even if the spanning trees themselves are not identical.

INSTRUCTIONAL NOTE An important part of any algorithm is knowing when you are done. In the algorithm given here, you are done when it is no longer possible to add an edge without creating a circuit. Another condition that could be used to check when you are done is to keep track of the number of edges that have been added. If a graph has n vertices, then a spanning tree for the graph will contain $n - 1$ edges (see Part c of Connections Task 10 on page 424). Thus, you are done when you have added $n - 1$ edges (since this algorithm does in fact produce a minimum spanning tree).

9 **a.** There are four minimum spanning trees. Each has total weight 260.

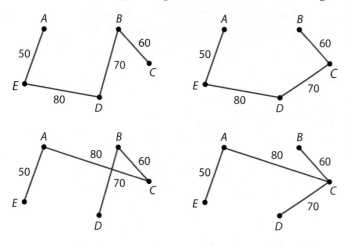

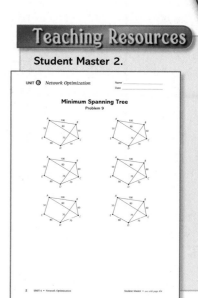
b. Since the second step of the algorithm includes the phrase, "If there is more than one such edge, choose any one," there is room for variation.

c. All minimum spanning trees produced by the algorithm are shown in Part a.

d. Student responses will depend on the algorithms they produced in Problems 4 and 5.

Complete Parts a–f to test this algorithm. First, make four copies of the graph below.

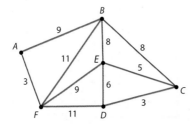

a. Apply the algorithm to the graph starting with vertex *E*. What is the total weight of the network you get?

b. Explain why this algorithm could be called a *nearest-neighbor algorithm*.

c. Apply the algorithm starting with vertex *F*. Record the total weight of the resulting network.

d. Apply the algorithm starting with vertex *A*. What happens?

e. Now use the best-edge algorithm described in Problem 8 to find a minimum spanning tree for this graph.

f. Do you think the nearest-neighbor algorithm is a good algorithm for finding a minimum spanning tree? Write a brief justification of your answer.

11 The best-edge algorithm from Problem 8 was first published by American mathematician Joseph Kruskal, and so it is often called **Kruskal's algorithm**. Kruskal discovered the algorithm while he was still a graduate student in the 1950s. How are the nearest-neighbor algorithm and Kruskal's algorithm similar? How are they different?

12 Two important questions about any algorithm are "Does it always work?" and "Is it efficient?".

a. Do you think Kruskal's algorithm (described in Problem 8) will always work to find a minimum spanning tree in any connected graph? Use vertex-edge graph software to investigate your conjecture. Create several connected weighted graphs. Use these test graphs and the software to help answer the following questions.

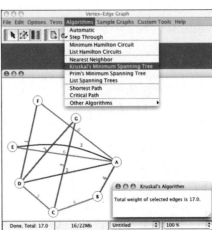

10 **a.** Starting at *E*, this algorithm generates the route *E-C-D-F-A-B* for a total length of 31. See the diagram at the right.

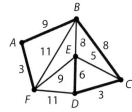

b. This algorithm could be called a nearest-neighbor because the tree is built by connecting a vertex to the vertex that is closest to it.

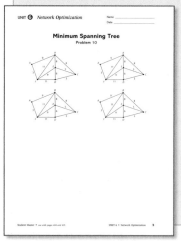
c. Starting at *F*, this algorithm generates two possible routes: (1) the route *F-A-B-E-C-D* for a total length of 28 and (2) the route *F-A-B-C-D-E* for a total length of 29. See the diagrams at the right.

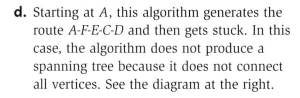

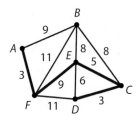

d. Starting at *A*, this algorithm generates the route *A-F-E-C-D* and then gets stuck. In this case, the algorithm does not produce a spanning tree because it does not connect all vertices. See the diagram at the right.

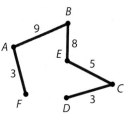

INSTRUCTIONAL NOTE
Be sure students are using the nearest-neighbor algorithm. There are 8 graphs on the master, so students can start with clean graphs if needed. Students may incorrectly think there are 8 minimum spanning trees.

e. One minimum spanning tree produced by the best-edge algorithm is shown at the right. The length of this tree is 28.

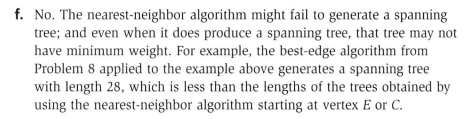

f. No. The nearest-neighbor algorithm might fail to generate a spanning tree; and even when it does produce a spanning tree, that tree may not have minimum weight. For example, the best-edge algorithm from Problem 8 applied to the example above generates a spanning tree with length 28, which is less than the lengths of the trees obtained by using the nearest-neighbor algorithm starting at vertex *E* or *C*.

INSTRUCTIONAL NOTE An important part of any algorithm is knowing when you are done. In the algorithm given here, Step 4 states that you are done when it is not possible to add another edge. You might not be able to add another edge because a spanning tree has been created, in which case you have used *n* − 1 edges (see the Instructional Note in Problem 8). However, this algorithm is not guaranteed to produce a spanning tree, so you might not be able to add another edge because you have reached a dead end, as in Part d.

11 Similarities: At each step, you choose an edge of least weight that does not create a circuit. Note that since both algorithms choose the least-weight edges we could call them both "best-edge" algorithms. (Do not worry about this subtle point unless students raise the issue. There is no confusion because the lesson refers to the name of the algorithms—Kruskal's or Nearest-Neighbor—or to the specific problem in which the algorithm is described.)

Differences: (1) In Kruskal's best-edge algorithm, you choose a least-weight edge from among all edges that have not yet been used; while in the nearest-neighbor algorithm, you choose a least-weight edge from among only those edges that are connected to the vertex of your current location. (2) Kruskal's algorithm seems always to produce a minimum spanning tree, while the nearest-neighbor algorithm does not. In fact, the nearest-neighbor algorithm does not always produce a spanning tree; and when it does produce a spanning tree, it may not be one with least total weight. (See Problem 12 for a definitive statement about the correctness and efficiency of Kruskal's algorithm.) (3) In Kruskal's algorithm, the edges you add may not form a connected network until the end of the procedure; while in the nearest-neighbor algorithm, you create a successively longer connected path at each step.

12 **INSTRUCTIONAL NOTE** Students can do the exploration this problem requests by using *CPMP-Tools* at home and then share their discoveries in class.

a. • Using *CPMP-Tools* or similar software, students should see that Kruskal's algorithm produces a spanning tree for every connected weighted graph they generate.

• Different runs of Kruskal's algorithm on the same graph could produce different spanning trees.

• Every spanning tree produced by Kruskal's algorithm for a given graph has the same total weight.

• A spanning tree produced by Kruskal's algorithm in a connected weighted graph has minimum total weight.

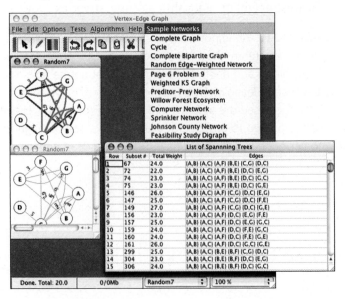

b. All this testing does *not* provide enough evidence to conclude that Kruskal's algorithm always works for any connected graph.

c. For the question "Does it always work?"—the nearest-neighbor algorithm is not guaranteed to work as a method for producing a minimum spanning tree in any connected graph. See, for example, Problem 10 Part d. (Even though this algorithm does not work in general, it is valuable to study, as discussed in the Instructional Note below following the Summarize the Mathematics.)

For the question "Is it efficient?"—students will not be able to give a technical answer to this question. Such analysis is beyond the scope of this course. If "efficient" is limited to "ease of use," students may very well argue that it is efficient since the steps are easy to carry out and it is similar to Kruskal's algorithm, which is efficient. (Efficiency of algorithms is an important issue to which students should be alerted. It is not possible to study it formally in this course, but the issue is dealt with again informally when brute-force methods are discussed in Investigation 2 of this lesson. A good introduction to these ideas is given in Chapter 6 of COMAP's *Principles and Practice of Mathematics*; New York: Springer, 1997.)

KEY IDEA It is important for students to realize that verification for some examples is not a proof. (A proof that Kruskal's algorithm does indeed work is beyond the scope of this course.)

- Does Kruskal's algorithm produce a spanning tree in a connected graph? (Use the software to run the algorithm on several graphs; check to see if the result is always a spanning tree.)

- Is it possible that different runs of Kruskal's algorithm could produce different spanning trees in the same graph? (Try different runs on the same graph for several different graphs. If Kruskal's algorithm produces just one spanning tree for each graph, create a new graph for which you think Kruskal's algorithm can generate different spanning trees, then test it.)

- If Kruskal's algorithm produces several different spanning trees for a given graph, do they all have the same total weight?

- Will any spanning tree produced by Kruskal's algorithm have the smallest possible total weight? (Use the software to generate and examine all possible spanning trees for a given graph. Check to see if a spanning tree generated by Kruskal's algorithm has smallest weight among all possible spanning trees.)

b. Suppose you run all these tests on many graphs, and each time Kruskal's algorithm produces a minimum spanning tree. Is this enough evidence to conclude that Kruskal's algorithm will always work to find a minimum spanning tree in any connected graph? Explain your reasoning.

c. The two questions—Does it always work? and Is it efficient?—should be considered for all algorithms. So far, you have only investigated the first question. For Kruskal's algorithm, mathematicians have proven that the answer to both questions is "yes." Kruskal's algorithm will efficiently find a minimum spanning tree for any connected graph. How would you answer these questions for the nearest-neighbor algorithm?

Summarize the Mathematics

In this investigation, you learned how to find and interpret minimum spanning trees.

a Does every connected graph have a minimum spanning tree? Explain your reasoning.

b Is it possible for a given graph to have more than one minimum spanning tree? Can different minimum spanning trees for the same graph have different total weights?

c What information does the total weight of a minimum spanning tree give you?

d Describe in your own words the basic strategy of Kruskal's best-edge algorithm. Do the same for the nearest-neighbor algorithm. Which of these two algorithms is guaranteed to produce a minimum spanning tree for any connected graph?

Be prepared to share your ideas and reasoning with the class.

Summarize the Mathematics

a Yes, every connected graph has a minimum spanning tree. This could be explained in several ways. One explanation involves constructing a minimum spanning tree with Kruskal's best-edge algorithm. That is, every connected graph has a minimum spanning tree because Kruskal's algorithm is guaranteed to produce one for any connected graph. (See Problem 12.) Another argument might be the following: since the graph is connected, all vertices are spanned already. Remove edges that create circuits to get a tree (which will still span all vertices). Thus, it is a spanning tree. There may be many ways to remove such edges, but there are only finitely many ways since there are finitely many edges. Among the total weights of the finitely many different possible spanning trees, there must be a minimum total weight. So, there must be a minimum spanning tree.

b A graph can have more than one minimum spanning tree, but all the minimum spanning trees must have the same minimum total weight.

c The specific information provided by the total weight of a minimum spanning tree depends on the context. For example, in the computer-network problem, the total weight of a minimum spanning tree is the minimum amount of cable needed to connect the hubs so that every hub is linked directly or indirectly to every other hub. Generally, the total weight of a minimum spanning tree is the minimum total weight of all the edges needed to join all the vertices in the graph.

d Students should be encouraged to characterize the algorithms in a simple, sensible, and accurate way. In Kruskal's best-edge algorithm, you successively add shortest edges without creating circuits, and any edge you add does not have to be connected to a previously added edge. In the nearest-neighbor algorithm, you likewise successively add shortest edges without creating circuits, but you start at a certain vertex and only add edges that are connected to the vertex where you are at each step.

Kruskal's best-edge algorithm is guaranteed to produce a minimum spanning tree. Although the nearest-neighbor algorithm does have an appeal, it is not a guaranteed method for finding a minimum spanning tree.

NOTE The solution to Problem 12 is on pages T405A and B.

PROMOTING MATHEMATICAL DISCOURSE

Teaching Resources

Transparency Master 4.

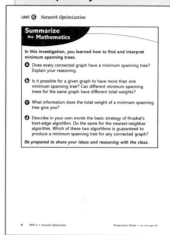

UNIT 6 · *Network Optimization*

Summarize the Mathematics

In this investigation, you learned how to find and interpret minimum spanning trees.

a Does every connected graph have a minimum spanning tree? Explain your reasoning.

b Is it possible for a given graph to have more than one minimum spanning tree? Can different minimum spanning trees for the same graph have different total weights?

c What information does the total weight of a minimum spanning tree give you?

d Describe in your own words the basic strategy of Kruskal's best-edge algorithm. Do the same for the nearest-neighbor algorithm. Which of these two algorithms is guaranteed to produce a minimum spanning tree for any connected graph?

Be prepared to share your ideas and reasoning with the class.

4   UNIT 6 • Network Optimization   Transparency Master • *on with page 406*

Unit 6

COLLABORATION PROMPT
I made sure _____
                                  (name)
was included by ... .

INSTRUCTIONAL NOTE Since the nearest-neighbor algorithm is not a method that works very well, students may wonder why they are studying it. There are several good reasons.

First, it is an algorithm that often comes up naturally in initial attempts to find minimum spanning trees (and in other graph problems); and therefore, it needs to be discussed and analyzed.

Second, by comparing two different algorithms, students gain experience in the important skill of algorithmic problem solving, which involves designing, using, comparing, and analyzing algorithms.

Third, although the algorithm does not generally work as an exact solution method, it is intuitive and easy to apply, and so it may have value for approximating solutions.

Fourth, students should understand that there may be algorithms that seem reasonable for a given problem, and yet they do not work well in general.

Finally, this algorithm illustrates an important situation: it optimizes at each step, and yet it does not optimize for the whole problem. This situation often occurs in optimization problems. We sometimes say that a *locally* optimum solution is not necessarily a *globally* optimum solution. A very rough analogy is getting the best deal on a video game system. You might find the best price for individual components but discover that a whole package deal is a lower price than the sum of all the component prices.

Summarize the Mathematics, *page 406*

Teacher: You have had time to think about the Summarize the Mathematics questions with your group members. Let's spend a few minutes discussing your summaries. In this investigation, you learned how to find and interpret minimum spanning trees. Does every connected graph have a minimum spanning tree? Tia, what did your group say?

Tia: We said that it does and that you can just use the best-edge algorithm to find it.

Jacob: We agree.

Kioko: Our group said the same.

Teacher: We examined a couple of different best-edge algorithms. Describe the best-edge algorithm you are referring to, Tia.

Tia: It was called Kruskal's best-edge algorithm. You draw the vertices and then draw in the shortest edge. If there are two that are shortest, you just pick either one. Then you draw the next edge that is shortest. It doesn't matter where it is; it just has to be the shortest edge remaining. Wait, it also cannot make a circuit. You just keep going until every vertex is connected by an edge.

Teacher: Does anyone want to make any changes to Tia's description? *(No students offer changes.)*

Teacher: Carmita, I noticed that your group used different reasoning to explain your answer. Could you please share that with the whole class?

Carmita: We started with a connected graph. Since all the vertices are already spanned in a connected graph, we just erased any edges that made circuits.

Teacher: That's interesting! If you do that will you always get a spanning tree?

Carmita: Yeah, I think so.

Teacher: Will the spanning tree be a *minimum* spanning tree?

Carmita: Well … help me … *(she talks to her group members for a few seconds)* … I guess it wouldn't necessarily be a minimum spanning tree; but if you kept trying, you'd find a minimum one.

Johnny: It seems easier if you just use the best-edge algorithm. I mean, think about it. When you have a large graph, it would be really hard to track down all the circuits to erase one edge. Besides if you were going to write a computer program, like we did earlier this year, it would seem easier to write one for the nearest-neighbor algorithm.

Teacher: Is it possible for a given graph to have more than one minimum spanning tree?

Madeline: Sure. That happened in our group on one of the investigation problems. Two of us had 28 for the length of the minimum spanning tree, but our edges connected different vertices.

Teacher: Are you saying that minimum spanning trees for the same graph must have the same total length (or weight)?

Madeline: Of course. If they were different lengths, then how could they both be minimum? One would be shorter than the other.

Teacher: What information does the total weight of a minimum spanning tree give you?

Selam: It gives you the shortest way to connect all the vertices.

Teacher: What would that mean in different situations? For example, what information would the minimum spanning tree give you in the computer-network problem?

Cindy: In that situation, it gives you the smallest amount of cable needed to connect all the hubs.

Teacher: Okay, good. Let's consider Part d. Tia described the basic strategy of Kruskal's best-edge algorithm for us a few minutes ago. How about the nearest-neighbor algorithm? Who can describe that one in your own words?

Iona: I can do it. You begin at any vertex. Then you choose the shortest edge leaving that vertex. This is like finding the closest vertex to your starting vertex. You just keep going until all the vertices or neighbors are connected.

Teacher: Any comments on Iona's description?

Melissa: You have to make sure that each edge you add doesn't create a circuit. So, you don't go back to the same vertex even if there is a shorter path out of your current vertex. I think about it by saying that I shouldn't visit the same neighbor twice—I need to visit the other neighbors.

Iona: That's true. I need to add that to my description.

Teacher: Which of these two algorithms is guaranteed to produce a minimum spanning tree?

Johnny: That is what I was talking about in Part a. Kruskal's algorithm guarantees a minimum spanning tree, so you might as well use it if you need to find a minimum spanning tree.

Teacher: As we continue looking at network optimization, let's look for instances where we choose one algorithm over another and think carefully about which one works best for various situations.

✓ Check Your Understanding

A landscape architect has been contracted to design a sprinkler system for a large lawn. There will be six sprinkler heads that must be connected by a buried network of pipes to the main water source. The possible connections and distances in yards are shown in the diagram below. The main water source is represented by vertex *B*. What is the least amount of pipe needed to construct the sprinkler network? Draw a landscape plan showing the optimum sprinkler network.

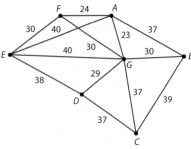

Main Water Source

Investigation 2 · The Traveling Salesperson Problem (TSP)

In the last investigation, you learned about a particular type of optimum spanning network—a minimum spanning tree. The vertex-edge graphs you investigated were *weighted graphs*, since they had *weights* (numbers) on the edges. Such numbers often represent distance, but they can also represent other quantities such as time or cost. In this investigation, you will study another type of optimum spanning network in weighted graphs, related to the following problem.

The **Traveling Salesperson Problem**, often simply referred to as the **TSP**, is one of the most famous problems in mathematics. Here is a statement of the problem.

A sales representative wants to visit several different cities, each exactly once, and then return home. Among the possible routes, which will minimize the total distance traveled?

✓ Check your Understanding

✓ Check your Understanding

Applying Kruskal's algorithm to the graph yields a minimum of 173 yards of pipe needed to construct the sprinkler network.

The two minimum spanning trees are shown below.

> **TECHNOLOGY NOTE** This Sprinkler System Network is in *CPMP-Tools*, Discrete Math, *Vertex-Edge Graph* software under Sample Graphs for Unit 6.

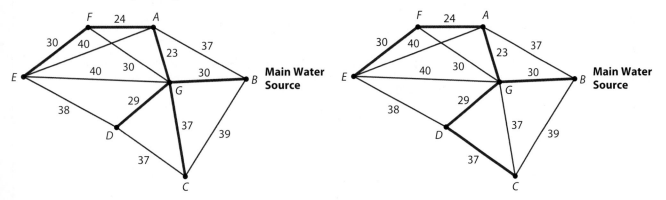

Investigation 2 · The Traveling Salesperson Problem

Students investigate the Traveling Salesperson Problem (TSP), its applications, and its solution, which is a minimum-weight Hamilton circuit. They use a best-edge algorithm and a brute-force method to try to solve the TSP, and learn that the best-edge algorithm is efficient but does not always find a solution, while the brute-force method always finds a solution but is very inefficient. Students learn about the fundamental limitations of brute-force computer solutions due to problems of "combinatorial explosion."

The TSP is a famous unsolved problem in mathematics. It is unsolved in the sense that no one knows an efficient algorithm that will find a solution to the TSP for any graph. Students find it interesting that they can understand and work on a problem that mathematicians are still trying to solve completely. Many students enjoy the feeling of being on a frontier. Also, this may give students a new view of mathematics as a growing field, rather than a dry and dusty collection of facts that have been known for centuries.

You might show the following video after this investigation as part of the closure and summary. (Showing the video before the investigation will impede students' exploration.) See For All Practical Purposes, Program 3: Trains, Planes, and Critical Paths, from Annenberg Media, produced by the Consortium for Mathematics and Its Applications (COMAP), 1988. There are three segments on this video; the first segment is on the TSP. You can purchase the video or view it online at www.learner.org/resources/series82.html.

Unit 6

This problem is historically known as the Traveling Salesman Problem since the original context for the problem referred to salespeople, almost all men at the time the problem was named in the 1950s, who traveled from city to city selling their products. As is common in the present day, we will typically refer to this problem simply by its initials—TSP. As you work through this investigation, look for answers to this question:

What are some ideas and methods that are helpful
as you try to solve the TSP?

1 Although the TSP is classically stated in terms of salesmen, cities, and distance, it also refers to similar problems in other contexts. Consider the TSP in the context of this airfare graph.

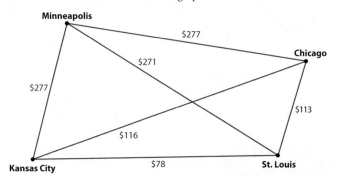

a. Solve the TSP for this weighted graph. What does "weight" represent in this case?

b. Compare your solution to those of other students. Resolve any differences.

c. How do you know that there is no circuit less expensive?

2 A route through a graph that starts at one vertex, visits all the other vertices exactly once, and finishes where it started is called a **Hamilton circuit**.

a. Describe the TSP in terms of Hamilton circuits.

b. How many different Hamilton circuits are there in the graph in Problem 1? For the purpose of finding the total weight of circuits, two circuits are different only if they have different edges. It does not matter where you start or which direction you go around the circuit.

3 Think about the method you used to find the optimum circuit in Problem 1.

a. Write a description of the method you used.

b. Could you generalize your method to find an optimum circuit for traveling to the capital cities of all 48 contiguous states in the United States? Explain your reasoning.

INSTRUCTIONAL NOTE The statement of Problem 1 differs from the classic statement of the TSP given in the introduction—the context is cost instead of distance and no home is specified. This may generate some initial questions. If so, let students discuss this. They will likely figure out what it means to solve the TSP in this context and realize that in terms of total cost of a circuit, it does not matter which city is designated "home." This latter point is further clarified in Problem 2.

 a. The cheapest circuit, *M-C-K-S-M*, would cost $742. At this time, students solve the problem in whatever way works for them. If students are struggling, give them advice or encourage them to move to Part b and compare and discuss with others. Students should reason from the diagram and the context of the problem that weight represents one-way airfare. Assume that the one-way airfare is the same in both directions.

KEY IDEA Although the TSP is classically stated in terms of salespersons, cities, and distance, it is formally stated as a more general graph theory problem—see Problem 2. Problem 1 is an example of the TSP. Students will see many other instances of the TSP in this lesson.

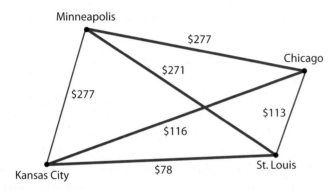

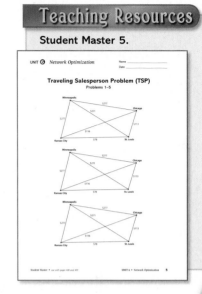
b. Students should compare and discuss and make sure that everyone gets the solution shown in Part a above.

c. For this small problem, students can check all possibilities to verify that the circuit in Part a is in fact the cheapest. There are only three possible circuits (see Problem 2). Besides the cheapest circuit shown in Part a, the other possible circuits are *M-C-S-K-M* and *M-S-C-K-M*.

Unit 6

INSTRUCTIONAL NOTE In this problem, students connect the TSP to Hamilton circuits and state the problem in its more general form related to vertex-edge graphs.

a. Students might describe the TSP in terms of Hamilton circuits as follows: find a minimum-weight Hamilton circuit in a weighted graph.

KEY IDEA Students should understand that to solve the TSP means to find a minimum-weight Hamilton circuit. More formally and as optional background knowledge, the TSP is the problem of finding a minimum-weight Hamilton circuit in a *complete* weighted graph. A complete graph is a graph in which there is exactly one edge between every pair of vertices. If a particular problem involves a noncomplete graph, we can think of the noncomplete graph as being embedded in a larger complete graph where edges labeled with infinite weight are added to the graph to make it complete.

b. If we needed to specify a starting point or direction of travel, then there would be many "different" circuits. Since our only concern is total cost, there are just three different Hamilton circuits, as shown below.

a. There is no known efficient algorithm for solving the TSP in general; so for students to be sure they have the minimum, they would need to have checked all possible circuits. They may describe that this is what they did. However, there are a variety of reasonable algorithms that students may have tried, similar to the algorithms in Lesson 1 for minimum spanning trees, so students should be encouraged to describe any methods they tried.

b. Students should discuss whether their method will work in a 48-vertex graph and if it will be efficient. This discussion sets the stage for subsequent problems. (It is extremely unlikely that the method described in Part a will be generalizable to a graph with 48 vertices in a way that will be efficient and guarantee the optimum circuit.)

INSTRUCTIONAL NOTE
Many students may be unfamiliar with the word "contiguous." You may need to clarify for them.

Unit 6

Teacher Notes

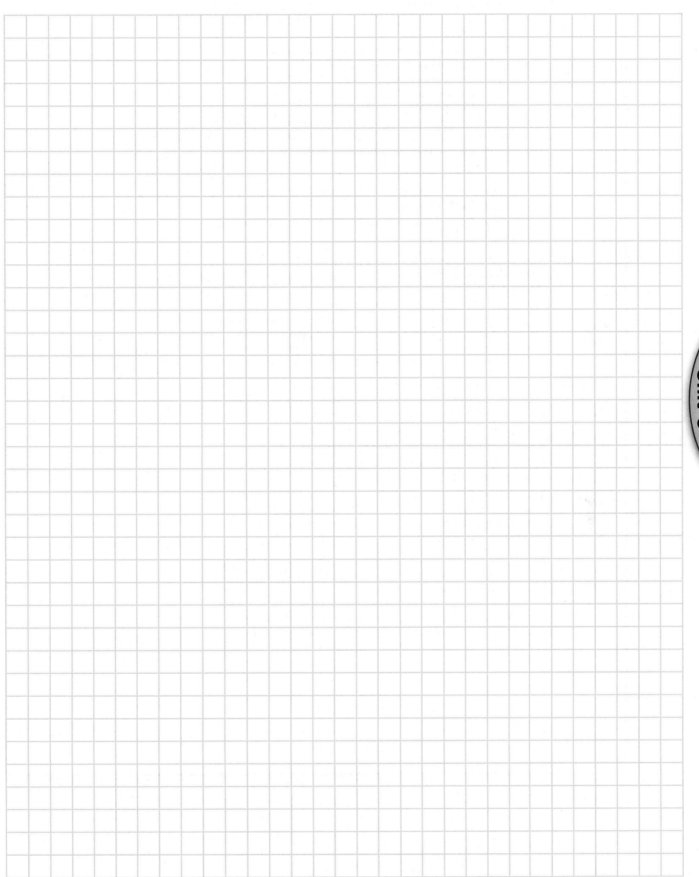

Best-Edge Algorithm In Investigation 1, you used Kruskal's best-edge algorithm to find a minimum spanning tree. One group of students devised the following best-edge algorithm for the TSP. They claim it will solve the TSP. Here is their algorithm:

Step 1: Make a copy of the graph with the edges drawn lightly.
Step 2: Darken the shortest edge not yet used, provided that:
  • you do not create a circuit of darkened edges, unless all of the vertices are included.
  • no vertex is touched by 3 darkened edges.
  (The edge you darken does not have to be connected to previously darkened edges.)
Step 3: Repeat Step 2 as long as it is possible to do so.

4 Analyze this best-edge algorithm.

  a. Why do you think the algorithm requires that you do not create a circuit of darkened edges unless all of the vertices are included?

  b. Why do you think the algorithm requires that no vertex is touched by 3 darkened edges?

5 Apply the algorithm to the airfare graph in Problem 1. Does this algorithm produce a solution to the TSP? Explain.

Brute-Force Method One method that certainly will work to solve the TSP is to list all possible Hamilton circuits, compute the weight of each one, and choose the minimum. This approach of checking all possibilities is sometimes called a *brute-force method*. With computers available to do all the calculations, you might naturally think this is the way to proceed.

6 Use vertex-edge graph software to try the brute-force method for a weighted complete graph with 5 vertices. That is, consider a graph with 5 vertices that has exactly one edge between each pair of vertices, and the edges are weighted. Do the following.

  a. Create a weighted complete graph with 5 vertices.

  b. Use a method of your choice to try to find a solution to the TSP for this 5-vertex graph, using software or not.

  c. Use a brute-force method to find a solution to the TSP for this graph. That is, find all possible Hamilton circuits, compute the total weight of each, and select a circuit with the minimum total weight. Compare to what you found in Part b.

In Problem 6, you were able to use a computer to carry out a brute-force method to solve the TSP for a 5-vertex graph. However, even though computers are fast, the amount of time required for a brute-force computer solution must be taken into account. For example, in the next two problems, you will determine how long it will take a computer to use a brute-force method to solve the TSP for the 26 cities shown in the following map. Assume each city is connected directly to all the others, and the tour starts at Atlanta.

Unit 6

4 **a.** If you create a partial circuit that does not include all the vertices, then the final circuit that does contain all the vertices must visit some vertex more than once, which is not allowed in a solution to the TSP.

b. Any vertex that is touched by three darkened edges must be visited more than once, which is not allowed in a solution to the TSP.

INSTRUCTIONAL NOTE
Be sure students are using the algorithm in Steps 1–3, not Kruskal's best-edge algorithm.

5 Applying this algorithm to the airfare graph in Problem 1 yields the circuit shown below, which is not the cheapest circuit. So, this algorithm does not produce a solution to the TSP.

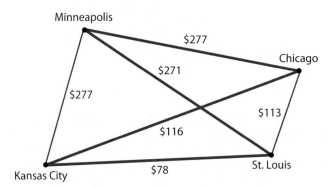

6 **a.** Students should use available software to create a weighted complete graph with five vertices.

TECHNOLOGY NOTE In the *CPMP-Tools*, Discrete Math, *Vertex-Edge Graph* software, holding the Shift key down as you click on edges allows you to select more than one edge at a time. Also, the List Hamilton Circuits option in the Algorithms menu will list all possible Hamilton circuits.

Unit 6

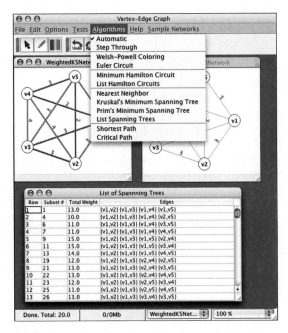

b. Students should choose edges of the graph that form a Hamilton circuit and calculate the total weight of the circuit.

c. Students should use software to generate all possible Hamilton circuits. Then they can compute the total weight of each and choose a circuit with the smallest weight. They will see that there are many possible Hamilton circuits, and the circuit they found in Part b may not be one with minimum weight.

7 Find the number of possible circuits for the 26-city TSP using the following reasoning.

  a. Starting from Atlanta, how many cities could be the first stop?

  b. Once you choose a city for this first stop, how many cities could be the second stop in the circuit? Remember that every city is connected directly to every other city, and each city is visited exactly once.

  c. How many different first-stop/second-stop possibilities are there? Justify your answer.

  d. How many cities could be the third stop of the circuit? How many different routes of first-stop/second-stop/third-stop are there?

  e. How many different circuits are possible using all the cities?

8 Suppose you could use the fastest computer in the world to solve the 26-city TSP.

  a. Using the brute-force method running on the world's fastest supercomputer, how long do you think it would take to solve the 26-city TSP? Make a quick guess.

  b. The TOP500 project, which began in 1993, keeps track of the world's fastest computers. Twice a year, they release a list of the 500 most powerful computer systems. In June 2007, they announced that the BlueGene/L System, developed jointly by IBM and the U.S. Department of Energy, was the world's fastest. The BlueGene/L shown at the left was officially rated at 280.6 TFLOPS (teraFLOPS). Thus, roughly speaking, it can carry out 280.6 trillion calculations per second. Suppose you could use the BlueGene/L System to solve the 26-city TSP. Consider how fast the BlueGene/L could compute the total weight of all the possible different Hamilton circuits. (It would take additional time to find all the circuits.) Assume that the BlueGene/L can compute the weight of 280 trillion circuits each second. How many seconds will it take to compute the weight of all the circuits? How many years? (Source: www.top500.org)

INSTRUCTIONAL NOTE Students may have been introduced to factorial notation in middle school. Hold off from (re)introducing it at this time to allow students an opportunity to recall the notation or develop a need for the notation by computing $25 \times 24 \times \cdots \times 1$ without it. If students have difficulty conceptualizing the 25×24 different combinations, ask them to consider 3 or 4 cities. Trying a simpler problem should be a problem-solving technique students develop. It is important to explicitly discuss this technique with students. Make sure students have a correct answer for Part e of Problem 7 before they move on to Problem 8 since the answer is used in Problem 8. Part c of Problem 8 may require a class discussion.

 7

a. Starting from Atlanta, 25 cities could be the first stop.

b. Once you choose a city for this first stop, 24 cities could be the second stop in the circuit.

c. There are 25×24, or 600, different first-stop/second-stop combinations.

d. Any of 23 cities could be the third stop of the circuit. There are $25 \times 24 \times 23$, or 13,800, different first-stop/second-stop/third-stop combinations.

e. It seems that $25 \times 24 \times 23 \times 22 \times 21 \times 20 \times \cdots \times 1$, or approximately 1.55×10^{25}, different circuits are possible using all the cities. (For the purposes of this problem, such an answer is appropriate. However, often traveling through a circuit in the reverse order is considered the same circuit, so a more accurate answer is actually $\dfrac{1.55 \times 10^{25}}{2}$.)

 8

a. Here, students should take a quick guess. It is likely that many students will think that surely such a fast computer could solve the problem quickly. This will be confronted and corrected in Part b.

b. Students might plausibly base this computation on 25! circuits or $\dfrac{25!}{2}$ circuits (see Problem 7, Part e). Using $\dfrac{25!}{2}$ circuits, the number of years required is $\dfrac{25!}{(2)(280 \times 10^{12})(60)(60)(24)(365)} \approx 878.32$ years. This may be very surprising to students!

NOTE 280.6 TFLOPS or "teraflops" means 280.6 trillion floating point operations per second. Thus, we are just using a rough approximation when we assume that the computer can compute the weight of 280 trillion circuits each second.

Unit 6

c. How fast do you think a computer would need to be to provide a brute-force solution to this problem in a reasonable amount of time?

More with Hamilton Circuits Early work with Hamilton circuits involved graphs that were not weighted. For example, around 1857, Sir William Rowan Hamilton, a famous Irish mathematician for whom Hamilton circuits are named, invented a game called the *Traveller's Dodecahedron, A Voyage Round the World.* Recall that a dodecahedron has 20 vertices and 12 faces which are regular pentagons.

9 The *Traveller's Dodecahedron* game includes a wooden compressed dodecahedron with a peg at each vertex and a silk cord. The vertices represent cities from around the world, like Canton, Delhi, and Zanzibar. The object of the game is to start at one city, visit the other 19 cities exactly once, and finish back where you started. The silk cord is wound around the pegs to keep track of the journey.

a. Explain how the wooden figure shown can be thought of as a "compressed" dodecahedron. Then think about completely flattening the compressed dodecahedron. The flattened figure looks like a vertex-edge graph with 20 vertices and 11 pentagonal regions. Draw this vertex-edge graph.

b. Instead of using string, use your pencil to trace a path in this graph that will win the game.

c. Explain why a winning path is a Hamilton circuit.

d. Does it matter where you start? Explain why or why not.

10 For the following two graphs, find a Hamilton circuit if one exists. If there is no Hamilton circuit, explain why not.

a.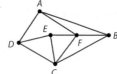

b.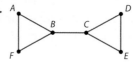

c. INSTRUCTIONAL NOTE Students may have a hard time getting started on this problem. If so, try asking them first to state a "reasonable time." Perhaps, for example, they will think 1 day is a reasonable time. Then ask them how many times bigger their current calculated time is than 1 day. Finding that factor should help them find the corresponding computer speed that would be needed.

The answer to this question depends on students' interpretation of "reasonable amount of time," as well as their computation in Part b, which may have used 25! circuits or $\frac{25!}{2}$ circuits. To illustrate one possible answer, assume $\frac{25!}{2}$ circuits and about 878 years, using the computation given above for Part b. Suppose students think that computing all circuits in 1 day is "reasonable." In this case, it would take a computer that is faster than the BlueGene/L computer by a factor of about $878 \times 365 = 320{,}470$. Thus, you would need a computer that is 320,470 times faster than the fastest supercomputer in the world in 2006. Such a computer may actually exist sometime in the near future (say within a couple decades); but keep in mind that this will only solve a 26-city problem, and most real-world problems are much larger.

⑨ INSTRUCTIONAL NOTE In this problem, students play a game whose solution turns out to be a Hamilton circuit. In the game, each vertex must be visited once but not necessarily each edge. To help students understand this game, a demonstration dodecahedron would be useful. If you do not have such a model, you or the students can construct one from the Teaching Master by cutting out the patterns on card stock and taping them together. Push pins work well for vertices, and students can try the game by winding thread from vertex to vertex.

a. Students should be able to draw the vertex-edge graph from the picture in the student text. Their graphs should be isomorphic to the one at the right. (That is, their visual placement of vertices and edges may be different, but all vertices should connect in exactly the same way.)

b. Paths may vary. A suggested path is indicated by the numbers in the graph at the right; start at 1 and move through in numerical order to 20, then connect from 20 to 1.

c. A winning path is a Hamilton circuit because, by definition of the game, a winning path starts and ends at the same vertex and visits all other vertices exactly once, and this is also the definition of a Hamilton circuit.

d. Since there is a circuit that includes all vertices, it does not matter where you start.

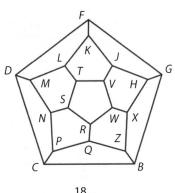

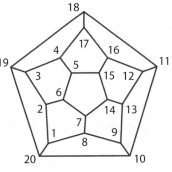

KEY IDEA The ultimate conclusion is that you cannot rely on advances in current computer technology to provide brute-force solutions to many real-world problems.

Teaching Resources

Student Master 6.

UNIT 6 *Network Optimization* Name _____ Date _____

Model Dodecahedron
Problem 9

6 UNIT 6 • Network Optimization   Student Master • see unit page 63

Unit 6

NOTE The solution to Task 10 is on page T412.

Summarize
the Mathematics

In this investigation, you learned about Hamilton circuits and explored algorithms for solving the TSP.

ⓐ What is the relationship between a Hamilton circuit and a solution to the TSP?

ⓑ Describe in your own words the best-edge algorithm for the TSP discussed in Problems 4 and 5. Can you always solve the TSP using this algorithm?

ⓒ Describe the brute-force method for solving the TSP. In theory, will this method always solve the TSP? Will this method provide a practical solution to the TSP? Explain.

Be prepared to share your descriptions and thinking with the class.

✔ Check Your Understanding

The matrix at the right shows the mileage between four cities.

$$\begin{array}{c} \\ A \\ B \\ C \\ D \end{array} \begin{array}{cccc} A & B & C & D \\ \begin{bmatrix} 0 & 20 & 25 & 40 \\ 20 & 0 & 35 & 45 \\ 25 & 35 & 0 & 30 \\ 40 & 45 & 30 & 0 \end{bmatrix} \end{array}$$

a. Represent the information in the matrix with a weighted graph.

b. Trace all the different Hamilton circuits starting at A. List the vertices in each circuit. Record the total length of each circuit.

c. Would you get different answers in Part b if the starting vertex was B?

d. Is there a difference between circuit A-B-C-D-A and circuit A-D-C-B-A? Explain your reasoning.

e. What is the solution to the TSP for this graph?

Investigation 3 · Comparing Graph Topics

So far in this lesson, you have studied minimum spanning trees, Hamilton circuits, and the TSP. In this investigation, you will compare different graph topics. As you work through the investigation, look for answers to this question:

What are similarities and differences among different graph topics that you have studied?

1 **TSP versus Minimum Spanning Trees** There are some interesting connections between these two graph topics.

a. Describe how a solution to the TSP is similar to, and yet different from, a minimum spanning tree.

10 **a.** There are several Hamilton circuits. Here are two: *A-B-C-F-E-D-A* and *A-B-C-D-E-F-A*.

b. There is no Hamilton circuit. One way to explain why not is to think of the edge between *B* and *C* as a bridge between the two triangular regions. Any circuit must travel that bridge twice in order to return to the starting vertex. But traveling the bridge twice means some vertices are repeated, which is not allowed in a Hamilton circuit.

Summarize
the Mathematics

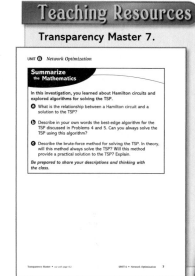

Teaching Resources

Transparency Master 7.

a The main point is that a solution to the TSP is a Hamilton circuit with minimum total weight. A few details are that Hamilton circuits in general may not be weighted while the TSP is always in terms of weighted graphs, and Hamilton circuits may apply in noncomplete graphs while the TSP is formally stated in terms of complete graphs (although see the Key Idea in Problem 2 on T408A).

b In the best-edge algorithm for the TSP, you keep choosing the shortest (best) edge possible and avoid the possibility of any vertex being visited more than once. That is, sequentially choose the shortest edge possible such that no vertex is touched by three chosen edges and no circuits are formed until the end. The best-edge algorithm does not always produce a solution.

c In a brute-force method for solving the TSP, you find all possible Hamilton circuits, compute the weight of each circuit, and choose a circuit with minimum weight. In theory, this method will always solve the TSP. However, it is not a practical solution method due to the huge number of circuits that need to be found and checked in large graphs. Even the fastest computer would take too long to solve a large TSP.

ADDITIONAL INFORMATION Since solving the TSP has applications for so many different kinds of networks, like telephone and transportation networks, mathematicians are always looking for better algorithms that will solve the problem for larger graphs. In 1954, it was considered a breakthrough when a 49-city problem was solved with an efficient algorithm. In 2004, the record was 24,978 cities. You can search the Internet to find the current record. For example, a good source as of 2006 was the TSP site at the Georgia Institute of Technology: www.tsp.gatech.edu. You might assign students to look this up as part of a report on the history of the TSP—see Extensions Task 25.

Unit 6

✓ Check Your Understanding

a.

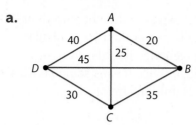

b. *A-B-C-D-A*, length 125
A-B-D-C-A, length 120
A-D-B-C-A, length 145

(If students choose to include the reverse order circuits, there will be six circuits. Students may indicate that reverse order circuits are the same or that they are different. They certainly are different in that the cities are visited in a different order, but they are the same in that they use the same undirected path through the graph. If you were finding and computing all circuits (i.e., using a brute-force method), you would not bother computing the reverse order circuit once you have the original. So, in terms of enumerating and checking all possible circuits, there are only three. In fact, when counting all possible circuits that need to be checked using brute force in the general case of a complete graph with n vertices, there are really only $\frac{(n-1)!}{2}$ circuits to check. In this case, students should see that there are only $\frac{(4-1)!}{2}$, or three "patterns," that is, if the cities are put in a rectangular pattern, then the three "different" patterns are shown below.

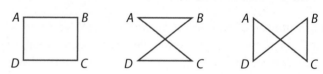

c. No. You will get the same answer for the total length of a circuit no matter where you start the circuit.

d. There is no difference between these two circuits other than they are listed in reverse order.

e. The solution is *A-B-D-C-A* with length of 120 miles. (You may start at any vertex.)

Students compare graph topics they have studied: TSP versus minimum spanning trees, Hamilton versus Euler circuits, and matrices and graphs. The intent of this investigation is to help students synthesize their knowledge of different graph topics and problems. In addition, distance matrices are introduced as a way to organize data on the shortest distance between two vertices. Row sums of distance matrices can be used to determine centrally located and isolated vertices.

 INSTRUCTIONAL NOTE In answering Part a of Problem 1, students may include answers to Parts b and c below, which is fine.

a. They are similar in that both are shortest networks—a solution to the TSP is a shortest circuit and a minimum spanning tree is a shortest tree. Also, they are both optimum spanning networks (see answer to Part b).

They are different in that one is a circuit and the other is a tree. They also differ significantly in terms of solutions (as elaborated in Part c).

b. The title of this lesson is "Optimum Spanning Networks."

   i. Explain how a minimum spanning tree can be viewed as an optimum spanning network.

   ii. Explain how a solution to the TSP can be viewed as an optimum spanning network.

c. A best-edge algorithm can be used to try to solve the TSP and to find a minimum spanning tree. For which of these two problems does this algorithm always work?

(2) **Hamilton versus Euler Circuits** In *Core-Plus Mathematics Course 1*, you may have studied *Euler circuits*—circuits that use each edge of a graph exactly once.

a. State the definition of a Hamilton circuit. Then describe the key difference between an Euler circuit and a Hamilton circuit.

b. Consider the graph at the right.

   i. Find an Euler circuit.

   ii. Find a Hamilton circuit.

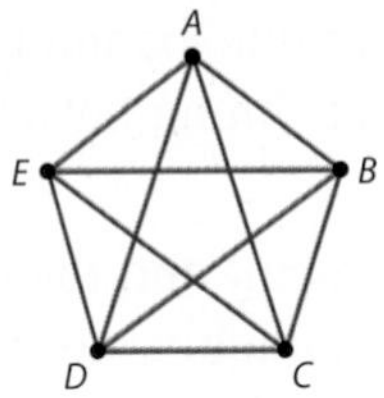

(3) The graph in Problem 2 has both an Euler and a Hamilton circuit. Draw the following graphs (if possible).

a. A graph that does not have an Euler circuit or a Hamilton circuit

b. A graph that does not have an Euler circuit but does have a Hamilton circuit

c. A graph that does have an Euler circuit but does not have a Hamilton circuit

(4) Some graphs have Euler or Hamilton circuits and some do not. You may recall that for Euler circuits there is a theorem that gives a simple, easily testable condition for whether or not an Euler circuit exists. This is not the case for Hamilton circuits. That is, no one knows a nice theorem that states, "A graph has a Hamilton circuit if and only if ...." However, there are some graph properties that give you some information about Hamilton circuits.

a. Look back at your work on Problem 3 above and on Problem 10 in Investigation 2 (page 411). Can you think of a property of a graph that will guarantee that it does *not* have a Hamilton circuit? Make a conjecture and give an argument to support it.

b. Using vertex-edge graph software, generate several graphs that have the property you conjectured in Part a, then test them to see if they have a Hamilton circuit. Does your conjecture still hold or do you need to revise it?

c. Generate and test other graphs to help you propose another property that you think will guarantee that a graph does not have a Hamilton circuit.

b. i. A minimum spanning tree is "optimum" because it is the shortest path. It is a spanning network because every vertex is on the path (network).

ii. A solution to the TSP is an optimum spanning network because it is the shortest circuit that contains each vertex (spans), and a circuit can be thought of as a network.

c. A best-edge algorithm works for finding a minimum spanning tree but does not work to solve the TSP. (There are several efficient algorithms for finding a minimum spanning tree, such as Kruskal's best-edge algorithm investigated in the lesson and Prim's algorithm investigated in Extensions Task 24. However, there are no known efficient algorithms for solving the TSP.)

a. A Hamilton circuit is a circuit in a graph that starts at one vertex, visits all the other vertices exactly once; and ends where it started. In a Hamilton circuit, you use each *vertex* exactly once; while in an Euler circuit, you use each *edge* exactly once.

b. i. An Euler circuit is *D-A-C-E-B-D-E-A-B-C-D*.

ii. A Hamilton circuit is *D-E-A-B-C-D*.

3 Graphs may vary. Examples are given.

a.  **b.** **c.**

4 A connected graph has an Euler circuit if and only if all vertices have even degree. Although there is no known similar theorem for Hamilton circuits, there are some known necessary conditions for a Hamilton circuit and some (different) sufficient conditions. See the solutions and discussion below for some examples.

a. One possible conjecture: Students may notice from Part b of Problem 10 on page 411 that if a graph has a "bridge" then it cannot have a Hamilton circuit. This is because any circuit must travel that bridge twice in order to return to the starting vertex. But traveling the bridge twice means some vertices are repeated, which is not allowed in a Hamilton circuit.

b. Students should use software to create several graphs and test to see if a Hamilton circuit exists in each case. If they find a counterexample, then they should revise their conjecture.

c. For example, students may conjecture that if a graph has a vertex of degree 1 then it cannot have a Hamilton circuit.

DIFFERENTIATION You might challenge some students to think about or research some conditions that guarantee that a graph does have a Hamilton circuit. For example, if G is a simple graph (i.e., a graph with no loops or multiple edges) with n vertices, where $n > 2$, and if each vertex of G has degree at least $\frac{n}{2}$, then G has a Hamilton circuit.

INSTRUCTIONAL NOTE
Since there are efficient algorithms for finding minimum spanning trees but not for solving TSP and since the two topics are similar in some ways, students may wonder whether a minimum spanning tree could be used to find an approximate solution to the TSP. In fact, this can be done. See Extensions Task 23.

INSTRUCTIONAL NOTE
Students may struggle with Parts b and c. Encourage them, as a general problem solving technique, to restrict their thinking to simple cases. For Parts b and c, suggest they consider graphs with a small number of vertices. Then, have students check each other's graphs.

Unit 6

NOTE ON PROOF
If students' conjectures hold for all graphs that they check, this is still not a proof of their conjectures.

(5) **Matrices and Graphs** You learned about adjacency matrices for graphs in previous units. In the next few problems, you will use a similar type of matrix called a *distance matrix*. Consider the following road network. There are seven small towns in Johnson County that are connected to each other by gravel roads, as in the diagram below. (The diagram is not drawn to scale and the roads are often curvy.) The distances are given in miles.

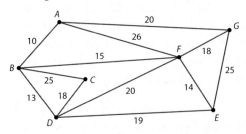

The county wants to pave some of the roads so that people can get from every town to every other town on paved roads, either directly or indirectly. To save money, they also want the total number of miles paved to be as small as possible.

a. Copy the vertices of this graph on a sheet of paper. Then draw a network of paved roads that will fulfill the county's requirements.

b. Each entry in a **distance matrix** for a graph is the length of a shortest path between the corresponding pair of vertices. For example, each entry in the partially completed distance matrix at the right is the shortest distance between the corresponding pair of towns on the paved road network that you found in Part a above.

$$
\begin{array}{c c}
& \begin{array}{c c c c c c c} A & B & C & D & E & F & G \end{array} \\
\begin{array}{c} A \\ B \\ C \\ D \\ E \\ F \\ G \end{array} &
\left[
\begin{array}{c c c c c c c}
— & — & 41 & — & 39 & — & — \\
— & — & — & — & 29 & 15 & — \\
— & 31 & — & — & — & — & — \\
23 & 13 & 18 & — & 42 & 28 & 46 \\
— & 29 & — & — & — & — & — \\
— & — & — & — & — & — & — \\
43 & — & — & — & 32 & — & —
\end{array}
\right]
\end{array}
$$

  i. Explain why the *A-C* entry is 41 and the *D-E* entry is 42.

  ii. Why will this matrix have symmetry about its main diagonal?

  iii. Fill in the remaining entries of the matrix. Divide the work among some of your classmates.

(6) Use the distance matrix to further analyze the road network in Problem 5.

a. Which two towns are farthest apart on the paved-road network?

b. Compute the row sums of the distance matrix. What information do the row sums give about distances on the paved-road network?

c. Which town seems to be most isolated on the paved-road network? Which town seems to be most centrally located? Explain how these questions can be answered by examining the distance matrix.

5 **INSTRUCTIONAL NOTE** Discuss the situation in Problem 5 with your students to be sure that they understand that, as far as the county government is concerned, an acceptable route from, say, *A* to *C* might be very circuitous. The officials are not concerned with the shortest driving time. They are only interested in making sure you can get from any town to any other town on paved roads and minimizing the total number of miles of paved roads. You can help students be more effective with their graphs by providing markers or colored pencils to color the edges that make the spanning tree or by suggesting that they draw a separate tree that only shows the paved roads. Using the supplied Teaching Master will help this problem go smoothly.

INSTRUCTIONAL NOTE
For now, it is best to have students draw (or redraw) their minimum spanning trees without any other edges of the graph shown, rather than darkening the edges of the minimum spanning tree on the entire graph. This will avoid confusion when finding paths and working with distance matrices in the following problems.

a. The paved-road network will be a minimum spanning tree. Students may or may not use Kruskal's best-edge algorithm. The minimum spanning tree shown at the right is unique.

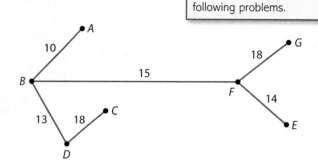

b. **i.** The 41 for the *A-C* entry represents the paved-road distance from *A* to *B* to *D* to *C* (10 + 13 + 18).

The 42 for the *D-E* entry represents the paved-road distance from *D* to *B* to *F* to *E* (13 + 15 + 14).

ii. Since the shortest distance between two points is the same in either direction, the matrix is symmetric about the diagonal.

INSTRUCTIONAL NOTE
It is important to note that the distances in the matrix are the shortest distances along the paved roads, not the shortest distance on any road.

iii.

$$
\begin{array}{c|ccccccc}
 & A & B & C & D & E & F & G \\
\hline
A & 0 & 10 & 41 & 23 & 39 & 25 & 43 \\
B & 10 & 0 & 31 & 13 & 29 & 15 & 33 \\
C & 41 & 31 & 0 & 18 & 60 & 46 & 64 \\
D & 23 & 13 & 18 & 0 & 42 & 28 & 46 \\
E & 39 & 29 & 60 & 42 & 0 & 14 & 32 \\
F & 25 & 15 & 46 & 28 & 14 & 0 & 18 \\
G & 43 & 33 & 64 & 46 & 32 & 18 & 0 \\
\end{array}
$$

6 **a.** Towns *C* and *G* are farthest apart on the paved-road network. The *C-G* entry is the largest number of miles (64).

b.

Row	A	B	C	D	E	F	G
Row Sum	181	131	260	170	216	146	236

The row sum for a given town is the sum of all the distances from the town to all other towns. If you were to take separate trips from the given town to each of the other towns, the sum of the distances of all the separate trips would be equal to the row sum. Since the matrix is symmetric, you can also think of a row sum as the sum of all the distances from all other towns to the town indicated by the row. If there is a meeting in the town indicated by the row, the row sum would be the total travel distance for one person from each town to attend.

c. A larger row sum indicates that a town is farther away from the other towns; i.e., it is relatively isolated. A smaller row sum indicates that there is less total distance to all other towns. Such a town would be centrally located. Thus, Town *C* is the most isolated, and Town *B* is the most centrally located.

Teaching Resources

Student Master 8.

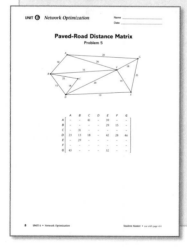

DIFFERENTIATION Some students may need assistance understanding "isolated" or "centrally located."

Unit 6

(7) Which towns might be dissatisfied with this paved-road network? Why? What are some other considerations that might be taken into account when planning an optimum paved-road network?

Solved and Unsolved Problems In this lesson, you examined four fundamental vertex-edge graph topics: minimum spanning trees, the TSP, Hamilton circuits, and Euler circuits. For two of these topics—the TSP and Hamilton circuits—the key problems are currently unsolved! New applications and new mathematics have been developed as researchers continue to work on these problems.

For the TSP, the key problem is to find an efficient solution method that will work in all situations. You have seen one method, a best-edge algorithm, that is efficient but does not guarantee a solution. You have seen another method, the brute-force method, that guarantees a solution but is not efficient. No one knows a method that is both efficient and works in all situations.

For Hamilton circuits, the key problem is to find some testable condition(s) that will completely describe graphs that have a Hamilton circuit. In Problem 4, you made some conjectures about properties of graphs that guarantee that a Hamilton circuit does *not* exist. In Extensions Task 22, you are asked to examine some special types of graphs for which it is possible to deduce whether or not a Hamilton circuit exists. However, there are no known general results for arbitrary graphs. That is, no one knows a theorem that completely characterizes graphs that have a Hamilton circuit; no one knows an efficient algorithm for determining if a graph has a Hamilton circuit; and no one knows an efficient algorithm that is guaranteed to find a Hamilton circuit if it exists.

In contrast, the general problems of finding a minimum spanning tree and finding an Euler circuit are well solved. There are known efficient algorithms that are proven to work in both cases. In addition, the problem of characterizing graphs that have Euler circuits is also solved (a connected graph has an Euler circuit if and only if all the vertices of the graph have even degree).

MATHEMATICAL MODELING Problem 7 is a good problem to include in a large-group summary discussion because it highlights the limitations of a mathematical model. Graphs and matrices are reasonable models for this situation, and they provide a useful solution. However, as with all mathematical models, they do not capture every aspect of the situation. Thus, whichever model is used, you should interpret the solution in terms of the original overall context and be alert to the limitations of the model.

7 In this case, there certainly are other factors that need to be considered when finding the "best" network. For example, it may be that the two most populous towns are connected only very indirectly, and so a different network would be better for more people. For almost any choice, the towns on the "fringes" of the minimum spanning tree probably would be dissatisfied. There may not be an absolute "best" answer.

Unit 6

Summarize
the Mathematics

In this investigation, you have compared several graph topics and problems.

a Describe similarities and differences between the problem of finding a minimum spanning tree and the TSP.

b Describe similarities and differences between Hamilton circuits and Euler circuits.

c What information does the distance matrix for a minimum spanning tree give you?

Be prepared to share your ideas with the class.

✓ Check Your Understanding

Consider the road network below, where distances shown are in miles.

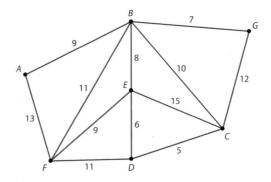

a. Suppose some of the roads need to be plowed after a snowstorm. Find the shortest possible network of plowed roads that will allow cars to drive from every town to every other town on plowed roads.

b. What is the shortest distance from *A* to *F* on the plowed-road network?

c. When there is no snow, all the roads can be used. Find the shortest distance from *A* to *F* when all the roads are clear.

d. Suppose you want to take a tour of all seven towns in the summer when all the roads are clear. Find a route that will visit all the towns without visiting any town more than once, except that you finish the tour where you started. Then, find the shortest such route.

e. Which of Parts a–d above involve finding:

   i. a minimum spanning tree?

   ii. a Hamilton circuit?

   iii. a solution to the TSP?

Summarize
the Mathematics

a A minimum spanning tree and a solution to the TSP are similar in that both are optimum spanning networks. They are different in that one is a tree and the other is a circuit. For other comparisons, see the solution to Problem 1 on pages T412B and T413.

b A Hamilton circuit is similar to an Euler circuit in that both are optimum circuits. They are different in that one uses each vertex exactly once and the other uses each edge exactly once.

c Each entry in the matrix gives the shortest distance between the two corresponding towns on the minimum spanning tree network. Furthermore, each row sum gives a measure of how centrally located a town is.

✓Check Your Understanding

a. This task asks students to find a minimum spanning tree. The only such tree is shown below. The length of this tree is 44 miles.

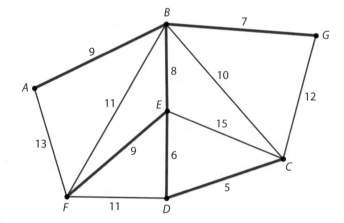

b. The shortest distance from *A* to *F* on the plowed road network above is 26 miles.

c. The shortest distance from *A* to *F* when roads are clear is 13 miles since you can travel there directly. The point here is that shortest paths and distances depend on the network being used—in this case, the plowed-road network or the original, entire network.

d. One such tour is *A-F-D-E-C-G-B-A* which has a length of 73. The shortest such tour is *A-B-G-C-D-E-F-A* with a minimum length of 61.

e. **i.** In Part a, you need to find a minimum spanning tree.

  ii. In the first part of Part d, you need to find a Hamilton circuit.

  iii. In the second part of Part d, you need to solve the TSP.

Applications

1. A restaurant has opened an outdoor patio for evening dining. The owner wants to hang nine decorative light fixtures at designated locations on the overhead latticework. Because of the layout of the patio and the latticework, it is not possible to install wiring between every pair of lights. The matrix below shows the distances in feet between lights that can be linked directly. The main power supply from the restaurant building is at location X. The owner wants to use the minimum amount of wire to get all nine lights connected.

	X	A	B	C	D	E	F	G	H	I
X	—	18	—	—	11	—	—	13	17	—
A	18	—	16	—	—	15	15	—	—	—
B	—	16	—	16	12	—	—	—	—	—
C	—	—	16	—	—	—	—	12	—	—
D	11	—	12	—	—	—	—	10	—	—
E	—	15	—	—	—	—	7	—	—	—
F	—	15	—	—	—	7	—	—	—	—
G	13	—	—	12	10	—	—	—	18	—
H	17	—	—	—	—	—	—	18	—	8
I	—	—	—	—	—	—	—	—	8	—

a. What is the minimum amount of wire needed to connect all nine lights?

b. Suppose the electrician decides to start at the power supply X, then go to the closest light, then go to the closest light from there, and so on. What algorithm does she seem to be using?

c. Apply the electrician's algorithm to the graph, starting at X. Describe what happens.

Applications

1   **a.** The minimum amount of wire needed is 108 feet. The following is one possible minimum spanning tree:

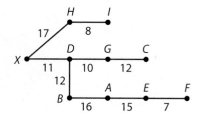

   b. The electrician is using the nearest-neighbor algorithm.

   c. Applying the algorithm starting at *X* yields: *X-D-G-C-B-A-E*(or *F*)-*F*(or *E*). It is not possible to continue at this point because the algorithm requires that we add edges without creating circuits; yet the only edge that now can be added is an edge back to *A*, which creates a circuit. But vertices *H* and *I* have not been reached. No spanning tree is found using this algorithm. (Note that even if we use the network produced by the algorithm and then wire in vertices *H* and *I*, the total amount of wire needed would be 112 feet, which is more than the minimum amount of 108 feet.)

2 There are many situations in which it is useful to detect *clustering*. For example, health officials might want to know if outbreaks of the flu are spread randomly over the country or if there are geographic clusters where high percentages of people are sick. Geologists might want to know if the distribution of iron ore is spread evenly through an ore field or if high densities of ore are clustered in particular areas. Economists might want to know if small business start-ups are more common, that is, clustered, in some areas. There are several techniques that have been devised to detect clustering. A technique involving minimum spanning trees is illustrated in the following copper-ore mining context.

Great Lakes Mining Company would like to know if copper ore is evenly distributed throughout a particular region or if there are clusters of ore. The company drills a grid of nine test holes in each of two ore fields. The following diagrams show the grid of test holes in each ore field along with the percentage of copper, expressed as a decimal, in the sample from each test hole.

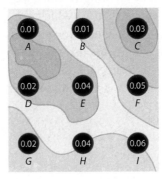
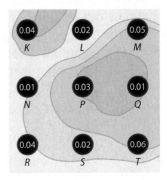

a. Construct a graph model for the grid in each ore field. Represent each test hole as a vertex, and connect two vertices with an edge if the test holes are next to each other (vertically, horizontally, or diagonally).

b. For each edge, compute the absolute value of the difference between the concentrations of copper at the two vertices on the edge. Label the edge with this number. For example, consider the grid on the left. Since the concentration at test hole *A* is 0.01 and the concentration at test hole *E* is 0.04, label the edge connecting *A* and *E* with $|0.01 - 0.04|$ or 0.03.

2 a.

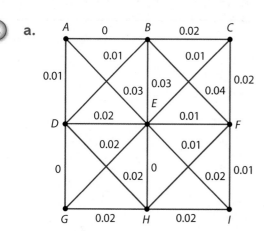
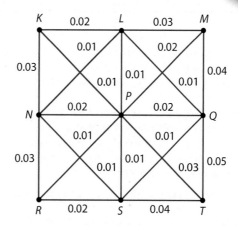

b. The weights of the edges are shown on the graph models above.

TECHNOLOGY NOTE
These graphs are available in *CPMP-Tools* under Discrete Math, *Vertex-Edge Graph* software under Sample Graphs menu. If you wish to reduce the time on this task, students can use *CPMP-Tools*. The tradeoff is losing the modeling opportunity and the arithmetic practice.

Teaching Resources

Student Master 11.

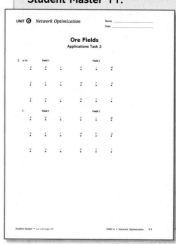

Unit 6

c. Find a minimum spanning tree for each of the two graphs. What is the total weight of each minimum spanning tree? (Note that "total weight" here refers to the sum of the concentration differences on each edge.)

d. Now consider the connection between the length of a minimum spanning tree and clusters of ore concentrations.

   i. In general, if there is a cluster of test holes with similar concentrations of copper, will the numbers on the edges in that cluster be large or small? Why?

   ii. If there is more clustering in one of the ore fields, will the length of the minimum spanning tree for that ore field be larger or smaller than the other one? Why?

   iii. Which of the two ore fields in this example has greater clustering of concentrations of copper? Explain in terms of minimum spanning trees.

3 The graph to the right shows a road network connecting six towns (not shown to scale). The distances shown are in miles. The Highway Department wants to plow enough roads after a snowstorm so that people can travel from any town to any other town on plowed roads. However, because of the time and cost involved, officials want to plow as few miles of road as possible.

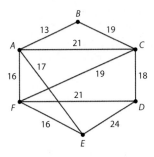

a. Find and draw a network that will meet the Highway Department's requirements. What is the total number of miles that must be plowed?

b. As you know from this lesson, there may be several networks that satisfy the Highway Department's requirements. Find all the plowed-road networks that will work. Check the total length of each such network and make sure that you get the same total mileage for each that you got in Part a.

c. Construct a distance matrix for each shortest network (that is, for each minimum spanning tree) that you found in Parts a and b. (List the vertices in alphabetical order in your matrix.)

d. For each plowed-road network, which town is most centrally located? On what quantitative (numerical) information did you base your decision?

e. Each plowed-road network that you found has the same total length. Despite this, do you think one is better than another? Justify your answer by using information from the graphs and the distance matrices.

c. The lengths of the minimum spanning trees are 0.06 and 0.11 for the left and right ore fields, respectively. One example of each minimum spanning tree is provided. Other trees are possible.

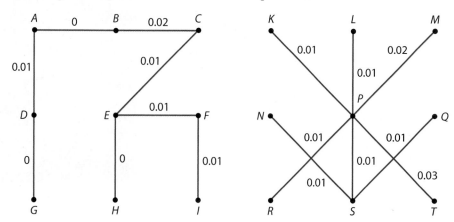

d. i. If there is a cluster of test holes with similar concentrations of copper, the differences between the concentrations will be small, and so the numbers on the edges also will be small.

ii. Clustering in an ore field leads to small differences between ore concentrations, which leads to many edges with small numbers on them, which in turn leads to a short minimum spanning tree. Thus, an ore field with more clustering than another will have a shorter minimum spanning tree length.

iii. The ore field diagram on the left has greater clustering. While the two fields have similar concentration levels, the minimum spanning tree of the one on the left has smaller total weight.

3 a. As shown below, there are two minimum spanning trees. Both trees have a total length (weight) of 82 miles.

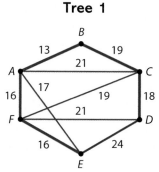

b. See Part a above.

c. **Tree 1**

	A	B	C	D	E	F
A	–	13	32	50	32	16
B	13	–	19	37	45	29
C	32	19	–	18	64	48
D	50	37	18	–	82	66
E	32	45	64	82	–	16
F	16	29	48	66	16	–

Tree 2

	A	B	C	D	E	F
A	–	13	35	53	32	16
B	13	–	48	66	45	29
C	35	48	–	18	35	19
D	53	66	18	–	53	37
E	32	45	35	53	–	16
F	16	29	19	37	16	–

INSTRUCTIONAL NOTE
Minimum spanning trees are useful for helping to detect clustering when the fields being compared have similar levels of ore concentrations. They may be less useful if this is not the case. For example, an ore field with no clustering but low concentrations will have a short minimum spanning tree length that could, in fact, be shorter than the minimum spanning tree length for a field with lots of clustering and high concentrations.

Unit 6

NOTE The solutions to Task 3 Parts d–e are on page T420.

4. Three different features appear in a local newspaper every day. The features are scheduled to be printed in three jobs, all on the same printing press. After each job, the press must be cleaned and reset for the next job. After the last job, the press is reset for the first job to be run the next morning. The time, in minutes, needed to set up the press between each pair of jobs is shown in the matrix below.

$$\begin{array}{c} \\ A \\ B \\ C \end{array} \begin{array}{c} \begin{array}{ccc} A & B & C \end{array} \\ \left[\begin{array}{ccc} - & 25 & 15 \\ 30 & - & 25 \\ 20 & 20 & - \end{array} \right] \end{array}$$

The newspaper production manager wants to schedule the jobs so that the total set-up time is minimum.

a. Model this situation with a *weighted digraph*.

b. Show how a solution to the TSP will tell you how to schedule the jobs so that the total set-up time is minimum.

c. In what order should the jobs be scheduled, and what is the minimum total set-up time?

5. Integrated circuit boards are used in a variety of electronic devices, including kitchen appliances, video games, automobile ignition systems, and the guidance systems in commercial airliners. To manufacture a circuit board, a laser must drill as many as several million holes on a single board. This is usually done with a laser in a fixed position; the circuit board is turned to the positions that must be drilled. For maximum efficiency, the board must end up in its original position, no hole should pass under the laser more than once, and the total distance that the board is moved should be as small as possible.

To see how this problem is solved using graphs, consider a simple situation in which there are just four holes to be drilled. The distance, in millimeters, that the board must be moved from one hole to another is given in the matrix below.

$$\begin{array}{c} \\ A \\ B \\ C \\ D \end{array} \begin{array}{c} \begin{array}{cccc} A & B & C & D \end{array} \\ \left[\begin{array}{cccc} - & 0.02 & 0.02 & 0.01 \\ 0.02 & - & 0.04 & 0.02 \\ 0.02 & 0.04 & - & 0.05 \\ 0.01 & 0.02 & 0.05 & - \end{array} \right] \end{array}$$

a. Represent the information in the matrix with a weighted graph.

b. Explain why solving the circuit board problem is the same as solving the TSP for this graph.

c. Find the order for drilling the holes that will minimize the total distance that the board has to be moved.

d. The row sums for Tree 1 are *A*: 143, *B*: 143, *C*: 181, *D*: 253, *E*: 239, *F*: 175. This indicates that *A* and *B* are the most centrally located on this network.

The row sums for Tree 2 are *A*: 149, *B*: 201, *C*: 155, *D*: 227, *E*: 181, *F*: 117. On this network, *F* is the most centrally located.

e. The primary effect of substituting *CF* for *BC* is to improve the *ED* route at the expense of the *BC* route. Geometrically, this makes a more equitable spanning tree. Also note that the sum of all row sums in the first matrix is more than the sum of all row sums in the second matrix, which again leads one to prefer the second. In practice, however, one should gather more data on road usage before making the decision.

4 **a.** In the digraph below, the numbers represent the time required to set up the press between jobs. For example, after Job *A*, 25 minutes are needed to set up for Job *B*.

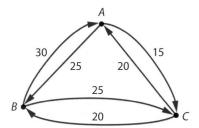

b. A solution to the TSP will give us a sequence of jobs in which each job is done exactly once and the sum of the set-up times between jobs is minimized.

c. There are only two circuits which visit every vertex exactly once, the outer one and the inner one. The outer one is shorter with length 65 minutes. The optimum schedule for the jobs has them in the order *A-C-B-A*. It does not matter which job is first. The minimum total set-up time is 65 minutes.

5 **a.**

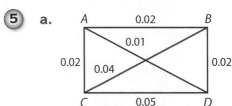

b. In the drilling problem, you have to visit each position once and return to the original position. In effect, the drill moves over the positions as if it were a traveling salesperson.

c. The minimum Hamilton circuit is *A-D-B-C-A*, with length 0.09. One can start at any point and go around in either direction.

(6) Information is processed by computers as strings of 1s and 0s—called **binary strings**. Suppose the information comes from a rotary mechanical controller like what is found on a motorized wheelchair. How can the rotary position of a controller be converted into a binary string so that a computer can process the information? One method, patented in 1953 by Frank Gray and still used today, is based on a set of binary strings called a *Gray code*.

A **Gray code** is an ordered set of binary strings with the following properties.

- Every string of a given length is in the list.
- Each string in the list differs from the preceding one in exactly one position.
- The first and last strings in the list differ in exactly one position.

a. Here is a Gray code using binary strings of length two:

10   00   01   11

Verify that the three properties of a Gray code are satisfied.

When the strings are short and there are so few of them, it is possible to find a Gray code by trial and error. Using Hamilton circuits is one way to find Gray codes with longer strings. Consider strings of length three. A binary string of length three has a 1 or a 0 in each of the three positions. For example, 100 and 011 are binary strings of length three.

b. Build a graph model by letting the vertices be the eight binary strings of length three. Two vertices are connected with an edge if the two strings differ in exactly one position. For example, 010 differs in exactly one position (the 3rd position) from 011, so the vertices representing 010 and 011 should be connected by an edge.

c. Find a Hamilton circuit in the graph. List all the distinct vertices in the circuit in order.

d. Is the list you made in Part c a Gray code? Why or why not?

e. The diagram at the right represents a rotary controller with 8 positions. A movable crank is centered at the inner circle of the diagram and extends to the outermost circle. As you rotate this crank, it passes over the circular sectors comprised of blue and yellow regions. For each sector to which the crank is moved, an electrical device converts the blue regions into 1s and the yellow regions into 0s. Thus, each of the 8 angular positions is converted into a 3-digit binary string. (The white inner circle is not part of the coding, since it represents the shaft of the crank.) On a copy of the diagram, moving clockwise, label the remaining sectors with binary strings. Is this a Gray code? If so, trace a Hamilton circuit in the graph model of Part b that corresponds to this code.

100

f. Why do you think a Gray code is desirable in the situation of a rotary controller as described in Part e?

6 **a.** There are four possible strings of length two, all of which are included in the list. The other two properties can be verified by inspection.

b.

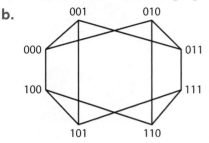

c. One possible Hamilton circuit is 000, 001, 011, 111, 101, 100, 110, 010.

d. Yes, the list is a Gray code: all eight possible strings are included; each string in the sequence differs from its predecessor in exactly one place; and the last string differs from the first in exactly one place. These last two properties are satisfied because, by definition of the edges, when you travel along an edge from one vertex to the next, you move from one string to another string that differs in exactly one position.

e. The eight binary strings, starting with the one o'clock position and moving clockwise, are: 100, 000, 001, 101, 111, 011, 010, 110. This is a Gray code; all three properties are satisfied; and it corresponds to a Hamilton circuit in the graph in Part c.

f. A Gray code is desirable since with a rotary controller the most common moves are small, from one circular sector to the next. For example, you gradually increase speed by turning the crank or gradually make a turn by turning the crank. Thus, it will be more efficient and less error-prone if only one electrical switch or one bit has to change between neighboring sectors, and this is a property provided by a Gray code.

Unit 6

(7) A family with seven members in different parts of the world wants to keep informed about family news at home in the United States. But international calling can be expensive. The family wants to set up a telephone-calling network so everyone will know the latest news for the least total cost. A family member in the United States will call Felix, and then Felix will start the message through the network. The table below shows the cost for a 30-minute phone call between each pair of family members who are abroad.

Phone Call Costs (in dollars)

	Amy	Felix	Eliza	Kit	Owen	Ruby	Raquel
Amy		3.50	4.75	3.80	4.10	2.85	5.10
Felix	3.50		3.75	2.50	4.50	4.10	3.40
Eliza	4.75	3.75		2.95	3.15	4.40	3.50
Kit	3.80	2.50	2.95		4.25	3.30	3.40
Owen	4.10	4.50	3.15	4.25		2.95	3.25
Ruby	2.85	4.10	4.40	3.30	2.95		3.60
Raquel	5.10	3.40	3.50	3.40	3.25	3.60	

a. What is the total cost of the least expensive calling network they can set up?

b. Write a description of who should call whom in this least expensive calling network.

(8) Martin and William have invited friends, who do not all know each other, for dinner. All eight people will be seated at a round table, and the hosts want to seat them so that each guest will know the people sitting on each side of him or her. In the graph below, two people who know each other are connected by an edge.

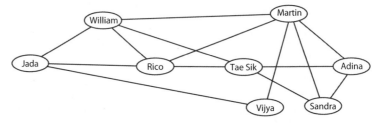

a. Find a Hamilton circuit. Explain how you can use the Hamilton circuit to seat the people according to Martin and William's requirement.

b. Sketch a diagram of the round table and show how the people should be seated.

7 **a.** The table presents the same information as a graph with vertices representing the names and edges representing the costs of phoning. A minimum spanning tree will give a solution to this problem. You can use Kruskal's algorithm directly on the table to select edges and build a minimum spanning tree. The result is the network shown below and a total network calling cost of $17.65.

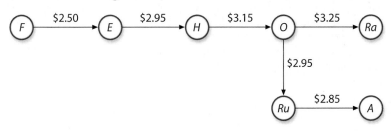

b. Felix calls Kit, Kit calls Eliza, Eliza calls Owen, Owen calls Ruby and Raquel, and Ruby calls Amy.

8 **a.** There are several Hamilton circuits. One is shown below.

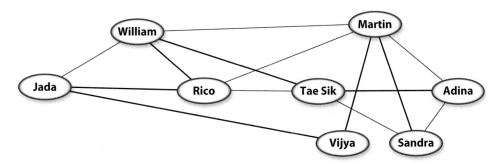

b. Simply wrap the Hamilton circuit around the table and then adjacent people will know each other. The seating chart that corresponds to the Hamilton circuit from Part a is shown here.

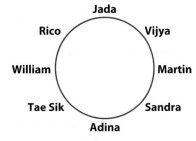

Connections

9 In this lesson, you found optimum networks by finding minimum spanning trees. Graphs for problems involving minimum spanning trees always have numbers associated with their edges. Now consider connected graphs that do not have numbers on the edges. In these cases, you might still be interested in finding a *spanning tree*.

a. Find a spanning tree for each graph below. Describe the method you used to find the spanning trees.

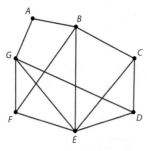 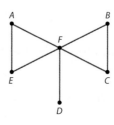

b. Find three different spanning trees for the following graph.

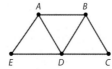

c. Write a rule relating the number of vertices *V* in a connected graph and the number of edges *E* in a spanning tree for the graph.

10 If you make a rectangular frame, like framing used for scaffolding, it is necessary to brace it with a diagonal strip. Without such a strip, it can deform, as illustrated below.

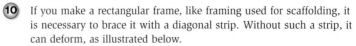

A shape like this will deform under a load to a shape like this, unless it is braced like this.

Buildings and bridges are often constructed of rectangular steel grids, such as those shown below. To make grids rigid, you do not have to brace each cell with a diagonal, but you do have to brace some of them.

a. One of the two grids at the right is rigid, and the other is not.

  i. Which is the rigid grid? Explain your choice.

  ii. For the rigid grid, remove some of the braces without making the grid nonrigid. (You may want to make a physical model to help.)

  iii. For the nonrigid grid, add some diagonal braces to make the grid rigid.

Grid A   **Grid B**

Connections

9 **a.** One possible spanning tree for each graph is shown below. One method for finding a spanning tree is to systematically remove edges that form circuits. Another way is to consider these unweighted graphs as graphs in which all edges have weight 1. Then minimum spanning tree algorithms can be applied, such as Kruskal's algorithm.

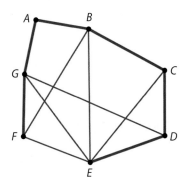 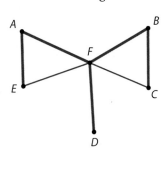

b. There are many possible spanning trees. Three are given.

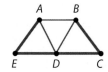 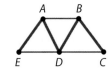 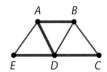

c. The number of edges E in a spanning tree is always one less than the number of vertices V in the graph. $E = V - 1$

10 **INSTRUCTIONAL NOTE** You may wish to have students build models to assist their thinking about this task. One inexpensive way to provide models is to have strips of plastic cut and holes drilled near the ends. Nuts and bolts can then be used to secure the strips as seen at the right. Alternatively, geometry strips could be used.

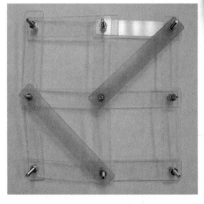

a. **i.** Grid A is rigid; Grid B is not. Student explanations may vary. Students simply may notice fewer braces on Grid B, but it is hoped that they will notice that the first column and last row could collapse.

ii. Three braces can be removed from Grid A. One possibility is shown at the right (top).

iii. At least two braces must be added to Grid B to make it rigid. One solution is shown at the right (bottom). Students may begin thinking about conjectures for how many and which braces make a grid rigid. An appealing conjecture is that if you have a brace in each row and each column, then the grid will be rigid. So, for example, put a brace in each diagonal cell for a total of three braces. However, this will not make the whole grid rigid. To see why not, take the upper left square, hold its shape fixed, and rotate it a few degrees counterclockwise. This movement will maintain the squareness of the square (and the other two braced squares), but the other two cells in the top row and left column will deform. For more on a rigidity criterion, see Part c.

Grid A Modified

Grid B Modified

b. You can use vertex-edge graphs to help solve problems like those on the previous page. The first step is to model the grid with a graph. Let the vertices represent the rows and columns of the grid. Then draw an edge between a row-vertex and a column-vertex if the cell for that row and column is braced. The graph for Grid A is drawn below.

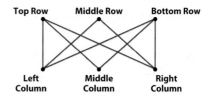

i. Explain why there is an edge from the top-row vertex to the middle-column vertex.

ii. Explain why there is no edge from the middle-row vertex to the middle-column vertex.

iii. Construct the graph for Grid B.

c. Compare the graphs for Grid A and Grid B.

i. Is the graph for Grid A connected? Is Grid A rigid?

ii. Is the graph for Grid B connected? Is Grid B rigid?

iii. Do you think connectedness of a graph model of a grid will ensure the corresponding grid is rigid? Draw another connected graph and another nonconnected graph, each of which could model a grid. What is true about the rigidity of the corresponding grids? Do these examples support your conjecture?

d. A rigid grid may have "extra" bracings. For example, in Part a, you discovered that it was possible to remove some of the cell bracings of Grid A and still maintain the rigidity. Investigate what this means in terms of the corresponding graph.

i. On a copy of the graph for Grid A, eliminate "extra" edges, one at a time. Stop when you think that removing another edge will result in a graph that represents a nonrigid grid. How is your final "subgraph" related to the original graph?

ii. Add the minimum number of bracings to Grid B to make it rigid. Draw the corresponding graph. Is there anything special about the graph?

iii. Describe as completely as you can what you think are the properties of a vertex-edge graph that represents a grid that is rigid and has the minimum number of bracings. Draw a graph that has the properties, then check to see if the graph corresponds to a grid that is rigid with the minimum number of bracings. Draw a rigid grid with the minimum number of bracings, then draw the graph that represents that grid. If necessary, use these and other examples to refine your graph description.

b. i. There is a brace where the top row intersects the middle column.

ii. There is no brace in the cell in the center of the grid.

iii. The graph for Grid B is at the right.

Graph for Grid B

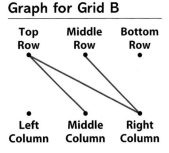

c. i. yes; yes

ii. No, the graph for Grid B consists of three pieces. No, Grid B is not rigid.

iii. See student grids and graphs. A grid is rigid if and only if the corresponding graph is connected.

For interested students, one possible, and partial, explanation using the terms post (vertical segment) and beam (horizontal segment) follows. Assume that the grid is positioned so that the upper left post is, in fact, vertical. For any grid, braced or not, all posts in a given row are parallel, and all beams in a given column are parallel since the cells are rhombuses. A brace in square (i, j) of the grid forces the posts and beams in that cell to be perpendicular, and thus all the posts in row i are forced to be perpendicular to all the beams in column j.

Now, if the graph is connected, then there is a path between every pair of vertices. Every edge in a path corresponds to a brace in a cell, which forces a perpendicular post-beam relation. Thus, since there is a path from the top-row vertex to all other row vertices, the posts in all rows are parallel. For example, suppose the top-row vertex is connected to the right-column vertex, which is connected to the bottom-row vertex. Then the top-row posts are perpendicular to the right-column beams, which are perpendicular to the bottom-row posts. So, the top-row posts must be parallel to the bottom-row posts. Similarly, since there is a path from the top-row vertex to all the column vertices, the beams in every column are perpendicular to the posts in every row. Thus, every cell is forced to be a square and the grid is rigid.

d. i. One subgraph is shown at the right. After eliminating all "extra" edges, the result should be a spanning tree for the graph.

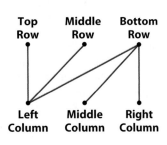

ii. Two more bracings must be added. Grids and graphs will vary. The graph will be a spanning tree for the vertices.

iii. In order to represent a grid, the graph must consist of two sets of vertices to represent the rows and columns of the grid and edges that connect vertices in one set to vertices in the other set but no edges between vertices within a set. (Such a graph is called a **bipartite graph**.) If the grid is rigid, then the graph must be *connected*. If the minimum number of bracings is used, then the graph must be a *spanning tree* for the vertices. Graphs and grids drawn by the students will vary.

Unit 6

11 For vertex-edge graphs, the position of the vertices, the lengths of the edges, and the shape of the graph are not essential. All that really matters is how the vertices are connected by the edges. So, for example, when drawing a graph that corresponds to a distance matrix, the graph does not need to be drawn to scale. On the other hand, in other areas of geometry, like coordinate geometry as studied in the *Coordinate Methods* unit, position, size, and shape *are* essential. Investigate this key difference between graph theory and other areas of geometry by considering the following distance matrix. Each entry is the shortest distance, in miles, between the two corresponding towns.

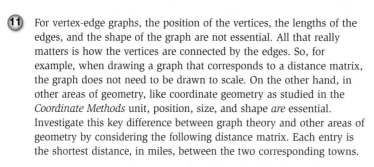

$$\begin{array}{c}\text{Woebegone (W)}\\\text{Rivendell (R)}\\\text{Troy (T)}\end{array}\begin{array}{ccc}W & R & T\\\left[\begin{array}{ccc}— & 60 & 100\\60 & — & 80\\100 & 80 & —\end{array}\right]\end{array}$$

a. Draw a vertex-edge graph that represents the information in the matrix.

b. Use a compass and ruler to draw a scale diagram showing the distances between the three towns. Assume straight-line roads between the towns.

c. State a question involving these three towns that is best answered using the scale diagram.

d. State a question that could be answered using either model—the scale diagram or the vertex-edge graph.

12 A **Hamilton path** is a route that uses each vertex of a graph exactly once. (Thus, a Hamilton circuit may be thought of as a special type of Hamilton path; it is a circuit that uses each vertex exactly once.) Hamilton paths can be used to analyze tournament rankings.

Consider a round-robin tennis tournament involving four players. The matrix below shows the results of the tournament. Recall that the matrix is read from row to column with a "1" indicating a win. For example, the "1" in the Flavio-Simon entry means that Flavio beat Simon.

Tournament Results

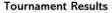

$$\begin{array}{c}\text{Josh (J)}\\\text{Simon (S)}\\\text{Flavio (F)}\\\text{Bill (B)}\end{array}\begin{array}{cccc}J & S & F & B\\\left[\begin{array}{cccc}0 & 0 & 0 & 1\\1 & 0 & 0 & 1\\1 & 1 & 0 & 1\\0 & 0 & 0 & 0\end{array}\right]\end{array}$$

a. Draw a digraph representing the information in the matrix.

b. Find all the Hamilton paths in the graph.

c. Use the Hamilton path to rank the players in the tournament. Explain the connection between your ranking and the Hamilton path.

d. In the *Matrix Methods* unit, you used row sums and powers of matrices to rank tournaments. Rank the tournament as you did in that unit and compare your ranking to that in Part c above.

11 **a.**

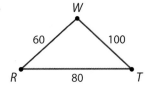

b.

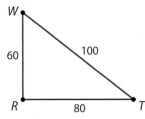

c. One possible question: What kind of angle is formed by the line segments representing the road from *R* to *W* and the road from *R* to *T*?

d. One possible question: Which two cities are closest to one another?

12 **a.**

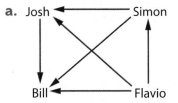

b. The only Hamilton path is *F-S-J-B*.

c. The Hamilton path provides a sequence of players in which each player beats the next. Thus, the Hamilton path *F-S-J-B* also serves as a ranking.

d. The ranking *F-S-J-B* determined by the Hamilton path corresponds to the ranking determined by the row sums of the tournament matrix.

Unit 6

13 In Investigation 2, you considered a Hamilton circuit on a dodecahedron. In fact, many other polyhedra permit Hamilton circuits. For example, all of the Platonic solids (regular polyhedra) permit Hamilton circuits. Consider the cube.

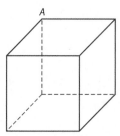

a. How many edges will be in a Hamilton circuit on a cube? Draw a diagram showing one such circuit.

b. Will all Hamilton circuits on a cube be congruent figures? Explain.

c. If a circuit is described by the sequence of vertices in the order visited, how many different Hamilton circuits begin at vertex *A* in the diagram above?

14 The Internet can be thought of as a huge vertex-edge graph (see figure on page 399). Such large graphs are sometimes called *massive graphs*. The degrees of vertices in massive graphs often obey an inverse power law. That is, the number of vertices of degree *d* is proportional to $\frac{1}{d^b}$, for some constant $b > 0$. In particular, for many Internet graphs, *b* is between 2 and 3. Explain what this inverse power law relationship tells you about the numbers of vertices with very large degree and those with very small degree. (You can read more about this at www.mathaware.org/mam/04/essays/graphs.html.)

Reflections

15 Think about the characteristics of those graphs which are also trees.

a. Explain why a tree can be considered a *minimum* connected graph.

b. Explain why a tree can be considered a *maximum* graph with no circuits.

16 Look back at Problem 8 (page 410) of Investigation 2. Find news about the world's fastest computer today. Using the power of that computer, how long will it take to solve the 26-city TSP using the brute-force method? How long will it take to solve a 27-city TSP problem?

17 With the rapid development of more and more powerful computers, do you think that any problem can eventually be solved with a brute-force method by having a computer check all possibilities? Or do you think that there is some fundamental limitation to the ability of computers to solve problems? Explain your thinking.

(13) **INSTRUCTIONAL NOTE** See MathWorld (mathworld.wolfram.com/IcosianGame.html) for more details about Hamilton circuits on polyhedra.

a. There are eight edges in a Hamilton circuit on a cube. One such circuit is shown below.

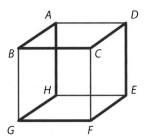

b. All Hamilton circuits on a cube are congruent figures. Each can be transformed into another by rotating the cube.

c. There are eight different ordered Hamilton circuits starting at A.

(14) According to this inverse power law relationship, there are fewer vertices of large degree than there are vertices of small degree.

Reflections

(15) a. A connected graph can have many circuits. In terms of keeping the graph connected, the edges that form circuits are redundant. That is, you can remove edges that form circuits and the resulting graph is still connected. But once there are no circuits, it is impossible to remove edges without disconnecting the graph. Thus, a connected graph with no circuits (a tree) has the fewest number of edges possible to maintain connectivity. In this sense, a tree is a minimum connected graph.

b. Since a tree is connected, there is a path from any vertex to any other vertex. Thus, adding an edge between any 2 vertices in the graph will introduce a circuit. In this way, a tree is a maximal graph with no circuits.

(16) Students should reflect on the limitations of using computers to solve problems. For example, they have already seen that even seemingly simple problems, like the 26-vertex TSP, can involve so many possibilities that even with the fastest computer, checking them all is unrealistic.

When thinking about using computers and algorithms to solve problems, there are two fundamental questions that need to be answered.

- Is there a solution algorithm?
- If there is a solution algorithm, is it efficient; that is, can it be executed in a reasonable amount of time?

Depending on the answers to these questions, problems may fall into one of four categories:

- problems for which no solution algorithm exists, for example, a safe, general computer virus-checking program (algorithm) is impossible;
- problems that have a solution algorithm but no efficient algorithm, thus no computer, no matter how fast, could solve these problems in a reasonable amount of time;

NOTE The remainder of the solutions to Tasks 16 and 17 are on page T427.

18 There is a story that composer Igor Stravinsky (1882–1971) was asked how he would describe his music pictorially. Pointing to the diagram below, he replied, "This is my music:"

 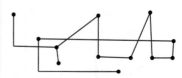

a. What do you think Stravinsky meant?

b. One of Stravinsky's most well-known compositions is *The Rite of Spring*. Listen to *The Rite of Spring*. Why do you think Stravinsky used a tree graph to describe his music? (Incidentally, because *The Rite of Spring* sounded so unexpectedly different and unusual, the premiere performance caused a riot in the audience.)

19 Kruskal's algorithm for minimum spanning trees was developed in the 1950s, and new results related to the TSP are discovered almost every year. It is estimated that more new mathematics has been developed in the last 20 years than in all the past history of mathematics. In fact, most of the mathematics you have investigated in this unit has been developed in the last few decades or even more recently. Do some research to find out about some recent development in mathematics. Write a brief essay on what you find. You might describe how current mathematics is used in the plot of a recent novel or television show, or you could explain a recent news story about mathematics from the radio, newspaper, or Internet. (One good source is Math in the Media from the American Mathematical Society: www.ams.org/mathmedia/.)

Extensions

20 The nearest-neighbor algorithm you investigated in Problem 10 on page 404 did not always produce a minimum spanning tree in a connected graph. Below is a modified version of that algorithm called *Prim's algorithm*.

Step 1: Make a copy of the graph with the edges drawn lightly.

Step 2: Choose a starting vertex. This is the beginning of the tree.

Step 3: Find all edges that have one vertex in the tree constructed so far. Darken the shortest such edge that does not create a circuit. If there is more than one such edge, choose any one.

Step 4: Repeat Step 3 until all vertices have been reached.

a. Test Prim's algorithm using three copies of the following graph from Problem 10.

   i. Apply the algorithm starting at vertex *E*.

   ii. Apply the algorithm starting at vertex *C*.

   iii. Apply the algorithm starting at vertex *A*.

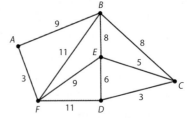

- problems that have efficient solution algorithms, like the minimum spanning tree problem; and
- problems which are believed to have no efficient solution algorithm, but no one knows for sure, like the TSP.

17 Check on the Internet for the speed of the current world's fastest computer. Do a search for this information, or the site at www.top500.org may have the information. Using that speed will likely still result in an impractically long time to solve the problem. However, even if this new computing speed makes the 26-city problem feasible using brute force, students will see that just adding one more city (27 city problem) makes the solution time 26 times longer. (In general, you can mention that real-world problems have many more vertices; so no matter how fast the current computer may be, a large problem in the real world will not be solvable using the brute force method on that computer.)

18 **a.** The graph suggests structural integration, lines, and angles rather than classical curves, continuous progress punctuated by angular passages, or strongly purposeful music with jagged inner content.

b. Students may suggest that Stravinsky chose a tree to emphasize that the themes in his music do not recur as was common in much of the classical music before his time.

19 Students may view mathematical knowledge as nothing new; it is all old knowledge, especially since they may not have studied much recent mathematics. They probably will be surprised at how fast mathematical knowledge is growing today. It is hoped that the current, and unsolved, problems they encountered in this unit will begin to change students' views of mathematics from seeing it as old and dull to seeing it as modern and vital.

Unit 6

Extensions

20 **a.** Responses may vary because Step 2 allows for choice between edges of the same length. One set of solutions is shown below.

i.

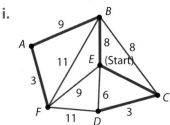

ii.

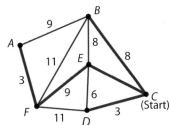

iii.

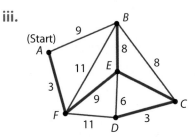

b. Compare Prim's algorithm with the nearest-neighbor algorithm in Problem 10 on page 404.

    i. How are they similar? How are they different?

    ii. Compare the results in Part a above to those you got with the nearest-neighbor algorithm in Problem 10.

c. Prim's algorithm is sometimes called a tree-growing algorithm. Explain why a tree is constructed at each stage of Prim's algorithm.

d. Compare Prim's algorithm to Kruskal's best-edge algorithm from Problem 8 on page 404.

    i. Using vertex-edge graph software, generate several weighted connected graphs. Then apply Kruskal's and Prim's algorithms to find a minimum spanning tree in each graph. Apply each algorithm in automatic mode and in user-activated edge-by-edge mode, if available.

    ii. Describe how Kruskal's and Prim's algorithms are similar. Describe how they are different.

    iii. Do you prefer one algorithm over the other to find a minimum spanning tree? Why?

e. Do you think Prim's algorithm is a good procedure for finding a minimum spanning tree? Write a brief justification of your answer.

21 To find a minimum spanning tree in a graph, you look for a network of existing edges that joins all the vertices and has minimum length. In some situations, you may want to create a minimum spanning network by adding new vertices and edges to the original graph. Such a network is called a **Steiner tree** (named after Jacob Steiner, a nineteenth century mathematician at the University of Berlin). You can find Steiner trees using geometry.

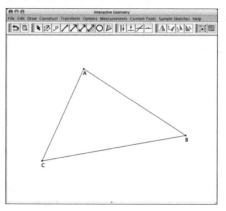

a. Using interactive geometry software, draw a triangle, *ABC*, in which all the angles are less than 120°. You can think of this triangle as a vertex-edge graph.

b. i. This algorithm is similar to the nearest-neighbor algorithm in that at each step, you add the shortest edge that does not create a circuit. The small but significant difference is that in the nearest-neighbor algorithm, the edge you add must be connected to the vertex where you are; while in Prim's algorithm, the edge you add must be connected to any vertex already reached. With this change, Prim's algorithm is guaranteed to find a minimum spanning tree.

ii. Prim's algorithm produced three different minimum spanning trees for this graph while the nearest-neighbor algorithm did not even guarantee a spanning tree or a minimum spanning tree.

c. At each step, the edge added must be connected to a vertex already reached, so at each step the graph that is constructed is connected. Also, no edge can be added that creates a circuit. Thus, at each step, you get a larger connected graph with no circuits, that is, a larger tree.

d. TECHNOLOGY NOTE Duplicate graphs can be made from the edit window. By creating duplicate graphs, students can easily try both algorithms (in both modes) with each graph. Select Sample Graphs, Unit 6, Connected Weighted Graph. Then choose the number of vertices for the graph, the probability that an edge is placed between each pair of vertices, and the highest edge weight. The screen to the right shows one graph of 6 vertices with probability 0.86 and maximum weight 6.

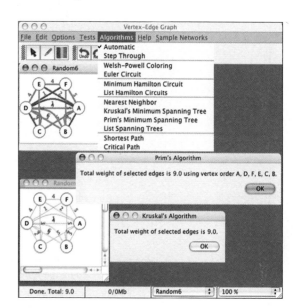

i. Students should use software to create weighted connected graphs and then find minimum spanning trees using both algorithms. By doing so, they will see some differences in how the algorithms generate a minimum spanning tree.

ii. In both algorithms, at each step, you add the shortest edge that does not create a circuit. The key difference is that the set of edges to choose from is different in the two algorithms. In Kruskal's algorithm, you choose from among all unused edges; while in Prim's algorithm, you consider only those unused edges adjacent to vertices already in the tree. Both algorithms are efficient and always produce a minimum spanning tree.

iii. Responses will vary. Students should explain their choice of algorithms.

e. Prim's algorithm is efficient, and it always yields a minimum spanning tree. Look for a sensible justification and evidence of understanding the algorithm. A technical answer is beyond the scope of this book, but students should at least comment that the algorithm worked on the examples they tried and it seems efficient.

21 a. Students will construct diagrams using the geometry software.

Unit 6

Your goal in Parts b and c is to find a shortest network that joins all three of the triangle's vertices.

b. A minimum spanning tree for this triangular graph is just the network consisting of the two shortest sides. Find the sum of the lengths of the two shortest sides. Now you have the length of a minimum spanning tree.

c. In Part b, you found a minimum spanning tree and its total length. Now consider a network that spans all three vertices, *A*, *B*, and *C*, and you are allowed to insert a new vertex and new edges to create this spanning network. You will investigate whether this new spanning network is shorter than the minimum spanning tree you found in Part b. Begin by using the software to perform the following construction.

    i. Insert a new point (vertex) inside the triangle; label it *D*.

    ii. Construct segments from the inside point *D* to each of the vertices of the triangle. This network, consisting of segments $\overline{DA}$, $\overline{DB}$, and $\overline{DC}$, is a network that spans all three of the triangle's vertices (but it uses a vertex and edges that are not part of the original triangle).

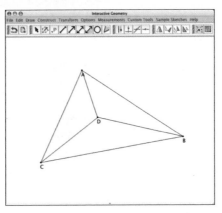

    iii. Measure the length of this network by measuring each segment and adding the three lengths.

    iv. Use the software to grab the inside point and drag it around. Note that the network length changes as the point is moved. Drag the point around until the network length is as small as possible.

Is this length smaller than the minimum spanning tree length from Part b?

d. Find the measure of the three central angles that surround the inside point. Make a conjecture about the measures of these angles when the inside point is moved to a position giving the shortest connected network. Test your conjecture on some other triangles.

b. Responses will depend on student-generated diagrams in Part a.

c. The length of this new network will be smaller than the minimum spanning tree length from Part b.

d. The triangle, its minimum spanning tree, and its Steiner tree will typically look something like the diagrams below. It will always be the case that the central angles surrounding the inside point will measure 120° each.

Triangle

Minimal Spanning Tree   **Steiner Tree**

Unit 6

22 You have learned in this lesson that there is no known theorem that provides complete and efficiently testable conditions for whether or not a graph has a Hamilton circuit. However, for some graphs, you can easily decide if they have a Hamilton circuit.

  a. Consider *complete graphs*. A **complete graph** is a graph that has exactly one edge between every pair of vertices. Complete graphs with three and five vertices are shown below.

  Draw the complete graphs with four and six vertices. Which complete graphs have a Hamilton circuit? Explain.

  b. Consider *complete bipartite graphs*. A **complete bipartite graph**, denoted $K_{n,m}$, is a graph consisting of two sets of vertices, one with n vertices and the other with m vertices. There is exactly one edge from each vertex in the one set to each vertex in the other set. There are no edges between vertices within a set.

  - Draw these complete bipartite graphs: $K_{2,2}$, $K_{2,3}$, $K_{3,3}$, $K_{3,4}$.
  - Which complete bipartite graphs have a Hamilton circuit? Justify your answer.

23 In this lesson, you have learned that there is no known efficient algorithm for solving the TSP. However, there are efficient algorithms for finding a minimum spanning tree. Since both minimum spanning trees and solutions to the TSP are optimum spanning networks (an optimum spanning tree and optimum spanning circuit, respectively), perhaps a minimum spanning tree could be used to find an approximate solution to the TSP.

  a. To test this idea, start with a weighted graph where the weights are regular Euclidean distance. Use one of the efficient algorithms you know (like Kruskal's algorithm) to find a minimum spanning tree.

  b. Suppose you have a circuit that is a solution to the TSP for the graph in Part a. Delete one edge from the circuit.

   i. Explain why the resulting network is a spanning tree for the graph.

   ii. Explain why the total weight of this spanning tree is greater than or equal to the total weight of the minimum spanning tree you have found.

   iii. Explain why the total weight of this spanning tree is less than the total weight of the circuit which is a solution to the TSP.

  Thus, the total weight of the minimum spanning tree is less than the total weight of a circuit that is a solution to the TSP.

22 a. **Complete graph on 4 vertices** **Complete graph on 6 vertices**

All complete graphs have a Hamilton circuit. For example, just make a circuit around the "perimeter" of the graph.

b. $K_{2,2}$ $K_{2,3}$ $K_{3,3}$ $K_{3,4}$

The complete graph $K_{n,m}$ has a Hamilton circuit if and only if $n = m$. If $n = m$, then you can create a Hamilton circuit by tracing "over and back" between the two sets of vertices. If $n \neq m$, then you cannot visit all the vertices in the larger set and end where you started. This is because "over and back" is the only way to trace the vertices (since there are only edges between the two sets, not within a set). Therefore, the vertices are traced in pairs, one from each set, and thus there will always be some untraced vertices in the larger set (or you cannot get back to the starting vertex). Hence, there is no Hamilton circuit.

 23 a. Students' methods may vary. This method uses a minimum spanning tree to find an approximate solution to the TSP when the weights are the usual Euclidean distance.

b. i. A circuit that is a solution to the TSP is a minimum-weight Hamilton circuit (MHC). If you remove one edge, then you get a tree (a connected graph with no circuits) that spans all the vertices.

ii. The weight of this spanning tree (ST) must be greater than or equal to the weight of our minimum spanning tree (MST) because a minimum spanning tree has the smallest possible weight.

iii. The weight of this spanning tree is less than the weight of the minimum Hamilton circuit (MHC) that is a solution to the TSP because we created the tree by removing an edge from the MHC.

Concluding statement:
Thus, in shorthand, we have: MST $\leq$ ST $<$ MHC.

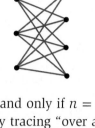

DIFFERENTIATION
Extensions Task 23 may be difficult for some students. You may wish to provide students some time on this task and then provide a copy of the solution. By analyzing this solution, students will gain some experience in reading and understanding others' reasoning.

Unit 6

c. Now consider the minimum spanning tree, and convert it into a Hamilton circuit, as follows:

- Duplicate each edge of the minimum spanning tree.

- Choose a starting point and begin traveling on the duplicated edges of what used to be the minimum spanning tree. Because of the duplicated edges you can backtrack and make a circuit out of what used to be the minimum spanning tree. Some vertices will get visited more than once in this circuit. Remember, you really want a Hamilton circuit; so eventually, you only want to use each vertex once. As you move along the circuit of duplicated edges, when you reach a vertex on the circuit you have visited before, look beyond it to the next unvisited vertex on the circuit. Take a shortcut to that unvisited vertex by simply "cutting the corner" and avoiding the vertex you have already visited. Explain why the "cutting the corner" distance is shorter than the distance that goes through the skipped vertex.

- Continue in this way, cutting the corners to skip vertices you have already visited, until you end up back at the starting vertex.

d. Using the Hamilton circuit you created in Part c, justify the following statements.

- The weight of this Hamilton circuit is less than the weight of the duplicated-edges circuit.

- The weight of the duplicated-edges circuit is twice the weight of the minimum spanning tree.

- Thus, the weight of the Hamilton circuit you have created is less than twice the weight of the minimum spanning tree.

e. By putting the concluding statements together from Parts b and d, explain why you have found a Hamilton circuit with weight that is within twice the optimum weight of a solution to the TSP. Thus, you have a reasonable approximate solution to the TSP.

 24 You have seen in this lesson that there is no known efficient method for solving the TSP. The same is true for finding Hamilton circuits and paths. Most experts believe that efficient solutions for these problems will never be found, at least not by using traditional electronic computers. In 1994, computer scientist Leonard M. Adleman of the University of Southern California in Los Angeles opened up the possibility of using nature as the computer to solve these problems. Dr. Adleman successfully carried out a laboratory experiment in which he used DNA to do the computations needed to solve a Hamilton path problem. Dr. Adleman stated, "This is the first example, I think, of an actual computation carried out at the molecular level." This method has not been shown to solve all Hamiltonian problems, and the particular problem solved was quite small, but it opens up some amazing possibilities for mathematics and computer science.

c. We began this method by finding an MST. Now you duplicate all the edges on this MST. This will create a graph with extra edges that you can trace to generate a circuit that visits all the vertices in the graph. Let's call this the duplicated-edges circuit DEC. The DEC will likely visit some of the vertices more than once. To avoid visiting vertices more than once, every time you come upon a vertex that you have already visited, you will skip it and "cut the corner" and add a new straight line Euclidean distance edge to the next vertex. By the triangle inequality, this new edge that cuts the corner will be shorter than going through the two existing edges that form the other two sides of the triangle.

Continuing in this way, you visit each vertex (because all vertices are included on the MST you started with), you do not visit any vertex more than once (because you cut the corner past vertices you have already visited), and you end up back at the vertex where you started (because with all the duplicate edges, you can get back to the start). Thus, you get a Hamilton circuit.

d. • The Hamilton circuit (HC) has less weight than the duplicated-edges circuit (DEC) because some of the duplicated edges were deleted and replaced with shorter edges that cut corners.

 • The DEC has twice the weight of the original MST since all the MST edges were duplicated to create it.

 • HC < DEC (as in the first bullet above). DEC = 2MST (as in the second bullet above). Thus, HC < DEC = 2MST.

e. Since a minimum Hamilton circuit must have weight that is less than or equal to the weight of any other Hamilton circuit, you can put together the conclusions of Parts b and d to get:

$$\text{MST} \leq \text{ST} < \text{MHC} \leq \text{HC} < \text{DEC} = 2\text{MST} < 2\text{MHC}$$

(The last inequality follows since MST < MHC implies 2MST < 2MHC.)

Thus, the Hamilton circuit (HC) has weight that is within twice the weight of a minimum Hamilton circuit (MHC). Since the HC was constructed from our MST (which can be done efficiently), an approximate solution to the TSP has been efficiently constructed that is within twice the optimum solution.

a. The graph that Dr. Adleman used in his experiment is shown below. All of the information in the graph was encoded using strands of DNA, and then the computations needed to find a Hamilton path were carried out by biochemical processes. Of course, this graph is small enough that the Hamilton path can also be found without gene splicing or conventional computers. Find the Hamilton path for this graph.

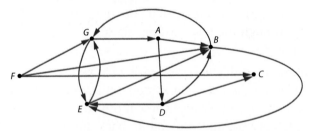

b. Find out more about this groundbreaking experiment in "molecular computation" by reading some of the articles below and conducting an Internet search. Write a short report incorporating your findings.

- Adleman, Leonard M. Molecular Computation of Solutions to Combinatorial Problems. *Science*, November 11, 1994.

- Delvin, Keith. Test Tube Computing with DNA. *Math Horizons*, April 1995.

- Kolata, Gina. Scientist At Work: Leonard Adleman: Hitting the High Spots of Computer Theory. *The New York Times*, Late Edition, December 15, 1994.

- Do an Internet search to find recent information.

25 Since solving the TSP has applications for so many different kinds of networks, like telephone and transportation networks, mathematicians are always looking for better algorithms that will solve the problem for larger graphs. In 1954, a 49-city instance of the TSP was solved. The record in 2004 was 24,978 cities—all cities in Sweden. Find the latest news about the TSP and write a brief report on the history of the TSP, the current record, and recent developments. A good source as of 2006 was the TSP site at the Georgia Institute of Technology: www.tsp.gatech.edu.

Review

26 Rewrite each expression in the shortest equivalent form without parentheses.

a. $3(15 - 8x) - 2x(x + 9)$ **b.** $\frac{2}{5}(3x) + \frac{1}{5}(4 + 7x) - 1$

c. $-6 + 5(-3 + 4x) - 8x$ **d.** $(x + 4)(2x + 7)$

27 Estimate the answer to each question. Then calculate the exact answers and compare to your estimates.

a. 15 is what percent of 75? **b.** What is 35% of 168?

c. 45 is 40% of what number?

TSP solved for 24,978 cities in Sweden

24 **a.** The Hamilton path is *F-B-E-G-A-D-C*.

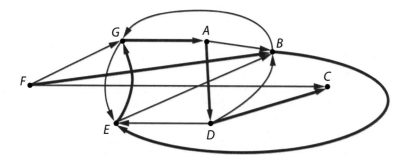

b. These articles are at different levels of scientific sophistication and ease of reading in the order given. The first article, from *Science*, might be best for the most motivated students. The second article is from *Math Horizons*, which is an expository magazine written for undergraduates in college who are interested in mathematics. The final article is a fairly detailed newspaper article from the *New York Times*.

25 Students can do an Internet search on "Traveling Salesman Problem" or "Traveling Salesperson Problem" or "TSP" to find information about the history of the TSP, the current record, and recent developments.

Review

26 **a.** $-2x^2 - 42x + 45$

b. $\frac{13}{5}x - \frac{1}{5}$

c. $12x - 21$

d. $2x^2 + 15x + 28$

27 Student answers should include estimates and the exact answers shown below.

a. 20%

b. 58.8

c. 112.5

28 Trapezoid *ABCD* has vertex matrix $\begin{bmatrix} 1 & 1 & 3 & 8 \\ 1 & 5 & 5 & 1 \end{bmatrix}$.

    a. Find the area of trapezoid *ABCD*.

    b. Find the perimeter of trapezoid *ABCD*.

    c. Trapezoid *A′B′C′D′* is the image of trapezoid *ABCD* after applying the transformation $(x, y) \rightarrow (x + 3, y - 2)$. Find the area and perimeter of trapezoid *A′B′C′D′* by using properties of the transformation. Explain your reasoning.

    d. Trapezoid *WXYZ* is the image of trapezoid *ABCD* after applying the transformation $(x, y) \rightarrow (5x, 5y)$. Find the area and perimeter of trapezoid *WXYZ* by using properties of the transformation. Explain your reasoning.

29 The registration cost per person on a softball team varies inversely with the number of people on the roster for the team.

    a. If only 10 people are on the roster, each person must pay $37. How much would each person have to pay if there were 15 people on the roster?

    b. Write a rule that expresses cost per person as a function of number of people. Then identify the constant of proportionality and explain what it means in this context.

    c. Describe how the cost per person changes as the number of people on the roster increases.

30 The histograms below show the ages of patients who were seen by two different doctors during one week in October. The scales on the Number of Patients axes are the same for both graphs.

Dr. Cabala

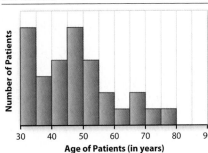

Dr. Dimas

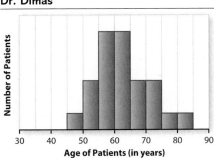

    a. For which office was the mean age of the patients seen greater? Explain your reasoning.

    b. For which office was there greater variation in the ages of the patients seen? Explain your reasoning.

31 Solve each equation algebraically—without use of the quadratic formula, if possible.

    a. $x^2 - 15x + 26 = 0$ **b.** $x^2 = -8x + 20$

    c. $48 = -x(x + 16)$ **d.** $2x^2 + 5x = 1$

28 a. 18 square units

b. $13 + \sqrt{41}$ units

c. The area and perimeter will be the same as that of the preimage trapezoid since distances are preserved under translations.

d. The area is $5^2(18)$, or 450 square units.
The perimeter is $5(13 + \sqrt{41})$, or $65 + 5\sqrt{41}$ units.

29 a. $\dfrac{(10)(37)}{15} \approx \$24.67$

b. $c(p) = \dfrac{370}{p}$
The constant of proportionality is 370—the total registration cost.

c. The cost per person decreases as the number of people on the roster increases.

30 a. Dr. Dimas. Most of Dr. Dimas' patients are older than 55, whereas most of Dr. Cabala's patients are younger than 55, making the mean age of Dr. Dimas' patients greater than the mean age of Dr. Cabala's patients.

b. Dr. Cabala. The range is one indicator that Dr. Cabala's office has greater variation in the ages of patients. The range of Dr. Cabala's patients is 50, whereas the range of Dr. Dimas' patients is 40.

31 a. $x^2 - 15x + 26 = 0$
$(x - 13)(x - 2) = 0$
$x = 13$ or $x = 2$

b. $x^2 = -8x + 20$
$x^2 + 8x - 20 = 0$
$(x + 10)(x - 2) = 0$
$x = -10$ or $x = 2$

c. $48 = -x(x + 16)$
$48 = -x^2 - 16x$
$x^2 + 16x + 48 = 0$
$(x + 12)(x + 4) = 0$
$x = -12$ or $x = -4$

d. $2x^2 + 5x = 1$
$2x^2 + 5x - 1 = 0$

$x = \dfrac{-5 \pm \sqrt{25 - 4(2)(-1)}}{4}$

$x = \dfrac{-5 \pm \sqrt{33}}{4}$

$x = \dfrac{-5}{4} \pm \dfrac{\sqrt{33}}{4}$

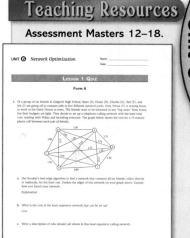

Teaching Resources

Assessment Masters 12–18.

Unit 6

Scheduling Projects Using Critical Paths

Careful planning is important to ensure the success of any project. This is particularly true in the case of planning large projects such as the construction of a new high school, shopping mall, or apartment complex. Even smaller projects such as house remodeling, organizing a school dance, or hosting a party can profit from careful planning. Network optimization using critical paths can help you plan well.

Scheduling Projects using Critical Paths

Students learn how to use critical paths to schedule projects. They find critical tasks and the earliest finish time for large projects that consist of many individual tasks. This method is called the Critical Path Method (CPM) or the Program Evaluation and Review Technique (PERT). It is one of the most widely used mathematical management techniques in business, industry, and government. Actually, PERT and CPM are slightly different techniques, but they both use critical paths. PERT was developed in the late 1950s to aid in the development of submarine defense systems. CPM was developed at about the same time in the private sector. These techniques are used extensively today in business, industry, and government.

You might show the following video after this lesson as part of the closure and summary. (Showing the video before the lesson will impede students' investigations.) See For All Practical Purposes, Program 3: Trains, Planes, and Critical Paths, from Annenberg Media, produced by the Consortium for Mathematics and Its Applications (COMAP), 1988. There are three segments on this video; the third segment is on the Critical Path Method. You can purchase the video or view it online at www.learner.org/resources/series82.html.

Lesson Objectives

- Construct and interpret a project digraph
- Determine earliest finish time for a project consisting of many tasks
- Understand and apply critical paths and critical tasks in the context of project scheduling
- Further develop skill in mathematical modeling, algorithmic problem solving, and optimization

Lesson Launch

Students should be focused on tasks that need to be done before the dance so that a poster advertising the dance can be displayed a month in advance. This focus on 30 days before the dance provides a definite deadline for completing the tasks and yet helps avoid complications that could occur if the project is simply stated as "plan the dance." (Such potential complications include worrying about advance-booking requirements and dealing with tasks that are not subject to scheduling methods because they must be done at specific times just before, during, or right after the dance, like set-up and clean-up.) It would be helpful to list the tasks where students can all see them.

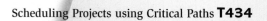

Think About This Situation

Suppose that you and some of your classmates are helping to plan a formal spring dance. You decide that a poster advertising the dance should be displayed around the school a month before the dance.

a What are some tasks related to putting on a spring dance that should be completed before advertising posters are printed and displayed?

b Describe two tasks that could be worked on at the same time by different teams.

c Do some tasks need to be done before others? A task that must be done before another task is called a *prerequisite*. Give an example of a task and a prerequisite for that task.

d How can you make sure that everything gets done on time?

In this lesson, you will learn how to use *critical paths* in vertex-edge graphs to schedule projects that involve many tasks. This technique is called the *Program Evaluation and Review Technique* (*PERT*) or the *Critical Path Method* (*CPM*). Critical path analysis is one of the most frequently used mathematical management techniques.

Investigation 1 — Building a Model

As you have seen before, a first step in modeling a situation is often to make a diagram. In the case of scheduling large projects like a school dance project, it is important to consider this question:

> *How can you create a vertex-edge graph model that will help in the analysis and scheduling of the project?*

Listed here are some of the tasks that you may have found necessary in planning a spring dance. These are the tasks that will be used for the rest of this investigation. The order in which these tasks would need to be completed may vary from school to school.

Tasks

Book a Band or DJ (*B*)
Design the Poster (*D*)
Choose and Reserve the Location (*L*)
Display the Posters (*P*)
Choose a Theme (*T*)
Arrange for Decorations (*DC*)

Think About This Situation

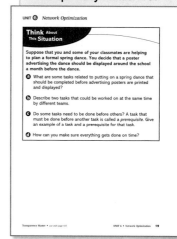

(a) Students might suggest some of the following tasks: choose a theme, find and book a band or DJ, find and book a location, find or make decorations, design or buy tickets, create a Web site for the dance, create a podcast or blog for the dance, design a poster, find chaperones, make transportation arrangements, decide who will do what to get everything done.

(b) An important part of the scheduling process is figuring out which tasks can be done at the same time and which tasks are prerequisites for others. Examples from the list above of tasks that could be done at the same time are book a band and find decorations.

(c) Using the sample tasks above, choosing a theme is a prerequisite for finding or making decorations since you cannot do the decorations until you know the theme.

(d) This is a very open-ended question designed to highlight the need for careful planning. Students might suggest making a list, using a spreadsheet, drawing a diagram, getting enough volunteers, etc. In this lesson, they will learn how to use critical paths to schedule all the tasks in a way that will help get everything done most efficiently.

COLLABORATION SKILL
Help each other to make sure answers make sense.

Unit 6

Investigation 1 Building a Model

In the context of a spring dance planning project, students learn how to construct a project digraph that shows tasks and prerequisite tasks.

At Marshall High School, the prerequisites for the various tasks are as follows:

- The tasks that need to be done just before booking the band are choosing the location and choosing a theme.
- The tasks that need to be done just before designing the poster are booking the band and arranging for decorations.
- There are no tasks that need to be done just before choosing and reserving the location.
- The task that needs to be done just before displaying the posters is designing the posters.
- There are no tasks that need to be done just before choosing a theme.
- The task that needs to be done just before arranging for decorations is choosing a theme.

Tasks to be done *just* before a particular task are called **immediate prerequisites**.

1. Using the prerequisite information for Marshall High School, complete a table like the one below showing which tasks are immediate prerequisites for others. Such a table is called an **immediate prerequisite table**.

Dance Plans

Task	Immediate Prerequisites
Book a Band or DJ (B)	L, T
Design the Poster (D)	
Choose and Reserve the Location (L)	
Display the Posters (P)	
Choose a Theme (T)	
Arrange for Decorations (DC)	

2. Using the procedure below, complete a diagram showing how all of the tasks are related to each other.

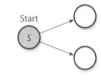

Step 1: Place the circle labeled S at the far left of your paper. Put a new circle at the far right of your paper, where the diagram will end. Label it F for "Finish." The circles labeled S and F do not represent actual tasks. They simply indicate the start and finish of the project.

Step 2: Draw two empty circles to the right of S representing tasks that do not have any immediate prerequisites. Which tasks in the immediate prerequisite table from Problem 1 should be represented by the two empty circles? Label the two circles with those tasks.

Step 3: Moving to the right again, draw a circle for each remaining task. Draw an arrow between two circles if one task (at the tail of the arrow) is an immediate prerequisite for the other task (at the tip of the arrow).

Step 4: Finish the diagram by drawing connecting arrows from the final task or tasks to the circle marked F.

Step 5: If necessary, redraw the diagram so that it looks orderly.

(1) **Dance Plans**

Task	Immediate Prerequisites
Book a Band or DJ (B)	L, T
Design the Poster (D)	B, DC
Choose and Reserve the Location (L)	None
Display the Posters (P)	D
Choose a Theme (T)	None
Arrange for Decorations (DC)	T

(2) One possible diagram is shown below.

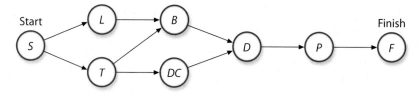

Unit 6

3 Compare your diagram with the diagrams of others.

a. Do the diagrams look different? Explain the differences.

b. Does everyone's diagram accurately represent the information in the immediate prerequisite table?

c. Decide on one organized, orderly diagram that best represents the situation. Make a copy of that diagram.

4 A diagram like the one you drew in Problem 3 is a vertex-edge graph where the edges are *directed*, that is, the edges are arrows. Graphs like this are called **directed graphs**, or **digraphs**. Use your digraph and the immediate prerequisite table to help answer the following questions.

a. Which of the following pairs of tasks can be worked on at the same time by different teams? Explain your reasoning.

   i. Tasks L and B

   ii. Tasks L and T

   iii. Tasks L and DC

   iv. Tasks L and D

b. Find one other pair of tasks that can be worked on at the same time.

Explain, in terms of the school dance project and the individual tasks, why it is reasonable for these tasks to be worked on at the same time.

Summarize
the Mathematics

In this investigation, you learned how to use a digraph to show how tasks involved in the dance project are related to each other.

a What do the vertices of the project digraph represent?

b How are prerequisite tasks represented in the project digraph?

c How are tasks that can be worked on at the same time represented in the project digraph?

Be prepared to share your ideas with the class.

(3) **a.** Diagrams could have different appearances depending on, for example, where students place vertices and how they draw the edges. Different looking diagrams may still be accurate representations or perhaps not. See Part b.

b. Students should check whether or not the immediate prerequisite relationships are accurately reflected in the diagram.

c. Students should compare and discuss their diagrams and then agree on one neat and clear diagram to use for the following problems.

INSTRUCTIONAL NOTE
A tip for making the diagrams look more orderly is to align vertically those tasks that share an immediate prerequisite.

(4) **a.** **i.** No; L is a prerequisite to B.

ii. Yes; neither has a prerequisite.

iii. Yes, as long as T has been done.

iv. No; L is a prerequisite for B which is a prerequisite for D.

b. Tasks B and DC can be worked on at the same time. Once the prerequisites L and T are done, then B and DC can be worked on at the same time. There is not a directed path between them. In terms of the school-dance context, it seems reasonable that you could book the band and arrange for decorations at the same time.

Summarize
the Mathematics

a The vertices of the digraph represent tasks.

b Prerequisite tasks have arrows which leave from them to their following tasks.

c Tasks that can be worked on at the same time have no directed paths between them.

Teaching Resources

Transparency Master 21.

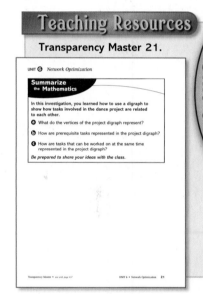

Unit 6

COLLABORATION PROMPT
We checked to make sure our answers made sense on Problem _____ by … .

✓ Check Your Understanding

"Turning around" a commercial
airplane at an airport is a
complex project that happens
many times every day.

   Suppose that the tasks
involved are unloading arriving
passengers, cleaning the cabin,
unloading arriving luggage,
boarding departing passengers,
and loading departing luggage.
The relationships among these
tasks are as follows:

- Unloading the arriving passengers must be done just before cleaning
  the cabin.

- Cleaning the cabin must be done just before boarding the
  departing passengers.

- Unloading the arriving luggage must be done just before loading the
  departing luggage.

- All activities in the cabin of the airplane (unloading and boarding
  passengers and cleaning the cabin) can be done at the same time as
  loading and unloading luggage.

Construct an immediate prerequisite table and project digraph for
this situation.

Investigation 2   Critical Paths and the Earliest Finish Time

You have seen that a large project, like a school dance or "turning around"
a commercial airplane, consists of many individual tasks that are related to
each other. Some tasks must be done before others can be started. Other
tasks can be worked on at the same time. A digraph is a good way to show
how all the tasks are related to each other.

   The real concern in a large project is to get all the tasks done most
efficiently. In particular, it is important to know the least amount of time
required to complete the entire project. This minimum completion time is
called the **earliest finish time** (**EFT**). As you work through the problems in
this investigation, look for answers to this question:

*How can you use the project digraph to find the
earliest finish time for a project?*

Check Your Understanding

Task	Immediate Prerequisite
Unload Passengers (*UP*)	none
Clean Cabin (*C*)	*UP*
Unload Luggage (*UL*)	none
Board Passengers (*BP*)	*C*
Load Luggage (*LL*)	*UL*

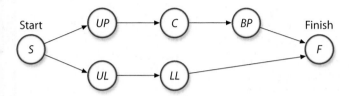

Investigation 2 — Critical Paths and the Earliest Finish Time

When task times are included, students learn to find a critical path and the earliest finish time (EFT) for the project. They learn that the length (weight) of a longest path through the project digraph, which is called a critical path, gives the EFT for the project; and they learn why the tasks on a critical path are indeed critical.

A general assumption throughout this lesson, unless otherwise stated, is that there are plenty of qualified people to work on each project. In particular, there are enough people to work on concurrent tasks as needed. Also, each task time is the time needed given the people who will be working on the task.

1 There are many reasonable estimates that you and your classmates might make for how long it will take to complete each task of the school dance project. Experience at one school suggested the task times and prerequisites displayed in the following table. These task times will be used for the rest of this lesson.

Planning a Dance

Task	Task Time	Immediate Prerequisites
Choose and Reserve a Location (*L*)	2 days	none
Choose a Theme (*T*)	3 days	none
Book a Band or DJ (*B*)	7 days	*L, T*
Arrange for Decorations (*DC*)	5 days	*T*
Design the Poster (*D*)	5 days	*B, DC*
Display the Poster (*P*)	2 days	*D*

Put these task times into the project digraph you constructed in the last investigation by entering the task times into the circles (vertices) of the digraph.

2 Assume that you have plenty of qualified people to work on the project. Use the immediate prerequisite table and the project digraph to help you figure out how to complete the project most efficiently.

   a. What is the least amount of time required to complete the whole project (that is, what is the EFT for the project)? Explain.

   b. Compare answers and explanations with some of your classmates. Resolve any differences.

   c. Is the earliest finish time for the whole project equal to the sum of all the individual task times? Explain why or why not.

3 Think about the EFT in terms of paths through the project digraph.

   a. Which path through the graph corresponds to the earliest finish time for all the tasks? Write down your answer and an explanation. Compare answers and explanations with some of your classmates. Resolve any differences.

   b. How many paths are there through the project digraph, from *S* to *F*? List in order the vertices of all the different paths. For each path, compute the total time of all tasks on the path. Explain how this is a brute-force method for finding the EFT.

4 A path through the project digraph that corresponds to the earliest finish time is called a **critical path**.

   a. Mark the edges of the critical path so that it is easily visible.

   b. Compare your critical path from Part a to the critical paths found by others. If the paths are different, discuss the differences and decide on the correct critical path.

   c. Describe the connections among the critical path, the EFT, and the longest path.

1 The graph should look something like this:

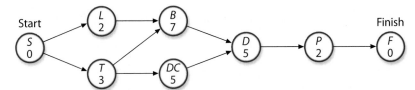

2 **a–b.** Students may suggest that the EFT is found by just adding up all the individual task times. But this is too long because some tasks can be worked on at the same time. Students may think that the EFT is 15 because 15 is the length of the shortest path. But this will not give enough time to finish all the tasks. It turns out that the EFT corresponds to the length of the longest path: *S-T-B-D-P-F*, which is 17 days. (Some students will see this now, and some students may need more time. They revisit this important idea right away in Problem 3.)

c. No, the EFT will be less than the sum of all the tasks as long as some tasks can be done at the same time.

POSSIBLE MISCONCEPTION Students may think that the EFT is the sum of all task times or that the EFT is the length of a shortest path. However, the EFT is the length of a longest path. The word "earliest" may incorrectly seem to imply "shortest" to students. These possible misconceptions are addressed in Problems 2 and 3, so be sure they are resolved by the time students finish Problem 3.

3 **a.** This question revisits the important ideas in Problem 2. The path that corresponds to the EFT is the longest path: *S-T-B-D-P-F*. Students should compare and discuss their answers until everyone agrees this is true and why. An explanation might be that we must use the longest path to make sure there is time allowed to do all the tasks, and we do not need to add in the task time for all tasks since some tasks can be done at the same time.

b. There are three paths through the project digraph: *S-L-B-D-P-F* (16 days), *S-T-B-D-P-F* (17 days), and *S-T-DC-D-P-F* (15 days). This is a brute-force method for finding the EFT since we know that the length of the longest path is the EFT, and we are finding the length of a longest path by finding all possible paths, computing the length of each path, and identifying the length of a longest path.

4 **a.** Students should darken the path *S-T-B-D-P-F*.

b. This comparison ensures that all students are getting the critical path.

c. Here is another opportunity for students to realize and explain that the EFT is 17 days, which is the length of the longest path, which is the critical path.

Unit 6

(5) If all the posters are to be displayed 30 days before the dance, how many days before the dance should work on the project begin? Justify your answer based on your work on the previous problems.

(6) Now consider what happens to the EFT and critical path if certain tasks take longer to complete than expected.

a. The project digraph below represents the school dance project you have been working on. Compare this digraph to the one you have constructed and used in the previous problems. If the graphs look different in some way, explain why this digraph and your digraph both accurately represent the project.

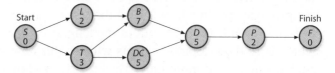

b. What happens to the earliest finish time if it takes 6 days, instead of 5 days, to design the poster (task D)?

c. What happens to the earliest finish time if it takes 9 days, instead of 7 days, to book the band (task B)?

d. A task on a critical path is called a **critical task**. What happens to the earliest finish time if one of the critical tasks takes longer than expected to complete?

e. What happens to the earliest finish time if it takes 6 days, instead of 5 days, to arrange for the decorations (task DC)?

f. Suppose it takes 3 days, instead of 2 days, to choose and reserve a location (task L).

  i. What happens to the EFT?

  ii. What is the critical path?

g. Suppose it takes 6 days, instead of 2 days, to choose and reserve a location (task L).

  i. What happens to the EFT?

  ii. What is the critical path?

h. What can happen to the earliest finish time and the critical path if one of the tasks that is *not on the critical path* takes longer than expected to complete?

Critical Paths, PERT, CPM, and Technology Finding a critical path and the EFT for a project are essential parts of the Program Evaluation and Review Technique (PERT) and the Critical Path Method (CPM). These methods are among the most widely-used mathematical tools in business, industry, and government. Of course, most projects are much larger than the school dance project you have been working on. Computer software is used to help solve large critical path problems. To explore how that might be done, use vertex-edge graph software or project management software to help solve the following problem.

5 $30 + 17 = 47$ days, so work should begin on the project 47 days before the dance. Students should justify their answer by explaining that 17 days is the EFT.

6 **a.** Students' graphs may look slightly different than the graph given here. This is fine as long as the graphs are identical in terms of how the vertices are connected.

> **KEY IDEA** An important point about vertex-edge graphs is that the size and shape of the graph is not essential; what is essential is how the vertices are connected by the edges.

b. The EFT increases by 1 day.

c. The EFT increases by 2 days.

d. The EFT increases by that much.

e. Nothing. The path through *DC* sums to only 16 days.

f. **i.** The EFT still is 17 days.

    ii. There are now two critical paths; *S-L-B-D-P-F* is also a critical path.

g. **i.** The EFT is now 20 days.

    ii. A new critical path is formed: *S-L-B-D-P-F*.

h. Three possibilities can occur when a noncritical task time is increased.

- No new longest path is created; the EFT and critical path are unchanged.

- A new longest path is created; the EFT and critical path change to correspond to the new longest path.

- A path is created that has the same length as the old longest path; the EFT is unchanged, but now there are two critical paths.

Unit 6

7 Suppose a car manufacturer is considering a new fuel-efficient car. Since this new car will cost a lot of money to produce, the company wants to be sure that it is a good idea before they begin production. So, they do a feasibility study. (In a feasibility study, you look at things like estimated cost and consumer demand to see if the idea is practical.) The feasibility study itself is a big project that involves many different tasks. The table below shows tasks, times, and prerequisites for the feasibility study project.

Feasibility Study Project

Task	Task Time	Immediate Prerequisites
Design the Car (A)	7 weeks	none
Plan Market Research (B)	2 weeks	none
Build Prototype Car (C)	10 weeks	A
Prepare Advertising (D)	4 weeks	A
Prepare Initial Cost Estimates (E)	2 weeks	C
Test the Car (F)	5 weeks	C
Finish the Market Research (G)	3.5 weeks	B, D
Prepare Final Cost Estimates (H)	2.5 weeks	E
Prepare Final Report (I)	1 week	F, G, H

a. Generate the feasibility study project digraph. What is a critical path and the EFT for this project?

b. Use the software to experiment with different task times and see the effect on the EFT and critical path. For example:

i. What happens to the EFT if you double all the task times? Explain why this is so.

ii. Modify some task times so that the critical path does not change but the EFT increases. State a general rule for when this will happen.

iii. Modify some task times so that neither the critical path nor the EFT changes. State conditions for when this will happen.

iv. Modify some task times so that the critical path changes, and there is only one critical path.

v. Modify some task times so there is more than one critical path.

vi. *Optional:* Experiment with adding new vertices, times, and edges to the graph. Describe the effects on the EFT and critical path(s).

7

a. Students can find the project digraph, critical path, and EFT with or without technology. However, it is useful to use software, both to solve this particular problem and to gain experience with software solutions since most real-world problems are solved using software. There is one critical path: *Start-A-C-F-I-Finish*. The EFT is 23 weeks.

TECHNOLOGY NOTE In the *Vertex-Edge Graph* Discrete Math software of *CPMP-Tools*, choose the Feasibility Study Digraph in the Sample Graphs, Unit 6 menu. Once loaded, apply the Critical Path algorithm to find a critical path and the EFT. The screen to the right shows the "Automatic" option.

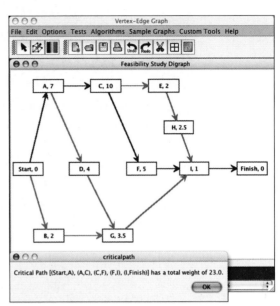

b. i. Doubling all the task times will not change the critical path, but it will double the task times for all the tasks on the critical path. Thus, the critical path is still *Start-A-C-F-I-Finish*, and the EFT is now $23 \times 2 = 46$ weeks.

ii. For example, increase the task time by 2 weeks for a task that is on the critical path. This will result in the same critical path but a new EFT $= 23 + 2 = 25$ weeks. General rule: Any increase in the task time for a task on the critical path will result in the same critical path but an increased EFT.

iii. Conditions: If you change the task time for a task off the critical path by an amount that is less than its "slack time," then neither the critical path nor the EFT change. Since slack time has not explicitly been studied, it is okay if students simply say that a task off the critical path should be increased by an amount that is not too large. You could also increase and decrease task times on the critical path but retain the same EFT.

iv. For example, increase *E* from 2 weeks to 3 weeks. Now the critical path is: *Start-A-C-E-H-I-Finish*, and the new EFT is 23.5 weeks.

v. For example, increase *E* from 2 weeks to 3 weeks, and increase *D* from 4 weeks to 12 weeks. Then there are two critical paths: *Start-A-C-E-H-I-Finish* and *Start-A-D-G-I-Finish*. Both of these paths have length 23.5 weeks; the EFT is 23.5 weeks.

vi. This is an opportunity for students to use the software to explore different "what-if" scenarios.

> **DIFFERENTIATION** You can accommodate some students who proceed through this problem more quickly, or those who particularly enjoy technology, by assigning part vi for them. Students should watch for vertex-edge configurations as shown in Connections Task 12 on page 447.

TECHNOLOGY NOTE In the *Vertex-Edge Graph* Discrete Math software of *CPMP-Tools*, you can edit task time by clicking on the arrow tool, double-clicking on a task, and then typing in a new task time number. You can add new vertices and edges by clicking on the "draw vertices or edges" tool, which is the pencil icon, and then clicking the space where you want a vertex; to create an edge, position the arrow over a vertex until it turns white and then click and drag to the endpoint vertex. The default setting for edge type is "Undirected." To construct a directed graph, choose "Directed" under the Options menu.

Summarize
the Mathematics

In this lesson, you have learned mathematical concepts and methods to help efficiently schedule projects. In particular, you have learned about critical paths and how to find the EFT for a project.

a How can you find the EFT by examining a digraph for a project?

b What is a critical path for a project, and why is it "critical"?

Be prepared to share your ideas with the entire class.

✔ Check Your Understanding

Examine the digraph below.

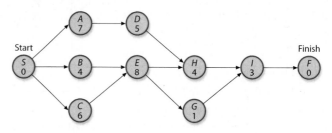

a. How many paths are there through this digraph, from S to F? List all the different paths, and compute the length of each path.

b. Find the critical path and the EFT.

c. Are there any tasks that can have their task times increased by 3 units and yet not cause a change in the EFT for the whole project? If so, which tasks? If not, why not?

It is important that each student can explain why the path which has the longest length gives the shortest amount of time needed to finish the project. You might ask each student to write an explanation, compare explanations with a neighbor, and then discuss as a whole class.

Summarize
the Mathematics

a The EFT is found by locating a path through the digraph that has the longest length.

b It is the critical path which determines the minimum total project time, thus the completion of tasks on time along the critical path is "critical" to the whole project being completed on time. If task times on the critical path are increased, then the critical path and the EFT become longer. Thus, tasks on the critical path are more sensitive to delays, i.e., they are more critical in terms of keeping the whole project on schedule. Also, if you wish to complete a project sooner, tasks along the critical path could be examined for earlier completion times.

INSTRUCTIONAL NOTE At this time, you might show a video segment about critical paths. For example, MATH TV—Management Science from COMAP (the first 10 minutes), or the video from the For All Practical Purposes series (from Annenberg/CPB) that includes critical paths. Either of these videos would provide a nice close to this investigation. (These two videos contain a segment concerning airline scheduling, which relates to the Check Your Understanding in Investigation 1.)

✔ Check Your Understanding

a. There are 5 paths.

Path	Length
S-A-D-H-I-F	19
S-B-E-H-I-F	19
S-B-E-G-I-F	16
S-C-E-H-I-F	21
S-C-E-G-I-F	18

b. The critical path is S-C-E-H-I-F with an EFT of 21 units.

c. The only possibilities would be noncritical tasks: A, B, D, or G. Of these, only G can be increased by 3 and not result in an increase in the EFT. One way to see this is to systematically examine changes that occur in path length to each of the paths listed in Part a. Or, you can see this more graphically by examining G's position opposite H in the graph.

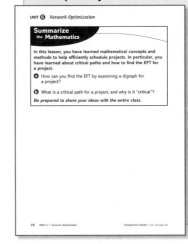

UNIT **6** *Network Optimization*

Summarize
the Mathematics

In this lesson, you have learned mathematical concepts and methods to help efficiently schedule projects. In particular, you have learned about critical paths and how to find the EFT for a project.

a How can you find the EFT by examining a digraph for a project?

b What is a critical path for a project, and why is it "critical"?

Be prepared to share your ideas with the entire class.

POSSIBLE MISCONCEPTION
It is *not* the case that only those tasks on the critical path need to be done. All tasks must be completed.

MATH TOOLKIT Write a summary of our discussion of the STM. Explain why the EFT is not the time for the shortest path through the digraph.

Unit 6

Applications

① Shown below is the immediate prerequisite table for preparing a baseball field.

Preparing a Baseball Field

Task	Task Time	Immediate Prerequisites
Pick up Litter (*L*)	4 hours	none
Clean Dugouts (*D*)	2 hours	*L*
Drag the Infield (*I*)	2 hours	*L*
Mow the Grass (*G*)	3 hours	*L*
Paint the Foul Lines (*P*)	2 hours	*I, G*
Install the Bases (*B*)	1 hour	*P*

a. Find at least two tasks that can be worked on at the same time.

b. Draw a digraph for this project.

c. Mark the critical path.

d. What is the EFT for the whole project? (Assume that you have enough people to work on the project and the task times shown are the times needed, given the people who will be working on the tasks.)

e. Do you think that the task times given in the table are reasonable? Change at least one task time. Use your new time(s) to find a critical path and the EFT.

② Suppose that your school is planning to organize an Earth Day. You will have booths, speakers, and activities related to planet Earth and its environment. Such a project will require careful planning and coordination among many different teams that will be working on it.

Here are six tasks that will need to be done as part of the Earth Day project and estimates for the time to complete each task.

Planning Earth Day

Task	Task Time
Decide on Topics	6 days
Get Speakers	5 days
Choose Date and Location	3 days
Design Booths	2 weeks
Build Booths	1 week
Make Posters	6 days

a. Decide on immediate prerequisites for each of the tasks and construct an immediate prerequisite table.

Applications

1 **a.** Tasks *D*, *I*, and *G* can be worked on at the same time as can *D* and *P* or *D* and *B*.

b.

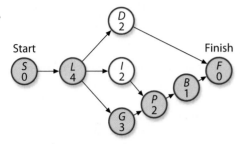

Start   Finish

c. The critical path is shaded in Part b.

Path	Length
S-L-D-F	6
S-L-I-P-B-F	9
S-L-G-P-B-F	10

d. The EFT is 10 hours. (See Extensions Task 19 for a more detailed analysis related to the number of people who are working on the project and on each task.)

e. Responses will vary. For example, you might decide that dragging the infield (task *I*) will take 4 hours instead of 2 hours. In this case, the new critical path is *S-L-I-P-B-F* and the EFT is 11 hours.

2 **a.** Responses may vary. An example is shown below.

Planning Earth Day

Task	Task Time	Immediate Prerequisites
Decide on Topics (*T*)	6 days	DL
Get Speakers (*SP*)	5 days	T
Choose Date and Location (*DL*)	3 days	none
Design Booths (*DB*)	2 weeks	T
Build Booths (*BB*)	1 week	DB
Make Posters (*P*)	6 days	T

b. Draw a project digraph.

c. Find a critical path and the EFT.

③ On a large construction project, there is usually a general contractor (the company that coordinates and supervises the whole project) and smaller contractors (the companies that carry out specific parts of the project, like plumbing or framing).

Suppose that the company responsible for putting in the foundation for a building estimates the times shown in the following prerequisite table. The general contractor wants the foundation done in 13 days. Can the foundation crew meet this schedule? If so, explain. If not, propose a plan for what they should do in order to shorten task times and finish on schedule.

Putting in a Foundation

Task	Task Time	Immediate Prerequisites
Measure the Foundation (A)	1 day	none
Dig Foundation (B)	4 days	A
Erect Forms (C)	6 days	B
Obtain Reinforcing Steel (D)	2 days	A
Assemble Steel (E)	3 days	D
Place Steel in Forms (F)	2 days	C, E
Order Concrete (G)	1 day	A
Pour Concrete (H)	3 days	F, G

④ Shown below is the immediate prerequisite table for building a house. Assume that three specialists are working on each task.

Build a House

Task	Task Time	Immediate Prerequisites
Clear Land (C)	2 days	none
Build Foundation (BF)	3 days	C
Build Upper Structure (U)	15 days	BF
Electrical Work (EL)	9 days	U
Plumbing Work (P)	5 days	U
Complete Exterior Work (EX)	12 days	U
Complete Interior Work (IN)	10 days	EL, P
Landscaping (H)	6 days	EX

a. Find at least two tasks that can be worked on at the same time.

b. Draw the digraph for this project.

c. Mark the critical path.

d. What is the EFT for the project?

e. Suppose that each specialist works 8 hours per day and is paid an average of $20 per hour. What will the total labor costs be?

f. Suppose that some plumbing supplies will be late in arriving, so installing the plumbing will take 10 days. How does this affect the EFT and critical path?

b.

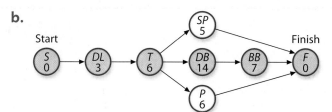

c. The critical path in this example is *S-DL-T-DB-BB-F*. The EFT is 30 days.

3

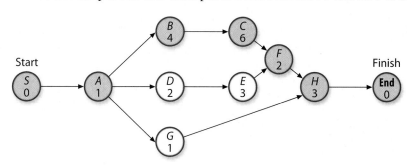

The critical path is *A-B-C-F-H* with an EFT of 16 days.

They cannot meet the 13-day deadline since the EFT is 16 days. There are a variety of ways to shorten the project EFT. For example, you might refine your task-time estimates, or you might shorten task times by hiring more workers, or you might try to relax some of the prerequisite relationships. Probably the most common answer will be to somehow shorten tasks on the critical path. Students should explain how the task times could be shortened, if this is the strategy they choose. Note that shortening tasks off the critical path will not help.

4 **a.** Some tasks that can be worked on at the same time are *EL*, *P*, and *EX*, or *IN* and *L*.

b.

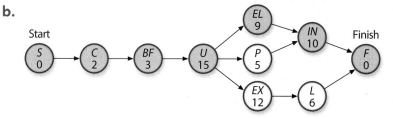

c. The critical path is *S-C-BF-U-EL-IN-F*, shown in the figure above.

d. The EFT is 39 days.

e. 62 total days × 8 hours × 3 workers × \$20 = \$29,760

f. The EFT is now 40 days. The critical path is now *S-C-BF-U-P-IN-F*.

> **INSTRUCTIONAL NOTE**
> The answer to Task 4 Part e may surprise students because here is a case where the critical path is *not* used. Since each task must be completed, all the task times must be totaled.

(5) A prerequisite table for putting on a school play is shown below.

Planning a School Play

Task	Task Time (in days)	Immediate Prerequisites
Choose a Play (*A*)	7	none
Tryouts (*B*)	5	*A*
Select Cast (*C*)	3	*B*
Rehearsals (*D*)	25	*C*
Build Sets and Props (*E*)	20	*A*
Create Advertising (*F*)	4	*C*
Sell Tickets (*G*)	10	*F*
Make/Get Costumes (*H*)	20	*C*
Lighting (*I*)	7	*E*, *H*
Sound and Music (*J*)	9	*E*
Dress Rehearsals (*K*)	5	*D*, *I*, *J*
Opening Night Prep (*L*)	1	*K*

a. You must report to the principal how long it will take before the play is ready to open. What will you report?

b. Suppose that because of a conflict with another special event, you find out that you must complete the project in 6 fewer days than the EFT. In order to meet this new timetable, you decide to shorten the time for some of the tasks.

   i. Describe which tasks you will shorten and how you will shorten them.

   ii. Show how this will result in a new EFT that is 6 days less than the original EFT. (Shortening task times like this is sometimes called **crashing** the task times.)

c. Another way to attempt to shorten the EFT is to figure out a way to change some of the prerequisites. Suppose that you decide to change the prerequisites for setting up the lighting by doing that task whether or not the set and props are built. Thus, task *E* is no longer an immediate prerequisite for task *I*. How much time will this save for the EFT?

d. Describe at least one other reasonable rearrangement of prerequisites to shorten this EFT. By how many days does your rearrangement change the EFT?

(6) Suppose that you and two friends are preparing a big dinner to serve 20 people.

a. List 4–8 tasks that must be done as part of this project.

b. Decide how long each task will reasonably take to complete.

c. Decide on the immediate prerequisites for each task and construct the immediate prerequisite table.

d. Draw the project digraph.

e. Find a critical path and the EFT.

5 **a.** The EFT is 48 days, so it will be 48 days before the play is ready to open. The critical path is *Start-A-B-C-H-I-K-L-Finish*. See the project digraph below.

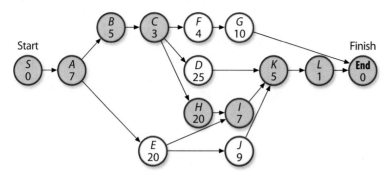

b. Responses will vary. For example, choose the play (task *A*) in 1 day instead of 7 days; this shortens all paths, including critical paths, by 6 days. Or, hire more helpers and cut the time to make costumes (task *H*) by 6 days. However, since this alone will change the critical path, you must also cut the time for rehearsals (task *D*) by at least 4 days.

c. Unfortunately, *E* is not on the critical path, so this option will not shorten the EFT.

d. Responses will vary. For example, make *H* (make/get costumes) an immediate prerequisite for *K* (dress rehearsals) but not for *I* (lighting). Make *I* an immediate prerequisite for *L* (Opening Night Prep) but not for *K*. This eliminates *I* (lighting) from the old critical path. The new critical path is then *Start-A-B-C-D-K-L-Finish* which yields an EFT of 46 days, or a decrease of 2 days.

6 **a–c.** Responses will vary based on students' lists of tasks for each project. Here is an example.

Task	Task Time	Immediate Prerequisites
Buy the Food (*B*)	50 min.	*M*
Select the Menu (*M*)	15 min.	none
Set the Table (*Se*)	15 min.	none
Cook the Food (*C*)	120 min.	*B*
Wash the Dishes (*D*)	30 min.	*E*
Eat (*E*)	60 min.	*C, Se*

d.

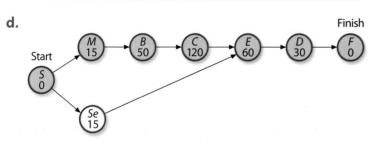

e. The critical path is *S-M-B-C-E-D-F*, which gives an EFT of 275 minutes.

Unit 6

7 Reproduced below is the digraph from the Check Your Understanding task on page 442. The critical path is shown by the red arrows. Verify that the EFT is 21.

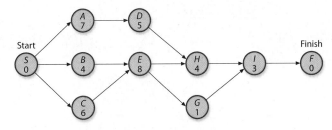

a. How do the critical path and EFT change if:

i. the time for task C decreases by 5?

ii. the time for task C increases by 5?

iii. the time for task D increases by 2?

iv. the time for task D increases by 3?

v. the time for task D decreases by 4?

b. Write a summary describing how changes in times for tasks on and off the critical path affect the EFT and the critical path.

c. Construct the immediate prerequisite table for the project digraph.

8 It is possible for a project digraph to have more than one critical path. Consider a modified version of the school dance project digraph shown below.

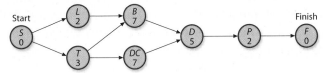

a. Find the EFT for the project.

b. How many critical paths are there?

c. List all the critical tasks.

9 Shown below is a modified version of the project digraph from the Check Your Understanding task on page 442.

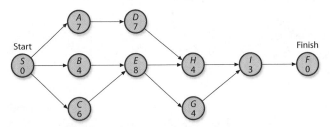

a. Find the EFT for the project.

7 **a.** **i.** Decreasing C by 5 changes the length of S-C-E-H-I-F to 16, and it is no longer the critical (longest) path. New critical paths are S-A-D-H-I-F and S-B-E-H-I-F. The new EFT is 19.

    ii. Increasing C by 5 gives the same critical path but an EFT of 26 units.

    iii. Increasing D by 2 gives the same EFT of 21 units, but now there is a new critical path S-A-D-H-I-F.

    iv. Increasing D by 3 gives a new critical path S-A-D-H-I-F with a new EFT of 22 units.

    v. Decreasing D by 4 gives the same original critical path with the same original EFT of 21 units.

  b. An increase of task times on the critical path keeps the critical path the same but increases the EFT. A decrease of task times on the critical path may result in a different critical path with a new EFT or simply a lower EFT on the same critical path. An increase of task times off the critical path may result in a new critical path with a new (or the same) EFT, or it may cause no change in critical path or EFT. A decrease of task times off the critical path does not change the critical path or the EFT.

  c.

Task	Task Time	Immediate Prerequisites
A	7	none
B	4	none
C	6	none
D	5	A
E	8	B, C
G	4	D, E
H	1	E
I	3	H, G

8 **a.** The EFT is 17 days.

  b. There are two critical paths. That is, there are two paths from S to F that have the maximum length of 17 days.

  c. The two critical paths are S-T-DC-D-P-F and S-T-B-D-P-F. The critical tasks are all tasks on critical paths (not including the "dummy" vertices S and F): T, B, DC, D, P.

9 **a.** The EFT is 21.

b. How many critical paths are there?

c. List all the critical tasks.

Connections

(10) The adjacency matrix for a graph can be used to enter the graph into a computer. You also can get information about the graph and the project just by looking at the adjacency matrix. Consider the digraph below.

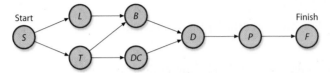

a. Construct the adjacency matrix for the digraph with vertices *L, T, B, DC, D,* and *P.*

b. Add up all the numbers in row *B*. What does this sum mean in terms of prerequisites?

c. Add up all the numbers in column *B*. What does this sum mean in terms of prerequisites?

d. What does a row of all zeroes mean in terms of prerequisites?

e. What does a column of all zeroes mean in terms of prerequisites?

(11) The **indegree** of a vertex in a digraph is the number of arrows coming into it. The **outdegree** is the number of arrows going out of it. Consider the digraph above in Connections Task 10.

a. What are the indegree and outdegree of *B*?

b. What is the outdegree of *T*?

c. Ignoring *S* and *F*, what is the indegree of *T*? The outdegree of *P*?

d. What do indegree and outdegree mean in terms of prerequisites?

e. How can you compute indegree and outdegree by looking at the rows and columns of the adjacency matrix for a digraph?

(12) Explain why the digraphs below could *not* be used to model a simple project.

a.
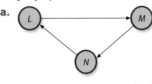

b.
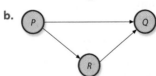

c. Are there any four-vertex configurations that can never occur in a project digraph? Explain and illustrate your answer.

LESSON 2 • Scheduling Projects Using Critical Paths **447**

b. There are three critical paths:

S-A-D-H-I-F

S-C-E-H-I-F

S-C-E-G-I-F

c. The critical tasks are all tasks except *B*.

Connections

10 **a.**

	L	T	B	DC	D	P
L	0	0	1	0	0	0
T	0	0	1	1	0	0
B	0	0	0	0	1	0
DC	0	0	0	0	1	0
D	0	0	0	0	0	1
P	0	0	0	0	0	0

b. The sum of row *B* is 1; this means *B* is an immediate prerequisite for 1 task.

c. The sum of column *B* is 2; this means *B* has 2 immediate prerequisite tasks.

d. The task of that row is not an immediate prerequisite for any other task. It is a task just before *Finish*.

e. The task of that column has no prerequisite tasks. It is a task just after *Start*.

11 **a.** The indegree of *B* is 2; the outdegree of *B* is 1.

b. The outdegree of *T* is 2.

c. The indegree of *T* is 0; the outdegree of *P* is 0.

d. The indegree is the number of immediate prerequisites a task has. The outdegree is the number of tasks for which the given task is an immediate prerequisite.

e. The indegree is the column sum; the outdegree is the row sum.

12 **a.** Every task (vertex) is a successor and prerequisite of every other task, which is impossible. Another way to say this is that the diagram implies that two tasks are prerequisites of each other (although not immediate prerequisites), which is impossible.

b. The arrow from *P* to *Q* implies that *P* is an immediate prerequisite of *Q*. However, the path from *P* through *R* to *Q* implies that *P* is not an immediate prerequisite of *Q* (since *R* is between *Q* and *P*). So, *P* is and *is not* an immediate prerequisite of *Q*. This is a contradiction.

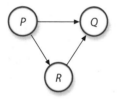

c.

This configuration is similar to that in Part a. Every vertex is a successor and prerequisite of every other vertex, which is impossible.

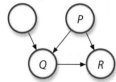

This configuration contains a configuration similar to that in Part b. Thus, as in Part b, it cannot be a project digraph.

13 Interview some adults in business or government who use PERT or the Critical Path Method to manage projects. Based on what you find out, describe one or two recent real-world examples of how critical paths are used to schedule projects.

Reflections

14 The title of this unit is *Network Optimization*. Optimize means find the best. The "best" may be different in different situations.

   a. Give an example in which the shortest path is not the best path.

   b. Explain why the best solution method for a small graph may not be the best solution method for a large graph. Give an example. (You may choose an example from this lesson or from Lesson 1.)

15 Initially, did you find something particularly difficult or confusing in finding critical paths and EFTs for projects? If so, how would you explain that idea to a friend to help her or him avoid the confusion?

16 The weighted graphs in Lesson 1 are sometimes called *edge-weighted graphs*. Explain why the project digraphs you worked with in Investigation 2 of Lesson 2 could be called *vertex-weighted graphs*.

17 What are similarities and differences among critical paths, Hamilton paths (Connections Task 12, page 425), and Euler paths?

Extensions

18 A leading contemporary researcher in discrete mathematics is Fan Chung Graham, a mathematician who earned her doctorate in 1974 and has worked at Bell Labs, Harvard University, the University of Pennsylvania, and the University of California at San Diego. Although some of the problems that Fan Chung works on look like games, they often have important applications in areas like communication networks and design of computer hardware and software. This task is an example of such a problem.

Fan Chung Graham

   In the following graph, suppose a person is standing at each vertex. The first letter of each vertex label is the name of the vertex; the second letter is the destination that each person must reach by walking along edges of the graph. The goal is for all of the people

13 Responses may vary with individual student reports.

Since critical path analysis is so widely used, this is a great opportunity for students to see the application of mathematics they are studying in the lives of adults they know. (It is also an opportunity for you to find guest speakers to come in and talk to your class.) Many companies use critical paths, that is, the Critical Path Method (CPM) or PERT charts, to organize and keep their projects on schedule. In fact, there are widely used commercial software packages, like *Microsoft Project*, that are used to construct critical paths. Consultant firms that design productivity plans and optimization plans for companies routinely recommend critical path analysis. One of the most common examples is the construction industry. On most large construction sites, you will find a critical path chart, or a modified version called a Gantt chart, on the wall of the general contractor's trailer. Another interesting example is the development of new calculators at Texas Instruments. During the development of the *Core-Plus Mathematics* curriculum, TI was developing one of its new graphing calculators. Upon seeing the *Core-Plus Mathematics* lesson on critical paths, one TI executive commented that they had an 8-foot critical path chart for the calculator project posted on the wall at their Texas headquarters. That chart was not used as a photo in the *Core-Plus Mathematics* materials because of the secrecy of the project at that time.

Reflections

14 **a.** There are many examples that students may give. The best path for a walk home with your best friend might be the longest path possible. The best path for an informative but not boring tour through a museum is neither the longest or shortest path. Also, a key example is a critical path, which is a best path and also a longest path.

   b. For a small graph, you might use the brute-force method or just "inspection" to find a solution. However, for large graphs, neither of these methods is likely to be effective. A key example is the TSP in which a brute-force method may work well as a solution method for very small graphs but is impractical for large graphs.

15 Student responses will vary. They may state that the idea of the *longest* path giving the *shortest* completion time was initially confusing to them. Or perhaps they had the initial misconception that once a critical path is found, only those tasks need to be done.

16 The project digraphs in this lesson could be called vertex-weighted graphs because there are weights (numbers) on the vertices in contrast to the graphs in Lesson 1 which had weights on the edges.

17 An overall similarity among critical paths, Hamilton paths, and Euler paths is that these are all optimum paths. They differ in that the criterion for "optimum" is different in each case—longest, visit all vertices exactly once, trace all edges exactly once, respectively. Critical paths also differ from Hamilton and Euler paths in this unit in that critical paths are based on directed graphs. (However, Hamilton paths and Euler paths can also be studied in directed graphs.)

to walk to their destinations without overusing any edge. By trying to solve a problem like this, you can find out how accessible a network is—that is, if it has any "bottlenecks" where there is excessive traffic.

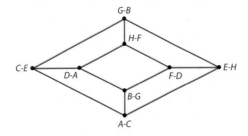

a. Assume that an edge is "overused" if it is used more than twice. Find routes for all walkers so that everyone reaches his or her destination but no edge is overused.

b. Are other routes possible? Describe the strategy you used to find the routes.

c. State and try to solve at least one other problem related to this situation.

 In an immediate prerequisite table, the task times given are the times needed to complete each task using the expected available resources. You might need to figure out what resources are needed (like how many workers are needed) so that you can maintain the task times. Or, if the available resources change, then the task times could change. You will explore such situations in this problem.

Reproduced below is the immediate prerequisite table for the project of preparing a baseball field for play from Applications Task 1. In that problem, you assumed that there are plenty of people to work on the project and that the task times shown are the times needed given the people who will be working on each task. In this problem, suppose the task times shown are how long it takes to complete each task when one person works on the task.

Preparing a Baseball Field

Task	Task Time	Immediate Prerequisites
Pick up Litter (L)	4 hours	none
Clean Dugouts (D)	2 hours	L
Drag the Infield (I)	2 hours	L
Mow the Grass (G)	3 hours	L
Paint the Foul Lines (P)	2 hours	I, G
Install the Bases (B)	1 hour	P

a. Suppose only one person will work on any given task, and you have plenty of people available to work on the whole project. In this situation, what is the EFT for the project?

Extensions

 18 a. There is more than one solution. In the solution below, the path used for each vertex label is shown. Recall that vertex labels include the vertex name and the destination vertex name. For example, label *B-G* means that the person at vertex *B*, which is the bottom vertex of the inside diamond, must walk to vertex *G*, which is the top-most vertex of the graph. A path for doing so is shown by listing the vertices in the path, for example, *B–D–C–G*.

> *A-C: A–C*
>
> *C-E: C–G–E*
>
> *E-H: E–F–H*
>
> *H-F: H–F*
>
> *F-D: F–B–D*
>
> *D-A: D–C–A*
>
> *B-G: B–D–C–G*
>
> *G-B: G–E–F–B*

b. Students should describe the strategy they used to find the routes in Part a. The descriptions could be specific algorithms, or they could be a statement of general guidelines. The more detailed the description, the better. Sample responses are given below.

- Trial and error

- Always taking the shortest path, start with some vertex and go to its destination; then proceed from that vertex to its destination. Continue in this way until you cannot proceed further. Then start with a new vertex and repeat the process. Continue until all people at all vertices have moved to their destination.

- Order the vertices in some manner, say alphabetically, and try to find paths for each vertex in the order in which it appears in the list.

- Whenever you have a choice, always choose a path that does not use an edge twice. That is, traverse an edge for the second time only as a last resort.

c. Some related problems are the following.

- What is the fewest number of repeated edges that must be used?

- Can you find routes if each edge can only be used once?

 19 a. The task times assume that one person is working on each task; and in this part of the problem, one person is indeed working on each task. Additionally, there are plenty of people available. So, to solve the problem, you simply find a critical path in the project digraph using the data directly from the table. The critical path is *S-L-G-P-B-F*, and the EFT is 10 hours. (Note that this is the same solution as in Applications Task 1.)

Unit 6

b. Suppose again that only one person will work on any given task. Each person can work on as many tasks as needed. In order to finish by the EFT in Part a, what is the fewest number of people needed to work on the project?

c. Suppose you have to complete the whole project by yourself. What is the EFT in this situation?

d. Suppose you and one friend are hired to prepare the field. You and your friend decide that you might work together or separately to complete any task. If you work together for an entire task, you can reduce the task time by half from that shown in the immediate prerequisite table. The only task that must be done by someone working alone is mowing the grass, since there is only one mower. How would you assign duties in order to complete the project in the least amount of time?

20 In this lesson, you have found critical paths in many different digraphs. In this task, you will explore several methods that might be used to try to find a critical path.

a. Recall the nearest-neighbor algorithm that you tried for minimum spanning trees in Lesson 1, on page 404. When using that algorithm, you move from vertex to vertex always choosing the "nearest-neighbor" vertex, with the goal of finding an overall *shortest* network. Although this type of algorithm has some appeal, it did not work for finding a minimum spanning tree. In the case of a critical path, you want a *longest* path. Thus, modify the nearest-neighbor algorithm so that it is a "farthest-neighbor" algorithm. Apply this algorithm to the project digraph in the Check Your Understanding task on page 442. Does it work to find a critical path?

b. Think about a method for finding the EFT for the whole project by starting at the Start vertex and working forward, finding the EFT for each task, until you reach the Finish vertex. Then once you have the task EFTs, work backwards to find a critical path. Try out this method and provide a more detailed description.

c. If you tried a method other than those in Parts a and b to find a critical path, write a step-by-step description of your method for how to find a critical path. Test your algorithm using several digraphs. Modify as needed based on your test results. You might use vertex-edge graph software or project management software to help test your algorithm.

b. Two is the fewest number of people needed to finish by the EFT of 10 hours. It may at first seem that three people are needed, so that tasks *D*, *I*, and *G* can all be worked on at the same time. However, that is not required to finish by the EFT. For example, Billie could do all the tasks on the critical path. It will take her 10 hours to complete all these tasks. As soon as she finishes task *L*, Marshall can begin work on tasks *D* and *I*, and Marshall will be done before Billie finishes all her tasks. This work arrangement will get all tasks done by the EFT of 10 hours.

c. If you are working by yourself, then you must do every task. Thus, the EFT is the total of all the task times, which is 14 hours.

d. We know from Part b that you and your friend can complete the project by the EFT of 10 hours if you work separately on every task. One way to work together under the conditions stated in the problem is the following: work together on *L* (2 hours); you work on *G* while your friend works on *D* and then *I* (3 hours); you join your friend for the last hour of *I* (0.5 hours); work together on *P* and *B* (1.5 hours). *Total time* = 7 hours

20 a. When this "farthest-neighbor" algorithm is applied in this case, you get the path *Start-A-D-H-I-Finish*. This path is *not* a critical (longest) path. Thus, this algorithm does not work in general to find a critical path.

b. A more detailed description could be the following:

Step I: Begin at the *Start* vertex.

Step II: Work forward and find the EFT for each vertex. Label each vertex with its EFT. To find the EFT for a vertex, use this formula: *(EFT for V)* = *(weight of V)* + *maximum of all the EFTs for all the immediate prerequisite vertices*

Step III: When you reach the Finish vertex, its label will be the EFT for the whole project.

Step IV: To find a critical path, start at the Finish vertex and move backwards, at each step choosing a vertex with EFT based on this formula: *(EFT for next vertex back)* = *(EFT of present vertex)* − *(weight of present vertex)*.

If you apply this to the project digraph in the Check Your Understanding task on page 442, you get the following EFTs for each task: *S*-0, *A*-7, *B*-4, *C*-6, *D*-12, *E*-14, *H*-18, *G*-15, *I*-21, *F*-21. Thus, the EFT for the whole project is the EFT for the *Finish* task *F*, which is 21. Working backwards from *F* using the procedure in Step IV above yields *F-I-H-E-C-S*. This is the critical path.

c. Students should consider how they went about finding a critical (longest) path. For example, as a very general strategy, they might have worked forward or worked backward. Or, very roughly and visually, they could have been keeping track of all vertically aligned tasks since these are the tasks that can be done concurrently. Students could experiment with the *Vertex-Edge Graph* Critical Path tool in the Discrete Math software of *CPMP-Tools* to help them devise and test an algorithm.

21 Besides finding the earliest finish time (EFT) for the whole project, it is often useful to find the EFT for each task. To see how to do this, consider the simple project digraph below.

a. The EFT for a given task is the least amount of time required to finish that task. Keep in mind that in order to finish the task, all of its prerequisites must be finished as well.

   i. What is the least amount of time needed to finish task *A*?

   ii. What is the least amount of time needed to finish task *C*?

   iii. Find the EFT for the rest of the tasks in this project.

b. Make a copy of the project digraph. Write the EFT for each task just above the vertex representing the task.

c. How does the EFT for the last task compare to the EFT for the whole project?

d. Describe the method you used to figure out the task EFTs.

Review

22 Solve each equation by reasoning with the symbols themselves.

a. $x^2 - 7x = 44$

b. $x(x + 8) = -6$

c. $\dfrac{12}{x} = x + 1$

d. $(x + 3)(x + 4) = 20$

23 Triangle *ABC* has vertices $A(-2, 3)$, $B(1, 7)$, and $C(2, 0)$.

a. What type of triangle is $\triangle ABC$? Be as specific as you can.

b. Draw $\triangle ABC$ and its reflection image across the *x*-axis. Label the coordinates of the image. What type of triangle is the image? Why?

c. Draw $\triangle ABC$ and its image after a 90° clockwise rotation about the origin. Label the coordinates of the image. What type of triangle is the image? Why?

24 Rewrite each radical expression in simplest form.

a. $\sqrt{24}$

b. $\sqrt{350}$

c. $\sqrt{\dfrac{80}{36}}$

d. $\dfrac{\sqrt{45}}{6}$

e. $\sqrt{6}\sqrt{72}$

f. $\sqrt{36 + 100}$

21 **a.** **i.** A: 3 units of time **ii.** C: 12 units of time **iii.** B: 9 units of time
D: 19 units of time

b.

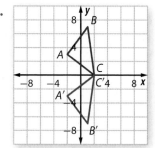

c. The EFT for task D is the EFT for the whole project. (Note that F is a "dummy" task.)

d. INSTRUCTIONAL NOTE Students should be encouraged to carefully describe their method for determining the EFT. Devising and describing step-by-step solution procedures or algorithms is an important part of solving many types of problems in mathematics—particularly in discrete mathematics. Sometimes this process of solving problems is called *algorithmic problem solving*. It is an important theme that should be highlighted throughout the curriculum.

One way to think about the EFT for a task is that it is the task time plus all the time needed to get all the prerequisites done. In terms of paths, the EFT for a task is the longest path to, and including, the task. More formally, the EFT for a task can be found using the following formula: *(EFT for V) = (weight of V) + maximum of all the EFTs for all the immediate prerequisite vertices.*

Review

22 **a.** $x = -4$ or $x = 11$ **b.** $x = -4 \pm \sqrt{10}$ **c.** $x = -4$ or $x = 3$ **d.** $x = -8$ or $x = 1$

23 **a.** Triangle ABC is an isosceles right triangle with right angle A.

b.

Triangle $A'B'C'$ is an isosceles right triangle since lengths are preserved under a line reflection.

$$\triangle A'B'C' = \begin{bmatrix} -2 & 1 & 2 \\ -3 & -7 & 0 \end{bmatrix}$$

c.

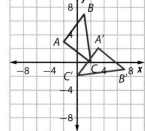

Triangle $A'B'C'$ is an isosceles right triangle since lengths are preserved under a rotation

$$\triangle A'B'C' = \begin{bmatrix} 3 & 7 & 0 \\ 2 & -1 & -2 \end{bmatrix}$$

24 **a.** $2\sqrt{6}$ **b.** $5\sqrt{14}$ **c.** $\dfrac{2\sqrt{5}}{3}$

d. $\dfrac{\sqrt{5}}{2}$ **e.** $12\sqrt{3}$ **f.** $2\sqrt{34}$

25 Find the values for x and y in the triangles below.

a.

b.

c.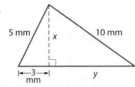

d.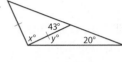

26 Would you expect each pair of variables below to have a positive, negative, or no correlation? Explain your reasoning.

a. The number of minutes that Grant has been running and the distance he has left to run if he plans on running three miles

b. The age of a person and the last digit of his or her zip code

c. The length of the grass on a baseball field during the summer and the number of days since it was last mowed

d. The number of phones in a house and the number of people living in the house

Just in Time

25
a. $x = 52°$; $y = 76°$

b. $x = \sqrt{72} = 6\sqrt{2}$; $y = 45°$

c. $x = 4$; $y = \sqrt{84} = 2\sqrt{21}$

d. $x = 94°$; $y = 23°$

26
a. These variables will have a negative correlation. It will be negative since the distance Grant has left to run will decrease and time increases.

b. These variables will have no correlation. This is because there is no relationship between a person's age and his or her zip code.

c. These variables will have a positive correlation since the more time that has passed since the grass has been mowed, the longer the grass will be.

d. These variables will have a positive correlation. This is because of the extensive personal cell-phone use.

Teaching Resources

Assessment Masters 23–28.

Unit 6

Looking Back

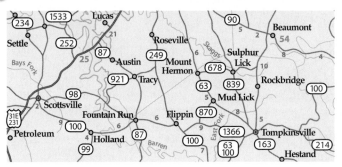

In this unit, you used vertex-edge graphs to optimize a variety of networks. For example, you used minimum spanning trees to optimize computer networks and road networks; you used Hamilton circuits and solutions to the TSP to optimize travel networks; and you used critical paths to find the optimum (earliest) finish time for large projects. Tasks in this final lesson will help you pull together and review what you have learned.

1 Consider the map below of a region in Kentucky.

Map © 1997 by Rand McNally, R.L. 97-S-79

a. State a problem related to this map that could be solved by finding a minimum spanning tree. Then describe how you would go about solving the problem.

b. State a problem related to this map that could be solved by finding a solution to an instance of the TSP. Describe how you would go about solving the problem.

Looking Back

In this lesson, students pull together and review what they have learned throughout the unit.

1. **a.** Student responses may vary. Here is one possible problem that involves finding a minimum spanning tree: since snowstorms are uncommon in Kentucky, the transportation departments do not have a lot of snowplows standing by. So when it does snow, they need to have an efficient plan for plowing the roads. Suppose the goal is to plow just enough roads so that there is a way to get from every town to every other town on plowed roads. What is the minimum number of miles that must be plowed in order to achieve this goal? This question could be answered by finding the minimum spanning tree using Kruskal's best-edge algorithm.

   b. Student responses may vary. Here is one possible problem that involves finding a solution to the TSP: suppose a truck driver must visit each town in the region to deliver packages, beginning and ending at Tompkinsville. What is the minimum number of miles the driver would have to drive? To find a solution, you could solve the TSP in this context. You could do this by finding all the circuits that start and end at Tompkinsville and visit each town exactly once. That is, find all the Hamilton circuits. Then compute the distances for each circuit and select the smallest distance. (In practice, some algorithm would be used to give an approximate solution.)

Suppose that you are the editor for a school newspaper. Study the following background information about the publishing process.

It takes 10 days for the reporters to research all the news stories. It takes 12 days for other students, working at the same time as the reporters, to arrange for the advertising. The photographers need 8 days to get all the photos. However, they cannot start taking photos until the research and the advertising arrangements are complete. The reporters need 15 days to write the stories after they have done the research. They can write while the photographers are getting photos. It takes 5 days to edit everything after the stories and the photos are done. Then it takes another 4 days to lay out the newspaper and 2 more days for printing.

Write a report to your teacher-advisor explaining how long it will take to turn out the next edition of the paper. State which steps of the publishing process will need to be monitored most closely. Include diagrams and complete explanations in your report.

 You have used vertex-edge graphs to model a variety of situations. You can also use vertex-edge graphs to represent and analyze relationships among the new concepts that you are learning. This is done using a type of graph called a *concept map*. In a concept map, the vertices represent ideas or concepts, and edges illustrate how the concepts are connected. The edges may or may not have labels. The first step in building a concept map for some area of study is to list all the concepts you can think of. Here is the beginning of such a list for this unit on network optimization:

- network

- spanning tree

- minimum spanning tree

- algorithms

- best-edge algorithm

a. Add to this list. Include all the concepts from this unit that you can recall.

2 Students should use a digraph model to find a critical path, the critical tasks, and the EFT. If they spend too much time working on the problem without using a vertex-edge graph model, direct them to use what they have learned from this lesson and think about how to use a graph model.

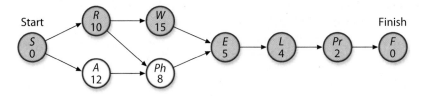

Task	Number of Days	Immediate Prerequisites
Research News (R)	10	none
Advertise (A)	12	none
Collect Photos (Ph)	8	R, A
Write Stories (W)	15	R
Edit Stories (E)	5	W, Ph
Layout Paper (L)	4	E
Print Paper (Pr)	2	L

EFT = 36 days

The tasks that should be carefully monitored are those on the critical path: R, W, E, L, and Pr.

3   a. Monitor the list of concepts and topics that the students generate and be prepared to augment their lists as needed from the list below. If your students studied Prim's algorithm in Extensions Task 20 in Lesson 1, then that topic could also be added to the list.

network (or vertex-edge graph)	distance matrices
spanning tree	algorithm
minimum spanning tree	nearest-neighbor algorithm
Kruskal's best-edge algorithm	brute-force method
Hamilton circuit	TSP
scheduling with prerequisites	digraph
circuit	critical path
earliest finish time	critical tasks

Teaching Resources

Student Master 29.

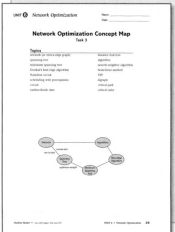

Unit 6

The next step in building a concept map is to let the concepts in the list be the vertices of a graph, and then draw edges between vertices to show connections between concepts. The edges should be labeled to show *how* the vertex concepts are connected. There are many different concept maps that can be drawn. The beginning of one concept map for this unit is drawn below.

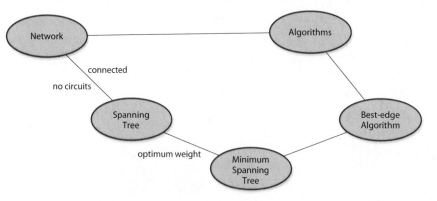

b. Interpret the sample concept map above.

  i. Why is there an edge between network and spanning tree?

  ii. There are two labels on the edge between network and spanning tree. Explain both of those labels. What other label could be put on this edge?

  iii. Why is there an edge between best-edge algorithm and minimum spanning tree? Put an appropriate label on this edge.

c. Complete the concept map by adding all the concepts (vertices) that you listed in Part a along with appropriate edges and labels that show connections among the concepts.

d. Compare your concept map with those of other classmates. Discuss similarities and differences.

b. **i.** A spanning tree is one type of network.

 ii. A tree is a connected graph (network) with no circuits. So by putting the labels "connected" and "no circuits," you are showing how a tree is a special type of network that has these two characteristics. You could also add a label that says "spanning" or "reaches all vertices."

 iii. It makes sense to have an edge between these two vertices in the concept map because Kruskal's best-edge algorithm can be applied to find a minimum spanning tree. You could put a label on this edge that says "Kruskal's" to show that this is a particular type of best-edge algorithm that works to find a minimum spanning tree.

c. A possible concept map is shown below.

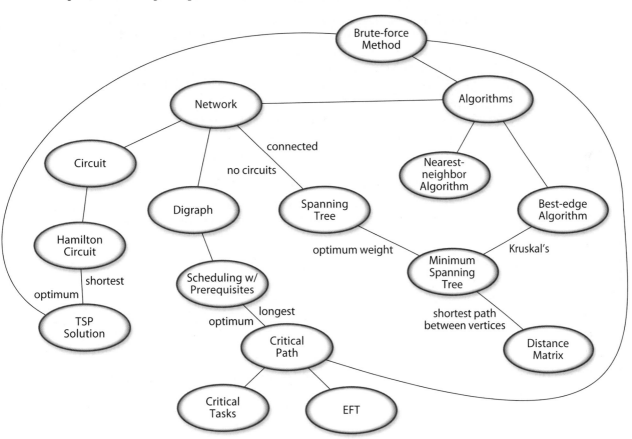

d. Comparing and discussing concept maps will help review and solidify students' understanding of key concepts and methods in this unit.

Summarize
the Mathematics

In this unit, you have studied important concepts and methods related to network optimization.

a Optimization or "finding the best" is an important theme throughout this unit. Describe three problem situations from the unit in which you "found the best." In each case, explain how you used a vertex-edge graph to solve the problem.

b The major topics you studied are minimum spanning trees, the TSP, and critical paths. For each topic, briefly describe what it is and what kinds of problems it can be applied to.

c You examined a variety of algorithms and methods for solving network optimization problems, including best-edge algorithms and brute-force methods. For each of these two solution procedures:

   i. describe the basic strategy,

   ii. give examples of problems that can be solved using the procedure, and

   iii. list some advantages and disadvantages of the procedure.

Be prepared to share your examples and descriptions with the entire class.

✔ Check Your Understanding

Write, in outline form, a summary of the important mathematical concepts and methods developed in this unit. Organize your summary so that it can be used as a quick reference in future units and courses.

Summarize
the Mathematics

(a) Some examples: (1) Find the best by finding the minimum amount of cable needed in a computer network using a minimum spanning tree. (2) Find the best by finding a route that visits each city exactly once with the least airfare costs using the brute-force method. (3) Find the best by finding the earliest finish time for a project consisting of many tasks such as those for preparing a baseball field by using a project digraph and critical paths.

(b) A minimum spanning tree is a tree in a graph that reaches all the vertices and has minimum total weight. Minimum spanning trees apply to problems in which you want to find an optimum network that includes all vertices and does not have any circuits. The TSP is the problem of finding a circuit through a weighted graph that visits each vertex exactly once and has minimum total weight. This problem applies to many network problems in which the goal is to find an optimum circuit that uses each vertex exactly once. A critical path is a longest path through a project digraph. Critical paths are used to find the earliest finish time (EFT) for a project and identify the critical tasks.

(c) **i–iii.** Best-edge algorithms are algorithms in which you choose the "best" (e.g., shortest, longest, cheapest) edge at each step. This "local" step-by-step optimization sometimes results in the overall optimum but not always. These are generally efficient algorithms, but they do not always work. For example, Kruskal's best-edge algorithm works to find a minimum spanning tree, but a similar best-edge algorithm does not work to solve the TSP.

The brute-force method involves finding and checking all possibilities and then choosing the best. This strategy was applied to all three major topics—minimum spanning trees, the TSP, and critical paths. This method works but is very inefficient and impractical for most large problems.

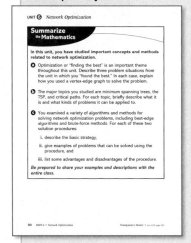

Transparency Master 30.

Student Masters 31–32, 56–57.

Assessment Masters 33–55.

✔ *Check Your Understanding*

You may wish to have students use the Teaching Master, *Network Optimization Unit Summary*, to help them organize the information. Above all, this should be something that is useful to the individual student.

Practicing for Standardized Tests

Each Practicing for Standardized Tests master presents 10 questions in the multiple-choice format of test items similar to how they often appear in standardized tests. Answers are provided below.

Answers to Practice Set 6

1. (b)   **2.** (c)   **3.** (b)   **4.** (c)   **5.** (c)
6. (c)   **7.** (c)   **8.** (a)   **9.** (e)   **10.** (c)

Unit 6

UNIT 7

TRIGONOMETRIC METHODS

Trigonometry, or triangle measure, is an important tool used by surveyors, navigators, engineers, builders, astronomers, and other scientists. Triangulation and trigonometry provide methods to indirectly determine otherwise inaccessible distances and angle measures. The same tools are useful in the design and analysis of mechanisms involving triangles in which the lengths of two sides of a triangle are fixed while the length of the third side is allowed to vary.

Through your work on the investigations in this unit, you will develop the understanding and skill needed to solve problems using trigonometric methods. Key ideas will be developed in two lessons.

Lessons

1 Trigonometric Functions

Use angles in standard position in a coordinate plane to define the trigonometric functions sine, cosine, and tangent. Interpret and apply those functions in the case of situations modeled with right triangles.

2 Using Trigonometry in Any Triangle

Develop the Law of Sines and the Law of Cosines, and use those relationships to find measures of sides and angles in triangles. Solve equations involving several variables for one of the variables in terms of the others.

TRIGONOMETRIC METHODS

Unit Overview

Trigonometry or "the measure of triangles" is an important and useful area of mathematics that naturally connects concepts and methods of geometry and algebra. *Trigonometric Methods* builds on the Course 1 geometry unit, *Patterns in Shape,* and the Course 2 unit, *Coordinate Methods.* In Course 1, students explored the rigidity of triangles and minimal conditions that are sufficient to completely determine a triangle's size and shape. Once a triangle is completely determined, a next logical question is "How can the measures of the triangle's unknown, but rigidly determined, sides and angles be calculated?". Trigonometry provides those methods, namely, trigonometric ratios for right triangles and the Law of Sines and Law of Cosines for any triangle. Interestingly, when angles are extended to include directed angles of rotation, powerful connections between trigonometric ratios and circular motion become evident. Trigonometric methods are extraordinarily useful for solving applied problems in land surveying, engineering, and various applied sciences and for designing and analyzing mechanisms whose function is based on either triangles or circles and their properties. Additionally, the trigonometric ratios, when viewed as functions of the measures of angles in standard position, have many mathematically interesting properties.

This unit builds on coordinate representations of geometric ideas developed in the *Coordinate Methods* unit in Course 2. The combined geometric and algebraic perspective of that unit is useful in defining the trigonometric ratios in terms of angles in standard position in a coordinate plane. Coordinates bring algebraic variables into the trigonometric ratios in a natural way, while the size transformation of right triangles is the key to viewing the trigonometric ratios as functions of angle measures. The focus in *Trigonometric Methods* is on acute, right, and obtuse angles of triangles. In later units when the perspective shifts to the algebraic study of the trigonometric functions over the domain of real numbers, the trigonometric functions will be extended beyond the domain of 0° to 360°.

Key Geometric Ideas—This unit builds on important geometric concepts and relationships developed in the previous *Core-Plus Mathematics* geometry units. These concepts and relationships are listed on pages T457A and T457B. Students should have the student activity master from Unit 3 that they augmented with Unit 3 concepts and relationships.

Definitions

Isosceles triangle A triangle with at least two sides of equal length

Parallelogram A quadrilateral with opposite sides of equal length

Rectangle A quadrilateral with four right angles

Kite A convex quadrilateral with two distinct pairs of consecutive sides the same length

Rhombus A quadrilateral with all four sides the same length

Congruent figures Figures that have the same shape and size, regardless of position or orientation

Perpendicular bisector of a segment A line that is perpendicular to a segment and contains its midpoint

Midpoint of a segment The point on the segment that is the same distance from each endpoint

Slope of a segment The slope of a segment that contains two points with coordinates (x_1, y_1) and (x_2, y_2) is $\frac{y_2 - y_1}{x_2 - x_1}$.

Size transformation of magnitude k A size transformation of magnitude k is defined by the rule $(x, y) \rightarrow (kx, ky)$.

Rotation A turning motion determined by a point called the center of rotation and a directed angle of rotation

Relationships

Pythagorean Theorem If the lengths of the sides of a right triangle are a, b, c, with the side of length c opposite the right angle, then $a^2 + b^2 = c^2$.

Converse of the Pythagorean Theorem If the sum of the squares of the lengths of two sides of a triangle equals the square of the length of the third side, then the triangle is a right triangle.

Triangle Inequality The sum of the lengths of any two sides of a triangle is always greater than the length of the third side.

Triangle Angle Sum Property The sum of the measures of the angles in a triangle is 180°.

Quadrilateral Angle Sum Property The sum of the measures of the angles in a quadrilateral is 360°.

Polygon Angle Sum Property The sum of the measures of the interior angles of a polygon with n sides is $(n - 2)180°$.

Base Angles of Isosceles Triangle Angles opposite congruent sides of an isosceles triangle are congruent.

Side-Side-Side (SSS) congruence condition If three sides of a triangle are congruent to the corresponding sides of another triangle, then the two triangles are congruent.

Side-Angle-Side (SAS) congruence condition If two sides and the angle between the sides of one triangle are congruent to the corresponding parts of another triangle, then the two triangles are congruent.

Angle-Side-Angle (ASA) congruence condition If two angles and the side between the angles of one triangle are congruent to the corresponding parts of another triangle, then the two triangles are congruent.

Opposite Angles Property of Parallelograms Opposite angles in a parallelogram are congruent.

Condition ensuring a parallelogram If the diagonals of a quadrilateral bisect each other, then the quadrilateral is a parallelogram.

Conditions ensuring a rectangle (1) If a parallelogram has one right angle, then it is a rectangle. (2) If the diagonals of a parallelogram are the same length, then the parallelogram is a rectangle.

30°-60° right triangle relationship For a right triangle with acute angles of measures 30° and 60°, the length of the leg opposite the 30° angle is half the length of the hypotenuse. The length of the side opposite the 60° angle is $\sqrt{3}$ times the length of the side opposite the 30° angle.

45°-45° right triangle relationship For a right triangle with acute angles of measures 45°, the length of the hypotenuse is $\sqrt{2}$ times the length of either of the equal legs of the right triangle.

Distance formula The distance d between two points with coordinates (x_1, y_1) and (x_2, y_2) is $d = \sqrt{(x_2 - x_1)^2 + (y_2 - y_1)^2}$.

Equation of a circle The equation of a circle with center at the origin and radius r is $x^2 + y^2 = r^2$.

Unit Objectives

- Explore the sine, cosine, and tangent functions defined in terms of a point on the terminal side of an angle in standard position in a coordinate plane
- Explore properties and applications of the sine, cosine, and tangent ratios of acute angles in right triangles
- Determine measures of sides and angles for nonright triangles using the Law of Sines and Law of Cosines
- Use the Law of Sines and Law of Cosines to solve a variety of applied problems that involve triangulation
- Describe the conditions under which two, one, or no triangles are determined given the lengths of two sides and the measure of an angle not included between the two sides

Unit 7

CPMP-Tools

The two custom tools available for use in this unit are "Auto Jack" and "Explore SSA." If you have *CPMP-Tools* available on a few classroom computers, groups could use these custom tools to explore the relationships at different times. The "Auto Jack" custom tool could be used on only one computer as part of the Lesson 1 launch using the TATS on page 459. It is best to allow students to control the dynamic feature of the tool. The "Explore SSA" custom tool is used in Lesson 2 to investigate why Side-Side-Angle is *not* a condition that ensures congruence of a pair of triangles.

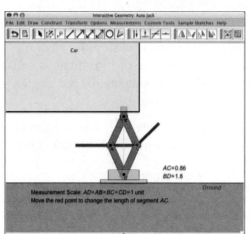
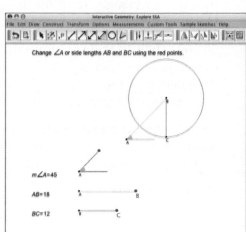

Lesson Objectives	On Your Own Assignments*	Suggested Pacing	Materials
Lesson 1 *Trigonometric Functions* • Determine values of the sine, cosine, and tangent functions of an angle in standard position in a square coordinate plane • Determine the sine, cosine, and tangent of an acute angle in a right triangle, and determine the angle given one of those ratios • Solve problems involving indirect measurement that can be modeled as parts of a right triangle • Explore basic properties of the sine, cosine, and tangent functions with reference to their interrelationships and their patterns of change as the angle measure changes	**After Investigation 1:** A1 or A2, A3, C9, C11, C12, R19, R20, E26 or E27, Rv32, Rv33 **After Investigation 2:** A4, A5, C13, C15, R21, E28 or E29, Rv34, Rv35 **After Investigation 3:** Choose two of A6–A8, C16, C17 or C18, choose two of R22–R25, E30 or E31, Rv36, Rv37	8 days (including assessment)	• *CPMP-Tools* custom tool "Auto Jack" • Unit Resources
Lesson 2 *Using Trigonometry in Any Triangle* • Determine measures of sides and angles of triangles using the Law of Sines and Law of Cosines • Use these laws to solve problems involving indirect measurement and analysis of mechanisms that use triangles with a side of variable length • Determine whether two, one, or no triangles are possible when the lengths of two sides and the measure of an angle not included between these sides are known	**After Investigation 1:** A1, A2, C9, C10, R16, R17, choose one of E21–E23, Rv28–Rv30 **After Investigation 2:** Choose two of A3–A6, C11, choose two of C12–C14, R18, E24 or E25, Rv31, Rv32 **After Investigation 3:** A7, A8, C15, R19, R20, E26 or E27, Rv33–Rv36	7 days (including assessment)	• Protractor • Centimeter rulers • Linkage strips that allow 12-cm and 16-cm sides • *CPMP-Tools* custom tool "Explore SSA" • Unit Resources
Lesson 3 *Looking Back* • Review and synthesize the major objectives of the unit		3 days (including assessment)	• Unit Resources

* When choice is indicated, it is important to leave the choice to the student.

Note: *It is best if Connections tasks are discussed as a whole class after they have been assigned as homework.*

LESSON
1

Trigonometric Functions

In Course 1 of *Core-Plus Mathematics*, you learned that triangles are rigid figures whose shapes and sizes are completely determined by conditions involving as few as three parts. In this unit, you will learn methods for determining the measures of the remaining parts of a triangle.

An automobile jack that comes with some makes of automobiles is shown below. It can be modeled by a pair of triangles with a common variable-length side. Points *A* and *C* are connected by a threaded rod, and the lengths *AB*, *BC*, *AD*, and *CD* are all 1 foot. The distance between points *A* and *C* increases or decreases depending on the direction the rod is turned.

The jack mechanism is a good example of how the measures of the six parts of a triangle (three sides and three angles) are interconnected. Altering the size of one part changes the size of other parts; and if you know measures of some parts, you can determine the measures of others.

Trigonometric Functions

T his lesson builds on the Courses 1 and 2 geometry units, *Patterns in Shape* and *Coordinate Methods*. The ratios of side lengths of right triangles are explored in order to observe that these ratios remain constant for a specific angle in standard position on the coordinate axes. These ratios are then identified as the sine, cosine, and tangent functions. Indirect measurement based on right triangles is developed in the second investigation. Besides their intrinsic mathematical interest, trigonometric functions are extraordinarily useful for solving applied problems in land surveying, engineering, and various applied sciences, and for designing and analyzing mechanisms whose function is based on triangles and their properties.

Lesson Objectives

- Determine values of the sine, cosine, and tangent functions of an angle in standard position in a square coordinate plane
- Determine the sine, cosine, and tangent of an acute angle in a right triangle, and determine the angle given one of those ratios
- Solve problems involving indirect measurement that can be modeled as parts of a right triangle
- Explore basic properties of the sine, cosine, and tangent functions with reference to their interrelationships and their patterns of change as the angle measure changes

Think About This Situation

Think about the design and function of this automobile jack. Use the "Auto Jack" custom tool to test your ideas.

a About how long would the threaded rod need to be if the jack is to be stored with points *B* and *D* as close together as possible?

b As the distance *AC* decreases, how do the angle measures of $\triangle ABC$ change? How does the distance between point *B* and the threaded rod change?

c How does the height of the jack, *BD*, compare to the length of the altitude of $\triangle ABC$ drawn from point *B*? Explain your thinking.

d Suppose the jack is set so that *AC* is as long as possible. As the threaded rod is turned at a constant rate, the distance *AC* decreases at a constant rate. How would you describe the rate at which the height *BD* of the jack changes?

In this lesson, you will use angles in a coordinate plane to define trigonometric functions and use those functions to determine measures of unknown parts in right triangles. These functions also form the basis for finding unknown parts of any triangle, as you will learn in the second lesson. Throughout this unit, you will see the practical power of trigonometric methods for solving a wide range of applied problems.

Investigation 1 Connecting Angle Measures and Linear Measures

One of the most effective strategies for calculating distances that cannot be measured directly is to represent the situation with a triangle in which the length of one side is the desired distance and other sides and/or angles can be measured. Trigonometry provides methods for using the known parts of a triangle to calculate those that are unknown. The key connections are the trigonometric ratios sine, cosine, and tangent defined as functions of angles in standard position in a coordinate plane. As you work on the problems in this investigation, look for answers to the following questions:

> *How are the sine, cosine, and tangent functions defined?*
> *How can their values be estimated?*

(a) $\overline{AC}$ would need to be about 2 feet long.

(b) As AC decreases, $m\angle A$ and $m\angle C$ increase, and $m\angle B$ decreases. The distance between B and the threaded rod increases.

(c) The length of $\overline{BD}$ is the sum of the lengths of the altitudes to $\overline{AC}$ of $\triangle ABC$ and $\triangle ADC$. Since the two triangles are congruent, if you superimpose them, you can see that the altitudes from B to $\overline{AC}$ and from D to $\overline{AC}$ are the same length. So, the height BD of the jack is twice the length of the altitude to side $\overline{AC}$ of $\triangle ABC$.

(d) The height BD increases rapidly at first; but as $\overline{AC}$ becomes shorter, BD increases more slowly.

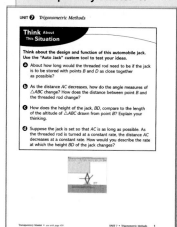
Investigation 1 — Connecting Angle Measures and Linear Measures

Students review, in an application setting, the use of the Pythagorean Theorem to determine the third side of a right triangle when the lengths of two sides are given. In the same setting, they recognize that they have no method to determine other side lengths when measures of an acute angle and a single side are known. Students are then introduced to angles as rotating rays in standard position on a coordinate system. They use points on terminal sides of angles in standard position to define the tangent, sine, and cosine ratios. Students estimate ratios for some angles from 0° to 90° in intervals of 10°. Then they derive the ratios for a 45° angle. Students are provided a partial trigonometric table and asked to describe the patterns of change for the sine, cosine, and tangent functions.

INSTRUCTIONAL NOTE
Some field-test teachers suggested doing a real-world trig measurement activity with students early in this lesson so they get a good idea of what trig will do for them. You might take the students outside and use an activity similar to the one described in Applications Task 3 in the On Your Own section.

Unit 7

1 Study the diagram below of a radio transmitter tower with two support wires attached to it at *A* and *E* and to the ground at *B* and *D*. First, focus on the triangle formed by the tower, the ground, and the shorter support wire.

 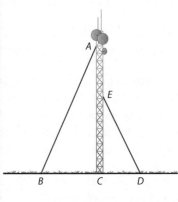

a. If *CD* = 50 feet and *CE* = 100 feet, is the size and shape of right △*DCE* completely determined? Why or why not?

b. How long is support wire $\overline{DE}$?

c. If you were asked to attach a support wire, 125 feet long, from point *D* to the tower, how far up the tower would you have to climb?

d. What relationship among sides of a right triangle have you used in Parts b and c?

2 Now focus on the right triangle formed by the tower, $\overline{BC}$, and the longer support wire $\overline{AB}$.

a. If *BC* = 75 feet and m∠*ABC* = 66°, is the size and shape of right △*ABC* completely determined? Why or why not?

b. Explain why the size and shape of a right triangle are completely determined when the measures of two sides are known or the measure of one acute angle and the length of one side are known.

c. It should be possible to use the information given in Part a to find *AC*, the distance above the ground at which support wire $\overline{AB}$ is attached to the tower. Will the Pythagorean Theorem help? Explain.

1　**a.** The shape of △*DCE* is determined because ∠*C* is fixed as a right angle and the lengths of the sides of ∠*C* are known. By the SAS congruence condition, there would be only one way to draw △*DCE*. Students might also respond by indicating that they can find the length of $\overline{ED}$ using the Pythagorean Theorem and that knowing the lengths of all three sides of a triangle determines exactly one triangle.

　b. $DE = \sqrt{50^2 + 100^2} \approx 111.803 \approx 112$ feet

　c. You would have to attach a wire at *E*, 114.6 feet up the tower.
$CE^2 + 50^2 = 125^2$
$CE \approx 114.564 \approx 115$ feet

　d. The Pythagorean Theorem was used in answering Parts b and c.

2　**a.** The size and shape of right △*ABC* is determined since ∠*C* is fixed as a right angle, *BC* is known, and m∠*B* = 66°. The ASA congruence condition tells us that there is only one triangle with the given parts.

　b. If the lengths of two sides of a right triangle are known, you can find the length of the third side using the Pythagorean Theorem. Either the SAS or the SSS triangle congruence conditions ensure the size and shape of the triangle are determined. If the measures of one side and one acute angle are known, then you can use either the AAS or ASA congruence condition to ensure the size and shape are determined.

　c. Only one side of the right triangle is known, so the Pythagorean Theorem will not help.

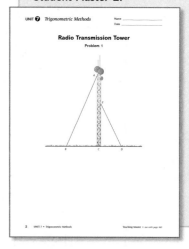
Unit 7

To solve problems like Problem 2 Part c, you need to find a connection between angle measures and segment lengths in a right triangle. In this case, it is helpful to think of an angle as being formed by rotating a ray about its endpoint from an *initial position* to a *terminal position*.

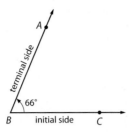

The point about which the ray is rotated is the **vertex** of the angle. The initial position of the ray is the **initial side** of the angle. The terminal position of the ray is the **terminal side** of the angle. To indicate the direction of rotation from initial side to terminal side, it is customary to say the angle has *positive measure* if the rotation is counterclockwise and has *negative measure* if the rotation is clockwise.

3 The diagram at the right shows four points on the terminal side of an angle in **standard position** in a coordinate plane. The vertex of the angle is at the origin and its initial side coincides with the positive *x*-axis.

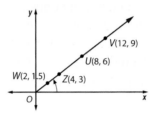

 a. For each point (x, y) shown on the terminal side, find the ratios $\frac{y}{x}$.

 i. $U(8, 6)$ **ii.** $V(12, 9)$

 iii. $W(2, 1.5)$ **iv.** $Z(4, 3)$

 b. How do the ratios $\frac{y}{x}$ compare in each case? Why does that make sense?

 c. For each point (x, y) in Part a, suppose r is the distance from the origin to the point. How do you think the ratios $\frac{x}{r}$ would compare in each case? The ratios $\frac{y}{r}$? Check your conjectures.

4 Your discoveries about the ratios of lengths in Problem 3 apply to any angle in standard position. Consider the diagram below that shows an angle with degree measure θ (Greek letter "theta") in standard position.

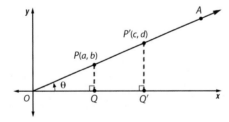

3 **a.** **i.** $\dfrac{y}{x} = \dfrac{6}{8}$

    ii. $\dfrac{y}{x} = \dfrac{9}{12}$

    iii. $\dfrac{y}{x} = \dfrac{1.5}{2}$

    iv. $\dfrac{y}{x} = \dfrac{3}{4}$

b. In each case, the ratios $\dfrac{y}{x}$ are equal. This makes sense because the ratio $\dfrac{y}{x}$ is the slope of the line that contains all four points. Alternatively, students may draw on the concept of similar triangles to indicate that the ratios are equivalent.

c. **i.** $r = \sqrt{8^2 + 6^2} = 10$. So, $\dfrac{y}{r} = \dfrac{6}{10}$ and $\dfrac{x}{r} = \dfrac{8}{10}$.

    ii. $r = \sqrt{12^2 + 9^2} = 15$. So, $\dfrac{y}{r} = \dfrac{9}{15}$ and $\dfrac{x}{r} = \dfrac{12}{15}$.

    iii. $r = \sqrt{2^2 + 1.5^2} = 2.5$. So, $\dfrac{y}{r} = \dfrac{1.5}{2.5}$ and $\dfrac{x}{r} = \dfrac{2}{2.5}$.

    iv. $r = \sqrt{4^2 + 3^2} = 5$. So, $\dfrac{y}{r} = \dfrac{3}{5}$ and $\dfrac{x}{r} = \dfrac{4}{5}$.

In each case, the ratios $\dfrac{x}{r}$ are equal to $\dfrac{4}{5}$, or 0.8. Likewise, all of the ratios $\dfrac{y}{r}$ are equal to $\dfrac{3}{5}$, or 0.6.

Let $P(a, b)$ and $P'(c, d)$ be any two points on the terminal side $\overrightarrow{OA}$, other than the origin O.

a. Find the slope of $\overleftrightarrow{OA}$ using points O and P. Find the slope of $\overleftrightarrow{OA}$ using points O and P'.

b. How are $\dfrac{PQ}{OQ}$ and $\dfrac{P'Q'}{OQ'}$ related? Why?

c. Explain why $\triangle OP'Q'$ is the image of $\triangle OPQ$ under a size transformation with center at the origin and magnitude $k = \dfrac{c}{a}$. Use the following questions to guide your thinking.

   i. What is the image of point O under this transformation?

   ii. Why is point Q' the image of point Q under this transformation?

   iii. Why is point P' the image of point P under this transformation?

d. Use your work in Part c to help explain each step in the reasoning below.

   i. $OQ' = k(OQ)$ and $OP' = k(OP)$.   **ii.** $OP' = k(OP)$ and $P'Q' = k(PQ)$.

   So, $\dfrac{OQ'}{OQ} = \dfrac{OP'}{OP}$.   So, $\dfrac{OP'}{OP} = \dfrac{P'Q'}{PQ}$.

   So, $OQ' \cdot OP = OQ \cdot OP'$.   So, $OP' \cdot PQ = OP \cdot P'Q'$.

   So, $\dfrac{OQ}{OP} = \dfrac{OQ'}{OP'}$.   So, $\dfrac{PQ}{OP} = \dfrac{P'Q'}{OP'}$.

e. Write a statement describing how your work in Parts b and d support your discoveries in Problem 3.

f. Draw diagrams similar to that above for cases where $\theta > 90°$. Does reasoning similar to that in Parts b–d hold in these cases? Explain.

Your work in Problem 4 shows that if $P(x, y)$ is a point (not the origin) on the terminal side of an angle in standard position and $r = \sqrt{x^2 + y^2}$, then the ratios $\dfrac{y}{x}$, $\dfrac{y}{r}$, and $\dfrac{x}{r}$ do not depend on the choice of P; they depend only on the measure of $\angle POQ$. That is, these ratios are functions of the measure θ of the angle. These functions are called **trigonometric functions** and are given special names as indicated below.

tangent of $\theta = \tan \theta = \dfrac{y}{x}$ $(x \neq 0)$

sine of $\theta = \sin \theta = \dfrac{y}{r}$

cosine of $\theta = \cos \theta = \dfrac{x}{r}$

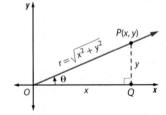

 The terminal side of an angle in standard position with measure θ contains the given point. In each case, draw the angle on a coordinate grid. Then find $\cos \theta$, $\sin \theta$, and $\tan \theta$.

a. $P(12, 5)$

b. $P(-6, 4)$

c. For any angle with measure θ, is it possible for $\sin \theta > 1$? For $\cos \theta > 1$? For $\tan \theta > 1$?

INSTRUCTIONAL NOTE This is a good opportunity for a class discussion to be sure that students have the correct ratios. Interpreting symbolic expressions is an important part of symbol sense. Parts c and d provide an opportunity with visual grounding for students to continue to develop their fluency with symbols.

a. The slope of $\overleftrightarrow{OA}$ using points O and P is $\frac{b-0}{a-0} = \frac{b}{a}$. The slope of $\overleftrightarrow{OA}$ using points O and P' is $\frac{d-0}{c-0} = \frac{d}{c}$.

b. $\frac{PQ}{OQ} = \frac{P'Q'}{OQ'}$ since each ratio represents the slope of $\overleftrightarrow{OA}$.

c. i. The image of point O under this transformation is O, since O is the center of the transformation.

   ii. In general, the ratio of the distance of the image point from the origin to the distance of the preimage point from the origin is the magnitude of the size transformation. $\frac{OQ'}{OQ} = \frac{c}{a} = k$. So, point Q' is the image of point Q.

   iii. Applying the size transformation $\frac{c}{a}$ to $P(a, b)$ gives $P'\left(c, \frac{bc}{a}\right)$. The slope of $\overleftrightarrow{OA}$ is $\frac{b}{a} = \frac{d}{c}$. So, we can write $P'\left(c, \frac{bc}{a}\right)$ as $P'\left(c, \frac{dc}{c}\right)$ or $P'(c, d)$. Thus, point P' is the image of point P.

   Since point O is the image of point O, point Q' is the image of point Q, and point P' is the image of point P under a size transformation with center at the origin and magnitude $k = \frac{c}{a}$, $\triangle OP'Q'$ is the image of $\triangle OPQ$.

d. i. From Part c, $\overline{OQ'}$ is the image of $\overline{OQ}$ under the size transformation with center at the origin and magnitude k, and $\overline{OP'}$ is the image of $\overline{OP}$ under the same transformation.

   Thus, $OQ' = k(OQ)$ and $OP' = k(OP)$ and $k = \frac{OQ'}{OQ} = \frac{OP'}{OP}$.

   Multiplying both sides of the equality by $OP \cdot OQ$ gives $OQ' \cdot OP = OQ \cdot OP'$.

   Dividing both sides of the equality by $OP \cdot OP'$ gives $\frac{OQ}{OP} = \frac{OQ'}{OP'}$.

   ii. Since $\overline{OP'}$ is the image of $\overline{OP}$ under the size transformation with center at the origin and magnitude k, and $\overline{P'Q'}$ is the image of $\overline{PQ}$ under the same transformation, $OP' = k(OP)$ and $P'Q' = k(PQ)$.

   Thus, $\frac{OP'}{OP} = k$ and $\frac{P'Q'}{PQ} = k$ and so $k = \frac{OP'}{OP} = \frac{P'Q'}{PQ}$.

   Multiplying both sides of the equality by $OP \cdot PQ$ gives $OP' \cdot PQ = OP \cdot P'Q'$.

   Dividing both sides of the equality by $OP \cdot OP'$ gives $\frac{PQ}{OP} = \frac{P'Q'}{OP'}$.

e. If point (x, y) is on the terminal side of an angle in standard position and r is the distance between the point and the origin, then the ratios $\frac{y}{x}$, $\frac{y}{r}$, and $\frac{x}{r}$ do not depend on the choice of (x, y) on the terminal side.

f. Since $\triangle OP'Q'$ is a size transformation of $\triangle OPQ$, the reasoning in Parts b–d applies for $\theta > 90°$ also.

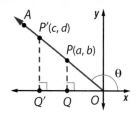

INSTRUCTIONAL NOTE In Part f, be sure that students draw angles in Quadrants II, III, and IV.

NOTE The solution to Problem 5 is on page T463.

6 The diagram below shows a portion of a circle with radius 10 cm, drawn on a 2-mm grid. Angles are marked off in 10° intervals, so $m\angle AOP_1 = 10°$, $m\angle AOP_2 = 20°$, $m\angle AOP_3 = 30°$, and so on. You can use this diagram to calculate approximate values of $\cos\theta$, $\sin\theta$, and $\tan\theta$ for angles with measure θ between 0° and 90°.

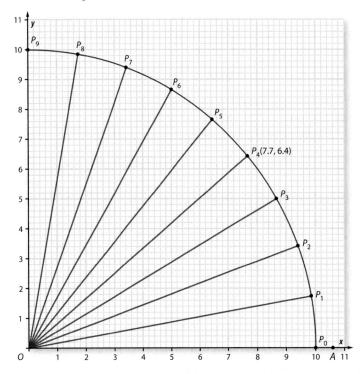

a. Verify the entries in the table below for the case of $\angle AOP_4$.

b. Make a copy of the table and then use the diagram to find the missing entries. Share the workload.

	P_n				
$m\angle AOP_n$	x	y	$\cos\theta$	$\sin\theta$	$\tan\theta$
0°					
20°	9.4	3.4			
40°	7.7	6.4	0.77	0.64	0.84
60°			0.50		
80°					
90°					

Unit 7

5 **a.**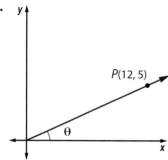

$$\cos \theta = \frac{12}{\sqrt{12^2 + 5^2}} = \frac{12}{13}$$

$$\sin \theta = \frac{5}{\sqrt{12^2 + 5^2}} = \frac{5}{13}$$

$$\tan \theta = \frac{5}{12}$$

b.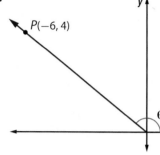

$$\cos \theta = \frac{-6}{\sqrt{(-6)^2 + 4^2}} = \frac{-6}{2\sqrt{13}}$$

$$\sin \theta = \frac{4}{\sqrt{(-6)^2 + 4^2}} = \frac{4}{2\sqrt{13}}$$

$$\tan \theta = \frac{4}{-6}$$

c. Sin θ and cos θ are less than or equal to 1 for all values of θ because for any point (x, y) on the terminal side of θ, r is greater than or equal to both x and y. (This is true because $r = \sqrt{x^2 + y^2}$. Some students may visualize a right triangle and recognize that the length of the hypotenuse r is longer than the lengths of the legs.) However, tan θ is greater than 1 for values of θ for which the slope of the line through the terminal side of θ is greater than 1, i.e., $45° < \theta < 90°$.

6 **INSTRUCTIONAL NOTE** Students should use the chart and trigonometric ratios to verify the entries and supply missing entries, not the trigonometric calculator functions. Since the x and y values are read from the graph, the trigonometric values will be rough estimates.

Student Master 3.

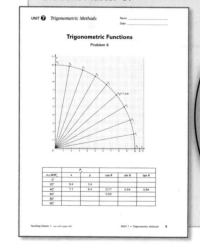

a–b.

m∠AOP$_n$	P_n		cos θ	sin θ	tan θ
	x	y			
0°	10.0	0.0	1.0	0.0	0.0
20°	9.4	3.4	0.94	0.34	0.36
40°	7.7	6.4	0.77	0.64	0.84
60°	5.0	8.7	0.50	0.87	1.74
80°	1.7	9.8	0.17	0.98	5.76
90°	0.0	10.0	0.0	1.0	not defined

7 In Problem 6, you were able to find approximate values of the trigonometric functions of 20°, 40°, 60°, and 80°. In the case of angles with measure 0° and 90°, you were able to determine *exact* values (with the exception of tan 90°). You can use geometric reasoning to find exact values of tangent, sine, and cosine of 45°.

  a. Draw an angle of 45° in standard position.

  b. What is an equation for the line that makes an angle of 45˚ with the positive *x*-axis?

  c. What do you know about the coordinates of any point on the terminal side of this angle?

  d. Choose a point (*x*, *y*) on the terminal side of the angle and then find tan 45°, sin 45°, and cos 45°. Give exact values, not decimal approximations.

8 Now return to Problem 2 about the radio transmitter tower. Suppose *BC* = 75 feet and m∠*ABC* = 66°.

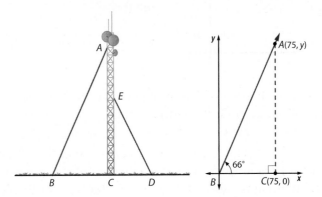

To determine *AC*, the distance above the ground at which support wire *AB* is attached to the tower:

  a. Draw ∠*ABC* in standard position as in the diagram above on the right. Explain why the coordinates of points *A* and *C* are labeled as shown.

  b. Write an expression for tan 66° in terms of the given information.

  c. Use the diagram in Problem 6 to calculate an approximate value of tan 66°.

  d. Using your results from Parts b and c, find the approximate height *AC*.

  e. How long is support wire $\overline{AB}$?

  f. Show how you could use a trigonometric function to find the approximate length of $\overline{AB}$ without first finding the height *AC*. Compare your answer to that obtained in Part e.

7 a.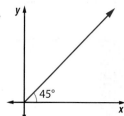

b. The slope of the line is 1 and the line passes through the origin, so the equation is $y = x$.

c. Any point on the terminal side lies on the line $y = x$ and will be of the form (a, a).

d. Choose, say, $(1, 1)$, then $\tan 45° = \frac{1}{1} = 1$; $\sin 45° = \frac{1}{\sqrt{2}}$; $\cos 45° = \frac{1}{\sqrt{2}}$.

8 a. $A(75, y)$ is directly above C, so A and C have the same x-coordinates. The vertical distance up from C is not known, so the y-coordinate is represented by a variable. $C(75, 0)$ is 75 feet from B and on the x-axis where $y = 0$.

b. $\tan 66° = \frac{y}{75}$

c. Students' choices of coordinates will vary. This solution uses a gridline intersection point.
$x \approx 4$, $y \approx 9.2$, so $\tan 66° \approx \frac{9.2}{4} = 2.3$.

d. $\tan 66° \approx 2.3$. So, $2.3 = \frac{y}{75}$ and $AC \approx 172.5 \approx 173$ feet.

e. $AB \approx \sqrt{75^2 + 172.5^2} \approx 188$ feet

f. If you knew the numerical value of $\cos 66°$, you could solve $\cos 66° = \frac{75}{AB}$ for AB. Using the diagram in Problem 6, $x \approx 4$ and $r \approx 10$. $\cos 66° \approx \frac{4}{10}$. So, solve $0.4 = \frac{75}{AB}$. $AB \approx 188$ feet. (There may be slight differences in solutions due to approximations.)

(9) The values of the trigonometric functions you found by using the grid on page 463 were rough approximations of the function values. Several centuries ago, mathematicians spent years calculating values of the trigonometric functions by hand to several decimal places so they could be used in surveying and astronomy. Today, more advanced mathematical methods are used. You will study those methods in a later course. A portion of a table of trigonometric function values with four-digit accuracy is shown below.

Angle	sin	cos	tan
45°	0.7071	0.7071	1.0000
46°	0.7193	0.6947	1.0355
47°	0.7314	0.6820	1.0724
48°	0.7431	0.6691	1.1106
49°	0.7547	0.6561	1.1504
50°	0.7660	0.6428	1.1918
51°	0.7771	0.6293	1.2349
52°	0.7880	0.6157	1.2799
53°	0.7986	0.6018	1.3270
54°	0.8090	0.5878	1.3764
55°	0.8192	0.5736	1.4281
56°	0.8290	0.5592	1.4826
57°	0.8387	0.5446	1.5399
58°	0.8480	0.5299	1.6003
59°	0.8572	0.5150	1.6643
60°	0.8660	0.5000	1.7321

Angle	sin	cos	tan
61°	0.8746	0.4848	1.8040
62°	0.8829	0.4695	1.8807
63°	0.8910	0.4540	1.9626
64°	0.8988	0.4384	2.0503
65°	0.9063	0.4226	2.1445
66°	0.9135	0.4067	2.2460
67°	0.9205	0.3907	2.3559
68°	0.9272	0.3746	2.4751
69°	0.9336	0.3584	2.6051
70°	0.9397	0.3420	2.7475
71°	0.9455	0.3256	2.9042
72°	0.9511	0.3090	3.0777
73°	0.9563	0.2924	3.2709
74°	0.9613	0.2756	3.4874
75°	0.9659	0.2588	3.7321

a. Compare the values of sine, cosine, and tangent of 45° that you found in Problem 7 with the values in the table above.

b. Compare the values of tan 66° and cos 66° that you used in Problem 8 with the values in the table above.

c. As the measure of an angle increases from 45° to 75°,

  i. how does the sine of the angle change?

  ii. how does the cosine of the angle change?

  iii. how does the tangent of the angle change?

d. Why do the patterns of change in Part c make sense in terms of the diagram on page 463?

a. Students should compare the values and notice that they are approximately the same. $\left(\dfrac{1}{\sqrt{2}} \approx 0.7071\right)$

b. Students should compare the values and notice that they are approximately the same.

c. **i.** As the measure of the angle increases from 45° to 75°, the sine of the angle increases from 0.7071 to 0.9659 at a nonconstant (decreasing) rate.

   ii. As the measure of the angle increases from 45° to 75°, the cosine of the angle decreases from 0.7071 to 0.2588 at a nonconstant (increasing) rate.

   iii. As the measure of the angle increases from 45° to 75°, the tangent of the angle increases from 1 to 3.7321 at a nonconstant (increasing) rate.

d. The sine values should be increasing as the angle increases from 45° to 75°, since the y-coordinates of P_n are increasing while the radius remains the same.

The cosine values should be decreasing as the angle increases from 45° to 75° since the x-coordinates of P_n are decreasing while the radius remains the same.

The tangent values should increase as the angle increases from 45° to 75°. At 45°, the x- and y-coordinates of P_n will be the same, so $\tan 45° = 1$. As the angle increases from 45° to 75°, the y-coordinates of P_n increase while the x-coordinates decrease. Thus, $\dfrac{y}{x}$ will increase. Alternatively, the tangent values increase from 45° to 75° because the slope of the lines increase as the angle size increases.

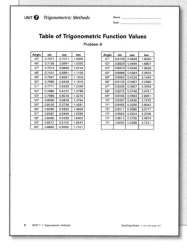

Teaching Resources

Student Master 4.

UNIT 7 Trigonometric Methods   Name _____
                                       Date _____

Table of Trigonometric Function Values
Problem 9

Angle	sin	cos	tan		Angle	sin	cos	tan
45°	0.7071	0.7071	1.0000		61°	0.8746	0.4848	1.8040
46°	0.7193	0.6947	1.0355		62°	0.8829	0.4695	1.8807
47°	0.7314	0.6820	1.0724		63°	0.8910	0.4540	1.9626
48°	0.7431	0.6691	1.1106		64°	0.8988	0.4384	2.0503
49°	0.7547	0.6561	1.1504		65°	0.9063	0.4226	2.1445
50°	0.7660	0.6428	1.1918		66°	0.9135	0.4067	2.2460
51°	0.7771	0.6293	1.2349		67°	0.9205	0.3907	2.3559
52°	0.7880	0.6157	1.2799		68°	0.9272	0.3746	2.4751
53°	0.7986	0.6018	1.3270		69°	0.9336	0.3584	2.6051
54°	0.8090	0.5878	1.3764		70°	0.9397	0.3420	2.7475
55°	0.8192	0.5736	1.4281		71°	0.9455	0.3256	2.9042
56°	0.8290	0.5592	1.4826		72°	0.9511	0.3090	3.0777
57°	0.8387	0.5446	1.5399		73°	0.9563	0.2924	3.2709
58°	0.8480	0.5299	1.6003		74°	0.9613	0.2756	3.4874
59°	0.8572	0.5150	1.6643		75°	0.9659	0.2588	3.7321
60°	0.8660	0.5000	1.7321					

4   UNIT 7 • Trigonometric Methods   Teaching Master • see unit page 465

e. Use the table to determine each of these trigonometric function values.

    i. sin 58°   **ii.** cos 48°   **iii.** tan 72°

f. Given the function values below, use the table to determine the measure of the angle θ whose terminal side is in the first quadrant.

    i. sin θ = 0.8910

    ii. cos θ = 0.5878

    iii. tan θ = 1.1106

Summarize the Mathematics

In this investigation, you explored the sine, cosine, and tangent, three members of a new family of functions called trigonometric functions.

a How do each of these functions provide a connection between angle measure and linear measure?

b Suppose the terminal side of an angle in standard position with measure θ lies on the line with equation $y = 2x$, $x \geq 0$.

    i. Find tan θ.   **ii.** Find cos θ.   **iii.** Find sin θ.

c Suppose θ is the measure of an angle in standard position whose terminal side is in the first quadrant and tan θ = $\frac{4}{5}$.

    i. Find cos θ.   **ii.** Find sin θ.

d Describe the pattern of change for each function as the measure of an angle in standard position increases from 0° to 90°.

    i. cos θ   **ii.** sin θ   **iii.** tan θ

Be prepared to explain your responses to the class.

✓ Check Your Understanding

The terminal side of an angle in standard position with measure θ contains the point $P(4, 7)$.

a. Draw a sketch of the angle.

b. Find sin θ, cos θ, and tan θ.

c. Use the table on page 465 to estimate θ to the nearest degree.

e. i. $\sin 58° \approx 0.8480$ **ii.** $\cos 48° \approx 0.6691$ **iii.** $\tan 72° \approx 3.0777$

f. i. $\theta = 63°$ **ii.** $\theta = 54°$ **iii.** $\theta = 48°$

Summary

In Part b, students might choose a specific point, such as (1, 2), on the terminal side of θ to calculate tan θ, cos θ, sin θ. Use this opportunity to reinforce the idea that any point on the terminal side of θ gives the same trig ratios as any other point on that side of θ. Then press for a generalization as shown in the solution below.

Students may want to look back at their work on Problems 6 and 9 to create a complete summary for Part d of the Summarize the Mathematics.

Teaching Resources

Transparency Master 5.

Summarize
the Mathematics

(a) The three functions, sine, cosine, and tangent, connect angle measure to linear measure by their definitions. Given an angle measure θ (the function input), you can estimate (or be given) the coordinates of a point $P(x, y)$ on the terminal ray of the given angle in standard position. Then the three linear measures, the horizontal distance of the point P from the y-axis (x), the vertical distance from the x-axis (y), and the distance from the origin $\left(r = \sqrt{x^2 + y^2}\right)$, are used to find the numerical outputs of the trigonometric functions as shown below.

$$\sin \theta = \frac{y}{r} \qquad\qquad \cos \theta = \frac{x}{r} \qquad\qquad \tan \theta = \frac{y}{x}$$

(b) **i.** $\tan \theta = \frac{2x}{x} = 2$

   ii. $\cos \theta = \frac{x}{\sqrt{x^2 + (2x)^2}} = \frac{x}{x\sqrt{5}} = \frac{1}{\sqrt{5}}$

   iii. $\sin \theta = \frac{2x}{\sqrt{x^2 + (2x)^2}} = \frac{2x}{x\sqrt{5}} = \frac{2}{\sqrt{5}}$

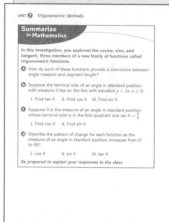

(c) Since $\tan \theta = \frac{4}{5}$, the point (5, 4) is on the terminal side of θ; so, $r = \sqrt{4^2 + 5^2} = \sqrt{41}$.

   i. $\cos \theta = \frac{5}{\sqrt{4^2 + 5^2}} = \frac{5}{\sqrt{41}}$

   ii. $\sin \theta = \frac{4}{\sqrt{4^2 + 5^2}} = \frac{4}{\sqrt{41}}$

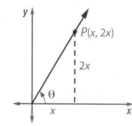

(d) **i.** As the measure of the angle increases from 0° to 90°, the cosine of the angle decreases at a nonconstant rate.

   ii. As the measure of the angle increases from 0° to 90°, the sine of the angle increases at a nonconstant rate.

   iii. As the measure of the angle increases from 0° to 90°, the tangent of the angle increases at a nonconstant rate.

Summarize the Mathematics, *Page 466*

Teacher: Our approach to this summary will be a little different this time. We will not have each group discuss the STM before we start. I will indicate how each part will be treated as we proceed with the discussion. So, Sophie, please read the STM introduction and Part a for us. Then each of you quietly think about how you would answer Part a.

Sophie: In this investigation, you explored the sine, cosine, and tangent, three members of a new family of functions called trigonometric functions. How do each of these functions provide a connection between angle measure and linear measure?

Teacher: *(After allowing a minute for students to think.)* What are your thoughts? Rod.

Rod: Well, I was thinking about how an angle makes a triangle and the functions are ratios of the side lengths.

Teacher: Okay, in Problem 8, you may have been thinking about the radio-transmitter tower as forming a triangle, but let's focus on the coordinates of points on the terminal side of an angle with vertex at the origin. How do the sine, cosine, and tangent functions connect angle measures and linear measures for a point on the terminal ray?

Merci: Well, the angle size determines where the ray lands. Once you know where the ray lands, a point on the ray helps you find the numbers to make trig ratios. Can I draw a picture of what I mean?

Teacher: Sure. *(Merci draws a sketch as shown below.)*

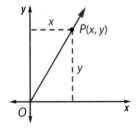

Merci: So, the distance P is from the y-axis (the x-coordinate) over the distance P is from the origin is the cosine of the angle. And the sine of the angle is the distance of the point P from the x-axis over the length OP. *(She points to the diagram.)*

Teacher: Which linear measures are then connected to the tangent of an angle?

Merci: Well, that is the vertical length from the point to the x-axis over the horizontal length of the point to the y-axis. You can think of a triangle, like Rod said, once you know where the ray lands.

Teacher: Thanks, Merci. You may have noticed that we have been referring to the sine, cosine, and tangent as "functions" in this investigation. In thinking of the angle measure and linear measure connection, which one is the input for trigonometric functions?

Vonisha: The angle.

Teacher: Remember, you should always explain your thinking for us.

Vonisha: Well, you need the angle size first. You input the angle, look at your trig function type, and pick the right ratio of lengths for the output.

Teacher: Nice description, Vonisha. Now let's consider Part b which is a little different type of question than you considered in the investigation. Part b says, "Suppose the terminal side of an angle in standard position with measure θ lies on the line with equation $y = 2x$, $x \geq 0$. Find $\tan \theta$." How would you begin to think about this task?

Sojo: Make a sketch.

Teacher: Good problem solving technique, Sojo. Individually, complete Part b. Then, compare your answers with a partner. I will be observing your work. *(Work time is provided.)*

Teacher: Let's take a minute to discuss your approaches to this task. Many of you noticed that you had a different strategy than your partner to find the requested trigonometric values. Some of you used specific points such as (1, 2) or (3, 6) while some of you used a general point $(x, 2x)$. So that everyone can think about the general strategy, Greg, please come to the front and show us how you thought about this task. *(Greg sketches the line $y = 2x$ and describes finding the ratios using the general point $P(x, 2x)$.)*

(The class continues with discussion of Parts c and d.)

Check Your Understanding

a.

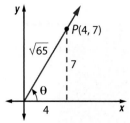

b. $\sin \theta = \dfrac{7}{\sqrt{65}} \approx 0.8682$

$\cos \theta = \dfrac{4}{\sqrt{65}} \approx 0.4961$

$\tan \theta = \dfrac{7}{4} = 1.75$

c. $\theta \approx 60°$

Unit 7

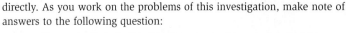

Investigation 2 · Measuring Without Measuring

The highest point on the Earth's surface is the peak of Mount Everest in the Himalaya mountain range along the Tibet-Nepal border in Asia. The most recent calculations indicate that Mount Everest rises 8,872 meters (29,108 feet) above sea level. As early as 1850, surveyors had estimated the height of that peak with error of only 0.4%. The first climbers known to actually reach the summit were Tenzing Norgay and Edmund Hillary in 1953.

In Investigation 1, you explored how the tangent and cosine functions could be used to calculate a height and distance that could not be measured directly. As you work on the problems of this investigation, make note of answers to the following question:

How can trigonometric functions be used to calculate heights like that of Mount Everest and other distances that cannot be measured directly?

1. The following sketch shows the start of one surveyor's attempt to determine the height of a tall mountain without climbing to the top herself.

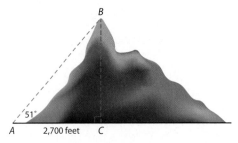

   a. Use the given information to calculate the lengths of $\overline{AB}$ and $\overline{BC}$. (Use the table on page 465 to calculate approximate values of trigonometric functions as needed.)

   b. Suppose that a laser ranging device allowed you to find the length of $\overline{AB}$ and the *angle of elevation* $\angle BAC$, but you could not measure the length of $\overline{AC}$. How could you use this information (instead of the information from the diagram) to calculate the lengths of $\overline{AC}$ and $\overline{BC}$?

This investigation introduces the right triangle definitions of the sine, cosine, and tangent. Using a variety of applications, students develop the ability to solve for missing side lengths and angle measurements of right triangles. Technology is introduced for finding trigonometric values and also angle measures using the inverse trigonometric functions.

Approximate Answers

For computations involving a trigonometric value, it is best to retain the full calculator display. You may wish to have students report answers to only four decimal places. In these solutions, when an answer to one part is used in a later computation, four decimal places will be used in the computation. Final answers are rounded to the same place value as the smallest place value for given information. The decision on whether or not to teach computation with significant digits is left to your discretion.

1   **a.** $\tan 51° = \dfrac{BC}{2{,}700}$

$BC = (1.2349)(2{,}700) \approx 3{,}334 \text{ ft}$

$\cos 51° = \dfrac{2{,}700}{AB}$

$AB = \dfrac{2{,}700}{0.6293} \approx 4{,}290 \text{ ft}$

b. $\sin \angle BAC = \dfrac{BC}{AB};\ BC = AB \sin \angle BAC$

$\cos \angle BAC = \dfrac{AC}{AB};\ AC = AB \cos \angle BAC$

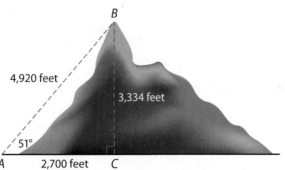

(2) The trigonometric functions are often used in problems modeled with right triangles, as in Problem 1. It is helpful to be able to use these functions without first placing an acute angle of the triangle in standard position in a coordinate plane. Examine the diagram of right $\triangle ABC$ with $\angle C$ a right angle.

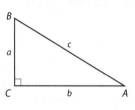

a. Explain why the following **right triangle definitions** of sine, cosine, and tangent make sense.

$$\text{tangent of } \angle A = \tan A = \frac{a}{b} = \frac{\text{length of side } opposite \ \angle A}{\text{length of side } adjacent \ to \ \angle A}$$

$$\text{sine of } \angle A = \sin A = \frac{a}{c} = \frac{\text{length of side } opposite \ \angle A}{\text{length of } hypotenuse}$$

$$\text{cosine of } \angle A = \cos A = \frac{b}{c} = \frac{\text{length of side } adjacent \ to \ \angle A}{\text{length of } hypotenuse}$$

b. Write expressions for $\tan B$, $\sin B$, and $\cos B$.

(3) Chicago's *Bat Column*, a sculpture by Claes Oldenburg, is shown below.

a. About how tall do you think the column is? What visual clues in the photo did you use to make your estimate?

b. In the diagram at the right, what lengths and angles could you determine easily by direct measurement (and without using high-powered equipment)?

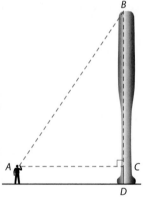

c. Which trigonometric functions of $\angle A$ involve side $\overline{BC}$? Of these, which also involve a measurable length?

d. Which of the trigonometric functions of $\angle B$ involve side $\overline{BC}$ and a measurable length? If you know the measure of angle of elevation $\angle A$, how can you find the measure of $\angle B$?

2 **INSTRUCTIONAL NOTE** If your students are having difficulty with the ratios, it may be that they have not recognized that *a* represents the side opposite of ∠*A*, and so on. Also, in this example, the given △*ABC* must be reflected in order for ∠*A* to be in the standard position with the right angle at *C* on the positive *x*-axis.

a. If the triangle is placed with ∠*A* in standard position as in the diagram at the right, you observe that point *B* would have coordinates (*b*, *a*) and the hypotenuse is length *c*.

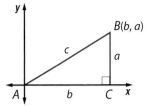

So, $\tan A = \dfrac{a}{b} = \dfrac{\text{length of side opposite } \angle A}{\text{length of side adjacent to } \angle A}$;

$\sin A = \dfrac{a}{c} = \dfrac{\text{length of side opposite } \angle A}{\text{length of hypotenuse}}$; and

$\cos A = \dfrac{b}{c} = \dfrac{\text{length of side adjacent to } \angle A}{\text{length of hypotenuse}}$.

b. $\tan B = \dfrac{b}{a}$

$\sin B = \dfrac{b}{c}$

$\cos B = \dfrac{a}{c}$

3

a. Student estimates of the height will vary. They may refer to the reflection of the sculpture in the windows of the building and the size of the people near the building to get an estimate.

b. ∠*BAC*, *AC*, ∠*ACB*, *CD*

c. tan *A* and sin *A*; tan *A* involves a measurable length *AC*

d. tan *B*

m∠*B* = 90° − m∠*A*

Unit 7

e. To find the height of *Bat Column*, Krista and D'wan proceeded as follows. First, Krista chose a spot (point *A*) 20 meters from the sculpture (point *C*). D'wan estimated the angle of elevation at *A* by sighting the top of the sculpture along a protractor and using a weight as shown. He measured ∠*A* to be 55°. What is the measure of ∠*B*?

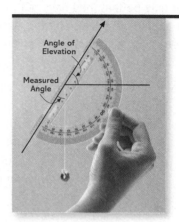

Angle of Elevation

Measured Angle

f. They next used the following reasoning to find the height *BC*.

> We need to find *BC*. We know that $\tan 55° = \frac{BC}{AC}$.
> But, $\tan 55° = 1.4281$ and $AC = 20$ m.
> So, we need to solve $1.4281 = \frac{BC}{20}$.
> If we multiply both sides of the equation by 20,
> we get $BC = 1.4281 \cdot 20$, or about 29 m.

   i. Why did they decide to use the tangent function rather than the sine function?

   ii. How did they know that $\tan 55° = 1.4281$?

   iii. Check that each step in their reasoning is correct.

   iv. How do you think Krista and D'wan used this information to calculate the height of *Bat Column*?

g. Ken said he could find the length *AB* (the line of sight distance) by solving $\cos 55° = \frac{AC}{AB}$.

   i. Use Ken's idea to find the length *AB*.

   ii. What is another way you could find *AB* by using a different trigonometric function?

   iii. Could you find *AB* without using a trigonometric function? Explain your reasoning.

4 As you have seen in Problems 1 and 3, an important part of solving problems using trigonometric methods is to decide on a trigonometric function that uses given information. For each right triangle below, write two equations involving trigonometric functions of acute angles that include *s* and the indicated length. Then rewrite each equation in an equivalent form "*s* = … ."

a.

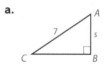

b.

c.

e. $m\angle B = 35°$

(You may need to explain how to sight along the protractor edge to measure the angle of elevation.)

f. **i.** They used the tangent function because they knew the length of one leg $\overline{AC}$ of the right triangle and wanted to find the length of the other leg $\overline{BC}$.

   ii. They used the table on page 465.

   iii. The reasoning is correct.

   iv. Their answer needs to be added to D'wan's height to get the full height of *Bat Column*.

g. **i.** $\cos 55° = \dfrac{AC}{AB}$

   $0.5736 = \dfrac{20}{AB}$

   $AB = \dfrac{20}{0.5736} \approx 34.8675 \approx 35$ feet

   ii. $\sin 55° = \dfrac{BC}{AB}$

   iii. Using the Pythagorean Theorem, $AB = \sqrt{AC^2 + BC^2}$.

NOTE The 55° angle is made by the edge of the protractor and the horizontal. The angle made by the edge of the protractor and the vertical is $90° - 55° = 35°$.

This method of measuring angles of elevation is based on some of the same principles as early sextants used by navigators to measure angles of elevation of particular stars.

(4) **a.** $\cos A = \dfrac{s}{7}; s = 7\cos A$

   $\sin C = \dfrac{s}{7}; s = 7\sin C$

b. $\cos F = \dfrac{8}{s}; s = \dfrac{8}{\cos F}$

   $\sin D = \dfrac{8}{s}; s = \dfrac{8}{\sin D}$

c. $\tan Q = \dfrac{s}{15}; s = 15\tan Q$

   $\tan P = \dfrac{15}{s}; s = \dfrac{15}{\tan P}$

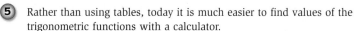

(5) Rather than using tables, today it is much easier to find values of the trigonometric functions with a calculator.

   a. To calculate a trigonometric function value for an angle measured in degrees, first be sure your calculator is set in *degree* mode. Then simply press the keys that correspond to the desired function. For example, to calculate sin 27.5° on most graphing calculators, press **SIN** **27.5** **)** **ENTER**. Try it. Then calculate cos 27.5° and tan 27.5°. Although your calculator displays 10 digits, you should report estimates of trigonometric function values to the nearest ten-thousandth.

   b. Use your calculator to find the sine, cosine, and tangent of 66°. Of 54°. Compare these results with those in the table on page 465.

   c. Use your calculator to find the sine, cosine, and tangent of 45°. Compare these results with the exact values you found in Problem 7 of Investigation 1.

(6) Each part below gives angle measure and side length information for right △ABC with ∠C a right angle. For each, sketch and label the triangle. Then find the lengths of the remaining two sides and find the measure of the third angle.

   a. ∠B = 52°, a = 5 m   **b.** ∠A = 48°, a = 15 mi

   c. ∠A = 31°, b = 8 in.   **d.** ∠A = 70°, c = 14 cm

Summarize
the Mathematics

The trigonometric functions sine, cosine, and tangent are useful in calculating lengths in situations modeled with right triangles. Refer to the right triangle below in summarizing your thinking about how to use trigonometric functions in the situations described.

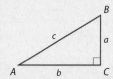

  a If you knew *b* and the measure of ∠A, how would you use that information to find *a*? How could you find m∠B? How could you find *c*?

  b If you knew *c* and the measure of ∠B, how would you use that information to find *a*? How could you find m∠A? How could you find *b*?

  c If you knew *a* and the measure of ∠A, how would you use that information to find *c*?

Be prepared to explain your methods to the entire class.

5. a. $\sin 27.5° \approx 0.4617$
$\cos 27.5° \approx 0.8870$
$\tan 27.5° \approx 0.5206$

b. $\sin 66° \approx 0.9135$ $\sin 54° \approx 0.8090$
$\cos 66° \approx 0.4067$ $\cos 54° \approx 0.5878$
$\tan 66° \approx 2.2460$ $\tan 54° \approx 1.3764$

c. $\sin 45° = \dfrac{1}{\sqrt{2}} \approx 0.7071$

$\cos 45° = \dfrac{1}{\sqrt{2}} \approx 0.7071$

$\tan 45° = 1$

6. a.

$\tan 52° = \dfrac{b}{5}$ $\cos 52° = \dfrac{5}{c}$

$b = 5 \tan 52°$ $c = \dfrac{5}{\cos 52°}$

$b \approx 6.4$ m $c \approx 8.1$ m

$m\angle A = 90° - 52° = 38°$

b.

$m\angle B = 42°$
$b \approx 13.5061 \approx 14$ mi
$c \approx 20.1845 \approx 20$ mi

c.

$m\angle B = 59°$
$a \approx 4.8069 \approx 5$ in.
$c \approx 9.3331 \approx 9$ in.

d.

$m\angle B = 20°$
$b \approx 4.7883 \approx 5$ cm
$a \approx 13.1557 \approx 13$ cm

Summarize the Mathematics

a $\tan A = \dfrac{a}{b}$; so, $a = b \tan A$; $m\angle B = 90° - m\angle A$; $c = \sqrt{a^2 + b^2}$ or
$c = \dfrac{b}{\cos A}$.

b $\cos B = \dfrac{a}{c}$; so, $a = c \cos B$; $m\angle A = 90° - m\angle B$; $b = \sqrt{c^2 - a^2}$ or
$b = c \sin B$.

c $\sin A = \dfrac{a}{c}$; so, $c = \dfrac{a}{\sin A}$.

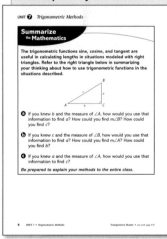

Teaching Resources

Transparency Master 6.

UNIT **7** *Trigonometric Methods*

Summarize *the* **Mathematics**

The trigonometric functions sine, cosine, and tangent are useful in calculating lengths in situations modeled with right triangles. Refer to the right triangle below in summarizing your thinking about how to use trigonometric functions in the situations described.

a If you knew *b* and the measure of ∠*A*, how would you use that information to find *a*? How could you find *m*∠*B*? How could you find *c*?

b If you knew *c* and the measure of ∠*B*, how would you use that information to find *a*? How could you find *m*∠*A*? How could you find *b*?

c If you knew *a* and the measure of ∠*A*, how would you use that information to find *c*?

Be prepared to explain your methods to the entire class.

6   UNIT 7 • Trigonometric Methods   Transparency Master • use with page 470

MATH TOOLKIT Record the right triangle definitions of the sine, cosine, and tangent functions. Use the definitions to make an example of finding a side length given the measures of an acute angle and one side.

✓ Check Your Understanding

Terri is flying a kite and has let out 500 feet of string. Her end of the string is 3 feet off the ground.

a. If ∠*KIT* has a measure of 40°, approximately how high off the ground is the kite?

b. As the wind picks up, Terri is able to fly the kite at a 56° angle with the horizontal. Approximately how high is the kite?

c. What is the highest Terri could fly the kite on 500 feet of string? What would be the measure of ∠*KIT* then?

d. Your answers in Parts a–c are estimates. When you actually fly a kite, what are some factors that might cause your answers to be somewhat inaccurate?

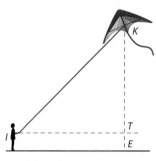

Investigation 3 — What's the Angle?

In Investigation 2, you used trigonometric functions to determine an unknown or inaccessible distance in situations that could be modeled with right triangles. In such situations, trigonometric functions can also be used to determine the measure of an angle when you know the lengths of two sides of a triangle. As you work on this investigation, look for answers to the following question:

> *How can trigonometric functions be used to determine the measure of an acute angle in a right triangle when the lengths of two sides are known?*

1 In Investigation 2, you explored ways to use trigonometric functions to indirectly measure the height of Chicago's *Bat Column* sculpture. Cal read some literature that said the *Bat Column's* height *BD* is about 30 meters.

a. Cal sighted to the top of the sculpture from a point *A*, 25 meters from point *C* and 1.5 meters above the ground. Experiment with your calculator to estimate, to the nearest degree, the measure of the angle of elevation that Cal should expect at point *A*.

b. Suppose Cal sighted from a point 18 meters from point *C* and 1.5 meters above the ground. Use the same method as in Part a to estimate the measure of the angle of elevation from this point.

c. Check your answers in Parts a and b using the table on page 465.

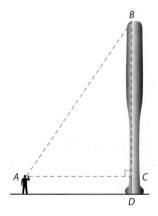

✓Check Your Understanding

a. Since $\sin 40° = \frac{KT}{500}$, $KT = 500 \sin 40°$, or approximately 321 feet. Thus, the kite is approximately $321 + 3$ or 324 feet off the ground.

b. This time, $\sin 56° = \frac{KT}{500}$; so $KT = 500 \sin 56°$, or approximately 415 feet. The kite is approximately 418 feet off the ground.

c. On 500 feet of string, with the string end 3 feet above the ground, 503 feet is the maximum that can be achieved. This would require the measure of $\angle KIT$ to be 90°, which is not likely to happen.

d. The main source of error is probably the sag in the kite string, so the triangle model probably overestimates the height of the kite for a given angle.

Investigation 3 — What's the Angle?

In this investigation, students will learn to use the inverse sine function to find the measure of an acute angle of a right triangle given lengths of two sides of the triangle. Before using the calculator's inverse sine function, students will be asked to use the table on page 465 in the opposite way that they had used it previously. Rather than read from the angle size to the value of the trigonometric function, they will use the trigonometric function value to estimate the angle size. Once this is done in Problem 1, students should use their calculator to estimate angle sizes *without* using the inverse sine key. This will be an estimating and refining process that will be verified again using the table on page 465. This development of the concept should help students understand the inverse trigonometric functions of the calculator when they are introduced in Problem 3.

1
a. Students will probably use $\tan A = \frac{28.5}{25} = 1.14$ and then try values for A. For example, $\tan 50° \approx 1.1918$, so try a value that is a little less than 50°. A good approximation is 48.7°, or to the nearest degree, 49°.

b. Students will probably use $\tan A = \frac{28.5}{18} \approx 1.5833$ and then try values for A. For example, $\tan 55° \approx 1.4281$, so try a value that is a little more than 55°. A good approximation is 57.7°, or to the nearest degree, 58°.

c. The values in Parts a and b check with those in the table.

Unit 7

2 Using your calculator, estimate (to the nearest degree) the measure of acute $\angle B$ for each of the following trigonometric functions. Check your estimate in each case using the table on page 465.

    a. $\sin B = \dfrac{3}{4}$ **b.** $\cos B = \dfrac{1}{2}$ **c.** $\tan B = 2$

3 You can also use the *inverse function* capabilities of your calculator to produce the acute angle measure when you know a trigonometric function value as in Problem 2. The function $\sin^{-1}$ (read "inverse sine") is related to the sine function for acute angles in a way similar to the way the square root and squaring operation are related. One function "undoes" the other. Thus, $\sin^{-1} x$ is the acute angle whose sine is x. The inverse cosine (denoted $\cos^{-1}$) and inverse tangent (denoted $\tan^{-1}$) are similarly related to the cosine and tangent functions.

    a. Suppose you know $\sin A = \dfrac{4}{5}$. Use the $\sin^{-1}$ function of your calculator to compute the measure of $\angle A$. (Make certain your calculator is set in degree mode.)

    b. Use inverse trigonometric functions to find the measure of $\angle B$ that corresponds to each of the function values given in Problem 2. Compare these values to the values you obtained in that problem.

    c. Use the calculator display at the right to find sin 37.58950296°.

    d. Use your calculator to find the degree measure of the acute angle in each of the following cases, where possible.

        i. $\tan B = 1.84$

        ii. $\sin A = 0.852$

        iii. $\sin A = 2.15$

        iv. $\cos B = 0.213$

4 House painters make decisions not only about the type of paint to use but also about what equipment to use. Suppose a house painter needs to buy a new extension ladder that will reach up to a vertical height of 30 feet when leaned against the side of a house. For safety reasons, it is recommended that the ladder is placed so the angle it makes with level ground measures 75°.

    a. What is the minimum fully-extended length of a ladder that meets these requirements?

    b. Suppose the painter's assistant extends the new ladder to 28 feet and leans it against a house from a point 11.5 feet from the house.

        i. What angle does the ladder make with the ground?

        ii. At what vertical height from the ground does the ladder meet the side of the house?

        iii. To what length should the ladder be adjusted if it is to reach the same point on the side of the house but make the recommended 75° angle with the ground?

        iv. How far will the ladder be placed from the house after it is adjusted as in part iii?

2 Students should try various values of B to estimate its value and then check using the table on page 465.

   a. 49°

   b. 60°

   c. 63°

3   **a.** $\sin^{-1}(0.8) \approx 53.1301°$

   b. 48.5904°; 60°; 63.4350°

   c. 0.61

   d. **i.** 61.5°

      ii. 58.4°

     iii. Not possible because $\sin A \leq 1$.

     iv. 77.7°

> **TECHNOLOGY NOTE**
> Note that the notation arcsin, arccos, and arctan is used by some calculators and computer programs instead of $\sin^{-1}$, $\cos^{-1}$, and $\tan^{-1}$.

4   **a.**

$$\sin 75° = \frac{30}{c}$$

$$c = \frac{30}{\sin 75°} \approx 31.0583 \text{ feet}$$

The ladder must extend slightly more than 31 feet.

   b. **i.** $\cos \angle A = \frac{11.5}{28} \approx 0.4107$

        $m\angle A \approx 65.75°$

      ii. $a = \sqrt{(28)^2 - (11.5)^2}$

        $a \approx 25.5$ feet

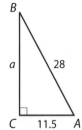

     iii. $\sin 75° = \frac{25.5}{c}$

        $c \approx 26.4$ feet

     iv. $\tan 75° = \frac{25.5}{b}$

        $b \approx 6.8$ feet

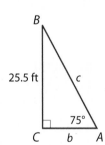

        Alternatively, students could use the Pythagorean Theorem.

Summarize
the Mathematics

The sine, cosine, and tangent functions are useful in finding the measures of acute angles of a right triangle using the lengths of two sides. Refer to the right triangle below to summarize your thinking about such situations.

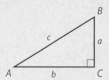

a If you knew a and c, how would you use that information to find the measure of $\angle B$? How could you then find m$\angle A$? How could you find b?

b If you knew b and c, how would you use that information to find the measure of $\angle B$? How could you then find m$\angle A$?

c If you knew a and b, how would you use that information to find the measure of $\angle A$?

Be prepared to explain your methods to the entire class.

✔Check Your Understanding

A person on an oil-drilling ship in the Gulf of Mexico sees a semi-submersible platform with a tower on top of it. The tower stands 130 meters above the platform floor.

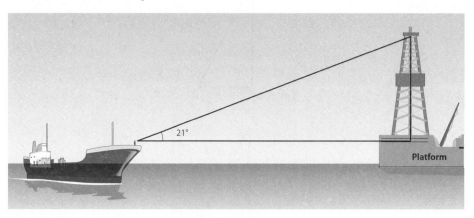

a. If the observer's position on the boat is 15 meters under the floor of the platform and the angle of elevation to the top of the rig is 21°, what three distances can you find? Find them.

b. Suppose the boat moves so the observer is 200 meters from the center line of the tower. What is the angle of elevation now?

Summarize the Mathematics

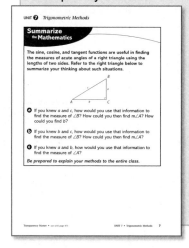
a $m\angle B = \cos^{-1}\left(\dfrac{a}{c}\right)$

$m\angle A = 90° - m\angle B;\ b = \sqrt{c^2 - a^2}$

b $m\angle B = \sin^{-1}\left(\dfrac{b}{c}\right)$

$m\angle A = 90° - m\angle B$

c $m\angle A = \tan^{-1}\left(\dfrac{a}{b}\right)$

✓ Check Your Understanding

MATH TOOLKIT Add to your right triangle trigonometry notes an example showing how to find the measure of the acute angles of a right triangle given two side lengths.

a. In the right triangle pictured, the side opposite the angle of elevation is $130 + 15$, or 145 meters. Call the adjacent side b, the distance from the observer to the center of the platform. Call the hypotenuse c. This latter distance is from the eye of the observer to the top of the tower. Both b and c can be determined as follows.

$\tan 21° \approx 0.3839 = \dfrac{145}{b};\ b = \dfrac{145}{0.3839} \approx 378$ meters

$\sin 21° \approx 0.3584 = \dfrac{145}{c};\ c = \dfrac{145}{0.3584} \approx 405$ meters

b. The angle of elevation can be determined from its tangent.

$m\angle A = \tan^{-1}\left(\dfrac{145}{200}\right) = \tan^{-1} 0.725 \approx 36°$

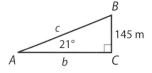

Unit 7

Applications

1 More people these days are exercising regularly. Exercise scientists measure the amount of work done by people in various forms of exercise so they can learn more about its effect. One popular form of exercise is walking on a treadmill.

Axle-to-Axle distance

Vertical rise

θ

a. What features of a treadmill do you think would increase or decrease the amount of work done by the walker?

b. One index that exercise scientists use is the *percent grade* of the treadmill. Percent grade is computed as 100 multiplied by the sine of the measure of the angle of elevation θ of the treadmill. Suppose θ is in standard position. Compute the percent grade of a two-meter (axle-to-axle) treadmill with a vertical rise of 0.25 meters. Of 0.33 meters.

c. How do you think the percent grade is related to the amount of work a person does on a treadmill?

2 Steep hills on highways are the scourge of long-distance bikers. To measure the percent grade of a section of highway, surveyors use transits to estimate the average angle of elevation (or inclination) over a measured distance of highway. Then the percent grade is computed in the same way as described in Task 1 Part b for a treadmill.

a. If you ride down a straight 3-mile section of highway that has an 8% grade, how far do you drop vertically?

b. If the angle of inclination of a 2-mile section of straight highway is about 4°, what is the percent grade?

3 Suppose the terminal side of an angle in standard position with measure θ contains the indicated point. Find sin θ, cos θ, and tan θ. Then find the measure of the angle to the nearest degree.

a. $P(3, 4)$

b. $P(5, 12)$

c. $P(0, -10)$

d. $P(-5, 5)$

Applications

① **a.** Answers may vary, but increases in the speed of the treadmill and in the angle of inclination will increase the work.

b. *percent grade* $= 100 \sin A = 100 \times \dfrac{0.25}{2} = 12.5\%$

percent grade $= 100 \sin A = 100 \times \dfrac{0.33}{2} = 16.5\%$

c. The amount of work increases as the percent grade increases.

② **a.** $8 = 100 \sin \theta$, so $\sin \theta = 0.08 = \dfrac{\textit{vertical rise}}{3}$;

therefore, *vertical rise* ≈ 0.24 miles $\approx 1{,}267$ feet.

b. *percent grade* $= 100 \sin 4° \approx 7\%$

③ **a.** $P(3, 4)$, $r = 5$

$\sin \theta = \dfrac{4}{5}$

$\cos \theta = \dfrac{3}{5}$

$\tan \theta = \dfrac{4}{3}$

$\theta \approx 53°$

(using the table on page 465)

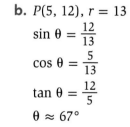

> **ASSIGNMENT NOTE**
> Applications Task 3 should be assigned immediately after completing Investigation 1. Students should not use calculators for this task.

b. $P(5, 12)$, $r = 13$

$\sin \theta = \dfrac{12}{13}$

$\cos \theta = \dfrac{5}{13}$

$\tan \theta = \dfrac{12}{5}$

$\theta \approx 67°$

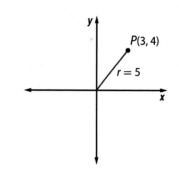

c. $P(0, -10)$, $r = 10$

$\sin \theta = \dfrac{-10}{10} = -1$

$\cos \theta = \dfrac{0}{10} = 0$

$\tan \theta$ is undefined because

$\tan \theta = \dfrac{-10}{0}$ is meaningless.

$\theta = 270°$

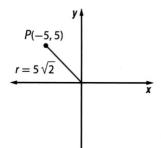

d. $P(-5, 5)$, $r = 5\sqrt{2}$

$\sin \theta = \dfrac{5}{5\sqrt{2}} = \dfrac{1}{\sqrt{2}}$

$\cos \theta = -\dfrac{5}{5\sqrt{2}} = -\dfrac{1}{\sqrt{2}}$

$\tan \theta = \dfrac{5}{-5} = -1$

$\theta = 135°$

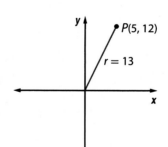

(4) In Fort Recovery, Ohio, there is a monument to local soldiers who died in battle. Mr. Knapke, a teacher at the local high school, challenged his class to find as many ways as they could to measure the height of the monument indirectly.

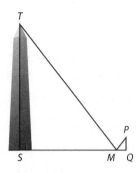

Pedro, whose eye level *P* is 5.8 feet, proposed a novel solution. He placed a mirror *M* on the ground 45 feet from the center of the monument's base and then moved to a point 2.6 feet further from the monument where he could just see to the top of the monument in the mirror. He recalled from his earlier studies that the angle of incidence and the angle of reflection are congruent.

a. On a copy of the diagram above, show all of the given information.

b. Figure out how Pedro found the height of the monument. What is the height?

c. Describe another method to find the height of the monument.

(5) A survey team was to measure the distance across a river over which a bridge is to be built. They set up a survey post on their side of the river directly across from a large tree on the other side. Then they walked downstream a distance that they measured to be 400 meters. From the downstream position, they sighted the survey post and then rotated their calibrated transit to the tree to find the sighting angle to be 31°.

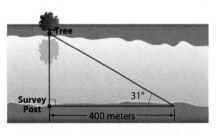

a. Determine the distance directly across the river, that is, from the survey post to the tree on the opposite bank.

b. Determine the distance from the surveyors' sighting point to the tree on the opposite bank.

4 **a.**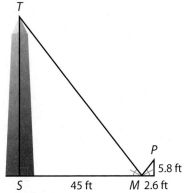

b. The acute angles at M in the small right triangle and in the large one have equal measures. In the small triangle, $\tan M = \frac{5.8}{2.6} \approx 2.2308$. In the large triangle, $\tan M = \frac{h}{45}$, where h is the height of the monument. Solve $2.2308 = \frac{h}{45}$ for h. $h = (2.2308)(45) \approx 100.4$ feet.

c. With an inclinometer or transit, you could measure the angle of elevation from a point at a measured distance away from the base of the monument. Then use the tangent of that angle, found with your calculator, to solve for the height. Students may propose other correct possibilities.

5 **a.** Using d to represent the distance across the river, $\tan 31° = \frac{d}{400}$ and $d = 400 \tan 31° \approx 240.344 \approx 240$ meters.

b. Using h to represent the length of the hypotenuse of the right triangle in the diagram, $h = \sqrt{400^2 + 240.344^2} \approx 467$ meters.

> **INSTRUCTIONAL NOTE**
> William J. Young invented the transit in 1831 to measure angles. By sighting from a fixed point to two other points marked by a surveyor's marker or some landmark, the measure of the angle at the transit and the measure of the angle of elevation or depression can be read on the transit's scales. You may wish to find a picture of surveyors using tripods and sighting poles to help students understand the process.

6 In each right triangle below, you are given two measures. Find the remaining side lengths and angle measures.

a.

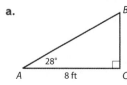

b.

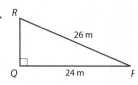

c.

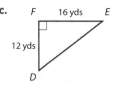

7 From the eye of an observer at the top of a cliff 125 m from the surface of the water, the *angles of depression* to two sailboats, both due west of the observer, are 16° and 23°. Calculate the distance between the sailboats.

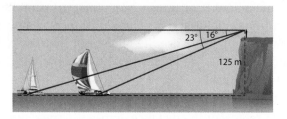

8 Commercial aircraft usually fly at an altitude between 9 and 11 kilometers (about 29,000 to 36,000 feet). When an aircraft is landing, its gradual descent to an airport runway occurs over a long distance. Assume the path of descent is a line.

a. Suppose a commercial airliner begins its descent from an altitude of 9.4 km with an angle of descent of 2.5°. At what distance from the runway should the descent begin?

b. Suppose a commercial airliner flying at an altitude of 11 km begins its descent at a horizontal distance 270 km from the end of the runway. What is its angle of descent?

6 a.

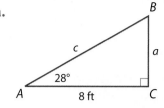

$$\cos 28° = \frac{8}{c}$$
$$c = \frac{8}{\cos 28°} \approx 9.0606 \approx 9 \text{ ft}$$
$$\tan 28° = \frac{a}{8}$$
$$a = 8 \tan 28° \approx 4.2538 \approx 4 \text{ ft}$$
$$m\angle B = 90° - m\angle A = 62°$$

b.

$$\cos P = \frac{24}{26} \approx 0.9231$$
$$m\angle P \approx 22.62° \approx 23°$$
$$m\angle R = 90° - m\angle P \approx 67°$$
$$RQ = \sqrt{26^2 - 24^2} = 10 \text{ m}$$

c.

$$\tan D = \frac{16}{12} \approx 1.3333$$
$$m\angle D \approx 53.13° \approx 53°$$
$$m\angle E \approx 90° - m\angle D \approx 37°$$
$$DE = \sqrt{16^2 + 12^2} = 20 \text{ yds}$$

7

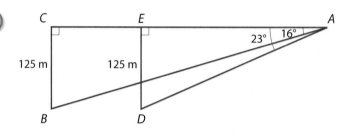

The distance between the sailboats is $BD = CE = AC - AE$. So, find AC and AE to compute $AC - AE$.

$$\tan 16° = \frac{125}{AC}; AC \approx 436 \text{ m}$$
$$\tan 23° = \frac{125}{AE}; AE \approx 294 \text{ m}$$
$$BD = 436 - 294 \approx 142 \text{ m}$$

8 a. Let d represent the horizontal distance from the runway when descent begins. Then $\tan 2.5° = \frac{9.4}{d}$, so

$$d = \frac{9.4}{\tan 2.5°} \approx 215.3 \text{ km}.$$

b. If the angle of descent is D, $\tan D = \frac{11}{270} \approx 0.0407$. Then $m\angle D = \tan^{-1} 0.0407 \approx 2.3°$.

c. The *cockpit cutoff angle* of an airliner is the angle formed by the pilot's horizontal line of sight and her line of sight to the nose of the plane. Suppose a pilot is flying an aircraft with a cockpit cutoff angle of 14° at an altitude of 1.5 km. In her line of sight along the nose of the plane, she sights the near edge of a lake.

 i. How far is she from the edge of the lake, measuring along her line of sight?

 ii. What is the horizontal distance to the near edge of the lake?

Connections

(9) The diagram below extends the diagram on page 463 to show several other angles, $\angle AOP_n$, in standard position in a coordinate plane. Angles are marked off in 10° intervals.

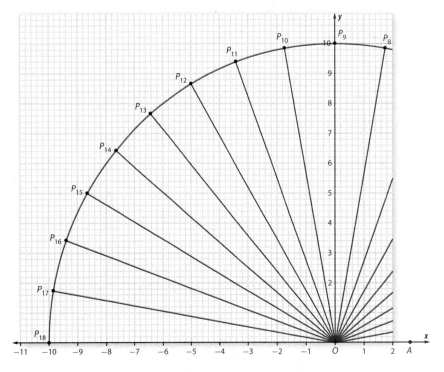

c. **i.** Let x represent the straight-line distance to the edge of the lake, $\sin 14° = \dfrac{1.5}{x}$. Then $x = \dfrac{1.5}{\sin 14°} \approx 6.2$ km.

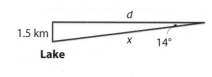

1.5 km

Lake

d

x 14°

ii. Let d represent the horizontal distance to the edge of the lake, $\tan 14° = \dfrac{1.5}{d}$. Then $d = \dfrac{1.5}{\tan 14°} \approx 6$ km.

a. Use the diagram to calculate approximate values of the following:

   i. cos 120°   **ii.** sin 120°   **iii.** tan 120°

   iv. cos 160°   **v.** sin 160°   **vi.** tan 160°

b. What is cos 180°? sin 180°? tan 180°?

c. How could you use symmetry of the semicircle and your completed copy of the table on page 463 to determine each of the trigonometric function values in Part a?

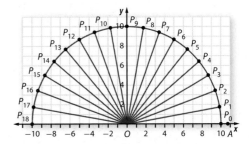

d. Refer to the diagram above. As the measure of $\angle AOP_n$ increases from 90° to 180°,

   i. how does the sine of the angle change?

   ii. how does the cosine of the angle change?

   iii. how does the tangent of the angle change?

10 The diagram at the right shows a portion of a circle with radius 1 and center at the origin. For acute angle θ in the diagram, the values sin θ, cos θ, and tan θ can all be seen as segment lengths. Explain why:

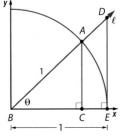

a. cos θ = BC

b. sin θ = AC

c. tan θ = DE

11 A portion of a circle with radius 1 and center at the origin is shown below. Point P_1 is the image of point A under a 45° counterclockwise rotation about the origin. Point P_2 is the image of point A under a counterclockwise rotation of θ degrees about the origin.

a. What is the length of $\overline{OP_1}$? Of $\overline{OP_2}$? Explain your reasoning.

b. Why does a = cos 45°? Why does b = sin 45°?

c. What is the x-coordinate c of point P_2 written as a trigonometric function of θ? What is the y-coordinate d?

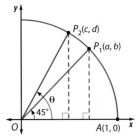

Connections

⑨ **a.** **i.** $\cos 120° \approx -0.5$

ii. $\sin 120° \approx 0.87$

iii. $\tan 120° \approx -1.73$

iv. $\cos 160° \approx -0.94$

v. $\sin 160° \approx 0.34$

vi. $\tan 160° \approx -0.36$

b. $\cos 180° = -1$; $\sin 180° = 0$; $\tan 180° = 0$

c. Since the trigonometric values result from ratios of the coordinates and the radius of the circle, you can find the trigonometric values for angles in Quadrant II (obtuse angles) by using the image of the point on the circle reflected across the y-axis. So, for example, a point $(-x, y)$ in Quadrant II has image point (x, y) in Quadrant I. The negative x-coordinate in Quadrant II means that the cosine and tangent values will be negative in Quadrant II. So, to use the table on page 465 for 120° or P_{12}, reflect P_{12} across the y-axis to P_6. Use the negative of the cos 60° and tan 60° function values from the table for a 120° angle. The $\sin 60° = \sin 120°$.

d. **i.** As the angle measure increases from 90° to 180°, the sine of the angle decreases at a nonconstant (increasing) rate from 1 to 0.

ii. As the angle measure increases from 90° to 180°, the cosine of the angle decreases at a nonconstant (decreasing) rate from 0 to −1.

iii. As the angle measure increases from slightly more than 90° to 180°, the tangent of the angle increases at a nonconstant (decreasing) rate from large negative values to 0.

⑩ $\cos \theta = \dfrac{BC}{AB} = \dfrac{BC}{1} = BC$

$\sin \theta = \dfrac{AC}{BC} = \dfrac{AC}{1} = AC$

$\tan \theta = \dfrac{DE}{BE} = \dfrac{DE}{1} = DE$

⑪ **a.** $OP_1 = OP_2 = 1$ since they are both radii of the given circle.

b. Since the radius of the circle is 1, $\cos 45° = \dfrac{a}{1} = a$ and $\sin 45° = \dfrac{b}{1} = b$.

c. $c = \cos \theta$; $d = \sin \theta$

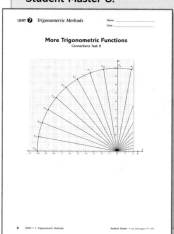

Unit 7

d. Based on your work in Parts a and b, what must be true about the expression $(\sin 45°)^2 + (\cos 45°)^2$? Evaluate the expression by calculating the function values.

e. What must be true about the expression $(\sin \theta)^2 + (\cos \theta)^2$? Explain your reasoning.

12 In Investigation 1, you used geometric reasoning to determine *exact* values of sin 45°, cos 45°, and tan 45°. You also determined exact values of these functions for angles of measure 0° and 90° (with the exception of tan 90°). Use equilateral triangle *ABC* to help you determine the *exact* trigonometric function values below. $\overline{AM}$ is a median of the triangle. (The side length 2 is chosen for ease of computation.)

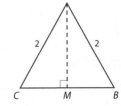

a. cos 60°   **b.** sin 60°   **c.** tan 60°

d. cos 30°   **e.** sin 30°   **f.** tan 30°

13 The diagram below shows a portion of a circle with radius 1 and center at the origin. Point *A′* is the image of point *A* and point *B′* is the image of point *B* under a 30° counterclockwise rotation about the origin.

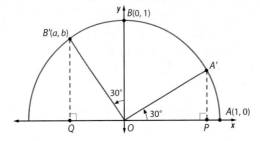

a. Explain why the coordinates of point *A′* are (cos 30°, sin 30°).

b. What is the length of $\overline{OB'}$? Why?

   i. Write the *x*-coordinate *a* of point *B′* as a trigonometric function of 30°.

   ii. Write the *y*-coordinate *b* of point *B′* as a trigonometric function of 30°.

c. In the *Coordinate Methods* unit, you learned that you could build a matrix representation of a rotation about the origin by knowing what happens to the points with coordinates (1, 0) and (0, 1). In that unit, you found the entries of the 30° counterclockwise rotation matrix to be

$$\begin{bmatrix} \dfrac{\sqrt{3}}{2} & -\dfrac{1}{2} \\ \dfrac{1}{2} & \dfrac{\sqrt{3}}{2} \end{bmatrix}.$$

Express the entries of this matrix in terms of cos 30° and sin 30°.

d. Transform the point *B*(0, 1) by multiplying by the matrix in Part c. Do you obtain the coordinates of *B′*?

d. $(\sin 45°)^2 + (\cos 45°)^2 = b^2 + a^2 = 1^2 = 1$ by the Pythagorean Theorem.

e. $(\sin \theta)^2 + (\cos \theta)^2 = 1$ since $d^2 + c^2 = 1$ for any angle θ, when $P(c, d)$ is the point where the terminal side of θ intersects the circle.

12

a. $\cos 60° = \frac{1}{2}$ **b.** $\sin 60° = \frac{\sqrt{3}}{2}$

c. $\tan 60° = \sqrt{3}$ **d.** $\cos 30° = \frac{\sqrt{3}}{2}$

e. $\sin 30° = \frac{1}{2}$ **f.** $\tan 30° = \frac{1}{\sqrt{3}}$

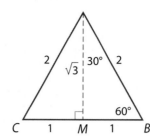

13 **INSTRUCTIONAL NOTE** Class discussions of Connections tasks allow you the opportunity to ensure that students fully understand the connections and, in some cases, press for additional understanding. In Task 13, you may wish to use *CPMP-Tools* geometry software to rotate a shape by angles other than the 30° and 90° rotations suggested in the student text to check that the trigonometric rotation matrix in Part c works for other angles of rotation. Use the "Rotate by" option to enter an angle size, such as 20°. Then choose "Show Matrix" to see the rotation matrix. Students can then check the sine and cosine values for 20° to see that they match the rotation matrix for 20°.

a. $\triangle OA'P$ is a 30°-60° right triangle. Using the diagram at the right, $x = \frac{\sqrt{3}}{2}$ and $y = \frac{1}{2}$. So, $A'\left(\frac{\sqrt{3}}{2}, \frac{1}{2}\right)$. As seen in Connections Task 12, $\cos 30° = \frac{\sqrt{3}}{2}$ and $\sin 30° = \frac{1}{2}$. So, the coordinates of point A' can be written as $(\cos 30°, \sin 30°)$.

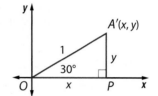

b. $OB' = 1$ because $\overline{OB'}$ is a radius.

   i. $a = -\sin 30°$

   ii. $b = \cos 30°$

c. $\begin{bmatrix} \cos 30° & -\sin 30° \\ \sin 30° & \cos 30° \end{bmatrix}$

d. $\begin{bmatrix} \frac{\sqrt{3}}{2} & -\frac{1}{2} \\ \frac{1}{2} & \frac{\sqrt{3}}{2} \end{bmatrix} \begin{bmatrix} 0 \\ 1 \end{bmatrix} = \begin{bmatrix} -\frac{1}{2} \\ \frac{\sqrt{3}}{2} \end{bmatrix}$

The result is equivalent to the coordinates of B'.

e. How could you use the sine and cosine functions to build a matrix for a counterclockwise rotation of θ degrees with center at the origin? Check your answer for the case of a 90° counterclockwise rotation.

14 At the opening of this lesson, you may have explored the operation of an automobile jack using the interactive geometry "Auto Jack" custom tool. Recall that points *A* and *C* are connected by a long threaded rod, and the lengths *AB*, *BC*, *AD*, and *CD* are all 1 foot. The distance *AC* is longer or shorter depending on the direction the rod is turned.

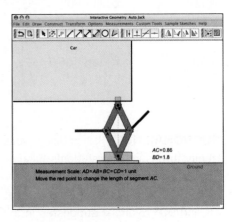

a. If *AC* = *x*, use the Pythagorean Theorem to write a rule that expresses the height *BD* as a function of *x*.

b. What is the domain of the function in Part a?

c. Use a graph of the function to explore how the height *BD* of the jack changes as *AC* changes. Sketch the graph and describe the shape of the graph as precisely as you can.

d. How is the pattern of change you saw in the graph reflected in the table of function values? Start at 0 and use increments of 0.1.

15 In the *Coordinate Methods* unit, Connections Task 18 (page 188) and Connections Task 21 (page 225), you prepared a table summarizing connections between important geometric ideas and their coordinate representations. Review the table you completed and then add to it coordinate representations and examples for the ideas of "angle in standard position" and "trigonometric functions of angle measure."

16 An angle in standard position has its terminal side in the first quadrant on a line whose equation is given. For each of the following lines, determine the measure of the angle.

a. $y = 20x$ **b.** $y = 8x$ **c.** $y = 0.5x$

17 The length of a side of a rectangle is 8 inches and the length of its diagonal is 9.5 inches.

a. What is the perimeter of this rectangle? What is its area?

b. What is the measure of an angle formed by a diagonal and an 8-inch side?

c. What is the measure of an angle formed by a diagonal and a side that is not 8 inches long?

e. $\begin{bmatrix} \cos\theta & -\sin\theta \\ \sin\theta & \cos\theta \end{bmatrix}$

14 a.

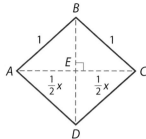

$BE = \sqrt{1 - 0.25x^2}$

$BD = 2\sqrt{1 - 0.25x^2}$

b. The domain is $0 \le AC < 2$. If the threaded rod is longer than 2 ft, then AC could be a maximum of 2 ft. If the jack is threaded so that it is as tall as possible, then AC would theoretically be 0.

c. The graph is a quarter circle with radius 2. When $AC = 0$, the jack is fully extended, that is, $BD = 2$. As the crank is turned at a constant rate, AC gets longer at a constant rate. At first, BD decreases slowly and then the rate of decrease gets faster as AC approaches 2 feet.

d. The table values decrease slowly at first and then more rapidly.

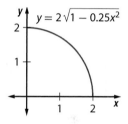

15

Geometric Idea	Coordinate Model	Example
Angle in standard position	When the initial side is the positive *x*-axis, an angle can be identified by a point (x, y) on the terminal side of the angle.	$P(-1, 4)$
Trigonometric functions of angle measure θ	For any point $P(x, y)$ on the terminal side of an angle in standard position and $r = \sqrt{x^2 + y^2}$	For the diagram above, $r = \sqrt{17}$
$\sin\theta$	$= \dfrac{y}{r}$	$= \dfrac{4}{\sqrt{17}}$
$\cos\theta$	$= \dfrac{x}{r}$	$= \dfrac{-1}{\sqrt{17}}$
$\tan\theta$	$= \dfrac{y}{x}$	$= \dfrac{4}{-1} = -4$

16 a. $\tan\theta = 20$; $\theta \approx 87°$

b. $\tan\theta = 8$; $\theta \approx 83°$

c. $\tan\theta = 0.5$; $\theta \approx 27°$

17 a. Using the Pythagorean Theorem:

$s = \sqrt{9.5^2 - 8^2} = \sqrt{26.25} \approx 5.1$ in.
Perimeter $= 2(8) + 2(5.1) = 26.2$ in.
Area $= (8)(5.1) = 40.8$ in.^{2}

b. Let A be the angle formed by the diagonal and an 8-inch side. Then $\cos A = \dfrac{8}{9.5} \approx 0.8421$ and $m\angle A = \cos^{-1} 0.8421 \approx 32.6°$.

c. $m\angle B = 90° - 32.6° = 57.4°$

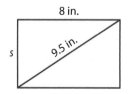

Unit 7

(18) The Pyramid of Cheops in Egypt is a square pyramid. The base edge measures 230 meters, and each face makes an angle of 51.8° with the horizontal floor.

a. Make a sketch of the Pyramid of Cheops.

b. Determine the vertical height of the pyramid.

c. If you were climbing the pyramid, what would be the shortest route to the top? What is the length of this route?

d. Determine the dimensions and angle measures of the triangular faces of the pyramid. Then determine the area of each face.

e. Determine the volume of the Pyramid of Cheops.

Reflections

(19) A line through the origin forms an acute angle with the positive x-axis of degree measure θ called the *angle of inclination* of the line. Express the slope of the line as a trigonometric function of θ. What is the equation of the line?

(20) Suppose $\triangle ABC$ is a right triangle with $\angle C$ a right angle.

a. If $m\angle A = 50°$, what is $m\angle B$? If $m\angle B = 10°$, what is $m\angle A$?

b. If you know the measure of one acute angle of a right triangle, explain why you can always determine the measure of the other acute angle.

c. Two angles whose measures sum to 90° are called **complementary angles**. In what sense do they complement each other?

d. The term "cosine" suggests that the cosine of an acute angle is the sine of the complement of that angle. Does $\cos 50° = \sin 40°$? Does $\cos 80° = \sin 10°$?

e. Suppose $\angle D$ and $\angle E$ are acute angles of a right triangle.

  i. Use a diagram to explain why $\cos D = \sin E$.

  ii. Why can the equation in part i also be written as $\cos D = \sin (90° - D)$? Why can it also be written as $\sin E = \cos (90° - E)$?

LESSON 1 • Trigonometric Functions **481**

18 a. See the figure at the right.

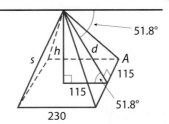

b. Since the base edge is 230 m, the center of the square base is 115 m from each side and directly below the vertex of the pyramid. The right triangle containing the center of the square base has one leg of 115 m and acute angle of 51.8°. The height h is the other leg. $\tan 51.8° = \frac{h}{115}$, so $h = 115 \tan 51.8° \approx 146.1389 \approx 146$ m.

c. The shortest distance to the vertex of the pyramid is straight up the center of a face. That distance d is the hypotenuse of the right triangle used in Part b.

$d^2 = 115^2 + 146.1389^2$

$d \approx 186$ m

Alternatively, students could solve $\cos 51.8° = \frac{115}{d}$.

d. Each face is an isosceles triangle with a base of 230 meters and an altitude d of approximately 186 meters. Since the altitude bisects the base, a base angle A can be found from this equation.

$\tan A = \frac{186}{115} \approx 1.617$; therefore, $m\angle A = \tan^{-1} 1.617 \approx 58.3°$.

The angle at the vertex of the pyramid in any face is $180° - 2(58.3°) = 63.4°$.

The common length s of the two congruent sides of the faces can be found using the Pythagorean Theorem:

$s^2 = 115^2 + 186^2 = 47,821$; so, $s \approx 219$ m.

The area of each face is $Area = 0.5(230)(186) = 21,390$ m^2.

e. $Volume = \frac{1}{3}(230^2)(146) \approx 2,574,467$ m^3

Reflections

 19 The slope is $\tan \theta$. The equation of the line is $y = (\tan \theta)x$.

20 a. $m\angle B = 40°$; $m\angle A = 80°$

b. The sum of the measures of all 3 angles is 180°, so the two acute angles of a right triangle must sum to 90°.

c. Together the angles make a right angle which is very useful.

d.

e. i.

	yes; yes
	$\cos D = \frac{e}{f}$
	$\sin E = \frac{e}{f}$

ii. Angles D and E are complementary. $m\angle E = 90° - m\angle D$. Since $\cos D = \sin E$, by substitution, $\cos D = \sin (90° - D)$. Similar reasoning can be used to show that $\sin E = \cos (90° - E)$.

Unit 7

21 What combinations of known facts about parts of a right triangle enable you to find information about other parts?

22 The label on a jar of creamy peanut butter claims that each serving (2 tablespoons) contains 16 grams of fat, 6 grams of carbohydrate, and 8 grams of protein. A recipe for peanut butter cookies calls for 5 tablespoons of peanut butter.

   a. Write proportions whose solutions would tell the number of grams of fat f, carbohydrate c, and protein p from peanut butter in the cookie recipe.

   b. Solve each of the equations in Part a.

   c. Explain how the equations solved in Part b are similar to equations with trigonometric functions used to find side lengths in right triangles.

23 When using trigonometric methods to solve a problem represented by a right triangle, how do you decide whether to use the sine, cosine, or tangent function?

24 If the angle of depression from point A at the top of a mountain to point B at a lower elevation is 20°, what is the angle of elevation from point B to point A? Explain why, using an appropriate diagram.

25 Do a search on "surveying" on the Internet. Look for ways in which surveyors use trigonometry, the instruments they use, and the training and skills that are required. Write a brief report describing your findings.

Extensions

26 As you learned in this lesson, two different points on the terminal side of the same angle in standard position determine two different right triangles, but ratios of corresponding sides of the two triangles are equal. In this task, you will examine another way of justifying this fact.

   a. Refer to Diagram I below. What is the equation of $\overleftrightarrow{OP}$?

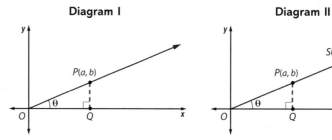

Diagram I　　　　　　　**Diagram II**

   b. Use the coordinates of P to write each of the following lengths as an algebraic expression:

    i. OQ **ii.** QP **iii.** OP

21 **INSTRUCTIONAL NOTE** Students should recognize that when using trigonometric ratios, there are three values: the angle measure and two lengths. Knowing two of the three values allows you to solve for the missing third value.

When you are given the measure of one acute angle and the length of one side of a right triangle, you can use the sine, cosine, or tangent function to find the lengths of the other two sides of the right triangle. The third angle measure is 90° minus the given angle size. Alternatively, once you have found the length of a second side, you can use the Pythagorean Theorem to find the length of the third side.

When you are given the length of two sides of a right triangle, you can find the length of the third side using the Pythagorean Theorem (or using trigonometric ratios, although this method is a little more complicated). The measure of an acute angle can be found using an inverse trigonometric function. The measure of the other acute angle can be found by subtracting the value from 90°.

22 **a.** $\frac{f}{5} = \frac{16}{2}; \frac{c}{5} = \frac{6}{2}; \frac{p}{5} = \frac{8}{2}$

b. $2f = (16)(5)$ or $f = 40$ grams of fat
$2c = (6)(5)$ or $c = 15$ grams of carbohydrate
$2p = (8)(5)$ or $p = 20$ grams of protein

c. When trigonometric functions are used to find side lengths in right triangles, usually one length ℓ and one acute angle A are known, and the equation is of the form $f(A) = \frac{x}{\ell}$ or $f(A) = \frac{\ell}{x}$, where f is sine, cosine, or tangent, and x is the unknown side length.

23 You need to choose a trigonometric function for which you know two of the three numbers in the function expression: the angle size and the two side lengths of the ratio.

24 Assuming the ground is horizontal and thus parallel to the horizontal side of the angle of depression, $\triangle ADB \cong \triangle BCA$ by the SAS congruence condition. Thus, $\angle BAC \cong \angle ABD$. (If students recall alternate interior angles of parallel lines from middle school, they might reason using that property.)

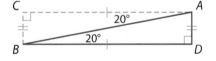

25 The Land Surveyor Reference Web site is www.lsrp.com. It gives many more links that students may be interested in visiting.

Extensions

26 **a.** $y = \frac{b}{a}x$

b. **i.** $OQ = a$

ii. $QP = b$

iii. $OP = \sqrt{a^2 + b^2}$

c. In Diagram II on page 482, $S(x, y)$ is any other point on $\overleftrightarrow{OP}$ other than the origin, $(0, 0)$. Explain why point S has coordinates of the form $\left(x, \frac{b}{a}x\right)$.

d. Use the coordinates of S to write each of the following lengths as an algebraic expression:

   i. OT **ii.** TS **iii.** OS

e. Compare the following pairs of ratios:

   i. $\frac{QP}{OQ}$ and $\frac{TS}{OT}$ **ii.** $\frac{QP}{OP}$ and $\frac{TS}{OS}$ **iii.** $\frac{OQ}{OP}$ and $\frac{OT}{OS}$

   What can you conclude?

 In $\triangle ABC$ shown here, $\overline{BD}$ is an altitude.

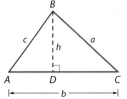

a. Express $\sin C$ in terms of h and a.

b. Explain why the following is true:

   area of $\triangle ABC = 0.5 \cdot ab \cdot \sin C$.

c. Write another formula for the area of $\triangle ABC$, this one in terms of $\sin A$.

d. Using Parts b and c, show that

   $a \cdot \sin C = c \cdot \sin A$.

 A surveyor made a sighting to the top of a mountain peak from point A, located on a flat plateau. The angle of elevation from point A was $28°$. He then moved 200 feet directly toward the mountain to point B on the same plateau. The angle of elevation from point B was $39°$. Find the height of the mountain peak above the plateau. Draw a figure, and explain your steps.

29 While camping by the Merced River in Yosemite Valley, a group of friends were admiring a particular tree on the opposite bank. Maria claimed that the height of the tree could be determined from the group's side of the river by the following method:

- Measure a 50-meter segment, $\overline{AB}$, on this shore.

- Consider the base of the tree to be located at point C and use a sighting device to measure $\angle BAC$ and $\angle ABC$.

- From A, measure the angle of elevation to the top of the tree, located at point D.

- Use the measurements above with some trigonometric functions to calculate the height.

The friends measured $\angle BAC$ to be $54°$ and $\angle ABC$ to be $74°$. The angle of elevation from point A to the treetop was $21°$. Draw a sketch of this situation and determine whether Maria was correct. If she was, compute the height; if she was not, explain why not.

c. Coordinates are of the form $\left(x, \frac{b}{a}x\right)$ because the equation of the line is
$y = \frac{b}{a}x$.

d. **i.** $OT = x$

    ii. $TS = y = \frac{b}{a}x$

    iii. $OS = \sqrt{x^2 + \left(\frac{b}{a}x\right)^2} = \sqrt{\frac{a^2x^2 + b^2x^2}{a^2}} = \sqrt{\frac{x^2}{a^2}(a^2 + b^2)} =$
    $\frac{x}{a}\sqrt{a^2 + b^2}$

    (Since students are using the diagrams, $x > 0$ and $a > 0$.)

e. **i.** $\frac{QP}{OQ} = \frac{b}{a}$; $\frac{TS}{OT} = \frac{\frac{b}{a}x}{x} = \frac{b}{a}$

    ii. $\frac{QP}{OP} = \frac{b}{\sqrt{a^2 + b^2}}$; $\frac{TS}{OT} = \frac{\frac{b}{a}x}{\frac{x}{a}\sqrt{a^2 + b^2}} = \frac{b}{\sqrt{a^2 + b^2}}$

    iii. $\frac{OQ}{OP} = \frac{a}{\sqrt{a^2 + b^2}}$; $\frac{OT}{OS} = \frac{x}{\frac{x}{a}\sqrt{a^2 + b^2}} = \frac{a}{\sqrt{a^2 + b^2}}$

Since the corresponding sides of $\triangle OPQ$ and $\triangle OST$ are in proportion,
$\triangle OST$ is a similarity transformation of $\triangle OPQ$.

27   **a.** $\sin C = \frac{h}{a}$

    b. *area of* $\triangle ABC = \frac{1}{2}bh = \frac{1}{2}b(a \sin C) = 0.5ab \sin C$

    c. In right triangle ABD, $\sin A = \frac{h}{c}$; so, $h = c \sin A$.

    Then, *area of* $\triangle ABC = \frac{1}{2}bh = \frac{1}{2}b(c \sin A) = 0.5bc \sin A$.

    d. $0.5ab \sin C = 0.5bc \sin A$ because both are equal to the area
    of $\triangle ABC$. Multiply both sides of the equation by $\frac{2}{b}$ to get
    $a \sin C = c \sin A$.

28   Call x the remaining distance from B to the
base of the mountain. Then $\tan 39° = \frac{h}{x}$,
$h = x \tan 39°$; so, $h \approx 0.8098x$.

$\tan 28° = \frac{h}{x + 200}$, and $h = (x + 200)(0.5317)$.
$h \approx 0.5317x + 106.34$.

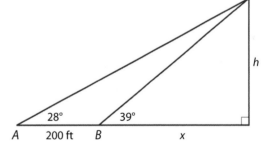

Equate the two expressions for h.
$0.8098x = 0.5317x + 106.34$
$0.2781x = 106.34$
$x \approx 382.2366 \approx 382$ feet

Substituting this value for x in $h = x \tan 39°$ gives $h = 382.2366 \tan 39°$.
So, $h \approx 310$ feet.

TECHNOLOGY NOTE
A CAS would be useful to
solve this equation.

NOTE The solution to
Task 29 is on page T484.

Unit 7

30 Find the tallest object on your school campus that cannot be easily measured directly. Prepare a plan to determine the height of the object. Carry out the plan, if it is plausible. Prepare a brief report of your method and findings.

31 Modern satellite communication systems make it possible for us to determine our exact (within a meter or so of accuracy) location on the Earth's surface by sending a signal from a handheld Global Positioning System (GPS) device. Perhaps you have GPS capability on your cell phone.

The GPS sends signals to satellites which relate the signal angle and distance to known reference sites. This technology makes it possible to have a system built into an automobile that shows a dashboard map giving both car and selected destination locations as well as how to reach the destination.

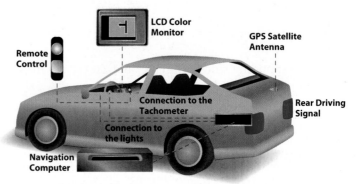

An actual GPS uses *spherical trigonometry* because of the spherical shape of the Earth. Consider a simpler problem of locating objects on a large flat surface, using sensors atop very tall towers.

Devise a system that you think would allow the sorts of calculations required to locate a GPS transmitter on this flat surface relative to a coordinate system.

29 First, determine $AE = x$ as follows:

$\tan 54° = \dfrac{d}{x}$ and $\tan 74° = \dfrac{d}{50 - x}$.

$x \tan 54° = (50 - x) \tan 74°$

$1.3764x = 174.3707 - 3.4874x$

$4.863x = 174.3707$

$x = 35.8566 \approx 36$ m

Then, determine $CE = d$:

$\tan 54° = \dfrac{d}{35.8566}$

$d \approx 49.3524 \approx 49$ m

Now, find AC:

$AC = \sqrt{x^2 + d^2} = \sqrt{35.8566^2 + 49.3524^2}$

$AC \approx 61$ m

Note $\triangle ACD$ is a right triangle.

$\tan 21° = \dfrac{h}{AC} = \dfrac{h}{61}$

$h \approx 61 \tan 21° \approx 23.4157 \approx 23$ m

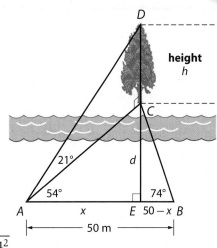

height
h

> **INSTRUCTIONAL NOTE**
> Note that $\triangle ABC$ lies in a horizontal plane and right $\triangle ACD$ lies in a vertical plane.

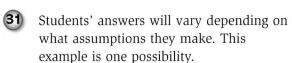

30 Plans will vary. The most likely scenario is to measure the distance on the ground between the tall object and a convenient point P. Then measure the angle of elevation from that point to the top of the object. In this case, the tangent ratio can be used to determine the object's height.

31 Students' answers will vary depending on what assumptions they make. This example is one possibility.

Assume that there is one tower whose height is known with base located at a position $(0, 0)$. Also, assume that the sensing device gives the bearing, the angle of depression, and the distance from the transmitter. In order to determine the location of the transmitter, you would use triangulation to determine the (x, y) coordinates on the grid. Let the positive y direction point north. For example, if the tower is 500 feet tall, the reported bearing is 140° east of north, and the distance from the transmitter is reported to be 2,000 feet, then the situation would look like this:

$OC = \sqrt{2,000^2 - 500^2} \approx 1,936.5$ ft

$\sin 50° = \dfrac{BC}{1,936.5}$, or $BC \approx 1,483.4$ ft

$\cos 50° = \dfrac{OB}{1,936.5}$, or $OB \approx 1,244.8$ ft

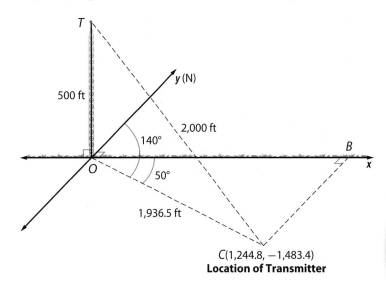

$C(1,244.8, -1,483.4)$
Location of Transmitter

> **NOTE** GPS are generally accurate to within 16 to 33 feet.

Unit 7

Review

32 Solve the following equations for x.

a. $\frac{5x}{12} = \frac{17}{23}$

b. $\frac{8 - x}{3} = \frac{x + 5}{10}$

c. $\frac{x + 6}{2x - 3} = \frac{7}{10}$

d. $\frac{10}{2x - 3} = \frac{7}{3x}$

33 Rewrite each expression with the smallest possible integer under the radical.

a. $\sqrt{60}$

b. $\sqrt{75}$

c. $3\sqrt{27}$

d. $\sqrt{25 + 144}$

34 Carl and Lisa are both drawing triangles ABC that meet each set of criteria below. Must the triangles they draw be congruent? Explain your reasoning.

a. The lengths of the three sides are 3 cm, 8 cm, and 7 cm.

b. The measures of the three angles are 120°, 20°, and 40°.

c. $AB = 5$ in., m∠$B = 60°$, and m∠$A = 50°$

d. m∠$C = 100°$, $BC = 10$ cm, and $AC = 8$ cm

e. m∠$B = 35°$, $BC = 10$ in., $AC = 8.5$ in.

35 Find the area of △ABC in each diagram.

a.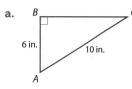

b.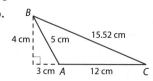

c.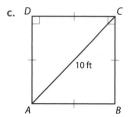

d.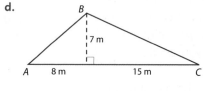

Review

Just in Time

32 **a.** $(5x)(23) = (12)(17)$
$115x = 204$
$x \approx 1.8$

b. $(8 - x)(10) = 3(x + 5)$
$80 - 10x = 3x + 15$
$-13x = -65$
$x = 5$

c. $(x + 6)(10) = (2x - 3)(7)$
$10x + 60 = 14x - 21$
$81 = 4x$
$x = 20.25$

d. $(10)(3x) = 7(2x - 3)$
$30x = 14x - 21$
$16x = -21$
$x \approx -1.3$

Just in Time

33 **a.** $2\sqrt{15}$
b. $5\sqrt{3}$
c. $9\sqrt{3}$
d. 13

ASSIGNMENT NOTE
Task 33 serves two purposes. It is a distributed review task that also prepares students for Lesson 2 content.

34 **a.** The triangles must be congruent by the SSS congruence condition.

b. The triangles could be different. Their shapes would be the same, but their sizes could be different.

c. The triangles must be congruent by the ASA congruence condition.

d. The triangles must be congruent by the SAS congruence condition.

e. The triangles could be different since SSA is not a congruence condition for all triangles.

35 **a.** *Area* $= 24$ in.^{2}
b. *Area* $= 24$ cm^2
c. *Area* $= 25$ ft^2
d. *Area* $= 80.5$ m^2

Unit 7

36 Solve each of these quadratic equations by factoring, if possible. If you don't see a way to factor, use the quadratic formula. Check your work by substituting your proposed solutions in the original equation.

a. $x^2 - 3x - 10 = 0$

b. $x^2 + 9x + 11 = 7$

c. $2x^2 - 12x + 16 = 0$

d. $3x^2 - x = 7$

37 Evaluate each of the following expressions, given $a = 4$, $b = 3$, $c = -3$, and $d = \frac{1}{3}$.

a. $2c + a^2 - (b + a)$

b. $a^2 + c^2 - 2abd$

c. $6d + 2(b - c)^2$

d. $(b - a) + abc$

e. $\sqrt{a^2 + b^2}$

38 Tim collected data about the amount of time he spent reading and the number of pages he read. His data are displayed in the scatterplot below.

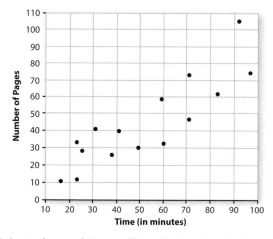

a. Estimate the correlation coefficient for the data. Explain your reasoning.

b. The regression equation is $y = 0.85x + 0.69$. Explain the meaning of the slope of this line in terms of the context.

c. One of the points on the graph has coordinates (92, 106). Find the residual for this point.

d. Tim has 50 pages left in the book he is currently reading. If he reads for 45 minutes before he goes to sleep, do you expect he will finish his book? Explain your reasoning.

36 **a.** $(x - 5)(x + 2) = 0$ Check:
$x - 5 = 0$ or $x + 2 = 0$ $5^2 - 3(5) - 10 = 25 - 15 - 10 = 0$
$x = 5$ or $x = -2$ $(-2)^2 - 3(-2) - 10 = 4 + 6 - 10 = 0$

b. $x^2 + 9x + 4 = 0$ Check:
$x = \dfrac{-9 \pm \sqrt{65}}{2}$ $(-0.47)^2 + 9(-0.47) + 4 \approx 0$
$x \approx -0.47$ or $x \approx -8.53$ $(-8.53)^2 + 9(-8.53) + 4 \approx 0$

c. $2(x^2 - 6x + 8) = 0$ Check:
$2(x - 4)(x - 2) = 0$ $2(4)^2 - 12(4) + 16 = 32 - 48 + 16 = 0$
$x - 4 = 0$ or $x - 2 = 0$ $2(2)^2 - 12(2) + 16 = 8 - 24 + 16 = 0$
$x = 4$ or $x = 2$

d. $3x^2 - x - 7 = 0$ Check:
$x = \dfrac{1 \pm \sqrt{85}}{6}$ $3(1.7)^2 - 1.7 - 7 \approx 0$
$x \approx 1.70$ or $x \approx -1.37$ $3(-1.37)^2 - (-1.37) - 7 \approx 0$

37 **a.** 3

b. 17

c. 74

d. −37

e. 5

38 **a.** Students' estimates should reflect strong positive correlation. A reasonable estimate is 0.8.

b. For each additional minute that Tim reads, he finishes 0.85 pages.

c. The residual is $106 - 78.89 = 27.11$.

d. The regression equation predicts that Tim will be able to read about 39 pages in 45 minutes ($0.85(45) + 0.69 = 38.94$). So if the book is similar to others he has read, he is not likely to be able to finish his book before he goes to sleep.

39 The matrix below gives the cost of building trails between five scenic areas in Baldy Mountain State Park.

$$
\begin{array}{c c c c c c}
 & A & B & C & D & E \\
A & \begin{bmatrix} 0 \\ 1{,}250 \\ 459 \\ 3{,}465 \\ 1{,}524 \end{bmatrix} & \begin{matrix} 1{,}250 \\ 0 \\ 875 \\ 1{,}300 \\ 1{,}600 \end{matrix} & \begin{matrix} 459 \\ 875 \\ 0 \\ 2{,}379 \\ 1{,}437 \end{matrix} & \begin{matrix} 3{,}465 \\ 1{,}300 \\ 2{,}379 \\ 0 \\ 889 \end{matrix} & \begin{matrix} 1{,}524 \\ 1{,}600 \\ 1{,}437 \\ 889 \\ 0 \end{matrix} \\
B & & & & & \\
C & & & & & \\
D & & & & & \\
E & & & & &
\end{array}
$$

a. Create a vertex-edge graph that could represent this situation.

b. The State Park rangers want to build trails so hikers can get from any one of these scenic areas to another. Which trails should they build to minimize the cost of building the trails? What is the minimum cost?

c. Use the best-edge algorithm to find a set of trails that would allow hikers to start at *A* and make a loop that visits all five of these attractions. Find the cost of building your loop trail. Are you guaranteed that you have found the cheapest way to build a loop trail that starts at *A*? Explain your reasoning.

a.

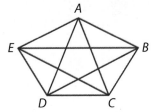

b. To minimize the cost, the rangers should build the trail as follows: *A-C-B-D-E* for a cost of $3,523. (The reverse ordering of vertices is also correct.)

c.

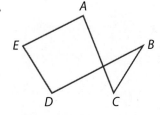

The cost of the loop is $5,047. The best-edge algorithm guarantees the cheapest way to build a loop that starts at *A* since you successively add the cheapest edge without creating a circuit.

Using Trigonometry in Any Triangle

In Lesson 1, you learned several strategies for using the Pythagorean Theorem and the trigonometric functions (sine, cosine, and tangent) to calculate unknown side lengths and angle measures in situations represented by right triangles. But often, problem situations are modeled by triangles that are not right triangles.

Consider, for example, the problem of developing an accurate map of the floor of the Grand Canyon.

Using Trigonometry in Any Triangle

The main goal of this lesson is to extend trigonometric measurement methods to general triangles by deriving and applying the Law of Sines and Law of Cosines. In Investigation 1, after providing reasons for steps in the derivation of the Law of Sines, students use the Law of Sines to solve for parts of a triangle in an application and in a triangulated parallelogram. In Investigation 2, students explore a triangle in which the lengths of two sides are fixed and the measure of the included angle varies, noting that the Law of Sines is not sufficient to determine the length of the opposite side. The Law of Cosines is then introduced and used in several triangle applications. Students also explore how the Law of Cosines extends the Pythagorean Theorem, in a sense, by including a "correction" for nonright triangles. Students are also asked to consider the conditions that require the use of each law. In Investigation 3, students explore, in a real-life setting and with software, triangles that are possible when two sides and an angle opposite one of those sides are given. They develop criteria for identifying the conditions under which this given information determines two, one, or no triangles.

The coordinate definitions of the trigonometric functions in Lesson 1 apply to all angles. However, trigonometric functions of acute angles were emphasized. In this lesson, students will also need values of the trigonometric functions for right and obtuse angles. Throughout this lesson, students will confront the facts that the sine of an obtuse angle equals the sine of its supplement and that the cosine and tangent of an obtuse angle are the negatives of the corresponding function values of its supplement. That is, $\sin \theta = \sin (180° - \theta)$, $\cos \theta = -\cos (180° - \theta)$, and $\tan \theta = -\tan (180° - \theta)$.

Lesson Objectives

- Determine measures of sides and angles of triangles using the Law of Sines and Law of Cosines
- Use these laws to solve problems involving indirect measurement and analysis of mechanisms that use triangles with a side of variable length
- Determine whether two, one, or no triangles are possible when the lengths of two sides and the measure of an angle not included between these sides are known

Suppose a surveyor sights point *C*, the tip of a pointed spur deep in the canyon, from triangulation points *A* and *B* on the south rim. $\overline{AB}$ was measured to be 2.68 miles. Using a transit, m∠*CAB* was found to be 64°; m∠*CBA* was found to be 34°.

a Draw and label a triangle representing this situation.

b Is the triangle a right triangle? How can you be sure of your answer?

c What side lies opposite the 34° angle in your triangle? Is sin 34° equal to a ratio of lengths of two sides of your triangle? If so, which ones? If not, why not?

d How might you go about determining the distances *AC* and *BC*?

In this lesson, you will investigate two important properties of any triangle that relate angle measures and side lengths known as the Law of Sines and the Law of Cosines. These properties will add to the trigonometric methods available to you for making indirect measurements and for analyzing mechanisms in which the lengths of two sides of a triangle are fixed but the length of the third side varies.

Investigation 1 The Law of Sines

If the triangle that models a situation involving unknown distances is not (or might not be) a right triangle, then it is not so easy to determine the distances; but it can be done. One method that is sometimes helpful uses the *Law of Sines*. As you work on the problems of this investigation, look for answers to the following question:

> *What is the Law of Sines, and how can it be used to find side lengths or angle measures in triangles?*

Suppose that two park rangers who are in towers 10 miles apart in a national forest spot a fire that is far away from both of them. Suppose that one ranger recognizes the fire location and knows it is about 4.9 miles from that tower.

During the launch, you might use an actual transit to discuss how it functions.

Think About This Situation

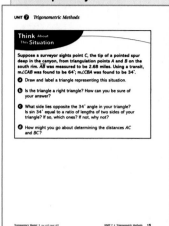

Teaching Resources
Transparency Master 15.

a See the sketch at the right.

b The angle at point C is $180° - 64° - 34° = 82°$. No angles are right angles, so the triangle is not a right triangle.

A   2.68   B
64°   34°
82°
C

c The side opposite the 34° angle is $\overline{AC}$. However, sin 34° is not a ratio of two sides in this triangle because it is not a right triangle. (Before moving to Part d, ask: *Will all triangles formed with the given measures be congruent?*)

d Students might suggest using an altitude to divide △ABC into two right triangles. If not, ask: *Could we divide △ABC into right triangles?* followed by: *Then what relationships could we use?*

Investigation 1   The Law of Sines

In this investigation, students provide reasons for steps in the derivation of the Law of Sines for right triangles and then use the Law of Sines to solve for parts of a triangle in applications. Once students have time to consider Problem 2 in groups, you may wish to have some students explain their thinking to the whole class before they consider Problem 3.

COLLABORATION SKILL
Seek ideas from others.

Unit 7

With this information and the angles given in the diagram below, the rangers can calculate the distance of the fire from the other tower.

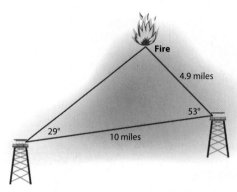

One way to start working on this problem is to divide the obtuse triangle into two right triangles as shown below:

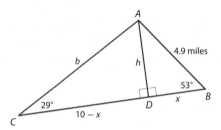

At first, that does not seem to help much. Instead of one segment of unknown length, there are now four! On the other hand, there are now three triangles in which you can see useful relationships among the known sides and angles.

1 Use trigonometry or the Pythagorean Theorem to find the length of $\overline{AC}$. When you have one sequence of calculations that gives the desired result, see if you can find a different approach.

2 In one class in Seattle, Washington, a group of students presented their solution to Problem 1 and claimed that it was the quickest method possible. Check each step in their reasoning and explain why each step is or is not correct.

(1) $\dfrac{h}{b} = \sin 29°$ (3) $\dfrac{h}{4.9} = \sin 53°$

(2) $h = b \sin 29°$ (4) $h = 4.9 \sin 53°$

(5) $b \sin 29° = 4.9 \sin 53°$

(6) $b = \dfrac{4.9 \sin 53°}{\sin 29°}$

(7) $b \approx 8.1$ miles

Compare your solution from Problem 1 with this reported solution.

(1) **INSTRUCTIONAL NOTE** While students work on this problem, encourage them to write down any relationships they can see. They may not see a way to reason all the way to the length AC, but they may well see some relationships that involve AC. Students who worked on Extensions Task 26 in Lesson 1 may recognize this as essentially the same situation. If any group arrives at a solution, you might have them write whatever relationships they find in the figure.

A solution for finding AC using trigonometry is shown in Problem 2 of the student text. The following solution uses the Pythagorean Theorem.

Since $AC^2 = (10 - x)^2 + h^2$, we need to find the values for x and h to find AC.

$\cos 53° = \dfrac{x}{4.9}$; so, $x \approx 2.95$ mi and $10 - x \approx 7.05$ mi.

$\sin 53° = \dfrac{h}{4.9}$; so, $h \approx 3.91$ mi.

$AC = \sqrt{7.05^2 + 3.91^2} \approx 8.1$ mi

(2) **INSTRUCTIONAL NOTE** You may choose to do Problem 2 as a whole group, as it foreshadows the Law of Sines.

$\dfrac{h}{b} = \sin 29°$	(1) Definition of sine ratio
$h = b \sin 29°$	(2) Multiplication Property of Equality
$\dfrac{h}{4.9} = \sin 53°$	(3) Definition of sine ratio
$h = 4.9 \sin 53°$	(4) Multiplication Property of Equality
$b \sin 29° = 4.9 \sin 53°$	(5) Substitution (using 2 and 4)
$b = \dfrac{4.9 \sin 53°}{\sin 29°}$	(6) Division Property of Equality
$b \approx 8.1$ miles	(7) Evaluation or Simplification

3 The approach used in Problem 2 to calculate the unknown side length of the given triangle illustrates a very useful general relationship among sides and angles of *any* triangle.

a. Explain why each step in the following derivation is correct for the acute △*ABC* below.

$$\frac{h}{b} = \sin A \qquad (1)$$

$$h = b \sin A \qquad (2)$$

$$\frac{h}{a} = \sin B \qquad (3)$$

$$h = a \sin B \qquad (4)$$

$$b \sin A = a \sin B \qquad (5)$$

$$\frac{\sin A}{a} = \frac{\sin B}{b} \qquad (6)$$

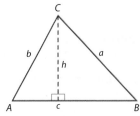

b. How would you modify the derivation in Part a to show that $\frac{\sin B}{b} = \frac{\sin C}{c}$?

The relationship derived in Problem 3 for acute angles *A*, *B*, and *C* holds in any triangle, for all three of its sides and their opposite angles. It is called the **Law of Sines** and can be written in two equivalent forms. The cases for a right triangle or an obtuse triangle are derived in Extensions Tasks 22 and 23.

In any triangle ABC with sides of lengths a, b, and c opposite ∠A, ∠B, and ∠C, respectively:

$$\frac{\sin A}{a} = \frac{\sin B}{b} = \frac{\sin C}{c}$$

or equivalently,

$$\frac{a}{\sin A} = \frac{b}{\sin B} = \frac{c}{\sin C}.$$

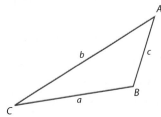

You can use the Law of Sines to calculate measures of angles and lengths of sides in triangles with even less given information than the fire-spotting problem at the beginning of this investigation. In practice, you only use the equality of two of the ratios at any one time.

Unit 7

3 **a.** $\dfrac{h}{b} = \sin A$ (1) Definition of sine ratio

$h = b \sin A$ (2) Multiplication Property of Equality

$\dfrac{h}{a} = \sin B$ (3) Definition of sine ratio

$h = a \sin B$ (4) Multiplication Property of Equality

$b \sin A = a \sin B$ (5) Substitution (using 2 and 4)

$\dfrac{\sin A}{a} = \dfrac{\sin B}{b}$ (6) Division Property of Equality

b. $\dfrac{h}{c} = \sin B$

$h = c \sin B$

$\dfrac{h}{b} = \sin C$

$h = b \sin C$

$b \sin C = c \sin B$

$\dfrac{\sin B}{b} = \dfrac{\sin C}{c}$

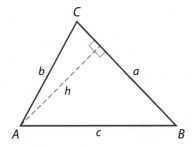

④ A class in San Antonio, Texas, agreed on the following representation of the surveying problem in the Think About This Situation (page 489). Use what you know about angles in a triangle and the Law of Sines to determine the distances *AC* and *BC*.

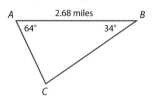

⑤ Suppose that two rangers spot a forest fire as indicated on the diagram below. Find the distances from each tower to the fire.

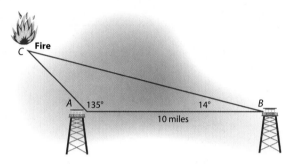

Summarize
the Mathematics

The Law of Sines states a relation among sides and angles of any triangle. It can often be used to find unknown side lengths or angle measures from given information. Suppose you have modeled a situation with △*PQR* as shown below.

ⓐ What minimal information about the sides and angles of △*PQR* will allow you to find the length of $\overline{QR}$ using the Law of Sines? How would you use that information to calculate *QR*?

ⓑ What minimal information about the sides and angles of △*PQR* will allow you to find the measure of ∠*Q*? How would you use that information to calculate m∠*Q*?

Be prepared to explain your thinking and methods to the entire class.

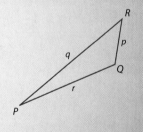

4 First, find $m\angle C = 180° - (64° + 34°) = 82°$.

$$\frac{BC}{\sin 64°} = \frac{2.68}{\sin 82°}; \quad BC = \frac{2.68 \sin 64°}{\sin 82°}; \quad BC \approx 2.43 \text{ miles}$$

$$\frac{AC}{\sin 34°} = \frac{2.68}{\sin 82°}; \quad AC = \frac{2.68 \sin 34°}{\sin 82°}; \quad AC \approx 1.51 \text{ miles}$$

5 $m\angle C = 180° - 135° - 14° = 31°$

$$\frac{\sin 135°}{BC} = \frac{\sin 31°}{10}$$

$$BC = \frac{10 \sin 135°}{\sin 31°} \approx 13.73 \approx 14 \text{ miles}$$

$$\frac{\sin 14°}{AC} = \frac{\sin 31°}{10}$$

$$AC = \frac{10 \sin 14°}{\sin 31°} \approx 4.70 \approx 5 \text{ miles}$$

Summary

If students seem unable to grasp the importance of the questions in the Summarize the Mathematics, it might help them to focus on the possible arrangements that will provide an answer for the length p. Write on the board the Law of Sines, $\frac{p}{\sin P} = \frac{q}{\sin Q} = \frac{r}{\sin R}$, and then the useful forms $\frac{p}{\sin P} = \frac{q}{\sin Q}$ and $\frac{p}{\sin P} = \frac{r}{\sin R}$. Ask students to think about how these last equations could be solved for p.

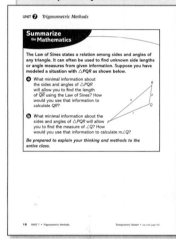

Summarize
the Mathematics

a In general, you need to know the measures of $\angle P$ and one other angle, along with the measure of either q or r. If you know the measure of two angles, you can find the measure of the third angle. So, you can solve for p if you know $m\angle P$, $m\angle Q$, and side q, or if you know $m\angle P$, $m\angle R$, and side r.

$$p = q \frac{\sin P}{\sin Q}$$

$$p = r \frac{\sin P}{\sin R}$$

b There are two sets of minimal conditions.

(1) You could find the measure of $\angle Q$ if you know $m\angle P$ and $m\angle R$ because the sum of the three angles is 180°.

(2) If you know the length of the side opposite $\angle Q$ and also one other side length and the measure of its opposite angle, you can use the Law of Sines to solve for $m\angle Q$. (See margin note.)

INSTRUCTIONAL NOTE
Unless the sine of an angle is 1, there are always two angles less than 180° that have the same sine value. (If one is x, the other is $180° - x$.) So, there may be two possibilities for $m\angle R$. This is the *side-side-angle* or *ambiguous case* for the Law of Sines. It is best not to discuss this at this time, unless one of your students mentions it. The side-side-angle case will be treated fully in Investigation 3.

COLLABORATION PROCESSING PROMPT
We encouraged everyone to contribute ideas by … .

Unit 7

✔ Check Your Understanding

A commuter airplane off course over the Atlantic Ocean reported experiencing mechanical problems around 9:15 P.M. The pilot sent two calls, one to Boston Logan International Airport and one to the regional airport in nearby Beverly. Air traffic controllers at the two airports reported the angles shown in the diagram below. How far was the plane from the closer airport?

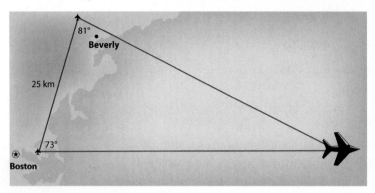

Investigation 2 The Law of Cosines

In the previous investigation, you examined how the Law of Sines is helpful in solving problems in which the measures of two angles and the length of one side of a triangle are known. For problems in which other combinations of side lengths or angle measures of a triangle are known, a second property of triangles called the *Law of Cosines* can be helpful. As you work on the following problems, look for answers to this question:

> What is the Law of Cosines, and how can it be used to
> find side lengths or angle measures in triangles?

In a right triangle, one angle is always known (the 90° angle), and the Pythagorean Theorem shows how the lengths of the two legs and the hypotenuse are related to each other. When that relationship is expressed as an equation, it is possible to solve for any side length in terms of the others. In Problems 1 and 2, you will investigate how the relationship among the sides changes as the right angle changes to an acute or obtuse angle.

1 Consider a linkage with two sides of fixed length: 12 cm and 16 cm. Here, $AC = 12$ cm and $BC = 16$ cm.

a. What is the distance from A to B when the angle at C is a right angle?

b. How does the distance from A to B change as $\overline{AC}$ is rotated to make smaller and smaller angles at C? How does that distance change if $\overline{AC}$ is rotated to make larger angles at C?

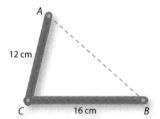

✔ Check Your Understanding

INSTRUCTIONAL NOTE Some students may not recognize that they can identify the closest airport by checking the angles opposite the sides of the triangle. Students who computed both distances will have benefited from one additional practice with the Law of Sines. If you do not help them notice this prior to doing the task, they may recognize it on their own the next time this occurs. It is likely that other students can share this more efficient strategy.

ASSIGNMENT NOTE
Be sure to assign and discuss Connections Task 10 prior to Investigation 2 Problem 6.

The distances can be determined using the Law of Sines. First, find the measure of the third angle: $180° - 81° - 73° = 26°$.

To find the distance to Beverly:

$$\frac{\sin 26°}{25} = \frac{\sin 73°}{x}$$

$$x = \frac{25 \sin 73°}{\sin 26°}$$

$$x \approx 54.5374 \text{ km}$$

To find the distance to Boston:

$$\frac{\sin 26°}{25} = \frac{\sin 81°}{x}$$

$$x = \frac{25 \sin 81°}{\sin 26°}$$

$$x \approx 56.3278 \text{ km}$$

The plane is closer to the Beverly airport.

Investigation 2 — The Law of Cosines

This investigation introduces the Law of Cosines. In Problems 1, 2, and 7, students use experimentation to see that the Pythagorean relationship for right triangles can be adjusted for acute and obtuse triangles. The Law of Cosines is explored as a multiple-variable relationship in which you need to know specific combinations of variables to solve for the required variable. The Law of Cosines is derived in Extensions Task 25 on page 512.

It is important that students realize that the Law of Sines is useful only with certain arrangements of sides and angles. If some students seem to be having difficulty with Problem 3, they probably did not develop a deep understanding of the combinations of information needed in the Summarize the Mathematics on page 492. If students have difficulty with Problem 3, you may wish to encourage them to try the Law of Sines on one part of Problem 2.

 a. $c = \sqrt{16^2 + 12^2} = 20$ cm

b. As $\overline{AC}$ is rotated to make smaller angles at C, the distance from A to B gets smaller until it is finally 4 cm when point A is located on $\overline{BC}$.

If $\overline{AC}$ is rotated to make larger angles at C, then the distance from A to B gets larger until it is finally equal to 28 cm when point A is located on $\overleftrightarrow{BC}$.

MATERIALS NEEDED
Students will need a 12-cm and a 16-cm linkage strip for this investigation.

Unit 7

(2) Using an actual physical linkage, interactive geometry software, or careful drawings, test your answers to Problem 1 by carefully measuring the distance from point A to point B in each case. Record your measures for further use in Problem 7.

    a. $m\angle C = 30°$ **b.** $m\angle C = 70°$

    c. $m\angle C = 130°$ **d.** $m\angle C = 150°$

(3) Why is it impossible to check the measured distances from A to B in Problem 2 by calculations using the Law of Sines without getting more information?

There is a second trigonometric principle for finding relationships among side lengths and angle measures of any triangle. It is called the **Law of Cosines**.

In any triangle ABC with sides of length a, b, and c opposite ∠A, ∠B, and ∠C, respectively:

$$c^2 = a^2 + b^2 - 2ab\,\cos C$$

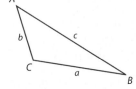

In Extensions Task 25, you are asked to provide a justification of this important relationship.

(4) The Law of Cosines states a relationship among the lengths of three sides of a triangle and the cosine of an angle of the triangle. If you know the lengths of two sides and the measure of the angle between the two sides, you can use the Law of Cosines to calculate the length of the third side.

    a. Write the Law of Cosines to calculate the length a in $\triangle ABC$ if you know the lengths b and c and the measure of $\angle A$.

    b. Write a third form of the Law of Cosines for $\triangle ABC$ for when you know the measure of $\angle B$.

    c. Suppose in $\triangle PQR$ you needed to calculate the length of $\overline{QR}$. What information would you need in order to use the Law of Cosines? Write the equation that you would use.

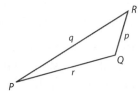

    d. Suppose in $\triangle PQR$ you knew $m\angle P$, $m\angle R$, and the lengths p and r.

        i. Could you find the length q using the Law of Cosines? Explain your reasoning.

        ii. Write an expression for calculating the length q.

    e. Using the information in Part d, write an expression for finding the length q using the Law of Sines. Which method would you prefer to use? Why?

(2) **a.** $AB \approx 8.2$ cm   **b.** $AB \approx 16.4$ cm

    c. $AB \approx 25.4$ cm   **d.** $AB \approx 27.1$ cm

INSTRUCTIONAL NOTE
If you have students organized in groups of four, each student can do one measurement. The data collected in Problem 2 will be needed in Problem 7.

(3) It is not possible to check these measurements directly using the Law of Sines because m∠C is the one angle measure that is known, and you would need to know either m∠A or m∠B in order to set up a proportion such as $\dfrac{\sin C}{AB} = \dfrac{\sin B}{12}$.

(4) **a.** $a^2 = b^2 + c^2 - 2bc \cos A$

    b. $b^2 = a^2 + c^2 - 2ac \cos B$

    c. You need to know the measure of the angle opposite $\overline{QR}$ (which is ∠P) and the lengths q and r.

      The equation would be $p^2 = q^2 + r^2 - 2qr \cos P$.

    d.   **i.** Yes, you can find the length of q. First, find m∠Q by subtracting the sum m∠P + m∠R from 180°. Then use the Law of Cosines written in the form $q^2 = r^2 + p^2 - 2rp \cos Q$.

      ii. $q = \sqrt{r^2 + p^2 - 2rp \cos Q}$

    e. Find m∠Q by subtraction: $180° - $ m∠P $-$ m∠R. Then $q = \dfrac{p \sin Q}{\sin P}$ or $q = \dfrac{r \sin Q}{\sin R}$.

      Responses may vary regarding preferred method, but students should support the method they used.

5 Surveyors are often faced with irregular polygonal regions for which they are asked to locate and stake out boundaries, determine elevations, and estimate areas. Some of these tasks can be accomplished by using a site map and a transit as shown in the photo below. In one subdivision of property near a midsize city, a plot of land had the shape and dimensions shown.

 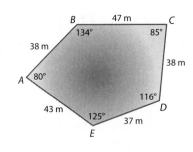

Examine the triangulation of the plot shown below.

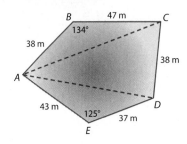

a. Find *AC* to the nearest meter.

b. Find *AD* to the nearest meter.

6 The Law of Cosines, $c^2 = a^2 + b^2 - 2ab \cos C$, states a relation among the lengths of three sides of a triangle *ABC* and the cosine of an angle of the triangle. If you know the lengths of all three sides of the triangle, you can calculate the cosine of any angle and then determine the measure of the angle itself.

a. Solve the equation $c^2 = a^2 + b^2 - 2ab \cos C$ for cos *C*.

b. Using your results from Problem 5, find the measure of ∠*BAC* to the nearest tenth of a degree. What is the measure of the third angle in △*ABC*?

c. Find the area of △*ABC*.

d. Explain how you could determine the area of the entire pentagonal plot.

(5) **INSTRUCTIONAL NOTE** Students may need to be asked "How can the Law of Cosines be used to find AC?". It helps to label the illustration so it is clear which segments and angles are to be used. In this problem, some of the given angles are *extraneous* to the solution. In the figure here, $BC = a$ and $AB = c$.

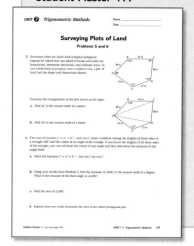

a. $AC^2 = a^2 + c^2 - 2ac \cos B$

$AC^2 = 47^2 + 38^2 - 2(47)(38) \cos 134°$

$AC^2 = 6{,}134.3197 \text{ m}^2$

$AC \approx 78 \text{ m}$

b. Using the two sides $\overline{AE}$ and $\overline{ED}$ and $\angle E$ in the Law of Cosines:

$AD^2 = 43^2 + 37^2 - 2(43)(37) \cos 125°.$

$AD^2 = 5{,}043.1202 \text{ m}^2$

$AD \approx 71 \text{ m}$

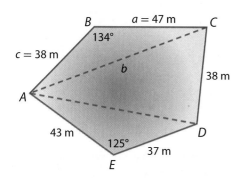

(6) **a.** **TECHNOLOGY NOTE** Students may struggle using their calculators and the order of operations to correctly calculate cos C. Some students benefit from using intermediate steps such as calculating $c^2 - a^2 - b^2$ and then computing ANS $\div (-2ab)$.

$$\cos C = \frac{c^2 - a^2 - b^2}{-2ab} \text{ or } \cos C = \frac{a^2 + b^2 - c^2}{2ab}$$

b. $\cos (\angle BAC) = \dfrac{47^2 - 78.3^2 - 38^2}{-2(78.3)(38)}$

$\cos (\angle BAC) \approx 0.9017$

$m\angle BAC \approx 25.6°$

$m\angle BCA \approx 180° - 134° - 25.6° \approx 20.4°$

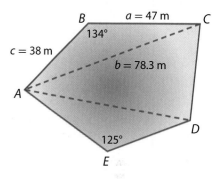

c. The diagram at the right shows the angle measures and the side lengths of $\triangle ABC$. Students who have completed Connections Task 9 may use the formula derived there. The area of $\triangle ABC = \frac{1}{2} bc \sin A = \frac{1}{2} ac \sin B = \frac{1}{2} ab \sin C$ results in approximately 642 m².

Alternatively, the following method using trigonometric ratios could be used.

$\sin 25.6° = \dfrac{h}{38}$

$h \approx 16.4$

$\triangle ABC \approx \frac{1}{2}(78.3)(16.4) \approx 642 \text{ m}^2$

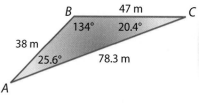

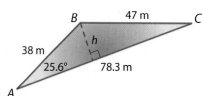

d. The area of the pentagonal plot will be the sum of the areas of the three triangles.

Unit 7

7 Now that you understand how to use the Law of Cosines, examine more closely its symbolic form and the information it conveys. Consider again the linkage with arms of lengths $b = 12$ cm and $a = 16$ cm positioned at various possible angles.

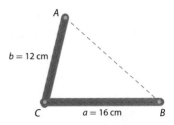

a. Record your data from Problem 2 in a copy of the table below. Then, using a physical linkage, interactive geometry software, or careful drawings, complete your table, showing how the distance between the ends of the linked arms changes as the angle at the link point C changes.

m∠C	30°	50°	70°	90°	110°	130°	150°
Length AB							

b. Add a row to your table from Part a showing corresponding values of $2ab \cos C$.

m∠C	30°	50°	70°	90°	110°	130°	150°
Length AB							
2ab cos C							

c. What is $\cos C$ when m∠C $= 90°$, and how does that simplify the equation for the Law of Cosines?

d. In what sense does the term "$2ab \cos C$" act as a *correction term*, adjusting the Pythagorean relationship for triangles in which ∠C is not a right angle?

8 As you have seen, the Law of Sines and the Law of Cosines can be used to find the measures of unknown angles as well as unknown sides of any triangle. You need to study given information about side and angle measurements to decide which law to apply. Then you work with the resulting equations to solve for the unknown angle or side measurements.

For example, suppose that two sides, $\overline{AB}$ and $\overline{BC}$, and a diagonal, $\overline{AC}$, of a parallelogram $ABCD$ measure 7 cm, 9 cm, and 11 cm, respectively.

a. Draw and label a sketch of parallelogram $ABCD$.

b. Which of the two trigonometric laws can be used to find the measure of an angle in that parallelogram?

c. Find the measure of that angle to the nearest tenth of a degree.

d. The diagonal $\overline{AC}$ splits the parallelogram $ABCD$ into two congruent triangles. Find the remaining measures of the angles in those triangles.

e. Find the length of diagonal $\overline{BD}$.

7 **INSTRUCTIONAL NOTE** This problem explores the fact that $ab\cos C$ is sometimes positive and sometimes negative. As students are working on this, you might ask them to recall the work they did with sine and cosine in Lesson 1, specifically, the signs of the coordinates of points in the second quadrant. Also, note that for supplementary angles C_1 and C_2, $|2ab\cos C_1| = |2ab\cos C_2|$.

a–b. Students' measurements should be close to those given below.

$m\angle C$	30°	50°	70°	90°	110°	130°	150°
Length AB	8.2	12.4	16.4	20	23.1	25.4	27.1
$2ab\cos C$	332.6	246.8	131.3	0	−131.3	−246.8	−332.6

c. When $m\angle C = 90°$, $\cos C = 0$. Therefore, the term $2ab\cos C$ would be equal to 0. So, $c^2 = a^2 + b^2$. (This is the Pythagorean Theorem.)

d. For angles less than 90°, the side opposite will be shorter than the hypotenuse of the right triangle; and therefore, $|2ab\cos C| = 2ab\cos C$ is subtracted. For angles greater than 90°, the side opposite will be longer than the hypotenuse of the right triangle; and therefore, $|2ab\cos C|$ is added. Note that when $m\angle C$ is greater than 90°, $\cos C < 0$. So, the values of $2ab\cos C$ are negative. In the Law of Cosines, $2ab\cos C$ is *subtracted* from $a^2 + b^2$, and consequently, for angles greater than 90°, subtracting $2ab\cos C$ is the same as adding $|2ab\cos C|$.

Teaching Resources

Student Master 18.

UNIT **7** *Trigonometric Methods*   Name _____
Date _____

The Law of Cosines
Problems 7

7. Now that you understand how to use the Law of Cosines, examine more closely its symbolic form and the information it conveys. Consider again the linkage with arms of lengths $b = 12$ cm and $a = 16$ cm positioned at various possible angles.

a. Record your data from Problem 2 in the table below. Then, using a physical linkage, interactive geometry software, or careful drawings, complete the first row of the table, showing how the distance between the ends of the linked arms changes as the angle at the link point C changes.

b. Complete the second row of the table showing corresponding values of $2ab\cos C$.

$m\angle C$	30°	50°	70°	90°	110°	130°	150°
Length AB							
$2ab\cos C$							

18   UNIT 7 • Trigonometric Methods   Student Master • *see unit page 496*

8 **a.**

b. In this figure, you know only the lengths of the three sides; and therefore, you would have to use the Law of Cosines to determine an angle measure.

c. Students may choose any angle in the triangle, but an easy one is $m\angle B$. It can be found using the equation $11^2 = 7^2 + 9^2 - 2(7)(9)\cos B$.

$$\cos B = \frac{11^2 - 7^2 - 9^2}{-2(7)(9)} \approx 0.0714$$

$$m\angle B \approx \cos^{-1} 0.0714 \approx 85.9°$$

Once $m\angle B$ is found, all other angle measures can be determined. $m\angle D = m\angle B$, and $m\angle A = m\angle C = 180° - m\angle B \approx 94.1°$.

d. Students can use the Law of Sines to find another angle in the triangle in Part c. For example,

$$\frac{\sin B}{11} = \frac{\sin 85.9°}{11} = \frac{\sin(\angle ACB)}{7}$$

$$\sin(\angle ACB) = \frac{7\sin 85.9°}{11} \approx 0.6347$$

$$m\angle ACB \approx 39.4°$$

So, $m\angle CAB = 180° - 85.9° - 39.4° = 54.7°$.
Then, since $\triangle ACD \cong \triangle CAB$, $m\angle ACD = m\angle CAB \approx 54.7°$, $m\angle CAD = m\angle ACB \approx 39.4°$, and $m\angle ADC = m\angle CBA \approx 85.9°$.

e. $BD^2 = AD^2 + AB^2 - 2(AD)(AB)\cos(\angle DAB)$
$BD^2 = 9^2 + 7^2 - 2(9)(7)\cos 94.1°$
$BD \approx 11.8 \approx 12$ cm

Summarize the Mathematics

In this investigation, you explored how the Law of Cosines can be used to find unknown side lengths or angle measures in a triangle. Consider △ABC shown below.

a What information would you need to know in order to use the Law of Cosines to find the length of $\overline{AC}$? What equation would you use to find that length?

b What information would you need to know in order to use the Law of Cosines to find the measure of ∠A? What equation would you use to find that angle measure?

c Suppose you know the lengths *a*, *b*, and *c*. What can you conclude about m∠B if $a^2 + c^2 > b^2$? If $a^2 + c^2 < b^2$? If $a^2 + c^2 = b^2$?

d What clues do you use to decide if an unknown side length of a triangle can be found using the Law of Cosines? Using the Law of Sines?

e What clues do you use to decide if an unknown angle measure of a triangle can be found using the Law of Cosines? Using the Law of Sines?

Be prepared to explain your ideas to the entire class.

✔ Check Your Understanding

A surveyor with transit at point *A* sights points *B* and *C* on either side of Asylum Pond. She finds the measure of the angle between the sightings to be 72°.

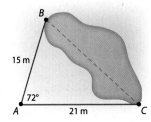

a. Find the distance *BC* across the pond to the nearest tenth of a meter.

b. Find m∠B and m∠C.

Summarize
the Mathematics

a You would need to know the measure of $\angle B$ and the lengths of sides $\overline{BC}$ and $\overline{AB}$.

$$AC = \sqrt{a^2 + c^2 - 2ac \cos B}$$

b You need to know the length of all three sides.

$$a^2 = b^2 + c^2 - 2bc \cos A$$
$$\cos A = \frac{a^2 - b^2 - c^2}{-2bc}$$
$$m\angle A = \cos^{-1}\left(\frac{a^2 - b^2 - c^2}{-2bc}\right)$$

c If $a^2 + c^2 > b^2$, then $m\angle B$ is less than $90°$. If $a^2 + c^2 < b^2$, then $m\angle B$ is greater than $90°$ but less than $180°$. If $a^2 + c^2 = b^2$, then $m\angle B$ is equal to $90°$.

d The Law of Cosines is useful to find an unknown side length when the lengths of two sides and the measure of the angle opposite the unknown side length are known. The Law of Sines can be used to find an unknown side length when the measures of two angles and one side length are known.

e An unknown angle measure can be found using the Law of Cosines if all three side lengths are known. The Law of Sines can be used *with caution* (as students will learn in the next investigation) if measures of two sides and an angle not included between them are known.

MATH TOOLKIT Summarize what you have learned about the Law of Sines and the Law of Cosines with examples. Include conditions that require using each law.

✓ Check Your Understanding

a. $BC^2 = 21^2 + 15^2 - 2(21)(15) \cos 72° \approx 471.3193$
$BC \approx 21.7099 \approx 22$ m

b. $\dfrac{\sin B}{21} = \dfrac{\sin 72°}{21.7099}$

$\sin B = \dfrac{21 \sin 72°}{21.7099} \approx 0.9200$

$m\angle B \approx 67°$

$m\angle C \approx 180° - (67° + 72°)$

$m\angle C \approx 41°$

Unit 7

Triangle Models— Two, One, or None?

The Law of Sines is useful in solving problems that involve triangles when the measures of two angles and the length of a side are known. The Law of Cosines is useful when the lengths of three sides or the lengths of two sides and the measure of the angle between them are known. In this investigation, you will seek clues that may help answer the following question:

> *What can you conclude about triangle models for situations in which you know the lengths of two sides and the measure of an angle not included between the sides?*

A cold frame is a box used to grow young plants in the spring. The top of the box is made of glass to let in light. The top can be propped open at various heights so the plants become accustomed to actual weather conditions before they are transplanted outside the box.

1 One cold frame has a rectangular top measuring 70 cm by 120 cm, hinged along the 120-cm edge. It can be held open by a prop 30 cm long. The prop is attached to the top 50 cm from the hinged end, as in the diagram at the right. Notches on the horizontal frame hold the prop in different positions, allowing the top to be opened at different angles.

  a. A triangle is formed by the hinged edges of the cold frame and the prop. Make and label a diagram of the triangle showing known side lengths.

  b. How do you think the measure of the angle at the hinged end changes as the prop is moved from one notch to the next? Imagine starting at the notch that is closest to the hinge and moving to the notch that is furthest from the hinge.

Triangle Models—
Two, One, or None?

The measures of two sides and an angle opposite one of the known sides (also called SSA) do not always determine the size and shape of a unique triangle, but sometimes that information is sufficient. For example, the lengths of two sides are sufficient if one angle of the triangle is a right angle. The Pythagorean relationship gives the length of the third side. In cases where the given information does not determine a unique triangle, it limits the possibilities to two triangles. In this investigation, students use the Law of Sines and Law of Cosines to explore the conditions under which SSA determines no triangle (if the Triangle Inequality fails), exactly one triangle, and exactly two triangles.

CPMP-Tools custom tool "Explore SSA" can be used with Problem 2.

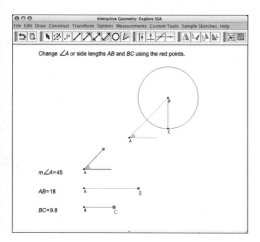

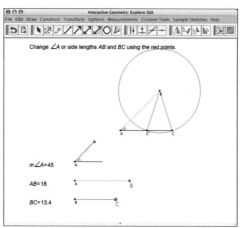

 a.

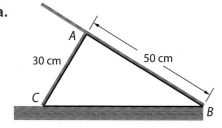

b. At first, the angle would increase; but after the point at which the prop made a right angle with the top, the angle would begin to decrease.

Unit 7

You will return to Problem 1 after first exploring how many differently shaped triangles can be formed given two side lengths (say, AB and BC) and the measure of an angle ($\angle A$) *not* included between them. In Problem 2, you will explore the side-side-angle (SSA) condition where $\angle A$ is acute. In Problem 3, you will explore the case where $\angle A$ is not an acute angle.

 Use a compass and ruler or software like the interactive geometry "Explore SSA" custom tool to conduct the following experiment.

a. Draw an acute angle, $\angle A$. Fix point B on one side of $\angle A$ by marking off length AB. Suppose $\overline{BC}$ is very short, as in the figure on the right. How many triangles ABC can be formed with the three given parts: $\angle A$, $\overline{AB}$, and $\overline{BC}$? Explain.

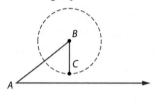

b. With the same $\angle A$ and length AB, try making $\overline{BC}$ longer. There is a minimum length of $\overline{BC}$ for which a triangle with the three given parts is formed, as shown in the next figure.

   i. In this case, what kind of triangle is ABC?

   ii. Is the triangle shown the only possible triangle determined by $\angle A$, AB, and BC?

   iii. Write the length BC in terms of length AB and a trigonometric function of $\angle A$.

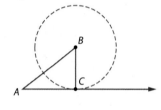

c. With the same $\angle A$ and length AB, continue to make $\overline{BC}$ longer. Try to find lengths BC for which two noncongruent triangles can be formed with the same three given parts.

   i. Draw a figure like those above that shows an example of this situation.

   ii. Over what interval of lengths BC will two noncongruent triangles be formed?

d. If BC is greater than or equal to all values in the interval you found in Part cii, how many triangles can be formed with the three given parts? Draw a figure like those above that shows an example of this situation.

e. In Parts a–d, you explored the SSA condition when $\angle A$ is acute. Summarize your findings by describing the lengths, or intervals of lengths, BC for which the given side-side-angle parts determine:

   i. no triangle.

   ii. exactly one triangle.

   iii. two noncongruent triangles.

a. No triangle can be formed since the length BC is not long enough to reach the side of $\angle A$ opposite point B.

b. i. Triangle ABC is a right triangle in this case.

    ii. Yes, because there is only one perpendicular from point B to the side of $\angle A$, opposite point B.

    iii. $BC = AB \sin A$ ($\overleftrightarrow{AC}$ is tangent to the circle.)

c. i.

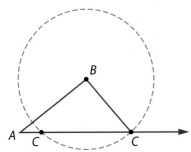

INSTRUCTIONAL NOTE
If students have difficulty finding the interval for Part cii, ask: *How large can BC become compared to other lengths you know and still have two noncongruent triangles?* followed by: *Can you find an expression for which BC must be slightly larger?*

    ii. We know from Part biii that when the circle centered at point B is tangent to the side of $\angle A$ opposite point B, there is one triangle determined (right triangle ACB) and $BC = AB \sin A$. When $BC > AB \sin A$ and $BC < AB$, the circle of radius BC has intersection points C and C_1 with the side of $\angle A$ opposite point B. In this case, there are two different triangles determined by $\angle A$, $\overline{AB}$, and $\overline{BC}$, namely $\triangle ACB$ and $\triangle AC_1B$. When the circle has radius $BC \geq AB$, there is exactly one triangle determined. So, the range of BC when there are two triangles determined by $\angle A$, $\overline{AB}$, and $\overline{BC}$ is the interval $AB \sin A < BC < AB$.

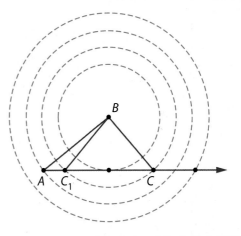

d.

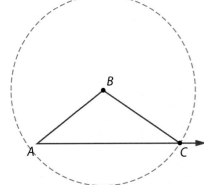

INSTRUCTIONAL NOTE
Some groups may not consider the upper bound on the radius BC while doing Part cii. If so, they will consider it in Part d.

e. i. If the radius of the circle BC is less than $AB \sin A$, then no triangle is determined. $BC < AB \sin A$

    ii. If the radius of the circle BC is equal to $AB \sin A$ or greater than or equal to AB, then exactly one triangle is determined. $BC = AB \sin A$ or $BC \geq AB$

    iii. If the radius of the circle BC is less than AB and greater than $AB \sin A$, then two noncongruent triangles are determined. $AB \sin A < BC < AB$

③ Suppose, as in Problem 2, $\overline{AB}$ and $\angle A$ are given, but now $\angle A$ is not an acute angle. Explore the two cases below.

   a. Consider the case in which $\angle A$ is an obtuse angle. Explore varying lengths BC and determine conditions for which two, one, or no triangles will be determined. Make sketches to illustrate your answer.

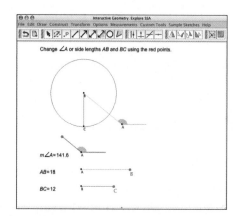

   b. Suppose $\angle A$ is a right angle. Describe the triangles determined by $\overline{BC}$, $\overline{AB}$, and $\angle A$, depending on how lengths AB and BC are related.

④ Now refer back to the cold frame in Problem 1.

   a. One possible placement of the prop so that the hinged angle is $20°$ is shown below. Do you think there could be a second position for the prop along the horizontal that would satisfy the given information? If so, sketch it. If not, explain why not.

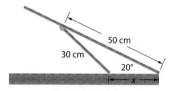

   b. Use the Law of Cosines to write a quadratic equation that relates x and the three given measures. Solve the equation for x. Explain how your solution(s) relate to the diagram in Part a.

3. **a.** (1) For $\angle A$ obtuse:
If the radius $BC \leq AB$, no triangle is determined.

(2) If the radius $BC > AB$, one triangle is determined.

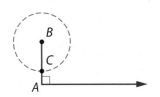

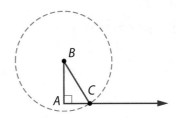

(3) It is never the case that two triangles are determined.

b. (1) For $\angle A$ right:
If $BC \leq AB$, no triangle is determined.

(2) If $BC > AB$, one triangle is determined.

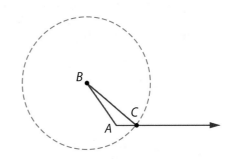

(3) It is never the case that two triangles are determined.

4. **a.** There would be a second position, as shown here, provided the horizontal part of the frame is long enough.

b. $30^2 = 50^2 + x^2 - 2(50)x(\cos 20°)$
$30^2 = 50^2 + x^2 - 2(50)x(0.9397)$
$x^2 - 93.97x + 1,600 = 0$
$x \approx \dfrac{93.97 \pm 49.30}{2}$

Thus, $x \approx 71.6$ cm or $x \approx 22.3$ cm.

Two triangles are theoretically possible with side measuring 22.3 cm and the other with side measuring 71.6 cm. Since the cold frame top measures 70 cm on the side with the notches, the second triangle in Part a is not possible.

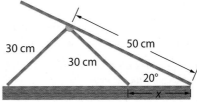

> **TECHNOLOGY NOTE**
> To solve the quadratic equation in Problem 4 Part b, you may wish to use a CAS or find the *x*-intercepts of the graph using technology.

Unit 7

c. Suppose the gardener wants to place a notch for the prop that makes the largest hinged angle for this cold frame. In which of the settings below is the hinged angle larger? Does the larger of the two settings below maximize the hinged angle? Explain your answer.

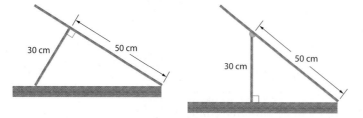

Summarize
the Mathematics

In this investigation, you explored conditions under which the measure of an angle together with the lengths of two segments—one of which is opposite the angle—is sufficient to determine a triangle.

Suppose you are given side lengths *a* and *b* and a given angle measure, m∠*A*, of a possible triangle *ABC*.

a If at least one triangle is determined by these three parts, what is the minimum length *a* in terms of *b* and ∠*A*?

b Suppose ∠*A* is an acute angle, and there is exactly one triangle that satisfies the given condition. How are the given sides and the given angle related?

c Suppose there are two triangles that satisfy the given condition. How are the given sides and the given angle related?

d Suppose ∠*A* is an obtuse angle. Is it possible that two noncongruent triangles satisfy the given condition? Explain your reasoning.

Be prepared to explain your thinking to the class.

✓ Check Your Understanding

The design and functioning of the automobile jack you examined in Lesson 1 and the cold frame in this lesson depend on triangle mechanisms where one side is able to vary in length. The functioning of a piston of a steam engine depends on a similar principle.

LESSON 2 • Using Trigonometry in Any Triangle **501**

c. For the setting on the left, the measure of the hinged angle is $\tan^{-1} 0.6 \approx 31.0°$. For the setting at the right, the measure of the hinged angle is $\sin^{-1} 0.6 \approx 37°$. The second setting gives the maximum possible hinged angle.

Summary

You may want to have students name this situation the "Ambiguous Case" as they may hear it referred to in a future mathematics or physics course.

Summarize
the Mathematics

a $a \geq b \sin A$

b Either $a = b \sin A$ and the triangle is a right triangle, or $a \geq b$.

c If two triangles are determined, $\angle A$ is acute. Furthermore, $a > b \sin A$ and $a < b$. So, $b \sin A < a < b$.

d It is not possible for two triangles to be determined when $\angle A$ is obtuse. That would require a triangle with two obtuse angles, which is impossible. Exactly one triangle is determined in the obtuse case provided $a > b$.

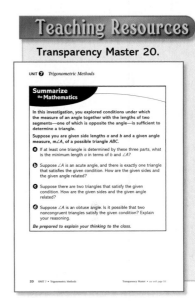

Teaching Resources

Transparency Master 20.

UNIT **7** *Trigonometric Methods*

Summarize
the **Mathematics**

In this investigation, you explored conditions under which the measure of an angle together with the lengths of two segments—one of which is opposite the angle—is sufficient to determine a triangle.

Suppose you are given side lengths a and b and a given angle measure, $m\angle A$, of a possible triangle ABC.

❶ If at least one triangle is determined by these three parts, what is the minimum length a in terms of b and $\angle A$?

❷ Suppose $\angle A$ is an acute angle, and there is exactly one triangle that satisfies the given condition. How are the given sides and the given angle related?

❸ Suppose there are two triangles that satisfy the given condition. How are the given sides and the given angle related?

❹ Suppose $\angle A$ is an obtuse angle. Is it possible that two noncongruent triangles satisfy the given condition? Explain your reasoning.

Be prepared to explain your thinking to the class.

20 UNIT 7 • Trigonometric Methods   Transparency Master • use with page 515

MATH TOOLKIT Draw a sketch that shows how two noncongruent triangles can sometimes be made when corresponding parts (SSA) are congruent.

Unit 7

In the design below of a simple steam engine, the piston rod is connected by a rod $\overline{BC}$ to a flywheel that rotates about a point A. The piston rod moves horizontally, the connecting rod is 48 inches long, and the crank is 16 inches long. In the diagram, the connecting rod is slanted below the horizontal at an angle of 14°.

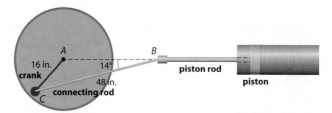

a. Are there other positions of the crank and connecting rod that set $m\angle ABC = 14°$? If so, illustrate with labeled sketches. If not, explain why not.

b. Find the measures of the other two angles in the diagram. If you found other triangles in Part a, determine the measures of their other two angles.

c. Find the length of the third side of the triangle(s).

d. How is the *throw* of the piston (the distance between the extreme points of its motion) related to the fixed lengths AC and BC?

✔ Check Your Understanding

a. Yes, there are other triangles that meet the same conditions. One of them is in the sketch below. Besides this triangle and the one shown on page 502, the reflections of the two triangles ACB across the horizontal line AB also satisfy these SSA conditions.

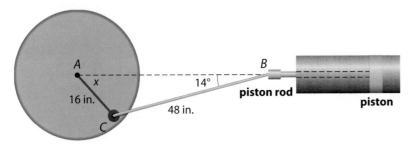

b. $\dfrac{\sin x}{48} = \dfrac{\sin 14°}{16}$; $\sin x = \dfrac{48 \sin 14°}{16} \approx 0.7258$

$x \approx \sin^{-1} 0.7258 \approx 46.5°$ or $x \approx 180° - 46.5° = 133.5°$

The triangle pictured in the student book (and its reflection across $\overleftrightarrow{AB}$) has the obtuse angle at A, and the one pictured above (and its reflection across $\overleftrightarrow{AB}$) contains the acute angle at A. The third angle, $\angle C$, measures $119.5°$ when $m\angle A \approx 46.5°$ and measures $32.5°$ when $m\angle A \approx 133.5°$.

c. Using the Law of Cosines, when $m\angle A \approx 46.5°$:

$c^2 = 16^2 + 48^2 - 2(16)(48) \cos 119.5°$

$c \approx 57.6$ inches

When $x \approx 133.5°$:

$c^2 = 16^2 + 48^2 - 2(16)(48) \cos 32.5°$

$c \approx 35.6$ inches

(Students may also use the Law of Sines.)

d. The throw is $2AC = 32$ in. Students might find this by considering the difference between the extreme positions of point C. Alternatively, they might focus on the two positions of the end of the piston rod when $\overline{AC}$ and $\overline{BC}$ are in line with each other.

Applications

(1) A pilot flying due east out of Denver gets word that a major thunderstorm is directly in his plane's path. The pilot turns 35° to the left of his intended course and continues on this new flight path. After avoiding the worst of the storm, he turns 45° to the right of the new course and flies until returning to his original intended line of flight. The plane reaches its original intended course at a point 80 kilometers from the start of the detour.

a. Draw a sketch of this situation.

b. How much farther did the aircraft travel due to the detour?

(2) Refer back to the Grand Canyon mapping problem in the Think About This Situation at the beginning of this lesson (page 489). In addition to calculating the distances of particular points in the Grand Canyon from triangulation points on the rim, the surveyors wanted to map the relative depths of these points in the canyon. Using their transits, they were able to measure the **angle of depression** (that is, the angle their line of sight made with the horizontal) to the point of interest in the canyon.

a. In Problem 4 of Investigation 1, you found that the distance from point A on the rim to the tip of the pointed spur at C was about 1.51 miles. Suppose the surveyor measured the angle of depression from point A to point C to be 28°. How far below point A is point C in vertical distance? Find the vertical distance in miles and in feet (1 mile = 5,280 feet).

b. If point A is 7,392 feet above sea level, how many feet above sea level is point C?

c. The Colorado River at the bottom of the Grand Canyon is 1,850 feet above sea level. How many feet above the Colorado River is point A? Point C?

LESSON 2 • Using Trigonometry in Any Triangle   **503**

Applications

1 **a.** The intended course is along $\overleftrightarrow{AC}$. The actual course is marked by arrows, and the distance $AB + BC$.

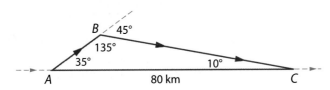

B 45°
135°
35°
10°
A   80 km   C

  b. $AB = \dfrac{80 \sin 10°}{\sin 135°} \approx 19.6460$ km; $BC = \dfrac{80 \sin 35°}{\sin 135°} \approx 64.8928$ km
   Extra travel distance $\approx AB + BC - 80 \approx 5$ km

2 **a.** $BC = 1.51 \sin 28°$
   $BC \approx 0.7089$ miles $\approx 3{,}743$ feet

A ---------- B
       28°
1.51 miles
              C

  b. Point C is $7{,}392 - 3{,}743 = 3{,}649$ feet above
   sea level.

  c. Point C is $3{,}649 - 1{,}850 = 1{,}799$ ft above the
   Colorado River.
   Point A is $7{,}392 - 1{,}850 = 5{,}542$ ft above the Colorado River.

3 Two lighthouses *A* and *B* are 50 km apart. At 2 A.M., a freighter moving parallel to line *AB* is sighted at point *C* as shown in the diagram below.

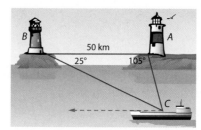

a. How far is the freighter from lighthouse *B*? From lighthouse *A*?

b. At 3 A.M., the angle at *A* is 86°. The angle at *B* is 29°. How far is the freighter from lighthouse *B*? From lighthouse *A*?

c. How far has the freighter moved in the hour between 2 A.M. and 3 A.M.?

4 The ninth hole at Duffy's Golf Club is 325 yards down a straight fairway. In his first round of golf for the season, Andy tees off and hooks the ball 20° to the left of the line from the tee to the hole. The ball stops 205 yards from the tee at point *P*, as shown in the figure.

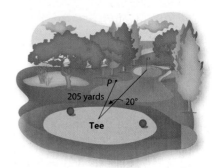

a. How far is his ball from the hole (marked by the flag)?

b. To decide which club to use on his next shot, Andy knows he hits an average of 135–145 yards with a five iron; with a four iron, he hits 145–155 yards; and with a three iron, he hits 155–165 yards. Which of these clubs would be his best choice?

5 A field is in the shape of quadrilateral *ABCD* as shown below.

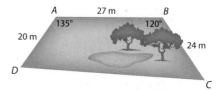

a. Find the length *CD* of its fourth side.

b. Find the measures of the remaining angles of the field.

c. Find the area of the field.

3 **a.** $\dfrac{BC}{\sin 105°} = \dfrac{50}{\sin 50°}$

$BC = \dfrac{50 \sin 105°}{\sin 50°} \approx 63.0463$ km

The freighter is approximately 63 km from lighthouse B.

$\dfrac{AC}{\sin 25°} = \dfrac{50}{\sin 50°}$

$AC = \dfrac{50 \sin 25°}{\sin 50°} \approx 27.5844$ km

The freighter is approximately 28 km from lighthouse A.

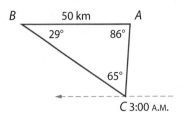

b. $\dfrac{BC}{\sin 86°} = \dfrac{50}{\sin 65°}$

$BC = \dfrac{50 \sin 86°}{\sin 65°} \approx 55.0345$ km

The freighter is approximately 55 km from lighthouse B.

$\dfrac{AC}{\sin 29°} = \dfrac{50}{\sin 65°}$

$AC = \dfrac{50 \sin 29°}{\sin 65°} \approx 26.7464$ km

The freighter is approximately 27 km from lighthouse A.

c. From Parts a and b, the lengths of the segments that form the 4° angle (see the diagram at the right) are 63.0463 km and 55.0345 km. Therefore, by the Law of Cosines,

$b = \sqrt{55.0345^2 + 63.0463^2 - 2(55.0345)(63.0463)\cos 4°} \approx 9$ km.

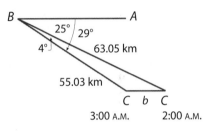

4 **a.** Let x represent the distance from the ball to the hole.

$x^2 = 205^2 + 325^2 - 2(205)(325)\cos 20°$

$x = \sqrt{22{,}435.96} \approx 149.79$

Andy's ball is approximately 150 yards from the hole.

b. Based on his distance estimates, Andy should choose a four iron.

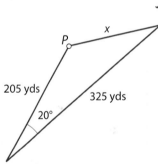

5 **a.** There are many ways to approach this multi-step task. Students may choose a different strategy from this one.

$BD = \sqrt{20^2 + 27^2 - 2(20)(27)\cos 135°} \approx 43.5049 \approx 44$ m

$m\angle CBD \approx 120° - m\angle ABD$

$\dfrac{\sin (\angle ABD)}{20} = \dfrac{\sin 135°}{43.5049}$

$\sin (\angle ABD) = \dfrac{20 \sin 135°}{43.5049} \approx 0.3251$

$\angle ABD = \sin^{-1}(0.3251) \approx 18.97° \approx 19°$

$m\angle CBD \approx 120° - 18.97° = 101.03° \approx 101°$

$CD = \sqrt{24^2 + 43.5049^2 - 2(24)(43.5049)\cos 101.03°} \approx 53.5512 \approx 54$ m

> **ASSIGNMENT NOTE**
> Applications Task 5 should be assigned following Investigation 2. If you assigned Connections Task 9 with Investigation 1, students can use the triangle area formula: *area* $\triangle ABC = \dfrac{1}{2} ab \sin C$.

Dimensions to Nearest Integer and Degree

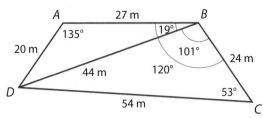

> **NOTE** Solutions to Task 5 Parts b and c are on page T505.

Unit 7

6 A side view of a reclining lawn chair is illustrated below. Its function is based on a triangle in which the lengths of two sides are fixed, and the length of the third side can vary. The key triangular component (△ABC) in the design of the lawn chair is shown in the diagram at the right. In △ABC, AB and BC are both 10 inches, and AC can be set to 8, 10, 12, or 14 inches. The reclining angle for someone sitting in the chair is ∠BCD.

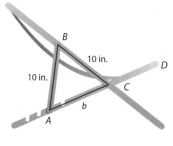

a. When the length AC, denoted b, is set, the lengths of all three sides of △ABC are fixed. How can you find m∠ACB? How is m∠BCD, the measure of the reclining angle, related to m∠ACB?

b. Write a rule that expresses m∠BCD in terms of b.

c. Use the rule in Part b to find the measure of the reclining angle for b = 8, 10, 12, and 14 inches. Describe how the measure of the reclining angle changes as b changes.

7 In the fall of 1986, three friends challenged each other to a pumpkin-throwing contest. The winner threw a pumpkin 126 feet. This event has since evolved into the annual Punkin' Chunkin' World Championship in which air compression cannons and catapult machines hurl pumpkins thousands of feet.

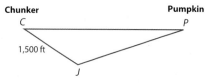

To measure the length of a throw, two judges and a spotter are involved. One judge is located at point C where the chunker releases the pumpkin. The second judge is on the right edge of the playing field at point J, a distance of 1,500 feet from point C. After a throw, the spotter stands at the location P at which the pumpkin landed. The two judges use transits to measure ∠C and ∠J, respectively. This information is then used to derive the length CP of the throw.

a. In 2004, Old Glory set a new world Punkin' Chunkin' record in the Adult Air Cannons category. To measure the record throw, the judges measured ∠C at 30.0° and ∠J at 135.6°. What was the distance CP of the record throw?

b. $m\angle C = \sin^{-1}\left(\dfrac{43.5049 \sin 101.03°}{53.5512}\right) \approx 53°$

$m\angle D = 360° - 135° - 120° - 53° = 52°$

c. *Area* $\triangle ABD = \dfrac{1}{2}(20)(27) \sin 135° \approx 191 \text{ m}^2$

Area $\triangle BCD = \dfrac{1}{2}(24)(53.5512) \sin 53° \approx 513 \text{ m}^2$

Area ABCD $\approx 191 \text{ m}^2 + 513 \text{ m}^2 = 704 \text{ m}^2$

Alternatively, students could use the following method:

In $\triangle ABD$, the length of the altitude from point A can be found by solving $\sin 19° = \dfrac{h}{27}$. So, $h = 27 \sin 19°$, and the area of $\triangle ABD = \dfrac{1}{2}(43.5)(27) \sin 19° \approx 191 \text{ m}^2$. In $\triangle CBD$, the length of the altitude from point B can be found by solving $\sin 53° = \dfrac{h}{24}$. So, $h = 24 \sin 53°$, and the area of $\triangle CBD = \dfrac{1}{2}(53.5)(24) \sin 53° \approx 513 \text{ m}^2$. *Area ABCD* $\approx 191 \text{ m}^2 + 513 \text{ m}^2 = 704 \text{ m}^2$.

6 **a.** You could use the Law of Cosines to find $m\angle ACB$. The measure of reclining angle $\angle BCD$ added to $m\angle ACB$ is $180°$.

b. $10^2 = 10^2 + b^2 - 2b(10) \cos (\angle ACB)$

$20b \cos (\angle ACB) = b^2$

$\cos (\angle ACB) = \dfrac{b^2}{20b} = \dfrac{b}{20}$

$m\angle ACB = \cos^{-1}\left(\dfrac{b}{20}\right)$

$m\angle BCD = 180° - \cos^{-1}\left(\dfrac{b}{20}\right)$

Alternatively, students might express $m\angle BCD$ as $\cos^{-1}\left(-\dfrac{b}{20}\right)$ if they use their knowledge from Lesson 1, Connections Task 8.

c. If $b = 8$, $m\angle BCD = 180° - \cos^{-1}\left(\dfrac{8}{20}\right) \approx 114°$.

If $b = 10$, $m\angle BCD = 180° - \cos^{-1}\left(\dfrac{10}{20}\right) = 120°$.

If $b = 12$, $m\angle BCD = 180° - \cos^{-1}\left(\dfrac{12}{20}\right) \approx 127°$.

If $b = 14$, $m\angle BCD = 180° - \cos^{-1}\left(\dfrac{14}{20}\right) \approx 134°$.

As b increases, the measure of the reclining angle increases at a nonconstant rate.

7 **a.** $m\angle P = 180° - 30.0° - 135.6° = 14.4°$

Use the Law of Sines to determine CP.

$\dfrac{CP}{\sin 135.6°} = \dfrac{1,500}{\sin 14.4°}$

$CP = \dfrac{1,500 \sin 135.6°}{\sin 14.4°} \approx 4,220 \text{ feet}$

(Old Glory's record throw is listed as 4,224.00 feet on the Punkin' Chunkin' Web site: www.atbeach.com/punkinchunkin/)

INSTRUCTIONAL NOTE If students use the Law of Sines in Part b to determine the measure of $\angle J$, they will get the measure of the supplement of $\angle J$. You can refer students back to Lesson 1, Connections Task 8, to help them make sense of this situation. From Connections Task 8, they know that two possible angles between $0°$ and $180°$ exist for any given sine value (except for $\sin 90° = 1$). Therefore, using $\sin^{-1}$ to determine the measure of an angle in any triangle should always reveal two possible solutions. To avoid this dilemma, students can use the Law of Cosines.

b. Another world record was set in 2004, this by Hypertension in the Adult Catapult category. Assume for this record throw of 2,112 feet that m∠C was 28.6°.

  i. What was the distance *JP* from the position of the judge at *J* to the position of the spotter at *P* where the pumpkin landed?

  ii. What was the measure of ∠*J*?

c. Suppose in a pumpkin throw, m∠C = 33.8° and the distance *JP* is 1,435 feet. Explain why this is not enough information to uniquely determine the length *CP* of the throw.

8 Suppose in △*ABC*, *a*, *b*, and *c* are the lengths of the sides opposites angles *A*, *B*, and *C*, respectively. Find the measures of the three unknown parts of △*ABC* to the nearest tenth, given each of the following sets of conditions.

a. $c = 5.4$ m, m∠A = 58.0°, m∠B = 42.8°

b. $a = 6.9$ m, m∠A = 47.2°, m∠C = 110.5°

c. $a = 12.9$ m, $b = 16.3$ m, $c = 8.8$ m

d. $b = 9.7$ m, $c = 10.2$ m, m∠C = 67.4°

Connections

9 To use the usual formula to find the area of a triangle, you need to know the length of one side and the altitude to that base. If you are given the lengths of two sides and the measure of the included angle, you can use the Law of Sines to find the area of the triangle.

a. Use the three diagrams below to show that in every case, area of △*ABC* = $\frac{1}{2}$ *bc* sin *A*.

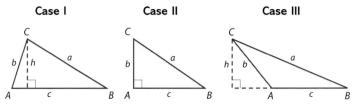

Case I **Case II** **Case III**

b. Explain as precisely as you can why it is also true that area of △*ABC* = $\frac{1}{2}$ *ac* sin *B* = $\frac{1}{2}$ *ab* sin *C*.

c. Determine the areas of triangles with the following side lengths and angle measures:

  i. m∠A = 73°, $b = 12$, $c = 17$

  ii. m∠A = 118°, $b = 21$, $c = 18$

b. **i.** Use the Law of Cosines to determine *JP*.

$$JP^2 = 1,500^2 + 2,112^2 - 2(1,500)(2,112) \cos 28.6°$$
$$JP \approx 1,071 \text{ feet}$$

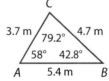

ii. Use the Law of Cosines to determine m∠*J*.

$$\cos \angle J = \frac{2,112^2 - 1,500^2 - 1,071^2}{-2(1,500)(1,071)}$$
$$m\angle J \approx 109.3°$$

c. Thinking back to exploring the SSA case, since 1,435 > 1,500 sin 33.8°, two triangles, △*CP′J* and △*CPJ*, could be formed as shown at the right.

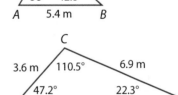

Alternatively, by the Law of Cosines,
$$1,435^2 = CP^2 + 1,500^2 - 2(1,500)(CP) \cos 33.8°.$$
$$CP^2 - 2,493CP + 190,775 = 0$$
CP is uniquely determined if and only if the above quadratic equation in *CP* has a unique positive solution. In fact, by the quadratic formula, the equation has two positive solutions.

$$CP = \frac{2,493 \pm \sqrt{2,493^2 - 4(1)(190,775)}}{2(1)} \approx \frac{2,493 \pm 2,335}{2} \approx 2,414 \text{ ft or } 79 \text{ ft}$$

Therefore, the given information does not uniquely determine *CP*.

8 In *a* and *b*, students might use either the Law of Sines or Law of Cosines to find the missing side lengths.

a. m∠*C* = 180° − 58.0° − 42.8° = 79.2°

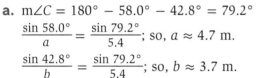

$$\frac{\sin 58.0°}{a} = \frac{\sin 79.2°}{5.4}; \text{ so, } a \approx 4.7 \text{ m}.$$

$$\frac{\sin 42.8°}{b} = \frac{\sin 79.2°}{5.4}; \text{ so, } b \approx 3.7 \text{ m}.$$

b. m∠*B* = 180° − 47.2° − 110.5° = 22.3°

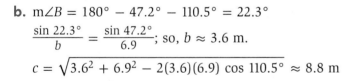

$$\frac{\sin 22.3°}{b} = \frac{\sin 47.2°}{6.9}; \text{ so, } b \approx 3.6 \text{ m}.$$

$$c = \sqrt{3.6^2 + 6.9^2 - 2(3.6)(6.9) \cos 110.5°} \approx 8.8 \text{ m}$$

c. $\cos A = \dfrac{12.9^2 - 16.3^2 - 8.8^2}{-2(16.3)(8.8)} \approx 0.6160;$

so, m∠*A* ≈ 52.0°.

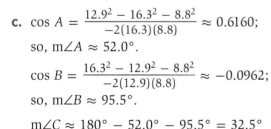

$$\cos B = \frac{16.3^2 - 12.9^2 - 8.8^2}{-2(12.9)(8.8)} \approx -0.0962;$$

so, m∠*B* ≈ 95.5°.

m∠*C* ≈ 180° − 52.0° − 95.5° = 32.5°

d. In this SSA situation, 10.2 > 9.7 so a unique triangle *ABC* is determined.

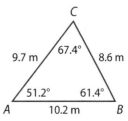

$$\frac{\sin B}{9.7} = \frac{\sin 67.4°}{10.2}; \text{ so, } m\angle B \approx 61.4°.$$

m∠*A* ≈ 180° − 67.4° − 61.4° = 51.2°

$$a = \sqrt{9.7^2 + 10.2^2 - 2(9.7)(10.2) \cos 51.2°}$$
$$\approx 8.6 \text{ m}$$

Unit 7

9 **a.** In each pictured triangle, $h = b \sin A$. In Case II, $\sin A = 1$; so, $h = b = b \sin A$. In Case III, $h = b \sin(180° - A) = b \sin A$. The base of each triangle is c, so the area is $\frac{1}{2}(base)(height) = \frac{1}{2}c(b \sin A) = \frac{1}{2}bc \sin A$. In the right triangle, the area reduces to the usual formula, $\frac{1}{2}bc$.

   b. The same reasoning as in Part a can be applied to $\triangle ABC$ using $\angle B$ and $\angle C$ and the corresponding heights.

   c. **i.** *Area* $= \frac{1}{2}(12)(17) \sin 73° \approx 98$ square units

   ii. *Area* $= \frac{1}{2}(21)(18) \sin 118° \approx 167$ square units

Unit 7

Teacher Notes

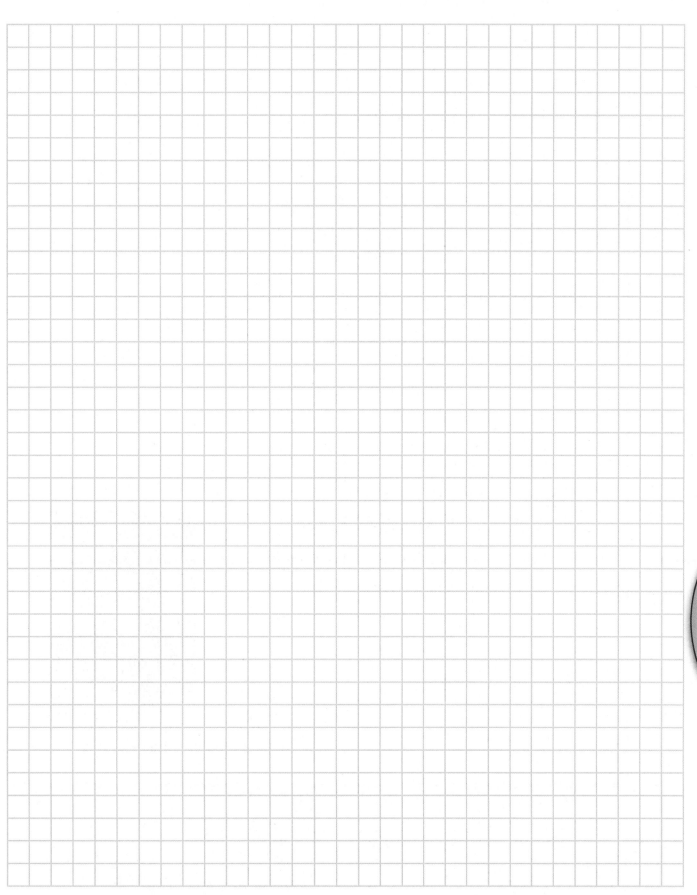

(10) In parallelogram *ABCD* below, information is given about one side and two angles formed by that side and the diagonals $\overline{AC}$ and $\overline{BD}$.

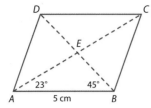

a. Verify that a parallelogram has 180° symmetry by tracing parallelogram *ABCD* on a sheet of paper and rotating the paper about point *E*.

b. Use facts about triangles and the rotational symmetry property of parallelograms to find the measures of as many of the other 7 segments and 10 angles in the given figure as you can. Do *not* use trigonometry.

c. Use the Law of Sines to find further information about the segments and angles in the figure.

(11) Use your calculator or computer software to graphically examine the behavior of the sine and cosine functions for angle measures between 0° and 360°. Be sure it is set in degree mode.

a. Set your graphing window to Xmin = 0, Xmax = 360, Xscl = 45, Ymin = −1.5, Ymax = 1.5, and Yscl = 0.5. Then graph $y = \sin x$ and $y = \cos x$.

  i. Describe the pattern of change for each function.

  ii. How do these graphs compare with those of linear, exponential, and quadratic functions?

  iii. For what values of x does $\sin x = \cos x$?

b. Use the definitions of the trigonometric functions to explain why your descriptions of the patterns of change for the sine and cosine functions make sense.

(12) Surveyors use triangulation and the methods in this lesson to determine the distance between two inaccessible points such as *P* and *Q* in the diagram. They begin by laying off a *base line* $\overline{AB}$ that can be accurately measured. Using a transit, they then measure the four angles at points *A* and *B* formed by $\overline{AB}$ and the diagonals $\overline{PB}$ and $\overline{QA}$. How can they use this information to determine *PQ*?

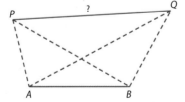

LESSON 2 • Using Trigonometry in Any Triangle **507**

10 a. Students should verify that parallelograms have 180° rotational symmetry. (The inclusion of the diagonals in their analysis of the symmetry will assist them in finding some of the information for Part b.)

b. Students should be able to determine the angle measures and lengths in the diagram shown here.

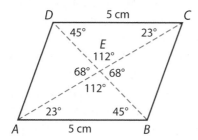

• $DC = 5$ cm because opposite sides of a parallelogram are of equal length.

• m∠$AEB = 112°$ because $180° - 23° - 45° = 112°$.

• Knowing that the measures of adjacent angles forming a line sum to 180°, students can find all of the angle measures at E.

• The 180° rotational symmetry implies that m∠$CDE = 45°$ and m∠$DCE = 23°$.

c. DIFFERENTIATION If you assign this task as suggested following Investigation 1, students will not have developed the Law of Cosines. Thus, many students will probably not be able to determine the measures of all the sides and angles in the diagram. This is a nice lead-in to the fact that another relationship between the sides and the angles would be helpful. However, it is possible to solve for all of the sides and angles of this parallelogram using only the Law of Sines and some calculator estimation. You may want to challenge your more able students to try to find the other measures and lengths as shown here.

First, in △AEB, $\dfrac{\sin 112°}{5} = \dfrac{\sin 23°}{BE} = \dfrac{\sin 45°}{AE}$.

$BE \approx 2.11$ cm; $AE \approx 3.81$ cm. By symmetry, $DE \approx 2.11$ cm and $CE \approx 3.81$ cm. Next, in △AED, let $x = $ m∠ADE, then m∠$DAE = 180° - (68° + x) = 112° - x$.

$$\dfrac{\sin x}{3.81} = \dfrac{\sin (112° - x)}{2.11}$$

$$\dfrac{\sin x}{\sin (112° - x)} = \dfrac{3.81}{2.11} \approx 1.81$$

By letting $Y_1 = \dfrac{\sin x}{\sin (112° - x)}$ and using tables or graphs, students can see that when $y \approx 1.81$, x is about 79°.

m∠$ADE \approx 79°$

m∠$DAE = 112° - x \approx 33°$

By applying the Law of Sines again, $\dfrac{\sin 79°}{3.81} = \dfrac{\sin 68°}{AD}$ and $AD \approx 3.60$ cm. Rotational symmetry allows you to use the measures for △AED to find the corresponding measures of △CEB.

NOTE This task uses values to hundredths for computations.

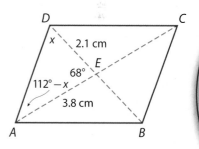

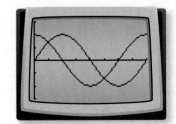

11 **a.** **i.** $y = \sin x$ starts at the origin and increases at a nonconstant rate until it reaches its maximum value of 1 at $x = 90°$. Then it decreases, crossing the x-axis at $x = 180°$, and continues to decrease until $y = -1$ when $x = 270°$. Then it increases again until $y = 0$ when $x = 360°$. $y = \cos x$ is at its maximum value of 1 when $x = 0°$. It then decreases, crossing the x-axis at $x = 90°$, and continues to decrease until it reaches its minimum of -1 at $x = 180°$. Then it increases, crossing the x-axis at $x = 270°$, and continues to increase until it again reaches its maximum value, when $x = 360°$. The cosine graph appears to be the same as the sine graph shifted horizontally by $-90°$.

ii. These functions differ from the other functions in many ways. For one, they have both a maximum and a minimum value in the interval $0° \le x \le 360°$. Their pattern of change is also different from the others in that the rates and directions in which they change alternate over consecutive intervals.

POSSIBLE MISCONCEPTION Students may incorrectly believe that the sine function is formed from two quadratic functions with restricted domains. As an extension and connection to the quadratic functions, students could fit a quadratic to the three points of the sine function, (0, 0), (90, 1), and (180, 0). Viewing these two functions on the window $0 \le x \le 180$, x-scale of 45, and $0 \le y \le 1.1$, y-scale of 0.1 will reveal differences.

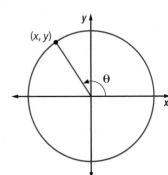

iii. $\sin x = \cos x$ when $x = 45°$ or when $x = 225°$.

b. Thinking about the angle θ in standard position and considering the trigonometric ratios as θ goes from $0°$ to $360°$ by quadrant:

$\sin \theta = \dfrac{y}{r}$, where $r = \sqrt{x^2 + y^2}$ goes from 0 to 1, 1 to 0, 0 to -1, and -1 to 0.

$\cos \theta = \dfrac{x}{r}$, where $r = \sqrt{x^2 + y^2}$ goes from 1 to 0, 0 to -1, -1 to 0 and 0 to 1.

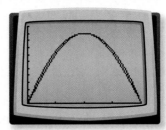

Unit 7

12 Let C be the point where $\overline{AQ}$ intersects $\overline{BP}$. Apply the Law of Sines four times in Steps 1–5 as follows:

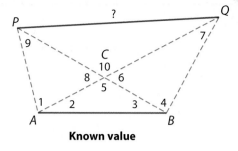

Known value

(1) Use m∠2 and m∠3 to find m∠5. Use m∠5 to find m∠6, m∠8, and m∠10. Use m∠1 and m∠8 to find m∠9. Use m∠4 and m∠6 to find m∠7.

(2) Use m∠2, m∠5, and AB to determine BC.

(3) Similarly, use m∠3, m∠5, and AB to determine AC.

(4) Use m∠4, m∠7, and BC to determine CQ.

(5) Similarly, use m∠1, m∠9, and AC to determine CP.

(6) Use the Law of Cosines and m∠10, CQ, and CP to determine PQ.

13. Find the lengths of the diagonal braces of kite *ABCD*.

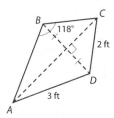

14. Make a model of a triangle *ABC* with a side whose length varies as the fixed length pieces *AB* and *BC* pivot about points *B* and *A* as shown below. Make *AB* = 10 cm and *BC* = 16 cm long (from endhole to endhole).

    a. Make strip $\overline{AD}$ with holes 2 cm apart (or draw a segment, $\overline{AD}$, on your paper and carefully mark points 2 cm apart).

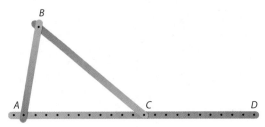

    i. What is the length needed for strip $\overline{AD}$ that would allow *C* to be extended so that *A*, *B*, and *C* are collinear?

    ii. What is the minimum length *AD* in this model?

    b. When you change the length *AC* in △*ABC*, what else changes?

    c. Adjust the length *AC* in 2-cm step sizes from its minimum to maximum possible values. At each step, use a ruler and protractor to obtain and record the length *AC* and m∠*A*.

    d. Make a scatterplot of the data pairs (*AC*, m∠*A*). Investigate whether a linear, exponential, or quadratic function would reasonably fit the pattern in the data. Do any of these appear to be a good fit for the data? Explain.

    e. Use the Law of Cosines to write an equation that gives m∠*A* as a function of *AC*. Graph the function over the interval from the minimum to the maximum length *AC*.

    f. How well does the graph of your function from Part e fit your measurement data? Is the symbolic form of your function rule that of a linear, exponential, quadratic, or some other kind of function?

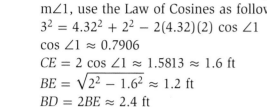

13 Since by symmetry, m∠ABC = m∠ADC, we have
$AC^2 = 2^2 + 3^2 - 2(2)(3) \cos 118°$.
$AC \approx 4.3^2 \approx 4$ ft
To find *BE*, you could find *CE* or *AE* and use the
Pythagorean Theorem.
To find *CE*, you could use $\cos \angle 1 = \frac{CE}{2}$. To find
m∠1, use the Law of Cosines as follows:
$3^2 = 4.32^2 + 2^2 - 2(4.32)(2) \cos \angle 1$
$\cos \angle 1 \approx 0.7906$
$CE = 2 \cos \angle 1 \approx 1.5813 \approx 1.6$ ft
$BE = \sqrt{2^2 - 1.6^2} \approx 1.2$ ft
$BD = 2BE \approx 2.4$ ft

14 **a.** **i.** If strip *AD* is 26 cm, the three strips lie on the same line. So, the
length *AD* should be greater than or equal to 26 cm.

ii. Since $AB + AC > BC$, $10 + AC > 16$ and since *AC* lies on *AD*,
$AD > 6$. The next hole is 2 cm larger, so the minimum length *AD*
is 8 cm.

b. The measures of the angles of △ABC change.

c. Some sample measurement data is provided below.

AC	8	10	12	14	16	18	20	22	24
m∠A	125°	105°	95°	85°	74°	62°	50°	40°	28°

d.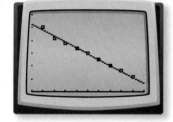

These points appear to be close to linear although the pattern
of consecutive points at the beginning and end of the scatterplot
are below and then above a regression line and so suggest a
different function.

e. Let $x = AC$.
Then $16^2 = 10^2 + x^2 - 2(10)x \cos A$.
$\cos A = \dfrac{x^2 - 156}{20x}$
$m\angle A = \cos^{-1}\left(\dfrac{x^2 - 156}{20x}\right)$

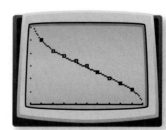

f. The data fit this symbolic function very
well. This function is obviously not a
linear, exponential, or power function.

Unit 7

15 In addition to examining the geometry of the SSA condition as you did in Investigation 3, it is revealing to consider the condition from trigonometric and algebraic points of view.

 a. Apply the Law of Sines to the two triangles *ABC* and *ABC′* in the diagram to the right.

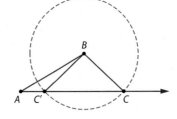

 i. What equation relates ∠*A*, *AB*, *BC*, and ∠*ACB* in △*ABC*?

 ii. What equation relates ∠*A*, *AB*, *BC′*, and ∠*AC′B* in △*ABC′*?

 iii. How can both equations be true when *BC* = *BC′* but m∠*ACB* ≠ m∠*AC′B*?

 b. Now suppose in △*ABC*, $a = 1$, $c = \sqrt{3}$, and m∠*A* = 30°.

 i. Using the Law of Cosines, write and then solve a quadratic equation that relates the unknown side length *AC* and the three given measures.

 ii. Sketch the triangle or triangles that are determined.

 c. Suppose in △*ABC*, $a = 8$, $b = 10$, and m∠*B* = 120°.

 i. Determine the number of possible triangles *ABC*—none, one, or two—that can satisfy these side and angle conditions.

 ii. Find the length of the third side of any triangles that were determined in part i.

Reflections

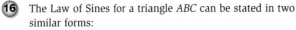

16 The Law of Sines for a triangle *ABC* can be stated in two similar forms:

I		II
$\dfrac{\sin A}{a} = \dfrac{\sin B}{b} = \dfrac{\sin C}{c}$	and	$\dfrac{a}{\sin A} = \dfrac{b}{\sin B} = \dfrac{c}{\sin C}$

 a. Why are these two forms equivalent?

 b. When is form I easier to use? When is form II easier to use?

17 Bradford Washburn, the leader of a group of surveyors that remapped the Grand Canyon in the 1970s, said that the work was "like mapping a mountain upside down." What do you think he meant by that?

15 **a.** **i.** $\dfrac{\sin A}{BC} = \dfrac{\sin (\angle ACB)}{AB}$

ii. $\dfrac{\sin A}{BC'} = \dfrac{\sin (\angle AC'B)}{AB}$

iii. Both equations can be true because $\angle ACB$ and $\angle AC'B$ are supplementary. It follows that their sines are equal.

b. **i.** Let $AC = b$.

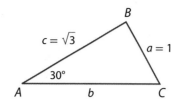

$$1^2 = b^2 + (\sqrt{3})^2 - 2b(\sqrt{3})(\cos 30°)$$
$$1 = b^2 + 3 - 2b\sqrt{3}\left(\dfrac{\sqrt{3}}{2}\right)$$
$$b^2 - 3b + 2 = 0$$
$$(b - 2)(b - 1) = 0$$
$$b = 2 \text{ or } b = 1$$

ii.

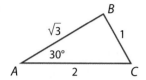

c. **i.** Since $\angle B$ is obtuse and $b > a$, exactly one triangle is determined.

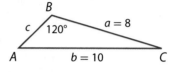

ii. $b^2 = a^2 + c^2 - 2ac \cos B$
$$10^2 = 8^2 + c^2 - 2(8)c(-0.5)$$
$$c^2 + 8c - 36 = 0$$
Using the quadratic formula, $c \approx 3.2$. (The negative value of c, -11.2, is not meaningful as a side of a triangle.)

Reflections

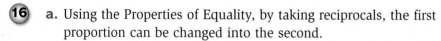

16 **a.** Using the Properties of Equality, by taking reciprocals, the first proportion can be changed into the second.

b. If you are solving for an angle, it is easier to use I $\dfrac{\sin A}{a} = \dfrac{\sin B}{b} = \dfrac{\sin C}{c}$. If you are solving for a side, it is easier to use II $\dfrac{a}{\sin A} = \dfrac{b}{\sin B} = \dfrac{c}{\sin C}$. Students should understand that the proportions can be solved in either form but that fewer steps are required if the variable for which you are solving is in the numerator.

17 A surveyor typically maps points on a mountain that are above the surveyor's vantage point, and the surveyor often measures angles of elevation. The Grand Canyon was mainly mapped from the rim of the canyon, well above the points to be mapped. Therefore, the surveyor often measures angles of depression.

Unit 7

18 Models of four problem situations are shown below. For each case, describe the trigonometric method that you would use to determine the indicated length or angle measure. Would you expect one, two, or no solutions? You do not have to perform the calculations.

a.

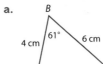

AC = ?

b.

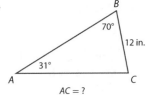

AC = ?

c.

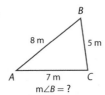

m∠B = ?

d.

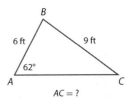

AC = ?

19 Look back at the statements of the Law of Sines (page 491) and the Law of Cosines (page 494). Write each law completely in words using no letter symbols for angles or sides of triangles.

20 The length of two sides *a* and *b* and the measure of ∠A opposite side *a* of a possible triangle *ABC* are given. Summarize in your own words the conditions under which (a) no triangle, (b) exactly one triangle, or (c) two triangles are determined.

Extensions

21 In Investigation 1, you examined a derivation of the Law of Sines for an acute triangle. In this task, you will derive the Law of Sines for the case of a right triangle. Use the fact that for right triangle *ABC* labeled as shown, sin *C* = sin 90° = 1.

a. Express sin *A* and sin *B* in terms of the sides *a*, *b*, and *c*.

b. Explain why $c = \frac{c}{\sin C}$.

c. Solve each equation in Part a for *c*. Use those results and your result in Part b to derive the Law of Sines.

d. What are the values of the common ratios in the formulation of the Law of Sines for △*ABC*?

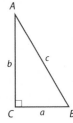

18 **a.** Use the Law of Cosines to find AC. $AC^2 = 6^2 + 4^2 - 2(6)(4) \cos 61°$. One solution is expected.

b. Use the Law of Sines to find AC. $\dfrac{AC}{\sin 70°} = \dfrac{12}{\sin 31°}$. One solution is expected.

c. Use the Law of Cosines to find $m\angle B$. $m\angle B = \cos^{-1}\left(\dfrac{7^2 - 8^2 - 5^2}{-2(8)(5)}\right)$. One solution is expected.

d. First, use the Law of Sines to find $m\angle C$. Then $m\angle B = 180° - (m\angle C + 62°)$. Then either use the Law of Sines or the Law of Cosines to determine AC. One solution is expected since $9 > 6$.

19 Students should express both the Law of Sines and the Law of Cosines relationships in their own words.

The Law of Sines: In any triangle, the ratios of the lengths of the sides to the sines of their opposite angles are equal.

The Law of Cosines: In any triangle, the square of the length of one designated side equals the sum of the squares of the two other side lengths minus twice the product of those other two side lengths with the cosine of the angle opposite the designated side.

20 If the given $\angle A$ is an acute angle, there is no triangle if $a < b \sin A$, two triangles if $a > b \sin A$ and $a < b$, and exactly one triangle if $a = b \sin A$ or $a \geq b$. If the given $\angle A$ is a right angle or an obtuse angle, there is no triangle if $a \leq b$ and exactly one triangle if $a > b$.

Extensions

21 **a.** $\sin A = \dfrac{a}{c}$

$\sin B = \dfrac{b}{c}$

b. Since $\sin C = 1$, $\dfrac{c}{\sin C} = \dfrac{c}{1} = c$.

c. $c = \dfrac{a}{\sin A}$, $c = \dfrac{b}{\sin B}$, and $c = \dfrac{c}{\sin C}$.

So, $\dfrac{a}{\sin A} = \dfrac{b}{\sin B} = \dfrac{c}{\sin C}$ or $\dfrac{\sin A}{a} = \dfrac{\sin B}{b} = \dfrac{\sin C}{c}$.

d. From Part c, we see that the common ratio of side length over sine of opposite angle is c, and the common ratio of sine of the angle over the length of the opposite side is $\dfrac{1}{c}$.

22 In this task, you will derive the Law of Sines for an obtuse triangle. Diagrams I and II below show the same triangle *ABC*, but the triangle is positioned differently.

Diagram I

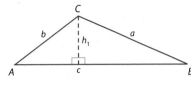

Diagram II

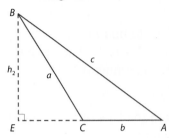

a. In Diagram I, the altitude from vertex *C* intersects side $\overline{AB}$.

   i. Write two expressions for h_1, one in terms of sin *A* and the other in terms of sin *B*.

   ii. Use your expressions in part i to show that $\frac{\sin A}{a} = \frac{\sin B}{b}$.

b. In Diagram II, the altitude from vertex *B* to opposite side $\overline{AC}$ falls outside the triangle.

   i. With reference to right triangle *ABE*, write an expression for h_2 in terms of sin *A*.

   ii. With reference to right triangle *BCE*, write an expression for h_2 in terms of $\sin(180 - m\angle C)°$.

   iii. Explain why the latter ratio is also equal to sin *C*. (The figure in Connections Task 9 Part c (page 478) may be helpful.)

   iv. Use your expressions in parts i–iii to show that $\frac{\sin A}{a} = \frac{\sin C}{c}$ or $\frac{a}{\sin A} = \frac{c}{\sin C}$.

c. Combine your results in Parts a and b to complete the derivation of the Law of Sines for an obtuse triangle.

 23 To find the area of a triangle using the usual formula, you need to know the length of one side and the length of the altitude to that side.

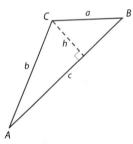

a. Suppose you know the lengths of the three sides *a*, *b*, and *c*. Explain how to calculate the height *h*.

b. How is your result in Part a related to the area formula in Connections Task 9?

22 **a.** **i.** $\sin A = \dfrac{h_1}{b}$; so, $h_1 = b \sin A$.

$\sin B = \dfrac{h_1}{a}$; so, $h_1 = a \sin B$.

ii. $b \sin A = a \sin B$, so dividing both sides by ab gives $\dfrac{\sin A}{a} = \dfrac{\sin B}{b}$.

b. **i.** $\sin A = \dfrac{h_2}{c}$; so, $h_2 = c \sin A$.

ii. $\sin (180 - \text{m}\angle C)° = \dfrac{h_2}{a}$; so, $h_2 = a \sin (180 - \text{m}\angle C)°$.

iii. Because of the symmetry of the semicircle formed from 0° to 180°, $\sin C = \sin (180° - \text{m}\angle C)$.

iv. $h_2 = c \sin A$ and $h_2 = a \sin C$; so, $a \sin C = c \sin A$. The Division Property of Equality gives $\dfrac{\sin A}{a} = \dfrac{\sin C}{c}$ or $\dfrac{a}{\sin A} = \dfrac{c}{\sin C}$.

c. Since $\dfrac{\sin A}{a} = \dfrac{\sin B}{b}$ and $\dfrac{\sin A}{a} = \dfrac{\sin C}{c}$, $\dfrac{\sin A}{a} = \dfrac{\sin B}{b} = \dfrac{\sin C}{c}$.

23 **a.** Use the Law of Cosines to determine m$\angle B$. Then $\dfrac{h}{a} = \sin B$ and $h = a \sin B$. Or, instead, find m$\angle A$ and write $h = b \sin A$.

b. The area of $\triangle ABC = \frac{1}{2}hc = \frac{1}{2}ac \sin B$ or $\frac{1}{2}bc \sin A$.

DIFFERENTIATION Another famous formula for the area of a triangle given its sides *a*, *b*, and *c* is attributed to Heron and is:
$Area = \sqrt{s(s - a)(s - b)(s - c)}$, where $s = \dfrac{a + b + c}{2}$ is the semiperimeter of the triangle. You may wish to have students verify it with some examples and find proofs of it in journal or Internet references.

24 You examined some of the geometric properties of one type of automobile jack in the Think About This Situation for Lesson 1 and in Connections Task 14 (page 480). Another kind of jack is used on racetracks and by service stations to perform quick tire changes. The jack has wheels so it can be easily moved around.

In the diagram of the automobile jack below, bar *DC* has one end *C* that can be moved between points *A* and *E* by turning a threaded rod at the back of the jack. The length *AE* is 24 inches, and *AB*, *BC*, and *BD* are each 12 inches.

a. If this jack is to be safe to use, what path must point *D* follow as point *C* moves toward point *A*?

b. What kind of triangles are △*ABC* and △*ABD*?

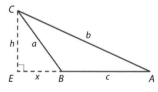

c. Use properties of isosceles triangles to explain why m∠*CAD* = 90° for any positive value of *CE* less than 24 inches.

d. Determine the height *AD* of the jack when *CE* = 6 inches. When *CE* = 13 inches.

25 Derivations of the Law of Cosines differ depending on whether the angle under consideration is acute or obtuse. In △*ABC* below, ∠*B* is an obtuse angle and *h* is the length of the altitude from vertex *C*.

a. Explain why each step in the following derivation is correct. The reason for Step 5 is that cos (180° − θ) = −cos θ as suggested by the figure in Connections Task 9, Part c (page 478).

(1) In right triangle *BCE*,
$h^2 = a^2 - x^2$.

(2) In right triangle *ACE*,
$h^2 = b^2 - (c + x)^2$.

(3) $b^2 - c^2 - 2cx - x^2 = a^2 - x^2$

(4) $b^2 = a^2 + c^2 + 2cx$

(5) In right triangle *BCE*,
$x = a \cos (m\angle CBE) = -a \cos B$.

(6) $b^2 = a^2 + c^2 - 2ac \cos B$

24 **a.** Point *D* must move vertically upward so that $\overleftrightarrow{AD}$ is a fixed, vertical line that is perpendicular to the base $\overline{AC}$ of the jack.

b. Triangles *ABC* and *ABD* are isosceles.

c. When *CE* < 24, triangles *ABC* and *ABD* are formed. Since the base angles in isosceles triangles have equal measures, m∠*ACB* = m∠*BAC* and m∠*ADB* = m∠*BAD*. Using these equations and the sum of the measures of the angles in △*CAD*, 2m∠*ACB* + 2m∠*ADB* = 180°. Dividing by 2, m∠*ACB* + m∠*ADB* = 90°. So, m∠*CAD* = 90°.

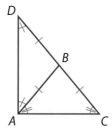

d. When *CE* = 6 inches, *AC* = 18. Using the Pythagorean Theorem for △*CAD*, $18^2 + AD^2 = 24^2$. So, *AD* ≈ 15.87 ≈ 16 inches. When *CE* = 13 inches and *AC* = 11 inches, $11^2 + AD^2 = 24^2$ and *AD* ≈ 21.33 ≈ 21 inches.

25 **a.** (1) Pythagorean Theorem

(2) Pythagorean Theorem

(3) Substitution Property using Steps 1 and 2

(4) Addition Property of Equality

(5) Definition of cosine; Multiplication Property of Equality; cos (180° − θ) = −cos θ

(6) Substitution Property using Steps 4 and 5

b. For the case of an acute angle, draw a new triangle ABC with $\angle B$ acute, and draw the altitude from vertex C to side $\overline{AB}$. Length c will then be divided into two parts of lengths x and $c - x$. The rest of the derivation of the Law of Cosines is similar to the obtuse case. Try to construct the argument.

c. Why is no additional proof needed for the case of m$\angle B = 90°$?

26 In $\triangle ABC$, ray BD bisects $\angle ABC$. Apply the Law of Sines to triangles ABD and CBD to show that the angle bisector of a triangle divides the opposite side into segments proportional in length to the adjacent sides. In symbols, show that $\frac{AD}{DC} = \frac{AB}{BC}$.

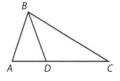

27 A carnival ride consists of six small airplanes attached to a vertical pole. As the pole rotates, the planes fly around the pole.

A rider can control the height of the plane by changing the length of the hydraulic cylinder $\overline{AC}$ attached at point C in the diagram below. In a typical design, $BD = 4$ m, $BA = 1.5$ m, $BC = 1.5$ m, $BE = 1.5$ m, and AC can vary between 1.5 and 2.2 m.

a. What is the smallest measure of $\angle ABC$? How far above the ground is the plane for that smallest angle?

b. If the hydraulic cylinder is fully extended, what is the measure of $\angle ABC$?

c. What is the lowest and what is the highest point of the plane above the ground?

d. How long should the hydraulic cylinder be so that the plane will fly 2.5 meters above the ground?

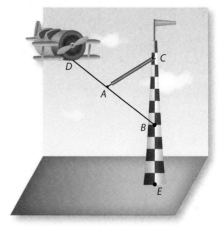

b. (1) In right triangle *CBE*, $h^2 = a^2 - x^2$.

(2) In right triangle *ACE*, $h^2 = b^2 - (c - x)^2$.

(3) $b^2 - c^2 + 2cx - x^2 = a^2 - x^2$

(4) $b^2 = a^2 + c^2 - 2cx$

(5) In right triangle *CBE*, $x = a \cos B$.

(6) $b^2 = a^2 + c^2 - 2ac \cos B$

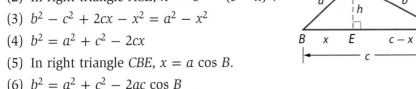

c. If m∠*B* = 90°, cos *B* = 0 and the Law of Cosines reduces to the Pythagorean Theorem, which was proved in Course 1.

 26 Apply the Law of Sines to △*ABD*:

$$\frac{AD}{\sin\left(\frac{m\angle B}{2}\right)} = \frac{AB}{\sin(m\angle ADB)} \text{ and } \frac{AD}{AB} = \frac{\sin\left(\frac{m\angle B}{2}\right)}{\sin(m\angle ADB)} \quad (1)$$

Now apply the Law of Sines to △*CBD*:

$$\frac{DC}{\sin\left(\frac{m\angle B}{2}\right)} = \frac{BC}{\sin(m\angle CDB)} \text{ and } \frac{DC}{BC} = \frac{\sin\left(\frac{m\angle B}{2}\right)}{\sin(m\angle CDB)} \quad (2)$$

Since m∠*ADB* = 180° − m∠*CDB*, sin (m∠*ADB*) = sin (m∠*CDB*).

Substituting into equation (2), we have $\frac{DC}{BC} = \frac{\sin\left(\frac{m\angle B}{2}\right)}{\sin(m\angle ADB)}$.

Substituting with equation (1), we have $\frac{AD}{AB} = \frac{DC}{BC}$, which is equivalent to $\frac{AD}{DC} = \frac{AB}{BC}$.

 27

a. When *AC* = 1.5, m∠*ABC* will be smallest. Then △*ABC* is equilateral; so, m∠*ABC* = 60°. In the diagram, △*BFD* is a 30°-60° right triangle with hypotenuse of length 4 m. Thus, *DF* = 2. Alternatively, *DF* = 4 sin 30° = 2. The height of the plane is *DG*, and *DG* = 2 + 1.5 = 3.5 m.

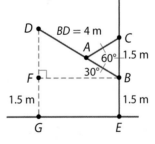

b. When the hydraulic cylinder is fully extended, *AC* = 2.2 m. By the Law of Cosines, $2.2^2 = 1.5^2 + 1.5^2 - 2(1.5)(1.5) \cos(\angle ABC)$. $\cos(\angle ABC) \approx -0.0756$; m∠*ABC* ≈ 94.3°

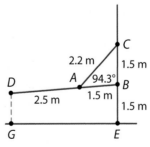

c. From Part a, the highest point is 3.5 m above the ground. The lowest point is when the hydraulic cylinder is fully extended; so, m∠*ABC* ≈ 94.3° and m∠*DBF* ≈ 4.3°. *DF* = 4 sin 4.3° ≈ 0.30 m. So, the distance, *DG*, of the plane above the ground is 1.5 − 0.3 ≈ 1.2 m.

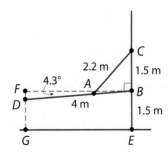

NOTE The solution to Part d is on page T514.

Unit 7

Review

28 Suppose the length, width, and height of a rectangular prism are all different.

  a. How many different lengths of edges does the prism have?

  b. How many different shapes of faces does it have?

  c. How many different lengths of diagonals does the prism have?

29 Solve each system of equations without using the graphing or table capabilities of your calculator or computer software.

  a. $6x + 4y = 58$
     $x - 2y = 7$

  b. $y = x^2 - 3x$
     $y = 2x + 6$

  c. $y = 2x + 1$
     $y = \dfrac{-5}{x - 3}$

30 Consider matrices A and B as given below. Evaluate each expression without the use of technology.

$$A = \begin{bmatrix} -2 & 3 \\ 0 & 5 \end{bmatrix} \qquad B = \begin{bmatrix} 4 & -6 \\ 1 & -2 \end{bmatrix}$$

  a. $A + 2B$ b. $B - A$

  c. $A \times B$ d. B^2

31 On a coordinate grid, make a sketch of the triangle with vertices at $A(-2, -1)$, $B(0, 3)$, and $C(8, -1)$.

  a. Verify that $\triangle ABC$ is a right triangle.

  b. Find the perimeter of the triangle.

  c. Find the coordinates of the midpoint of the hypotenuse of $\triangle ABC$. Does the line segment that joins vertex B to the midpoint of the hypotenuse divide $\triangle ABC$ into two triangles with equal areas? Explain your reasoning.

32 Write each of the following in equivalent factored form.

  a. $12x^2 + 2x$

  b. $x^2 - 12x + 36$

  c. $x^2 - 81$

  d. $2x^2 + 20x + 48$

  e. $x^2 - 2x - 35$

  f. $2x^2 + 11x - 21$

d. INSTRUCTIONAL NOTE A student who does not round off m∠ABC but directly evaluates $\cos\left(90° - \sin^{-1}\left(\frac{1}{4}\right)\right) = \frac{1}{4}$ may wonder if this is coincidence. It is not: $\cos(90° - \sin^{-1} x) = x$ for $0 \le x \le 1$. The right triangle below demonstrates:

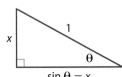

$$\sin\theta = x$$
$$\cos(90° - \theta) = x$$
$$\theta = \sin^{-1} x$$

If $DG = 2.5$, then $DF = 1$.

$\text{m}\angle DBF = \sin^{-1}\left(\frac{1}{4}\right) \approx 14.5°$

$\text{m}\angle ABC \approx 90° - 14.5° = 75.5°$

$AC^2 = 1.5^2 + 1.5^2 - 2(1.5)(1.5)\cos 75.5°$

$AC \approx 1.8$ m

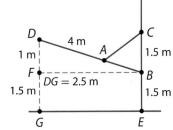

Review

28
a. The prism has three different lengths of edges.
b. The prism has three different shapes of faces.
c. The lengths of diagonals of the prism are all equal.

29 Students should use substitution or elimination to solve the systems.
a. (9, 1)   b. (6, 18), (−1, 4)   c. (2, 5), $\left(\frac{1}{2}, 2\right)$

30
a. $\begin{bmatrix} 6 & -9 \\ 2 & 1 \end{bmatrix}$ b. $\begin{bmatrix} 6 & -9 \\ 1 & -7 \end{bmatrix}$

c. $\begin{bmatrix} -5 & 6 \\ 5 & -10 \end{bmatrix}$ d. $\begin{bmatrix} 10 & -12 \\ 2 & -2 \end{bmatrix}$

31
a. Using slopes:
slope of $\overline{AB} = 2$
slope of $\overline{BC} = -\frac{1}{2}$
So, $\overline{AB} \perp \overline{BC}$. Therefore, △ABC is a right triangle. (Students might choose to find the lengths of the sides as requested in Part b and use the converse of the Pythagorean Theorem.)

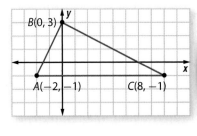

b. $AB = \sqrt{20} = 2\sqrt{5}$
$BC = \sqrt{80} = 4\sqrt{5}$
$AC = 10$
So, the perimeter is $10 + 6\sqrt{5}$.

c. Midpoint of $\overline{AC}$: (3, −1)
Yes. The two triangles will have equal heights and both bases are half the length of $\overline{AC}$. Therefore, the areas of the triangles will be equal.

32
a. $2x(6x + 1)$ or $x(12x + 2)$ b. $(x - 6)^2$
c. $(x + 9)(x - 9)$ d. $2(x + 6)(x + 4)$
e. $(x - 7)(x + 5)$ f. $(2x - 3)(x + 7)$

NOTE Solutions to Task 33 Parts a–e are on page T515.

33 Write each expression in the equivalent $ax^2 + bx + c$ form.

   a. $(x + 5)^2$

   b. $3x(x - 6) + 8(2 - 4x)$

   c. $3(2x - 10)(x + 2)$

   d. $\left(x - \frac{1}{2}\right)\left(x + \frac{1}{2}\right)$

   e. $(x + 5)(x + 4)$

34 Suppose you roll two dice and subtract the smaller number from the larger. Make a chart that shows all of the possible outcomes.

   a. What is the probability that the difference is greater than 4?

   b. What is the probability that the difference is less than or equal to 4?

   c. Explain why the probabilities you found in Parts a and b should add to 1.

   d. What is the probability that you will roll doubles and get a difference of zero?

35 Suppose that Alejandro bought a new car that cost $25,595, and the value of the car depreciates by 12% each year.

   a. What will the car be worth after two years?

   b. Write a rule that could be used to find the value V of the car for any number of years t in the future.

   c. In what year will the car be worth only half of what Alejandro originally paid for it?

36 Draw a vertex-edge graph that fits each description.

   a. Has an Euler circuit but does not have a Hamilton circuit

   b. Has a Hamilton circuit but does not have an Euler circuit

   c. Requires at least four colors to color the vertices of the graph

33 **a.** $x^2 + 10x + 25$

b. $3x^2 - 50x + 16$

c. $6x^2 - 18x - 60$

d. $x^2 - \dfrac{1}{4}$

e. $x^2 + 9x + 20$

Just in Time

34

	1	2	3	4	5	6
1	0	1	2	3	4	5
2	1	0	1	2	3	4
3	2	1	0	1	2	3
4	3	2	1	0	1	2
5	4	3	2	1	0	1
6	5	4	3	2	1	0

a. $\dfrac{2}{36}$, or $\dfrac{1}{18}$

b. $\dfrac{34}{36}$, or $\dfrac{17}{18}$

c. The probability is 1 because all possible outcomes are used exactly once in the two probabilities.

d. $\dfrac{6}{36} = \dfrac{1}{6}$

35 **a.** \$19,820.77

b. $V = 25,595(0.88^t)$

c. Half of the original value is \$12,797.50, a value the car will reach in its sixth year.

36 **a.** Responses will vary. One example is .

b. Responses will vary. One example is .

c. Examples will vary. Any graph that contains (as a subgraph) a complete graph on four vertices $\left(\text{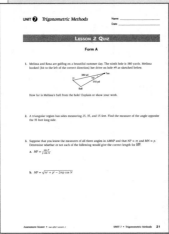} \right)$ will require four colors to color.

Looking Back

In this unit, you extended your work with coordinates to describe angles in standard position in a coordinate plane. The coordinates of points on the terminal side of an angle in standard position were used to define a new family of functions, the trigonometric functions: sine, cosine, and tangent. These functions provide important connections between angle measure and linear measure.

When interpreted as ratios of side lengths of a right triangle, the trigonometric functions have many important applications. You also learned to use trigonometric methods, including use of the Law of Sines and the Law of Cosines for any triangle, to solve problems such as indirect measurement of inaccessible distances or angles, measurement of polygonal shapes using triangulation, and modeling mechanisms with triangles in which the measures of two parts remain fixed while the length of a side varies.

The following tasks will help you review, pull together, and apply what you have learned as you solve new problems.

1 In the 19th and early 20th centuries, water wheels were commonly used to operate grist mills that ground wheat and corn for flour. The Wayside Inn Grist Mill, Sudbury, Massachusetts, pictured below, first ground corn in 1929. Power for the grinding was provided by a water wheel driven by flowing water.

Looking Back

Trigonometry draws on and supports important connections across different strands of mathematical content. For example, this unit drew on ideas from coordinate geometry, which itself connects geometry and algebra, to define the trigonometric functions in terms of angles in standard position. The unit built on ideas from synthetic geometry including triangles and other polygons, the congruence conditions for triangles, and the Pythagorean Theorem. The trigonometric ratios are functions, a concept that is most central to algebra. As students also learned, trigonometry provides methods for solving a wide variety of real-world problems that involve indirect measurement and the analysis of mechanisms based on triangles or circles.

Each task in the Looking Back lesson illustrates one or more of these connections or methods. Contexts include the motion of a water wheel, the functioning of a drafting table, and indirect measurements along the Platte River and with respect to a lighthouse located on a cliff. In the tasks, students will have the opportunity to review and apply trigonometric right triangle methods and the Law of Sines and Law of Cosines. Summary questions at the end of the lesson are designed to stimulate student articulation of the key principles and methods.

In the diagram below, the 30-foot diameter water wheel has been positioned on a coordinate system so the center of the wheel is the origin and the wheel reaches 3 feet below water level. As the wheel rotates counterclockwise, it takes 24 seconds for point A on the circumference of the wheel to rotate back to its starting position.

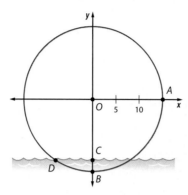

a. At its current position, how far is point A from the surface of the water? What are the coordinates of point A?

b. What are the coordinates of points B, C, and D?

c. Determine the distance from point A to the water surface as the water wheel rotates counterclockwise through each angle.

   i. 45°

   ii. 75°

   iii. 90°

   iv. 150°

d. Through what angle does point A rotate to first reach the water at point D? How many seconds does it take point A to first reach the water?

1 **a.** Since the radius of the circle is 15 feet and the water level is 3 feet above the wheel, point C is at $(0, -12)$ and point A is 12 feet above the surface of the water. $A(15, 0)$

b. $B(0, -15)$; $C(0, -12)$. Note that point D is at water level, so the y-coordinate of D is -12. In right triangle DOC, the length of the hypotenuse $\overline{DO}$ is 15 feet and the length of the leg $\overline{OC}$ is 12 feet. By the Pythagorean Theorem, DC is 9 feet, so the coordinates of D are $(-9, -12)$.

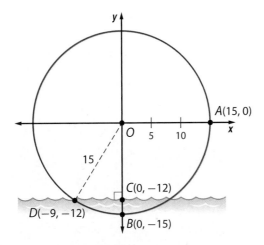

c. Point A will be $15 \sin \theta$ feet above the x-axis for each angle θ and thus A is $12 + 15 \sin \theta$ feet above the water's surface.

i. $12 + 15 \sin 45° \approx 22.6$ ft

ii. $12 + 15 \sin 75° \approx 26.5$ ft

iii. $12 + 15 = 27$ ft

iv. $12 + 15 \sin 150° = 19.5$ ft

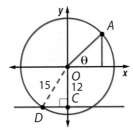

d. As shown in Part b, $CO = 12$ feet and $DO = 15$ feet; so, in right triangle DOC, $m\angle DOC = \cos^{-1}\left(\frac{12}{15}\right) \approx 36.9°$.

So, $m\angle AOB \approx 270° - 36.9° \approx 233.1°$.

It takes $\frac{233.1}{360}(24) \approx 15.5$ seconds for A to first reach the water at point D.

Unit 7

(2) At places along the south bank of the Platte River, the river is substantially below ground level. From the edge of the water at one location, the land slopes upward with an angle of inclination of 63°. The best way to get to the water is to go directly down the slope to the water's edge, a distance of approximately 123 meters.

a. Make a sketch of this situation showing distances and angles.

b. How far, horizontally, is the edge of the water from the edge of the bank, just where the land begins to slope downward?

c. How far above the surface of the Platte River is the land on the south bank?

(3) In route to sea, a freighter travels 50 km due west of its home port. It then turns, making an angle of 132° with its former path. It travels 80 km before radioing its home port.

a. Draw a diagram showing the path of the freighter.

b. How far is the freighter from its home port?

c. If sea conditions permitted, through what angle could the freighter have turned from its original course to go directly from its home port to the position at which it radioed the port?

d. Describe a second way in which you could find an answer for Part c.

2 a.

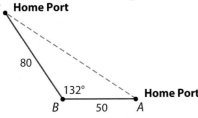

b. $BD = AC$; $\cos 63° = \dfrac{AC}{123}$; $AC = 123 \cos 63° \approx 55.8408 \approx 56$ m

c. $AD = BC$; $\sin 63° = \dfrac{BC}{123}$; $BC = 123 \sin 63° \approx 109.5938 \approx 110$ m

3 a.

Location when radioing
Home Port

C

80

132°

B   50   A

Home Port

b. Using the diagram and the Law of Cosines:
$AC^2 = 50^2 + 80^2 - 2(50)(80) \cos 132° \approx 14{,}253$
$AC \approx 119.3861 \approx 119$ km

c–d. Either the Law of Sines or the Law of Cosines may be used to find
$m\angle A$. Both will need the distance AC found in Part b. As before,
students should carry a few decimal places if not using the full
calculator value while computing.

Law of Cosines: $\cos A = \dfrac{80^2 - 119.3861^2 - 50^2}{-2(119.3861)(50)} \approx 0.8671$

$m\angle A \approx 30°$

Law of Sines: $\dfrac{\sin A}{80} = \dfrac{\sin 132°}{119.3861}$

$\sin A = \dfrac{80 \sin 132°}{119.3861} \approx 0.4980$

$m\angle A \approx 30°$

Unit 7

4 Architects sometimes use drafting tables that can be tilted forward, as shown in the photo and sketch below.

 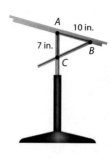

a. Explain how the structure of the table allows the top to be tilted at different angles.

b. Suppose in the sketch, $AB = 10$ inches and $AC = 7$ inches. When the tabletop is horizontal, what is the measure of $\angle ABC$? What is the length of the adjustable side BC?

c. What is the measure of $\angle ABC$ when the tabletop is tilted downward at a 30° angle with the horizontal? What is the length BC?

 5 A lighthouse 30 meters high stands at the top of a cliff. The angle of elevation from a point X on the bow of a ship to point A at the top of the lighthouse is 18°. The angle of elevation from X to point B at the bottom of the lighthouse is 14°.

a. Draw a sketch of the situation and then determine to the nearest meter the height of the cliff (above the level of point X).

b. Determine to the nearest meter the horizontal distance from the lighthouse to point X.

4 **a.** The adjustable prop fastened at B, which can slide through a wingnut at C, makes a triangle with a portion of the tabletop ($\overline{AB}$) and a portion of the stand ($\overline{AC}$). Because a triangle is a rigid shape, the angles of the triangle will change as the variable prop is adjusted.

b. When the tabletop is horizontal, $\angle B$ is an acute angle in a right triangle and $\tan B = \frac{7}{10}$; so, $m\angle B \approx 35.0°$. The length of the adjustable side BC is $\sqrt{10^2 + 7^2} \approx 12.2$ inches.

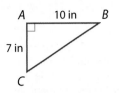

c. When the tabletop makes a 30° angle with the horizontal, $m\angle A = 60°$.
By the Law of Cosines,
$BC^2 = 7^2 + 10^2 - 2(7)(10) \cos 60° = 79$.
$BC \approx 8.8882 \approx 9$ inches
By the Law of Sines, $\frac{\sin B}{7} = \frac{\sin 60°}{8.8882}$.
So, $\sin B = \frac{7 \sin 60°}{8.8882}$; $m\angle B \approx 43°$.

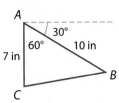

5 **a.**

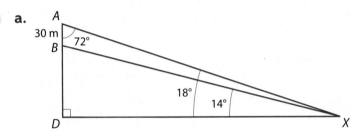

The (vertical) height of the cliff and a horizontal line or plane form a 90° angle; so, $m\angle A = 90° - 18° = 72°$. Consider $\triangle ABX$ where $m\angle AXB = 18° - 14° = 4°$. $\frac{\sin 4°}{30} = \frac{\sin 72°}{BX}$; so, $BX = \frac{30 \sin 72°}{\sin 4°} \approx 409.0186$ m. Using $\triangle BXD$, $\sin 14° = \frac{BD}{409.0186}$; so, $BD = 409.0186 \sin 14° \approx 98.9507 \approx 99$ m.

b. Using the Pythagorean Theorem in right triangle BDX,
$DX = \sqrt{409.0186^2 - 98.9507^2} \approx 397$ meters.

Summarize the Mathematics

In this unit, you extended your understanding of coordinate methods to include trigonometric methods that relate angle measures and linear measures. These methods are especially useful when solving problems involving triangulation and indirect measurement. In the process, you also extended your toolkit of basic functions to include the sine, cosine, and tangent functions for angles ranging from 0° to 360°.

a Suppose $P(a, b)$ is a point on the terminal side of an angle in standard position with measure θ.

 i. How can you find the value of $\sin \theta$? Of $\cos \theta$? Of $\tan \theta$?

 ii. How can you find the measure of θ?

b Imagine rotating a ray $\overrightarrow{OP}$ counterclockwise with initial position along the positive branch of the x-axis. As the measure θ of the angle formed increases from 0° to 360°, describe the pattern of change in:

 i. $\cos \theta$ **ii.** $\sin \theta$ **iii.** $\tan \theta$

 How are these patterns of change similar to, and different from, those of other functions you have previously studied?

c How are the definitions of the sine, cosine, and tangent of an acute angle of a right triangle related to the more general definitions of the functions in terms of an angle in standard position?

 i. How can these ratios be used to determine lengths in a right triangle that cannot be measured directly?

 ii. How can these ratios be used to determine acute angle measures that cannot be measured directly?

d Suppose you had modeled a problem with a triangle. What clues do you look for when deciding whether to use the Law of Sines? The Law of Cosines?

e Suppose for an angle A in a triangle, you know:

 i. $\sin A = p$ **ii.** $\cos A = q$ **iii.** $\tan A = r$

 In each case, can you find exactly one value for $m\angle A$? If so, how? If not, why not?

Be prepared to explain your ideas to the class.

✓ Check Your Understanding

Write, in outline form, a summary of the important mathematical concepts and methods developed in this unit. Organize your summary so that it can be used as a quick reference in future units and courses.

Summarize the Mathematics

a   **i.** Find $r = \sqrt{a^2 + b^2}$, then $\sin \theta = \dfrac{b}{r}$, $\cos \theta = \dfrac{a}{r}$, and $\tan \theta = \dfrac{b}{a}$.

     ii. $\theta = \tan^{-1}\left(\dfrac{b}{a}\right)$, $\theta = \cos^{-1}\left(\dfrac{a}{r}\right)$, or $\theta = \sin^{-1}\left(\dfrac{b}{r}\right)$.

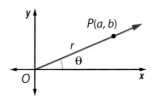

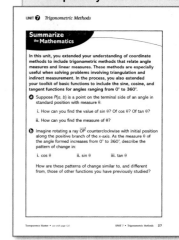
b   **INSTRUCTIONAL NOTE** Help students recognize the periodic nature of the tangent function and the symmetry in these graphs. They should also notice that for all three functions, the same y values occur more than once.

As the measure of θ increases from 0° to 360°:

   i. The value of $\cos \theta$ decreases from a maximum of 1 to a minimum of -1 (at 180°) and then back up to 1. The rates of decrease and increase are nonconstant.

  ii. The value of $\sin \theta$ increases from 0 to a maximum of 1 (at 90°), decreases to a minimum of -1 (at 270°), and then increases again to end at 0. The rates of increase and decrease are nonconstant.

iii. From 0° to 90°, the value of $\tan \theta$ increases at a nonconstant rate from 0 to positive infinity. $\tan \theta$ is undefined at $\theta = 90°$ and 270°. From 90° to 270°, the values of $\tan \theta$ increase at a nonconstant rate from negative infinity to positive infinity. The x-intercept occurs when $x = 180°$. From 180° to 270°, the pattern of change is the same as from 0° to 90°. From 270° to 360°, the pattern of change is the same as from 90° to 180°.

The pattern of change for the tangent function in the interval $[0°, 180°]$ resembles functions of the form $y = \dfrac{a}{x}$ because it has two parts that approach a vertical line as the denominator of the function approaches 0.

The pattern of change for the sine function in the interval $[0°, 180°]$ resembles a quadratic function (with a negative coefficient on the x^2 term) because it increases and then decreases. (See page T507A.)

The pattern of change for the cosine function is not like other functions studied. Some students may suggest it looks like an upside-down normal distribution curve.

Summarize
the Mathematics

c Every right triangle can be placed in the coordinate plane so that an acute angle B is at the origin in standard position as shown.

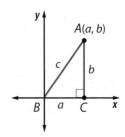

The trigonometric ratios are defined as follows and coincide with the more general definitions.

$$\text{sine of } \angle B = \sin B = \frac{\text{length of side } \textit{opposite } \angle B}{\text{length of } \textit{hypotenuse}} = \frac{b}{c}$$

$$\text{cosine of } \angle B = \cos B = \frac{\text{length of side } \textit{adjacent to } \angle B}{\text{length of } \textit{hypotenuse}} = \frac{a}{c}$$

$$\text{tangent of } \angle B = \tan B = \frac{\text{length of side } \textit{opposite } \angle B}{\text{length of side } \textit{adjacent to } \angle B} = \frac{b}{a}$$

  i. If the measure of $\angle B$ and one of the sides (either a, b, or c) are known, then the trigonometric ratio that involves the known side and the unknown side can be solved for the length of the unknown side. For example, if a is known and b is to be determined, then $\tan B = \dfrac{b}{a}$ can be solved for b.

  ii. If both sides in a trigonometric ratio are known, then the corresponding inverse trigonometric function can determine the measure of the acute angle B. For example, if sides b and c are known, $\sin B$ is the ratio $\dfrac{b}{c}$. Then $m\angle B = \sin^{-1}\left(\dfrac{b}{c}\right)$, which can be determined with a calculator or computer.

d The Law of Sines has fewer computations to do than the Law of Cosines. So, if you know a side length, its opposite angle measure, and a third angle or side measure, then use the Law of Sines.

When you know the measures of two sides and the angle between those sides or the measures of all three sides and no angle measures, then use the Law of Cosines.

e **i.** There are two different angles of measures between 0° and 180° for which $\sin A = p$. One is an acute angle and one is an obtuse angle.

  ii–iii. There is only one angle between 0° and 180° for which the $\cos A = q$ and $\tan A = r$. When the x-coordinate is negative and the y-coordinate is positive, $\cos A = \dfrac{x}{r}$ and $\tan A = \dfrac{y}{x}$ are less than zero, and A is obtuse.

✓ Check your Understanding

You may wish to have students use the Teaching Master, *Trigonometric Methods* Unit Summary, to help them organize the information. Above all, this should be something that is useful to the individual student.

Practicing for Standardized Tests

Each Practicing for Standardized Tests master presents 10 questions in the multiple-choice format of test items similar to how they often appear in standardized tests. Answers are provided below.

Answers to Practice Set 7

1. (c)   **2.** (a)   **3.** (b)   **4.** (e)   **5.** (c)
6. (e)   **7.** (b)   **8.** (a)   **9.** (c)   **10.** (d)

Student Masters 29–30.

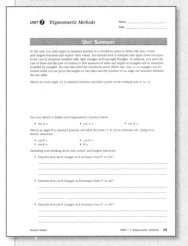

Assessment Masters 31–47.

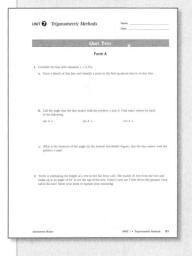

Student Masters 48–49.

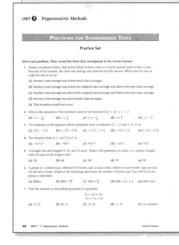

Unit 7

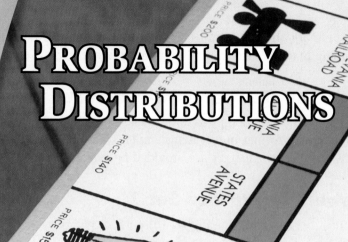

UNIT 8

PROBABILITY DISTRIBUTIONS

From lotteries, to weather, to disease, to your genetic make-up, to meeting the love of your life, you live in a world governed by chance. In the Course 1 unit, *Patterns in Chance*, you learned to use the Addition Rule to find the probability that event *A* happens *or* event *B* happens. In this unit, you will learn to use the Multiplication Rule to find the probability that event *A* happens *and* event *B* happens. In *Patterns in Chance*, you learned to use simulation to approximate probability distributions, such as the waiting-time distribution for the number of flips of a coin needed to get a head. In this unit, you will learn to use the Addition and Multiplication Rules to construct waiting-time distributions exactly.

Key ideas will be developed through your work on problems in three lessons.

Lessons

1 Probability Models

Use an area model to find the probability that two independent events both happen, find probabilities using the definition of conditional probability, decide whether two events are independent, use the Multiplication Rule for independent events and for dependent events.

2 Expected Value

Understand how the word "expect" is used in probability, compute the mean of a relative frequency distribution, compute the expected value of a probability distribution.

3 The Waiting-Time Distribution

Construct and analyze frequency distributions for simulations and relative frequency distributions for waiting-time situations, construct and analyze the (exact) probability distribution for a waiting-time situation, and discover the formula for the expected value of a waiting-time distribution.

Unit 8

PROBABILITY DISTRIBUTIONS

Unit Overview

Probability Distributions is the second unit on probability. In *Patterns in Chance* in Course 1, students learned to use the Addition Rule to find the probability that event *A* happens *or* event *B* happens. In the first lesson of this unit, students will learn to use the Multiplication Rule to find the probability that event *A* happens *and* event *B* happens. In *Patterns in Chance*, students used simulations to approximate probability distributions, such as the waiting-time distribution for the number of flips of a coin needed to get a head. In this unit, they will learn to use the Addition and Multiplication Rules to construct waiting-time distributions exactly.

After students complete this second probability unit in *Core-Plus Mathematics*, they will know the most important basic concepts of probability: sample spaces, equally likely outcomes, simulation and use of random digits, Addition Rule for Mutually Exclusive Events, the general Addition Rule, the Law of Large Numbers, the definition of conditional probability, the Multiplication Rule for independent events, the Multiplication Rule for dependent events, and expected value. Infinite series are introduced in the Lesson 3 Extensions tasks.

Unit Objectives

- Interpret and compute conditional probabilities
- Use the Multiplication Rule to find $P(A \text{ and } B)$, when events A and B are independent and when they are not independent
- Compute the expected value (mean) of a probability distribution
- Identify waiting-time situations and construct waiting-time distributions

Goals of This Unit

Perhaps the main goal in teaching probability is for students to understand that while they may not know the next outcome in a random process, they often have a very good idea of what the distribution of the next ten thousand outcomes will look like. Further, students should understand that the distributions for related random processes have characteristic shapes. Waiting-time distributions are skewed right. Binomial distributions are symmetric when $p = 0.5$, skewed right when $p < 0.5$, and skewed left when $p > 0.5$. (Students will study the binomial distribution formally in Unit 4, *Samples and Variation*, in Course 3 and in Unit 9, *Binomial Distributions and Statistical Inference*, in Course 4.) For each of these distributions, you can compute a measure of center, typically the mean (expected value), and a measure of spread, typically the standard deviation. These distributions can be constructed approximately using simulation or constructed exactly using mathematical theory.

Another important goal of this unit is for students to understand why, when events *A* and *B* are independent, we multiply to find the probability of *A* and *B* both occurring. This idea was introduced in Course 1 in *Patterns in Chance* and will be developed further through area models and through the intuitive idea that in a waiting-time situation, the proportion of people who have their first success on the *x*th trial is *p* times the proportion of people who were left after the previous trial.

Short Path in Course 1 Unit 8, *Patterns in Chance*

If your students have not studied the probability unit in Course 1 of *Core-Plus Mathematics*, they should complete the following parts of that unit before beginning this unit.

Course 1 Unit 8, *Patterns in Chance*

Lesson 1

Investigation 1, Problems 1–4, Check Your Understanding, OYO A2, R13

Investigation 2, Problems 1–7 and OYO A4, A5, R14

Lesson 2

Investigation 1, Problems 1–5, discuss Law of Large Numbers, OYO A2, R15

Investigation 2, Problems 1, 2, 4, 6, 7 and Check Your Understanding

Investigation 3 omit

Investigation 4, Problems 1–3 and OYO C14

CPMP-Tools

CPMP-Tools contains simulation software that can be used for selected problems in this unit. The software can quickly simulate experiments such as rolling two dice until doubles occur. Students can perform the entire simulation rather than add five runs to the frequency table in the text.

Misconceptions about Probability

People tend to have incorrect intuition when it comes to many probabilistic events. This unit, like Course 1 Unit 8, *Patterns in Chance*, continues to confront misconceptions people tend to have about probability. For references to the literature on misconceptions, see the section "Misconceptions about Probability and the Importance of Simulation" in the overview to the Teacher's Guide for *Patterns in Chance*.

Sensitivity about Gambling Contexts

Games of chance are used frequently in this unit because it is easy for students to understand the probabilities concerned with the flip of a coin or the roll of a die. The games described typically are based on family games such as Monopoly or the Game of Life or on common carnival games. However, emphasize to your students that knowing the basics of probability can help them make better decisions about everyday issues such as buying insurance, choosing a medical treatment, and understanding public opinion surveys. This unit includes many problems you can assign that illustrate this type of decision-making.

Gambling is a serious problem in the United States and is thoroughly discouraged in some cultures and in many households. If it is appropriate to discuss these issues in your class, you may want to have students read this information, which is from a longer article in the *Cincinnati Enquirer*, and ask the questions that follow. This should be done following Lesson 1 where students learn about independent events.

National studies show the number of young people gambling on poker and other card games has skyrocketed in recent years.

But while poker is a harmless diversion for most teens, some experts caution that the risks of gambling addiction are being overlooked.

"Most people can drink and they don't become alcoholics. Most people can gamble and they don't become compulsive gamblers," says Dr. Lori Rugle, a clinical psychologist and president of the Ohio Council on Problem Gambling.

"But for that small percentage—which is comparable to the percentage that develops serious drug problems—(gambling addiction) is a life-threatening disorder." She says about one-fourth of people in compulsive-gambling treatment programs attempt suicide.

Michael R. Stone, executive director of the Kentucky Council on Problem Gambling, says studies have shown that nearly 4 percent of teens are pathological, or compulsive, gamblers.

In any given week in this country, about 2.9 million people ages 14–22 are gambling on cards, and more than 80 percent are male, according to a report released this fall by the Annenberg Public Policy Center of the University of Pennsylvania, which has tracked teen gambling rates for several years.

Source: Do teens know when to hold 'em? Poker's popularity raises compulsive gambling concerns, by John Johnston, *Cincinnati Enquirer*, December 6, 2005; news.enquirer.com/apps/pbcs.dll/article?AID=/20051206/LIFE/512060321

Questions

1. How many males ages 14–22 gamble on cards each week in the United States? Females?

2. Do you think that 4% of the 2.9 million people ages 14–22 who gamble on cards each week are pathological gamblers?

3. Can you determine from this article whether being male and being a pathological gambler are independent events?

Solutions

1. 80% of 2.9 million or 2,320,000 males; 20% of 2.9 million or 580,000 females

2. No. The 4% is for all people this age. Presumably, the percentage of pathological gamblers would be much higher among those who gamble on cards.

3. No, you cannot tell for sure. A much larger percentage of gamblers are male, but there is no indication that more than 4% of males are compulsive gamblers. However, it is reasonable that that would be the case. Otherwise, a very large percentage of female gamblers would have to be compulsive gamblers.

Lesson Objectives	On Your Own Assignments*	Suggested Pacing	Materials
Lesson 1 *The Multiplication Rule* • Use an area model to find the probability that two independent events both occur • Use the Multiplication Rule to find the probability that two independent events both occur • Find conditional probabilities and determine if two events are independent • Use the Multiplication Rule to find the probability that two events both occur when the events are not independent	**After Investigation 1:** A1, A2, C9, C10, R14, R15, E19, Rv22–Rv24 **After Investigation 2:** A3–A5, C11, R16, Rv25–Rv27 **After Investigation 3:** A6, A7, C12, C13, R17, R18, E20 or E21, Rv28, Rv29	5 days (including assessment)	• *Optional:* Dice, game of Monopoly®, Game of LIFE® • Unit Resources
Lesson 2 *Expected Value* • Compute the fair price (expected value) of insurance and games of chance • Develop a formula for the expected value of a probability distribution • Compute the expected value of a probability distribution using the formula • Estimate the expected value from the graph of the probability distribution	**After Investigation 1:** A1, A2, C8, R14, E16, Rv19–Rv21 **After Investigation 2:** A4, Choose two of A3, A5 or A6, C9, C10, R11, R12 or R13, R14 or R15, E17 or E18, Rv22–Rv24	3 days (including assessment)	• Unit Resources
Lesson 3 *The Waiting-Time Distribution* • Use simulation to construct an approximate waiting-time distribution and understand why the shape is skewed to the right • Recognize rare events in a waiting-time situation • Use the formula to construct the probability distribution for a waiting-time situation • Discover the formula for the expected value of a waiting-time distribution • Understand that some infinite series have a finite sum	**After Investigation 1:** A1, A2, C9, R16, Rv24–Rv27 **After Investigation 2:** Choose two of A3–A6, C10, C11, R17–R19, E22, Rv28, Rv29 **After Investigation 3:** A7, A8, C12, C13, C14 or C15, R20, E23, Rv30	5 days (including assessment)	• *Optional:* game of Monopoly®, decks of cards • Unit Resources
Lesson 4 *Looking Back* • Review and synthesize the major objectives of the unit		2 days (including assessment)	• Unit Resources

• *When choice is indicated, it is important to leave the choice to the student.*

Note: *It is best if Connections tasks are discussed as a whole class after they have been assigned as homework.*

LESSON 1

Probability Models

Some physical characteristics, such as freckles, eyelash length, and the ability to roll one's tongue up from the sides, are determined in a relatively simple manner by genes inherited from one's parents. Each person has two genes that determine whether or not he or she will have freckles, one inherited from the father and one from the mother. If a child inherits a "freckles" gene from either parent or from both parents, the child has freckles. In order not to have freckles, the child must inherit a "no-freckles" gene from both parents. This explains why the gene for freckles is called *dominant*, and the gene for no freckles is called *recessive*. A parent with two freckles genes must pass on a freckles gene to the child; a parent with two no-freckles genes must pass on a no-freckles gene. If a parent has one of each, the probability is $\frac{1}{2}$ that he or she will pass on the freckles gene, and the probability is $\frac{1}{2}$ that he or she will pass on the no-freckles gene.

Unit 8

Probability Models

In Investigation 1, students will learn how to use an area model and the Multiplication Rule to find the probability that two independent events both occur: $P(A \text{ and } B) = P(A) \cdot P(B)$. In Investigations 2 and 3, students will learn how to modify the Multiplication Rule to account for the situation when the two events are not independent.

Lesson Objectives

- Use an area model to find the probability that two independent events both occur
- Use the Multiplication Rule to find the probability that two independent events both occur
- Find conditional probabilities and determine if two events are independent
- Use the Multiplication Rule to find the probability that two events both occur when the events are not independent

Lesson Launch

The genetic model presented here somewhat oversimplifies the real situation. A biology teacher can provide additional information about this basic Mendelian genetics model. The diagrams presented in the answers to Parts c and d on the following page are called Punnett squares. Students may suggest them if they have studied genetics in their biology class.

Think About This Situation

Consider the chance of inheriting freckles.

a) In what sense does the gene for freckles "dominate" the gene for no freckles?

b) What is the probability that a child will have freckles if both parents do not have freckles?

c) What is the probability that a child will not have freckles if each parent has one freckles gene and one no-freckles gene?

d) Can you determine the probability that a child of freckled parents also will have freckles?

As you work on the investigations of this lesson, you will learn how to find the probability that two (or more) events, such as inheriting the freckle gene from the mother and inheriting the freckle gene from the father, both happen. In the process, you will discover the importance of distinguishing between events that are *independent* and events that are *mutually exclusive* (*disjoint*).

Investigation 1 — The Multiplication Rule for Independent Events

You have found that graphical representations of data or quantitative relationships can reveal important underlying patterns and that making a "picture" of a mathematical situation can often help you understand that situation better. In Course 1 of *Core-Plus Mathematics,* you used an area model to explore patterns in chance situations. As you work on the problems of this investigation, look for answers to these questions:

How can you use an area model to find the probability that two events both happen?

How can you calculate that probability using the individual probabilities?

Think About This Situation

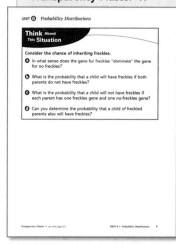
a) If a person has both a freckles gene and a no-freckles gene, then the person will have freckles. So, we say the freckles gene dominates the no-freckles gene.

b) The probability that the child of parents without freckles will have freckles is 0. Each parent must have two no-freckles genes (or else they would have freckles), and so the child must inherit a no-freckles gene from each parent.

c) The Punnett square below shows this situation:

Gene from Mother

	F	f
F	FF	Ff
f	fF	ff

Gene from Father

The uppercase F stands for a freckles gene, and the lowercase f stands for a no-freckles gene. The F for freckles is capitalized because it is the dominant gene: a person with Ff genes has freckles. From the Punnett square, students can see that there are four equally likely outcomes: FF (child has freckles), Ff (child has freckles), fF (child has freckles), and ff (child does not have freckles). Thus, the probability that the child will not have freckles is $\frac{1}{4}$.

Alternatively, students may notice that this situation is equivalent to flipping a coin twice and getting tails (no freckles) both times. From the sample space of four equally likely outcomes, HH, HT, TH, TT, the probability is $\frac{1}{4}$.

d) There is no way to determine the probability that the child of freckled parents will have freckles unless we know whether the parents have two freckles genes or one freckles gene and one no-freckles gene. If both parents are of the type FF, then the child is certain to have freckles. If both parents have only one freckles gene, then there is a $\frac{3}{4}$ chance the child will have freckles (as seen in the diagram in Part c). If one parent is of the type Ff and the other is FF, we can see from the Punnett square below that the child is certain to have freckles.

Gene from Mother

	F	f
F	FF	Ff
F	FF	Ff

Gene from Father

1 About half of all U.S. adults are female. According to a survey published in *USA Today*, three out of five adults sing in the shower.

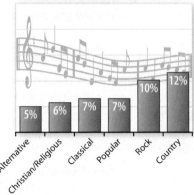

Singing in the Shower
Three out of five adults say they sing in the shower. Top types of showering music:

Alternative 5%, Christian/Religious 6%, Classical 7%, Popular 7%, Rock 10%, Country 12%

Source: Guideline Research and Consulting Corporation for Westin Hotels and Resorts

a. Suppose an adult from the United States is selected at random. From the information above, do you think that the probability that the person is a female *and* sings in the shower is equal to $\frac{3}{5}$, greater than $\frac{3}{5}$, or less than $\frac{3}{5}$?

b. Now examine the situation using the area model shown below.

i. Explain why there are two rows labeled "No" for "Sings in Shower" and three labeled "Yes."

ii. What assumption does this model make about singing habits of males and females?

c. On a copy of this area model, shade in the region that represents the event: *female* and *sings in the shower*.

d. What is the probability that an adult selected at random is a female and sings in the shower?

e. What is the probability that an adult selected at random is a male and does not sing in the shower?

Multiplication Rule for Independent Events

The principal idea in this investigation is that if two events A and B are independent, then we can multiply their probabilities to find the probability that A and B both occur: $P(A \text{ and } B) = P(A) \cdot P(B)$. In Problems 1–4, the use of an area model is developed. The area model builds on the model of multiplication that students have used since elementary school and is equivalent to the Multiplication Rule. The area model is based on the idea that the total probability of all possible events is 1, and this is modeled by the whole rectangular area. Each margin of the rectangle can be subdivided to model the probabilities of the events that can happen on each trial. This, in turn, subdivides the internal area proportionally to represent the probability that both events in the margin occur. In Problem 5, the Multiplication Rule is introduced formally. The Multiplication Rule is then used in Problems 6–8.

In Problems 7 and 8, students extend their understanding of the Multiplication Rule to situations in which there are more than two events.

Reducing Fractions As in the Course 1 unit, *Patterns in Chance*, it is usually not important that fractions be reduced when computing probabilities. In fact, reducing fractions can make it more difficult to relate the probability to the original situation and to compare the probabilities of two events. Students should also realize that probabilities expressed as fractions should not automatically be converted to decimals unless there is some reason to do so.

1
a. The probability is less than $\frac{3}{5}$. The probability that the adult is female is only about half, so the probability of getting an adult who is female and who also sings in the shower will be less than half.

b. i. There are two No's under "Sings in Shower," so the area model will have two-fifths of its area devoted to the event of not singing in the shower and three-fifths of its area devoted to the event of singing in the shower.

ii. The model assumes that females are just as likely to sing in the shower as are males. If this assumption is not true, the area model will not work.

c.

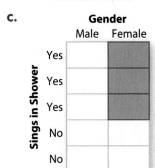

d. $\frac{3}{5}$ of half of the population, or $\frac{3}{10}$

e. $\frac{2}{10}$

Teaching Resources

Student Master 2.

(2) Consider this problem: What is the probability that it takes exactly two rolls of a pair of dice before getting doubles for the first time?

a. Explain why it makes sense to label the rows of the area model as shown below. On a copy of this area model, label the six columns to represent the possible outcomes on the second roll of a pair of dice.

Rolling a Pair of Dice Twice

Second Roll of the Pair of Dice

First Roll of the Pair of Dice
- Doubles
- Not Doubles
- Not Doubles
- Not Doubles
- Not Doubles
- Not Doubles

b. On your copy of the area model, shade the squares that represent the event *not getting doubles on the first roll* and *getting doubles on the second roll.*

c. What is the probability of not getting doubles on the first roll and then getting doubles on the second roll?

d. Use your area model to find the probability that you will get doubles both times.

e. Use your area model to find the probability that you will not get doubles either time.

(3) Make an area model to help you determine the probabilities that a child will or will not have freckles when each parent has one freckles gene and one no-freckles gene.

a. What is the probability that the child will not have freckles?

b. Compare your answer to Part a with your class' answer to Part c of the Think About This Situation on page 523.

2 **a.** It makes sense to label the rows as shown because the probability of rolling doubles is $\frac{1}{6}$ and the probability of not rolling doubles is $\frac{5}{6}$. One of six equally-spaced columns should be labeled "Doubles" and the others "Not Doubles," as in the diagram in Part b below.

b. Rolling a Pair of Dice Twice

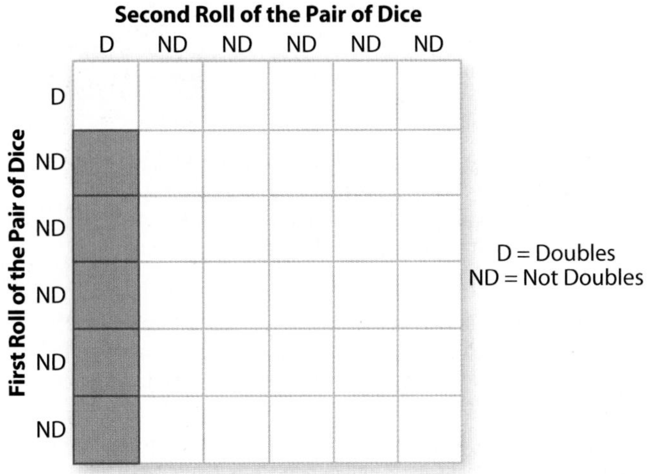

Second Roll of the Pair of Dice

	D	ND	ND	ND	ND	ND

First Roll of the Pair of Dice: D, ND, ND, ND, ND, ND

D = Doubles
ND = Not Doubles

c. $\frac{5}{36}$

d. $\frac{1}{36}$

e. $\frac{25}{36}$

3

Gene from Mother

Gene from Father	Freckles	No-freckles
Freckles	Freckles	Freckles
No-freckles	Freckles	No-freckles

a. $\frac{1}{4}$

b. Responses will vary depending on the class' answer to the Think About This Situation question.

INSTRUCTIONAL NOTE
Now is a good time to emphasize to students that probability models may be useful models of reality, but they seldom are exact models of reality. For example, it is useful to say that each side of a die has probability $\frac{1}{6}$ of coming up on top when rolled, but it would be a rare die for which that was true *exactly*.

4 Use area models to answer these questions:

a. About 25% of Americans put catsup directly on their fries rather than on the plate. What is the best estimate for the probability that both your school principal and your favorite celebrity put catsup directly on their fries?

b. About 84% of Americans pour shampoo into their hand rather than directly onto their hair. What is the best estimate of the probability that both your teacher and the President of the United States pour shampoo into their hand before putting it on their hair?

5 Look back at the situations described in Problems 1 through 4. The pairs of events in each of those problems are (or were assumed to be) **independent events**: knowing whether one of the events occurs does not change the probability that the other event occurs.

a. For each situation, explain whether you think the assumption of independence is realistic. If independence is not a reasonable assumption, how would you change the model?

b. Describe how you could compute the probability in each situation without making an area model (if independence is a reasonable assumption).

c. Suppose A and B are independent events. Express your method in Part c by completing the following rule using symbols:

$$P(A \text{ and } B) = \underline{\hspace{3cm}}$$

The notation $P(A \text{ and } B)$ is read "the probability of event A and event B."

d. Compare your rule with those of your classmates and resolve any differences.

e. State your agreed-upon **Multiplication Rule** in words.

Often a probability problem is easier to understand if it is written in words that are more specific than the words the original problem uses. For example, consider the problem:

What is the probability of taking exactly two tries to roll doubles?

You could express and calculate this probability in the following manner:

$P(\text{don't roll doubles on the first try and do roll doubles on the second try})$
$= P(\text{don't roll doubles on the first try}) \cdot P(\text{do roll doubles on the second try})$
$= \left(\frac{5}{6}\right)\left(\frac{1}{6}\right) = \frac{5}{36}$

4 a. You must assume that what the celebrity does is independent of what your principal does. The best estimate of the probability that both your principal and the celebrity put catsup directly on their fries is $\frac{1}{16}$.

b. You must assume that what the President does is independent of what your teacher does. If you visualize dividing the area into one-percent by one-percent squares, there will be (100)(100) or 10,000 small squares, of which (84)(84) or 7,056 represent the event that both the teacher and the President pour shampoo into their hand. The best estimate of the probability is $\frac{7,056}{10,000}$ or 0.7056.

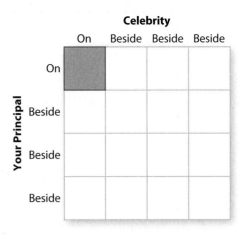

CHECKING UNDERSTANDING Before going on to Problem 5, all students should be able to compute probabilities using area models. To be sure, you may wish to ask students to do an area model problem individually. Here is an example of one you could give them: The last U.S. census found that 34% of the households in the United States rent the housing units they occupy. Suppose you select two American households at random. Make an area model to find the probability that they both rent their housing units. The answer is 0.1156.

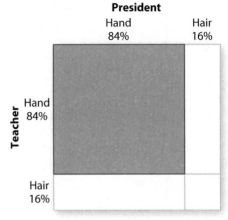

a. In Problem 1, the events were assumed to be independent as there is no reason to think that males are more likely or less likely to sing in the shower than females. In other words, knowing that someone is male does not change the probability that the person sings in the shower. In this situation, some students may think that independence is not a useful model of reality. If, for example, a larger proportion of males sing in the shower than females, the model might look more like the one at the right.

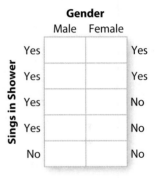

In Problems 2 through 4, independence is a reasonable assumption. In Problem 2, knowing the outcome on one die does not change the probabilities for the various outcomes on the other die. In Problem 3, knowing that the father passed on a freckles gene does not change the probability the mother passed on a freckles gene. In Problem 4, knowing what the principal does would not change your estimate of the probability that your favorite celebrity puts catsup directly on their fries. Similarly, knowing that your teacher pours shampoo on his or her hands does not change your estimate of the probability that the President does this.

b. To find the probability that two independent events both occur, multiply the probability that one event occurs by the probability that the other occurs.

c. $P(A \text{ and } B) = P(A) \cdot P(B)$

d. Students should compare their rules.

e. The probability that event A and event B both happen is equal to the probability that event A happens times the probability that event B happens.

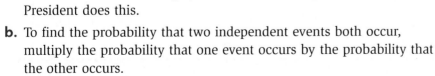

Unit 8

(6) Suppose Shiomo is playing a game in which he needs to roll a pair of dice and get doubles and then immediately roll the dice again and get a sum of six. He wants to know the probability that this will happen.

a. Which of the following *best* describes the probability Shiomo wants to find?

> **Option 1:** P(*gets doubles on the first roll* or *gets a sum of six on the second roll*)
>
> **Option 2:** P(*gets doubles on the first roll* and *gets a sum of six on the second roll*)
>
> **Option 3:** P(*gets doubles* and *a sum of six*)

b. Explain why the Multiplication Rule can be used to find the probability that this sequence of two events will happen. What is the probability?

(7) A modification of the game in Problem 6 involves rolling a pair of dice three times. In this modified game, Shiomo needs to roll doubles, then a sum of six, and then a sum of eleven.

a. Find the probability that this sequence of three events will happen.

b. Suppose *A*, *B*, and *C* are three independent events. Write a rule for calculating P(*A* and *B* and *C*) using the probabilities of each individual event.

c. Write the Multiplication Rule for calculating the probability that each of four independent events occurs.

(8) For each of the following questions, explain whether it is reasonable to assume that the events are independent. Then, if it applies, use the Multiplication Rule to answer the question.

a. What is the probability that a sequence of seven flips of a fair coin turns out to be exactly HTHTTHH?

b. What is the probability that a sequence of seven flips of a fair coin turns out to be exactly TTTTTTH?

c. According to the National Center for Education Statistics, 27.9% of public school students live in a small town or rural area. (Source: nces.ed.gov/pubs2006/2006307.pdf) If you select 5 students at random, what is the probability that they all live in a small town or rural area?

d. According to the National Center for Education Statistics, the percentage of students who are homeschooled in the United States is 2.2 percent. (Source: nces.ed.gov/pubs2006/homeschool/) If you pick 10 students at random in the United States, what is the probability that none of the 10 are homeschooled?

e. Refer to Part d. You pick a family with two school-age children at random in the United States. What is the probability that both children are homeschooled?

(6) **INSTRUCTIONAL NOTE** In Part a, students often miss the word "best" and so do not see the difference between Options 2 and 3. Option 2 is the best answer because it describes the outcome precisely. Option 3 is vague and sloppy. Specifically, because *P*(*gets doubles* and *a sum of six*) and *P*(*a sum of six* and *gets doubles*) are equivalent in English, Option 3 could apply equally well to getting a sum of six on the first roll and then getting doubles on the second roll.

a. Option 2:
   P(*gets doubles on the first roll* and *gets a sum of six on the second roll*)

b. The probability of rolling doubles is $\frac{1}{6}$, the probability of rolling a sum of six is $\frac{5}{36}$, and the two rolls are independent. So, the probability of Shiomo getting what he needs is $\left(\frac{1}{6}\right)\left(\frac{5}{36}\right) = \frac{5}{216}$.

(7) **a.** Since the probability of rolling a sum of 11 is $\frac{2}{36}$ and the three events are independent, this probability is $\left(\frac{1}{6}\right)\left(\frac{5}{36}\right)\left(\frac{2}{36}\right) = \frac{10}{7,776}$.

b. $P(A \text{ and } B \text{ and } C) = P(A) \cdot P(B) \cdot P(C)$

c. $P(A \text{ and } B \text{ and } C \text{ and } D) = P(A) \cdot P(B) \cdot P(C) \cdot P(D)$

(8) **INSTRUCTIONAL NOTE** In each situation, the events are independent, although it is reasonable for students to question in Parts c and d whether the gender of children in the same family is independent. Many people believe that some families are more likely to produce, say, girls than boys because they see many families with a preponderance of female children. However, statisticians who have looked at the entire U.S. population do not find more such families than one would expect from chance alone. That is, having boys or having girls does not tend to run in families. See "Does Having Boys or Girls Run in the Family?" (*Chance Magazine*, Vol. 14, No. 4, 2001, pages 8–13.)

Students will probably be surprised that the answer to Part b is the same as the answer to Part a. The sequence HTHTTHH looks more random to students than the sequence TTTTTTH, so they think that it is more likely to occur. But, in fact, any specific sequence such as HTHTTHH is just as difficult to get when tossing a coin as is TTTTTTH.

a. $\left(\frac{1}{2}\right)^7 = 0.0078125$

b. $\left(\frac{1}{2}\right)^7 = 0.0078125$

c. $(0.279)^5 \approx 0.0017$

d. The probability that a randomly selected student is not homeschooled is $1 - 0.022 = 0.978$. The probability that none of 10 randomly selected students is homeschooled is $(0.978)^{10} \approx 0.801$.

e. The event that the second child in the family is homeschooled is not independent of whether the first child is homeschooled. In fact, if the first child is homeschooled, the probability that the second child also is homeschooled is very high. So, the Multiplication Rule cannot be used in this situation and the question cannot be answered.

Summarize
the Mathematics

In this investigation, you learned how to find the probability that an event *A* and an event *B* both happen, when the two events are independent.

a How can you use an area model to find the probability that an event *A* and an event *B* both happen?

b Why does it make sense to multiply the individual probabilities when you want to find the probability that two independent events both happen?

c Explain which event has the higher probability: You roll a pair of dice twice and get a sum of 7 both times. You roll a pair of dice three times and get a sum of 7 all three times.

Be prepared to share your ideas and reasoning with the class.

✓ Check Your Understanding

While playing a board game, Jenny is sent to jail. To get out of jail, she needs to roll doubles. She wants to know the probability that she will fail to roll doubles in three tries.

a. Rewrite Jenny's situation using $P(\underline{\quad})$ notation, describing the sequence of events.

b. Find the probability that Jenny fails to roll doubles in three tries.

c. Explain why you can use the Multiplication Rule for this situation.

Investigation 2 — Conditional Probability

Sometimes you are interested in the probability of an event occurring when you know another event occurs. For example, a high school athlete might be interested in knowing the probability of playing professional basketball if he or she first plays basketball at the college level. As you work on the following problems, keep in mind this basic question:

> *How can you find probabilities in situations with conditions?*

Some boys wear sneakers and some do not. The same holds true for girls. However, in many places in the United States, boys are more likely to wear sneakers to school than are girls.

Unit 8

Summarize
the Mathematics

a Divide one margin of a rectangle proportionally into lengths representing the probabilities of events *A* and *not A*. Divide the other margin proportionally into lengths representing the probabilities of events *B* and *not B*. These divisions, in turn, subdivide the inside area of the rectangle proportionally to represent the probability that both events in the margin occur. This procedure can be used only if events *A* and *B* are independent.

b Students may reason as in the following example: Suppose that half of all children are girls, and one-third of all children have freckles. What is the probability that a randomly selected child is a girl with freckles? Assuming gender and freckles are independent, half of all children are girls, and $\frac{1}{3}$ of the girls have freckles. So, $\frac{1}{3}$ of half of the children, or $\left(\frac{1}{3}\right)\left(\frac{1}{2}\right)$, or $\frac{1}{6}$, have freckles. Alternatively, students may explain using an area model.

c You are more likely to roll a pair of dice twice and get a sum of 7 both times than you are to roll a pair of dice three times and get a sum of 7 all three times. You can see this by thinking about the Multiplication Rule. To get the probability of getting a sum of 7 on all three rolls, you must multiply the probability of getting a sum of 7 on the first two rolls by $\frac{1}{6}$, which makes a smaller number. The two probabilities are $\left(\frac{1}{6}\right)\left(\frac{1}{6}\right)$ and $\left(\frac{1}{6}\right)\left(\frac{1}{6}\right)\left(\frac{1}{6}\right)$.

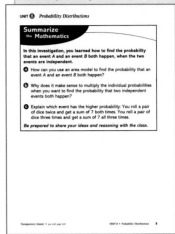

MATH TOOLKIT Record the Multiplication Rule for independent events in your toolkit. Give an example of two events for which it is appropriate to use the rule. Also, give an example of two events for which it is inappropriate to use the rule, explaining your reasoning.

✓ Check Your Understanding

a. P(*does not roll doubles on first roll* and *does not roll doubles on second roll* and *does not roll doubles on third roll*)

b. $\left(\frac{5}{6}\right)\left(\frac{5}{6}\right)\left(\frac{5}{6}\right) = \frac{125}{216}$

c. Each roll is independent of the others. The results of the first roll do not change the probability of getting doubles on the second roll, and so on.

Summarize the Mathematics, *page 528*

Teacher: In this investigation, you learned how to find the probability that an event *A* and an event *B* both happen when the two events are independent. Without talking, think for a minute about how you could use an area model to find the probability that both events happen. Then I will randomly select one of you to give us your thoughts. *(The teacher gives a minute or less for students to gather their thoughts. The teacher has wooden sticks with each student's name that she uses for randomly selecting students throughout the year.)* Okay, Darnell, please pick a name to identify the respondent.

Darnell: Mona.

Mona: You make a rectangle and label one side with the options for event *A* and the other side with the options for event *B*. Then you shade the sections that say that both event *A* and event *B* happen.

Teacher: Anyone wish to add to Mona's explanation? *(No responses. Realizing that the silence gives little information on whether or not others agree and understand the explanation, the teacher proceeds as follows.)* Okay, then Mona, please repeat your explanation and let's all consider whether someone who had not been in our class, like maybe your parent, might be able to understand how to use an area model from the explanation.

Mona: Is it okay if I add some to make it clearer? *(The teacher indicates approval knowing that it is important to give students an opportunity to improve their own explanations as well as add to others' explanations or thoughts.)* I'll explain with a diagram. *(She sketches a rectangle that looks almost square and subdivides one side into five sections and the other side into two sections.)* Now let's say that event *A* on this side happens $\frac{3}{5}$ of the time and event *B* on the top has probability $\frac{1}{2}$ of happening. *(She writes $\frac{1}{5}$ by each row and $\frac{1}{2}$ by each column.)* I will shade the first 3 rows of my diagram but only one of the two boxes across each row, like this. Does anyone wish to add or ask questions?

Samuel: Yeah, what is the answer?

Teacher: Good question, Samuel. Please answer the question, "What is the probability that both events *A* and *B* will happen?" and provide your reasoning.

Samuel: Well, there are 3 boxes shaded, so the probability is $\frac{3}{5}$. Wait, no, it is 3 of 10 boxes, so the probability is $\frac{3}{10}$. Three fifths does not make sense because that is the probability of event *A* by itself.

Teacher: So, are you thinking that the probability of both events *A* and *B* happening should be less than either one of the events happening?

Samuel: Right. When thinking about both, sometimes *A* happens and *B* does not happen or *B* happens and *A* does not. Getting both doesn't happen as often as each one separately.

Teacher: Your comment leads us right into considering why it makes sense to multiply the individual probabilities when you want to find the probability that two independent events both happen. Any thoughts on why multiplying makes sense?

Niyol: Well, to pick up on what Mona said, event *A* happens three-fifths of the time. Half of those times *B* will happen, too. So, we take half of three fifths, which is three tenths.

Teacher: How is that multiplying?

Niyol: $\frac{1}{2} \times \frac{3}{5} = \frac{3}{10}$

Mike: You can see that in the area diagram too. When you find the area of the shaded region, you multiply the length of one side, three fifths, times the length of the other side, one half, to get the area.

Teacher: Mike's comment brings up an interesting issue about lengths of area models. Notice that Mona's area model is almost square. Does it need to be square?

Jill: No, you could make the model skinny one way, like this.

(She draws a tall narrow rectangle, then divides and labels the sides as shown.)

Teacher: Does this model show that the probability is three tenths also? *(Students indicate agreement.)* Jill, what do you notice about the dimensions of the small rectangles labeled one fifth and one half?

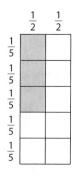

Jill: Well, they look like squares. If you were using a measuring tool, the lengths would be off. Like, this one fifth is almost the same size as the one half. Maybe it is like when we have different scales on our *x*- and *y*-axes. The one half is just half of the length across the top and the one fifth is just the side made into five equal pieces. This means the shaded area is just three of ten pieces that make up the whole.

Peta: Yeah, we are not really measuring lengths. Lengths do not matter. The percentage that they represent matters.

Teacher: That is an interesting way to think about it. So, we want the subdividing of each side to be proportional to represent the probabilities. That is the important feature of an area model. Now individually read Part c of the STM and decide on an answer and explanation. Again we will randomly select someone to report their thinking. This time I've drawn Bill.

Bill: It is harder to get 3 sevens in a row than 2 sevens. That is obvious.

Teacher: Let's think about the mathematics of this idea, to support or refute our instincts. Bill, can you talk about how to compute these probabilities for us?

Bill: Well, the probability of rolling a seven is 6 of 36 or one sixth. So, the probability of rolling 2 sevens is $\left(\frac{1}{6}\right)\left(\frac{1}{6}\right)$, or $\frac{1}{36}$. The probability of getting 3 sevens is $\left(\frac{1}{6}\right)\left(\frac{1}{6}\right)\left(\frac{1}{6}\right) = \frac{1}{216}$. That is smaller than $\frac{1}{36}$.

Teacher: What probability rule was Bill using to find these probabilities? Susan?

Susan: The Multiplication Rule for independent events.

Teacher: Good discussion. There is a number concept that I want to draw your attention to at this point. In learning and doing probability, the probability of an event is between 0 and 1. So, when rolling a pair of dice, the probability of getting a sum of seven is $\frac{1}{6}$. As Bill indicated, the probability of rolling a sum of seven twice is one sixth of one sixth, or $\frac{1}{36}$. In general, when you take a value and multiply by a number between 0 and 1, how does the result of the multiplication compare to the original value? Jon?

Jon: The result is less than the original value since you are multiplying by a positive number less than 1. I think of it as taking a piece of the original value, like taking half of the original value.

Teacher: *(The teacher knows that some students in the class can be pushed to generalize this idea with variables and wants to provide that opportunity, but will not expect that all students will be able to do this at this time.)* Let's try this idea with variables. If $0 < p < 1$, and $0 < q < 1$, which is larger, p or pq? And how do you know this?

Esther: p is larger. That is because multiplying by a number between 0 and 1 makes the original number smaller. So, pq is smaller. You can see this by using specific numbers like take $\frac{1}{4}$ and $\frac{1}{2}$. If you multiply $\frac{1}{4}$ by $\frac{1}{2}$, the result is $\frac{1}{8}$ which is smaller than $\frac{1}{4}$. You took half of $\frac{1}{4}$. So, there is less there now.

Teacher: Thinking about relative size of values is important when checking to see if your computations make sense. While working on this unit, you should please take the time to think about whether your numerical computation results make sense before moving on to the next problem.

Sarah: I thought about the answer to Part c without actually finding the probabilities. Is that okay?

Teacher: Why don't you tell us what you were thinking.

Sarah: I thought that if I was going to get 3 sevens in a row, I would first have to get 2 sevens in a row. Then after getting 2 sevens, you will only get a third seven some of the time, so it must be harder to get 3 sevens in a row than 2 sevens in a row. Getting 2 sevens in a row is included in getting 3 sevens in a row.

Teacher: That is another good way to think about it.

1 Count the number of students in your classroom who are wearing sneakers. Count the number of girls. Count the number of students who are wearing sneakers and are girls. Record the number of students who fall into each category in a copy of the following table.

	Wearing Sneakers	Not Wearing Sneakers	Total
Boy			
Girl			
Total			

a. Suppose you select a student at random from your class. What is the probability that the student is wearing sneakers?

b. Suppose you select a student at random from your class. What is the probability that the student is a girl?

c. Does the Multiplication Rule from Investigation 1 correctly compute the probability that the student is wearing sneakers and is a girl?

d. How is this situation different from previous situations in which the Multiplication Rule gave the correct probability?

2 The phrase *"the probability event A occurs given that event B occurs"* is written symbolically as $P(A \mid B)$. This **conditional probability** sometimes is read as "the probability of A given B." The table below categorizes the preferences of 300 students in a junior class about plans for their prom.

		Preference for Location	
		Hotel	Rec Center
Preference for Band	Hip-Hop	73	80
	Classic Rock	55	92

Suppose you pick a student at random from this class. Find each of the following probabilities.

a. *P(prefers hotel)*

b. *P(prefers hip-hop band)*

c. *P(prefers hotel* and *prefers hip-hop band)*

d. *P(prefers hotel* or *prefers hip-hop band)*

e. *P(prefers hotel | prefers hip-hop band)*

f. *P(prefers hip-hop band | prefers hotel)*

Investigation 2 — Conditional Probability

In this investigation, students learn the definition of conditional probability. They learn to compute a conditional probability using the idea of restricting the sample space to include only the outcomes specified by the "condition." Emphasize that the condition has the effect of changing the denominator when computing the probability.

Deciding when two events are independent is difficult for students, especially since they tend to confuse *independent* with *mutually exclusive*.

There are three equivalent definitions of the independence of events A and B: (1) $P(A) = P(A \mid B)$, (2) $P(B) = P(B \mid A)$, and (3) $P(A \text{ and } B) = P(A) \cdot P(B)$.

"Equivalent" means that if you know that any one of the equations holds, you can prove that the other two also hold.

This lesson follows standard practice and uses the first as the definition of independence. You may wish to point out explicitly that the second equation is the same as the first equation, but the events are renamed. The third equation is connected through the formal definition of conditional probability:

$$P(A \mid B) = \frac{P(A \text{ and } B)}{P(B)}$$

1 **INSTRUCTIONAL NOTE** This problem should be done with the entire class.

This is a key problem as students see that the form of the Multiplication Rule in Investigation 1 does not always apply. To find $P(\textit{student is a girl} \text{ and } \textit{wearing sneakers})$, you cannot compute $P(\textit{is a girl})$ times $P(\textit{wearing sneakers})$ because the events of being a girl and wearing sneakers are not independent. Although it may vary in different localities and cultures, typically the percentage of boys who wear sneakers is larger than the percentage of girls who wear sneakers.

If you have a single-gender class, you may have to have students collect data from outside the classroom. Other examples, which are less visual and thus not as effective as this example, might include pairs of events such as *has a pet* and *likes dogs* or *has younger siblings* and *has babysat*.

a. Answers will vary depending on your class. For an example, suppose that a classroom has 12 girls, 3 of whom are wearing sneakers, and has 16 boys, 10 of whom are wearing sneakers, as in the table at the right. Then the probability a student is wearing sneakers is $\frac{13}{28}$.

	Wearing Sneakers	Not Wearing Sneakers	Total
Boy	10	6	16
Girl	3	9	12
Total	13	15	28

b. For the sample data above, the probability is $\frac{12}{28}$.

c. Students need to check whether $P(\textit{girl}) \cdot P(\textit{wearing sneakers}) = P(\textit{girl} \text{ and } \textit{wearing sneakers})$. This will probably not be the case. For our sample data, $P(\textit{girl}) \cdot P(\textit{wearing sneakers}) = \left(\frac{12}{28}\right)\left(\frac{13}{28}\right)$ is not equal to $P(\textit{girl} \text{ and } \textit{wearing sneakers}) = \frac{3}{28}$.

d. The events are not independent. Knowing that a student is a girl changes the probability that the student is wearing sneakers. The Multiplication Rule from Investigation 1 works for independent events only, and so it does not give the correct probability for this situation.

NOTE The solution to Problem 2 is on page T530.

Unit 8

(3) Recall that events *A* and *B* are independent if knowing whether one of the events occurs does not change the probability that the other event occurs.

a. Using the data from Problem 1, suppose you pick a student at random. Find *P*(*wearing sneakers* | *is a girl*). How does this compare to *P*(*wearing sneakers*)?

b. Are the events *wearing sneakers* and *is a girl* independent? Why or why not?

c. Consider this table from a different class.

	Wearing Sneakers	Not Wearing Sneakers
Boy	5	9
Girl	10	18

Suppose you pick a student at random from this class.

    i. Find *P*(*wearing sneakers*).

    ii. Find *P*(*wearing sneakers* | *is a girl*).

    iii. Are the events *wearing sneakers* and *is a girl* independent? Why or why not?

d. If events *A* and *B* are independent, how are *P*(*A*) and *P*(*A* | *B*) related?

(4) Suppose that you roll a pair of dice.

a. Which is greater? *P*(*doubles*) or *P*(*doubles* | *sum is 2*)?

b. Are the events *getting doubles* and *getting a sum of 2* independent? If not, how would you describe the relationship?

(5) Refer to the table in Problem 2.

a. If you select a junior at random, are the events *prefers hotel* and *prefers hip-hop band* independent? Explain.

b. Recall from your work in Course 1 that two events are **mutually exclusive** if they cannot both occur on the same outcome. If you select a junior at random, are the events *prefers hotel* and *prefers hip-hop band* mutually exclusive? Explain.

c. Are the events *prefers hotel* and *prefers rec center* mutually exclusive? Explain.

(6) Suppose you pick a high school student at random. For each of the pairs of events in Parts a, b, and c, write the mathematical equality or inequality that applies:

$$P(A) = P(A \mid B), \quad P(A) > P(A \mid B), \quad \text{or} \quad P(A) < P(A \mid B).$$

a. *A* is the event that the student is male, and *B* is the event that the student is over six feet tall.

b. *A* is the event that the student is female, and *B* is the event that the student has brown eyes.

Unit 8

(2)

	Preference for Location		
	Hotel	**Rec Center**	**Total**
Hip-Hop	73	80	153
Preference for Band **Classic Rock**	55	92	147
Total	128	172	300

a. $\dfrac{128}{300}$ b. $\dfrac{153}{300}$ c. $\dfrac{73}{300}$

d. $\dfrac{208}{300}$ e. $\dfrac{73}{153}$ f. $\dfrac{73}{128}$

INSTRUCTIONAL NOTE
Students should begin this problem by adding the marginal totals to a copy of the table. There is no need to reduce fractions or change them to a decimal until Problem 5.

(3)

a. For our sample data, $P(wearing\ sneakers \mid is\ a\ girl) = \dfrac{3}{12}$, which is not equal to $P(wearing\ sneakers) = \dfrac{13}{28}$.

b. The events *wearing sneakers* and *is a girl* are not independent because if you are given the condition that the person is a girl, the probability that the person is wearing sneakers decreases from $\dfrac{13}{28}$ to $\dfrac{3}{12}$.

c. i. $P(wearing\ sneakers) = \dfrac{15}{42} = \dfrac{5}{14}$

   ii. $P(wearing\ sneakers \mid is\ a\ girl) = \dfrac{10}{28} = \dfrac{5}{14}$

   iii. Since knowing that a student was a girl did not change the probability of wearing sneakers, the events *wearing sneakers* and *is a girl* are independent.

d. If events A and B are independent, $P(A) = P(A \mid B)$.

	Wearing Sneakers	Not Wearing Sneakers	Total
Boy	5	9	14
Girl	10	18	28
Total	15	27	42

(4)

a. $P(doubles) = \dfrac{1}{6}$ but $P(doubles \mid sum\ is\ 2) = 1$, so $P(doubles \mid sum\ is\ 2)$ is greater.

b. The events *getting doubles* and *getting a sum of 2* are not independent. If you know that you rolled a sum of 2, you are sure that you have rolled doubles.

(5)

a. $P(prefer\ the\ hotel) = \dfrac{128}{300} \approx 0.427$ but $P(prefer\ the\ hotel \mid prefer\ the\ hip\text{-}hop\ band) = \dfrac{73}{153} \approx 0.477$. Because these probabilities are not equal, the events are not independent.

b. These events are not mutually exclusive because 73 students fall into both categories of *prefer the hotel* and *prefer the hip-hop band*. In other words, $P(prefer\ the\ hotel\ and\ prefer\ the\ hip\text{-}hop\ band) \neq 0$.

c. Yes, because each student had to choose between *prefer the hotel* and *prefer the rec center*. No one is counted under both categories.

(6)

a. $P(male) < P(male \mid over\ six\ feet\ tall)$ or $P(A) < P(A \mid B)$ because only half of all students are male, but most students over 6 feet tall are male.

b. $P(female) = P(female \mid brown\ eyes)$ or $P(A) = P(A \mid B)$ because there is no reason to think that females are any more or less likely to have brown eyes than students in general.

c. *A* is the event that the student is a member of the French club, and *B* is the event that the student is taking a French class.

d. Which of the pairs of events is it safe to assume are independent? Explain your reasoning.

Summarize
the Mathematics

In this investigation, you learned how to find conditional probabilities.

a What is the difference between $P(A)$ and $P(A|B)$?

b Use the two symbolic expressions in Part a to write a definition (in if-and-only-if form) that tells when events A and B are independent.

c Suppose you ask 30 juniors and 70 seniors whether they studied the previous night. Make three possible tables where the events *being a junior* and *studied last night* are independent events in this group of 100 students.

Be prepared to share your ideas and examples with the class.

✓ Check Your Understanding

A survey of 505 teens by the American Academy of Dermatology included 254 boys and 251 girls. Thirty-three percent of the boys said they wear sunscreen, and 53% of the girls said they wear sunscreen.

a. Fill in a copy of the following table, showing the number of teenagers who fell into each category.

	Boy	Girl	Total
Wear Sunscreen			
Don't Wear Sunscreen			
Total			505

Source: www.aad.org/public/News/NewsReleases/Press+Release+ Archives/Skin+Cancer+and+Sun+Safety/Teen+Survey+Results.htm

b. Suppose you pick one student at random from these 505 teens. Find the probability of each of the following events.

   i. $P(wears\ sunscreen)$

   ii. $P(is\ a\ boy)$

  iii. $P(wears\ sunscreen$ and $is\ a\ boy)$

  iv. $P(wears\ sunscreen$ or $is\ a\ boy)$

   v. $P(wears\ sunscreen\ |\ is\ a\ boy)$

  vi. $P(is\ a\ boy\ |\ wears\ sunscreen)$

c. Are being a boy and wearing sunscreen independent events? How could you tell this from the information given about the survey? How could you tell this from your table?

c. $P(French\ club) < P(French\ club\ |\ French\ class)$ or $P(A) < P(A\ |\ B)$ because students taking a French class are more likely to belong to a French club than students in general.

d. Only the two events in Part b because for A and B to be independent, you must have $P(A) = P(A\ |\ B)$.

Summarize
the Mathematics

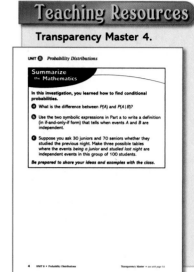
a $P(A)$ stands for the probability that event A happens when you have no additional information about whether other events happen. $P(A\ |\ B)$ stands for the probability that event A happens given the additional information that B happens for sure. Sometimes this additional information increases the probability that event A happens, sometimes it decreases the probability, and sometimes the probability that event A happens is unchanged.

b Events A and B are independent if and only if $P(A) = P(A\ |\ B)$.

c Three possible tables appear below. Note that the rows and columns are proportional. For example, in the first table, each entry in the first column is $\frac{3}{7}$ times the corresponding entry in the second column, and each entry in the first row is equal to 1 times the corresponding entry in the second row.

	Junior	Senior	Total
Studied	15	35	50
Did Not Study	15	35	50
Total	30	70	100

	Junior	Senior	Total
Studied	12	28	40
Did Not Study	18	42	60
Total	30	70	100

	Junior	Senior	Total
Studied	30	70	100
Did Not Study	0	0	0
Total	30	70	100

MATH TOOLKIT Explain the difference between $P(A)$ and $P(A\ |\ B)$. Record the definition of independent events A and B with an example.

Unit 8

✓Check Your Understanding

NOTE For Part a, other tables are possible. For example, the survey could have found 134 girls and 83 boys wearing sunscreen.

a.

	Boy	Girl	Total
Wear Sunscreen	84	133	217
Do Not Wear Sunscreen	170	118	288
Total	254	251	505

b. **i.** $P(\textit{wears sunscreen}) = \frac{217}{505}$

    ii. $P(\textit{is a boy}) = \frac{254}{505}$

    iii. $P(\textit{wears sunscreen and is a boy}) = \frac{84}{505}$

    iv. $P(\textit{wears sunscreen or is a boy}) = \frac{217 + 170}{505} = \frac{387}{505}$

    v. $P(\textit{wears sunscreen} \mid \textit{is a boy}) = \frac{84}{254}$

    vi. $P(\textit{is a boy} \mid \textit{wears sunscreen}) = \frac{84}{217}$

c. Being a boy and wearing sunscreen are not independent events. You can tell this from the information given about the survey because the percentage of boys who wear sunscreen is less than the percentage of girls who wear sunscreen. That must mean that if you know a person is a boy, the probability he wears sunscreen is less than the overall probability. Using the table, $P(\textit{wears sunscreen}) = \frac{217}{505} \approx 0.430$ while $P(\textit{wears sunscreen} \mid \textit{boy}) = \frac{84}{254} \approx 0.331$.

Teacher Notes

Investigation 3   **The Multiplication Rule When Events Are Not Independent**

In Investigation 1, you discovered a rule for calculating the probability that two *independent* events, *A* and *B*, both happen. As you saw in Investigation 2, sometimes the occurrence of one event influences the probability that another event occurs—that is, the events are *not* independent. As you work on the problems of this investigation, look for an answer to this question:

How do you find P(A and B) when A and B are not independent?

1 About half of all U.S. adults are male. The *USA Today*-reported data in Investigation 1 indicate that three out of five adults sing in the shower. Some people think that males are more likely to sing in the shower than are females. Suppose that they are right and 80% of males sing in the shower, but only 40% of females sing in the shower.

a. Make an area model that represents this situation.

b. Suppose you pick an adult at random. What is the probability that you get a female who sings in the shower?

c. Complete the following equation (in words) that describes how you found the probability in Part b.

$$P(\textit{female and sings in shower}) =$$

d. Suppose you pick an adult at random. What is the probability that you get a male who sings in the shower?

e. Write an equation in words that describes how you found the probability in Part d.

2 As you have seen in Problem 1, if events *A* and *B* are not independent, you can find *P(A and B)* by using either of the following rules.

$$P(A \text{ and } B) = P(A) \cdot P(B \mid A)$$
$$P(A \text{ and } B) = P(B) \cdot P(A \mid B)$$

The Multiplication Rule When Events Are Not Independent

In this investigation, students learn to use a form of the Multiplication Rule to find $P(A \text{ and } B)$ when A and B are not independent:

$$P(A \text{ and } B) = P(A) \cdot P(B \mid A)$$
$$P(A \text{ and } B) = P(B) \cdot P(A \mid B)$$

① **INSTRUCTIONAL NOTE** Some students might make a 10 × 2 or 2 × 10 area model representing 10% increments. If so, you may wish to have students show and explain their models to the entire class. Also, it would be valuable to have students compare this area model for dependent events to the area model for singing in the shower in Problem 5 of Investigation 1.

a.

Gender

	Male	Female	
Yes			Yes
Yes			Yes
Yes			No
Yes			No
No			No

Sings in Shower

b. Forty percent of half of the adults, or 20% of all adults, are females who sing in the shower, so the probability is $(0.5)(0.4) = 0.2$.

c. $P(female \text{ and } sings \text{ in } shower) = P(female) \cdot P(sings \text{ in the shower given female})$

d. Eighty percent of half of the adults, or 40% of all adults, are males who sing in the shower, so the probability is $(0.5)(0.8) = 0.4$.

e. $P(male \text{ and } sings \text{ in } shower) = P(male) \cdot P(sings \text{ in the shower given male})$

a. For the situation of rolling a pair of dice once, let event A be rolling doubles and event B be getting a sum of 8.

    i. Using the sample space below, find each of the following probabilities.

- $P(A)$
- $P(B)$
- $P(A \mid B)$
- $P(B \mid A)$
- $P(A \text{ and } B)$

Number on Second Die

	1	2	3	4	5	6
1	1, 1	1, 2	1, 3	1, 4	1, 5	1, 6
2	2, 1	2, 2	2, 3	2, 4	2, 5	2, 6
3	3, 1	3, 2	3, 3	3, 4	3, 5	3, 6
4	4, 1	4, 2	4, 3	4, 4	4, 5	4, 6
5	5, 1	5, 2	5, 3	5, 4	5, 5	5, 6
6	6, 1	6, 2	6, 3	6, 4	6, 5	6, 6

(Number on First Die)

    ii. Verify that both rules for $P(A \text{ and } B)$ hold for the probabilities that you found in part i.

b. Show that both rules also work for each of the following situations.

    i. You roll a pair of dice once. Event A is rolling doubles. Event B is getting a sum of 7.

    ii. You roll a pair of dice once. Event A is getting 1 on the first die. Event B is getting a sum of 7.

(3) A Web site at Central Michigan University collects data from statistics students. In one activity, students were asked whether they were right-handed or left-handed. Students were also asked which thumb is on top when they fold their hands (intertwining their fingers).

The following table shows the results for the first 80 students who submitted their information.

	Left-Handed	Right-Handed	Total
Left Thumb on Top	2	46	48
Right Thumb on Top	4	28	32
Total	6	74	80

Source: stat.cst.cmich.edu/statact/index.php

Suppose you pick one of these 80 students at random.

a. Find each probability.

    i. $P(left\text{-}handed)$

    ii. $P(left\ thumb\ on\ top)$

    iii. $P(left\ thumb\ on\ top \mid left\text{-}handed)$

    iv. $P(left\text{-}handed \mid left\ thumb\ on\ top)$

(2) The sum for each cell is in parentheses in the chart below.

Number on Second Die

		1	2	3	4	5	6
Number on First Die	1	1, 1 (2)	1, 2 (3)	1, 3 (4)	1, 4 (5)	1, 5 (6)	1, 6 (7)
	2	2, 1 (3)	2, 2 (4)	2, 3 (5)	2, 4 (6)	2, 5 (7)	2, 6 (8)
	3	3, 1 (4)	3, 2 (5)	3, 3 (6)	3, 4 (7)	3, 5 (8)	3, 6 (9)
	4	4, 1 (5)	4, 2 (6)	4, 3 (7)	4, 4 (8)	4, 5 (9)	4, 6 (10)
	5	5, 1 (6)	5, 2 (7)	5, 3 (8)	5, 4 (9)	5, 5 (10)	5, 6 (11)
	6	6, 1 (7)	6, 2 (8)	6, 3 (9)	6, 4 (10)	6, 5 (11)	6, 6 (12)

a. **i.** $P(A) = \frac{1}{6}$

$P(B) = \frac{5}{36}$

$P(A \mid B) = \frac{1}{5}$

$P(B \mid A) = \frac{1}{6}$

$P(A \text{ and } B) = \frac{1}{36}$

ii. $P(doubles \text{ and } sum\ 8) = \frac{1}{36}$ and $P(doubles) \cdot P(sum\ 8 \mid doubles) = \left(\frac{6}{36}\right)\left(\frac{1}{6}\right) = \frac{1}{36}$

$P(doubles \text{ and } sum\ 8) = \frac{1}{36}$ and $P(sum\ 8) \cdot P(doubles \mid sum\ 8) = \left(\frac{5}{36}\right)\left(\frac{1}{5}\right) = \frac{1}{36}$

b. **i.** $P(doubles \text{ and } sum\ 7) = 0$ and $P(doubles) \cdot P(sum\ 7 \mid doubles) = \left(\frac{6}{36}\right)\left(\frac{0}{6}\right) = 0$

$P(doubles \text{ and } sum\ 7) = 0$ and $P(sum\ 7) \cdot P(doubles \mid sum\ 7) = \left(\frac{6}{36}\right)\left(\frac{0}{6}\right) = 0$

ii. $P(1 \text{ on first die and } sum\ 7) = \frac{1}{36}$ and

$P(1 \text{ on first die}) \cdot P(sum\ 7 \mid 1 \text{ on first die}) = \left(\frac{1}{6}\right)\left(\frac{1}{6}\right) = \frac{1}{36}$

$P(1 \text{ on first die and } sum\ 7) = \frac{1}{36}$ and

$P(sum\ 7) \cdot P(1 \text{ on first die} \mid sum\ 7) = \left(\frac{6}{36}\right)\left(\frac{1}{6}\right) = \frac{1}{36}$

(3) **a.** **i.** $P(\text{left-handed}) = \frac{6}{80}$, or $\frac{3}{40}$

ii. $P(\text{left thumb on top}) = \frac{48}{80}$, or $\frac{3}{5}$

iii. $P(\text{left thumb on top} \mid \text{left-handed}) = \frac{2}{6}$, or $\frac{1}{3}$

iv. $P(\text{left-handed} \mid \text{left thumb on top}) = \frac{2}{48}$, or $\frac{1}{24}$

b. Are being left-handed and having the left thumb on top independent events? Are they mutually exclusive events?

c. Use your results from Part a and the formula to find P(*left-handed* and *left thumb on top*). Check your answer by using the table directly.

4 Think about a single roll of two dice. For each of the situations below, tell whether the two events are mutually exclusive. Then tell whether they are independent.

a. Event A is rolling doubles. Event B is getting a sum of 8.

b. Event A is rolling doubles. Event B is getting a sum of 7.

c. Event A is getting 1 on the first die. Event B is getting a sum of 7.

d. Event A is getting 1 on the first die. Event B is getting doubles.

5 Recall that the rule for finding the probability that event A *or* event B occurs is

$$P(A \text{ or } B) = P(A) + P(B) - P(A \text{ and } B).$$

When A and B are mutually exclusive, the rule simplifies to

$$P(A \text{ or } B) = P(A) + P(B).$$

a. Use the appropriate formula and your results from Problem 3 to find P(*left-handed* or *left thumb on top*). Check your answer by using the table directly.

b. Suppose you know P(A) and P(B). When you find P(A or B) when A and B are mutually exclusive, why is there no need to subtract P(A and B)?

c. Suppose you know P(A) and P(B). How can you find P(A or B) when A and B are independent?

d. Suppose you know P(A) and P(B). Can you find P(A or B) when A and B are neither mutually exclusive nor independent? Explain your thinking.

b. Being left-handed and having the left thumb on top are not independent events because the probabilities $P(left\text{-}handed)$ and $P(left\text{-}handed \mid left\ thumb\ on\ top)$ from Part a are not equal. They are not mutually exclusive events because 2 students are both left-handed and have their left thumb on top.

c. Using the formula, $P(left\text{-}handed\ and\ left\ thumb\ on\ top) =$
$P(left\text{-}handed) \cdot P(left\ thumb\ on\ top \mid left\text{-}handed) = \left(\frac{6}{80}\right)\left(\frac{2}{6}\right) = \frac{2}{80}$.
Using the table directly, we see that 2 students out of 80, or $\frac{2}{80}$, are left-handed and have their left thumb on top.

4 **a.** Rolling doubles and getting a sum of 8 are not mutually exclusive because both happen on the same roll if you roll a 4 on both dice. They are not independent events because $P(doubles) = \frac{1}{6}$ is not equal to $P(doubles \mid sum\ 8) = \frac{1}{5}$.

b. Rolling doubles and getting a sum of 7 are mutually exclusive events because both events cannot happen on the same roll. They are not independent events because $P(doubles) = \frac{1}{6}$ is not equal to $P(doubles \mid sum\ 7) = 0$.

c. Getting 1 on the first die and getting a sum of 7 are not mutually exclusive events because both happen on the same roll if you roll a 1 on the first die and a 6 on the second die. They are independent events because $P(1\ on\ the\ first\ die) = \frac{1}{6}$ is equal to $P(1\ on\ the\ first\ die \mid sum\ 7) = \frac{1}{6}$.

d. Getting 1 on the first die and getting doubles are not mutually exclusive events because both happen on the same roll if you roll a 1 on the first die and a 1 on the second die. They are independent events because $P(1\ on\ the\ first\ die) = \frac{1}{6}$ is equal to $P(1\ on\ the\ first\ die \mid doubles) = \frac{1}{6}$.

5 **INSTRUCTIONAL NOTE** You may help students recall how the Addition Rule was developed in *Patterns in Chance*. The example in that unit was to count the number of students who own white shoes and count the number who own black shoes. If you want to know how many students own either white or black shoes, you cannot just add the two counts because you would be counting students twice who own shoes of both colors. You can correct the sum by subtracting off the number of students who own shoes of both colors. If it turns out that no student owns shoes of both colors, you can just add the number who own black shoes to the number who own white shoes; there is no "overlap" to subtract off.

a. Using the formula, $P(left\text{-}handed\ or\ left\ thumb\ on\ top) =$
$P(left\text{-}handed) + P(left\ thumb\ on\ top) - P(left\text{-}handed\ and$
$left\ thumb\ on\ top) = \frac{6}{80} + \frac{48}{80} - \frac{2}{80} = \frac{52}{80}$. Using the table directly,
$\frac{2 + 4 + 46}{80} = \frac{52}{80}$.

b. You do not need to subtract $P(A\ and\ B)$ because there is no "overlap" in events A and B. (See explanation above.)

c. Start with $P(A\ or\ B) = P(A) + P(B) - P(A\ and\ B)$. Because A and B are independent, $P(A\ and\ B) = P(A) \cdot P(B)$. So $P(A\ or\ B) = P(A) + P(B) - P(A) \cdot P(B)$.

NOTE The solution to Problem 5 Part d is on page T535.

Unit 8

Probability Models   **T534**

Summarize
the Mathematics

In this investigation, you learned how to compute probabilities when two events are not independent.

a How do you find the probability that event *A* and event *B* both happen when the two events are not independent?

b Does the method in Part a work when events *A* and *B* are independent? Explain.

c What is the difference between mutually exclusive and independent events?

Be prepared to share your ideas with the class.

✔ Check Your Understanding

Rebekka has 75 books in her library. She categorized them in the following way.

	Fiction	Non-Fiction	Total
Book for Teens	20	30	50
Book for Adults	10	15	25
Total	30	45	75

Suppose Rebekka picks a book at random.

a. Find *P*(*book for teens*), *P*(*fiction*), *P*(*book for teens* | *fiction*), and *P*(*fiction* | *book for teens*).

b. Are *book for teens* and *fiction* independent events?

c. Are *book for teens* and *fiction* mutually exclusive events?

d. Use your results from Part a and the formula to find *P*(*book for teens* and *fiction*). Check your answer by using the table directly.

e. Use your results from the previous parts of this task and the formula to find *P*(*book for teens* or *fiction*). Check your answer by using the table directly.

d. No. Suppose that A is the event of rolling doubles with a pair of dice, so $P(A) = \frac{1}{6}$ and B is the event of rolling a sum of 8, so $P(B) = \frac{5}{36}$. As you saw in Problem 4 Part a, these are not mutually exclusive, and they are not independent. You cannot find $P(A \text{ or } B) = \frac{10}{36}$ using just $\frac{1}{6}$ and $\frac{5}{36}$. You need to know the extent to which A and B "overlap" in the distribution of possible rolls of the dice.

Summarize
the Mathematics

Teaching Resources

Transparency Master 5.

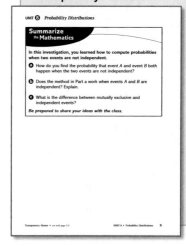

a Use either of the following forms of the Multiplication Rule:
$P(A \text{ and } B) = P(A) \cdot P(B \mid A)$ or $P(A \text{ and } B) = P(B) \cdot P(A \mid B)$

b Yes, because if events A and B are independent, $P(A) = P(A \mid B)$ and $P(B) = P(B \mid A)$. Thus, the two rules reduce to the Multiplication Rule for independent events: $P(A \text{ and } B) = P(A) \cdot P(B \mid A) = P(A) \cdot P(B)$ and $P(A \text{ and } B) = P(B) \cdot P(A \mid B) = P(B) \cdot P(A)$.

c Mutually exclusive events are two events that cannot happen on the same outcome; that is, if A and B are mutually exclusive, $P(A \text{ and } B) = 0$. Independent events are events such that if you know that one of them happened on a certain outcome, it does not change the probability that the other happened on that same outcome; that is, if A and B are independent, $P(A) = P(A \mid B)$ and $P(B) = P(B \mid A)$.

MATH TOOLKIT Explain how to find the probability that two events both happen when the events are not independent. Explain the difference between mutually exclusive and independent events using examples.

✓Check Your Understanding

a. $P(\text{book for teens}) = \frac{50}{75}$, or $\frac{2}{3}$; $P(\text{fiction}) = \frac{30}{75}$, or $\frac{2}{5}$;

$P(\text{book for teens} \mid \text{fiction}) = \frac{20}{30}$, or $\frac{2}{3}$;

$P(\text{fiction} \mid \text{book for teens}) = \frac{20}{50}$, or $\frac{2}{5}$.

b. *Book for teens* and *fiction* are independent events because the two probabilities $P(\text{book for teens})$ and $P(\text{book for teens} \mid \text{fiction})$ are both $\frac{2}{3}$.

c. *Book for teens* and *fiction* are not mutually exclusive events because Rebekka has 20 books that are both fiction and a book for teens.

d. Using the formula, $P(\text{book for teens and fiction}) = P(\text{book for teens}) \cdot P(\text{fiction} \mid \text{book for teens}) = \left(\frac{2}{3}\right)\left(\frac{2}{5}\right) = \frac{4}{15}$. Using the table directly, 20 of the 75 books, or $\frac{4}{15}$, are for teens and fiction.

e. Using the formula, $P(\text{book for teens or fiction}) = P(\text{book for teens}) + P(\text{fiction}) - P(\text{book for teens and fiction}) = \frac{50}{75} + \frac{30}{75} - \frac{4}{15} = \frac{60}{75}$, or $\frac{4}{5}$. Using the table directly, there are $(20 + 30 + 10) = 60$ books out of the 80, or $\frac{4}{5}$, that are a book for teens or fiction.

On Your Own

Applications

1 In a famous trial in Sweden, a parking officer had noted the position to the nearest "hour" of the valve stems on the tires on one side of a car. For example, in the following picture, the valve stems are at 3:00 and at 10:00. The officer issued a ticket for overtime parking. Upon returning later, the officer noted that the valve stems were still in the same position. However, the owner of the car claimed he had moved the car and returned to the same parking place.

   a. Use an area model to estimate the probability that if a vehicle is moved, both valve stems return to the same position (to the nearest hour) that they were in before the car was moved.

   b. Use the Multiplication Rule to estimate the probability that if a vehicle is moved, the valve stems return to the same position (to the nearest hour) that they were in before the car was moved.

   c. What assumption are you making? How can you find out if it is reasonable?

   d. Do you think that the judge ruled that the owner was guilty or not guilty?

2 Refer to your area model for the probabilities of whether a child will have freckles if both parents have one freckles gene and one no-freckles gene. (See Problem 3 on page 525.)

   a. Compare the following.

   P(*freckles gene inherited from father*)

   P(*freckles gene inherited from father* and *freckles gene inherited from mother*)

   b. How is the independence of the events *freckles gene inherited from father* and *freckles gene inherited from mother* shown in your area model?

Unit 8

Applications

1 **a.** Suppose the stems were at 10 o'clock on the back tire and 3 o'clock on the front tire, as in the photo. Then, from the diagram at the right, the probability is $\frac{1}{144}$.

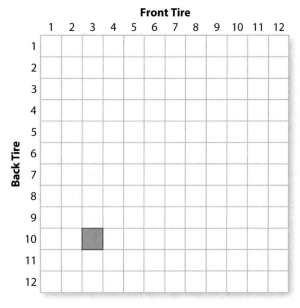

b. *P(back tire is in same position* and *front tire is in same position)* = *P(back tire is in same position)* • *P(front tire is in same position)* = $\left(\frac{1}{12}\right)\left(\frac{1}{12}\right) = \frac{1}{144}$.

c. The computations in Parts a and b assume that the tires rotate independently. This is a reasonable assumption, although some students may believe otherwise. To verify this, students could note the position of the valve stems on each of the two tires on one side of a car and see if the valve stems are at the same relative positions after a trip. This should be done many times and with various cars.

Note that if the tires rotate exactly together, the probability is $\frac{1}{12}$; they both will return to the same hour.

d. Most students usually think that the man should have been issued a ticket. In the actual trial, the judge said that 1 chance in 144 was reasonable doubt and the man was acquitted.

2 **a.** *P(freckles gene inherited from father)* = $\frac{1}{2}$

P(freckles gene inherited from father and *freckles gene inherited from mother)* = $\frac{1}{2} \cdot \frac{1}{2} = \frac{1}{4}$

b. With independent events, the probabilities for outcomes for one event do not depend on the outcomes for the other event. Thus, each partitioning line runs the entire width or length of the region. In other words, the columns are identical for each row.

3 Suppose you draw one card from a shuffled standard deck of cards.

    a. Find the following probabilities.

- P(*card is an ace*)
- P(*card is a heart*)
- P(*card is an ace* | *card is a heart*)
- P(*card is a heart* | *card is an ace*)
- P(*card is an ace* and *card is a heart*)
- P(*card is an ace* or *card is a heart*)

    b. Are the events *card is an ace* and *card is a heart* independent? Explain.

    c. Are the events *card is an ace* and *card is a heart* mutually exclusive? Explain.

    d. Give an example of two events that would be mutually exclusive.

4 For each situation below,

- find $P(A)$ and $P(A \mid B)$.
- say whether the pair of events A and B are independent or dependent.
- say whether events A and B are mutually exclusive or not mutually exclusive.

    a. You roll a pair of tetrahedral dice once. Event A is getting doubles, and event B is getting a sum of 3.

    b. You flip a coin twice. Event A is getting a head on the second flip, and event B is getting a head on the first flip.

    c. You pick a day of the week at random. Event A is getting a Monday, and event B is getting a school day.

5 Suppose you are trying to draw a heart from a regular deck of 52 cards.

    a. After each draw, you do not replace that card before you draw again.

      i. What is the smallest number of cards you might have to draw in order to get a heart?

      ii. What is the largest number of cards you might have to draw in order to get a heart?

      iii. Are the draws independent? Explain.

    b. After each draw, you do replace that card (and reshuffle) before you draw again.

      i. What is the smallest number of cards you might have to draw in order to get a heart?

      ii. What is the largest number of cards you might have to draw in order to get a heart?

      iii. Are the draws independent? Explain.

    c. Should you replace the card or not if you want to get a heart in the fewest number of draws? Why does this make sense?

3 **a.** $P(card\ is\ an\ ace) = \frac{4}{52}$, or $\frac{1}{13}$

$P(card\ is\ a\ heart) = \frac{13}{52}$, or $\frac{1}{4}$

$P(card\ is\ an\ ace\ |\ card\ is\ a\ heart) = \frac{1}{13}$

$P(card\ is\ a\ heart\ |\ card\ is\ an\ ace) = \frac{1}{4}$

$P(card\ is\ an\ ace\ and\ card\ is\ a\ heart) = \frac{1}{52}$

$P(card\ is\ an\ ace\ or\ card\ is\ a\ heart) = \frac{16}{52}$

INSTRUCTIONAL NOTE
Some students may not be very familiar with a deck of cards. Before assigning this problem, you may want to discuss how many and what kinds of cards make up a standard deck of 52 cards.

b. The events are independent because $P(card\ is\ an\ ace) = \frac{4}{52} = \frac{1}{13}$ is equal to $P(card\ is\ an\ ace\ |\ card\ is\ a\ heart) = \frac{1}{13}$.

c. No, because if you draw the ace of hearts, both *card is an ace* and *card is a heart* have occurred.

d. The events *card is a heart* and *card is a spade* are mutually exclusive.

4 **a.** • $P(getting\ doubles) = \frac{4}{16}$ and $P(doubles\ |\ sum\ of\ 3) = 0$.

• Because these two probabilities are not equal, the events are not independent.

• However, they are mutually exclusive because you cannot get doubles and a sum of 3 on the same roll.

b. • $P(head\ on\ the\ second\ flip) = \frac{1}{2}$ and $P(head\ on\ the\ second\ flip\ |\ head\ on\ the\ first\ flip) = \frac{1}{2}$.

• Because these two probabilities are equal, the events are independent.

• They are not mutually exclusive because you can get a head on the second flip and a head on the first flip.

c. • $P(Monday) \approx \frac{1}{7}$ and $P(Monday\ |\ school\ day) \approx \frac{1}{5}$ (depending on the particular year and your school schedule).

• Because these probabilities are not equal, the events are not independent.

• They also are not mutually exclusive because you can select a day that is both a Monday and a school day.

5 **a.** **i.** 1

ii. 40. You might draw all 39 of the diamonds, clubs, and spades before drawing a heart.

iii. No. The probability of getting a heart increases after each unsuccessful draw because the proportion of hearts to total cards increases. For example, $\frac{13}{52} < \frac{13}{51}$.

b. **i.** 1

ii. You might draw forever.

iii. Yes. The probability of getting a heart on each draw is $\frac{1}{4}$, no matter what has happened on previous draws.

c. Do not replace the card. This makes sense because if you do not replace the card, the probability of getting a heart increases on the next draw.

6 Consider the table below, which shows how many juniors and seniors at a small high school have a driver's license.

	Juniors	Seniors	Total
Have Driver's License	60	55	115
Do Not Have License	20	15	35
Total	80	70	150

Suppose you pick a student at random.

a. Find P(*junior*), P(*has driver's license*), P(*junior | has driver's license*), and P(*has driver's license | junior*).

b. Are being a junior and having a driver's license independent events? Are they mutually exclusive events?

c. Use your results from Part a and the formula to find P(*junior and has driver's license*). Check your answer by using the table directly.

d. Use your results from the previous parts of this problem and the formula to find P(*junior or has driver's license*). Check your answer by using the table directly.

7 There were about 300 million people in the United States in 2006. About 14.3 million of them watched Game 5 of the 2006 National Basketball Association championship between the Miami Heat and the Dallas Mavericks. About 15.7 million people watched the sixth and final game. (Source: en.wikipedia.org/wiki/National_Basketball_Association_Nielsen_ratings)

a. What proportion of people watched the fifth game? The sixth game?

b. Why is it unreasonable to multiply your two numbers in Part a to find the proportion of people who watched both Game 5 and Game 6?

c. What would be a better estimate?

Connections

8 Refer to Applications Task 1 about the Swedish overtime parking ticket. Design a simulation to estimate the probability that if a car is moved, the valve stems return to the same position (to the nearest hour) that they were in before the car was moved. You must make an assumption about how tires rotate. Will your simulation give approximately the same answer you found in Applications Task 1?

6 a. $P(junior) = \frac{80}{150}$, or $\frac{8}{15}$; $P(has\ driver's\ license) = \frac{115}{150}$, or $\frac{23}{30}$;

$P(junior \mid has\ driver's\ license) = \frac{60}{115}$, or $\frac{12}{23}$;

$P(has\ driver's\ license \mid junior) = \frac{60}{80}$, or $\frac{3}{4}$.

b. Being a junior and having a driver's license are not independent events because $P(junior) = \frac{80}{150} = \frac{8}{15}$ is not quite equal to

$P(junior \mid has\ driver's\ license) = \frac{60}{115} = \frac{12}{23}$. They are not mutually exclusive events because there are 60 students who are both juniors and have a driver's license.

c. $P(junior\ and\ has\ driver's\ license) = P(junior) \cdot P(has\ driver's\ license \mid junior) = \left(\frac{80}{150}\right)\left(\frac{60}{80}\right) = \frac{60}{150}$, or $\frac{2}{5}$. Reading directly from the table, 60 out of the 150 students are juniors and have a driver's license, so the probability is $\frac{60}{150}$, or $\frac{2}{5}$.

d. $P(junior\ or\ has\ driver's\ license) = P(junior) + P(has\ driver's\ license) - P(junior\ and\ has\ driver's\ license) = \frac{80}{150} + \frac{115}{150} - \frac{60}{150} = \frac{135}{150}$, or $\frac{9}{10}$. Reading directly from the table, $60 + 20 + 55$, or 135, out of 150 students are juniors or have their driver's license for a probability of $\frac{135}{150}$, or $\frac{9}{10}$. Alternatively, all but 15 students are either juniors or have their driver's license, so the probability is $\frac{135}{150}$, or $\frac{9}{10}$.

7 a. About 0.048; about 0.052

b. It is not reasonable to multiply $(0.048)(0.052)$ because the two events are undoubtedly not independent. If, for example, you know that a person watched the fifth game, your estimate of the probability that the person also watched the sixth game would be greater than 0.052.

c. A better, but not perfect, assumption is that it was pretty much the same people who watched both games. The estimate of the percentage of people who watched both games would then be close to 4.8%.

Connections

8 A possible simulation would be to have two spinners with clock faces on them, one for the front tire and one for the back tire. Students would spin both spinners and note how often they both end up where they started. Alternatively, students could use random integers selected from 1, 2, 3, ... , 12. The simulation should give approximately the same answer you found in Applications Task 1; and the more runs of the simulation, the closer the approximation is likely to be.

9 *Tree graphs* are a way of organizing all possible sequences of outcomes. For example, the tree graph below shows all possible families of exactly three children (with no twins or triplets). Each *G* means a girl was born, and each *B* means a boy was born. In the United States, the probability that a girl is born is approximately 49%.

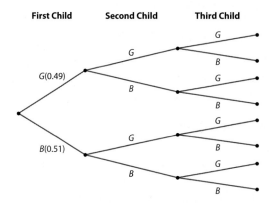

First Child   Second Child   Third Child

a. Use the graph to find the probability that a family of three children will consist of two girls and a boy (not necessarily born in that order).

b. Make a tree graph that shows all possible outcomes if you roll a die twice and each time read the number on top. What is the probability you will get the same number twice?

c. Make a tree graph that shows all possible outcomes if you flip a coin four times. What is the probability you will get exactly two heads?

d. Make a tree graph that shows all possible outcomes if you buy three boxes of cereal, each equally likely to contain one of the following stickers: bird of paradise, tiger, elephant, or crocodile. What is the probability that you will get three different stickers?

10 A board game has several PAY DAY spaces throughout the board. On each turn, the player spins a spinner similar to the one below and moves the indicated number of spaces around the board.

9 **a.** There are three paths through the tree that give two girls and a boy: GGB, GBG, and BGG. Their probabilities are (0.49)(0.49)(0.51), (0.49)(0.51)(0.49), and (0.51)(0.49)(0.49). The probability of two girls and a boy is $3(0.49)^2(0.51)$ or approximately 0.367.

b.

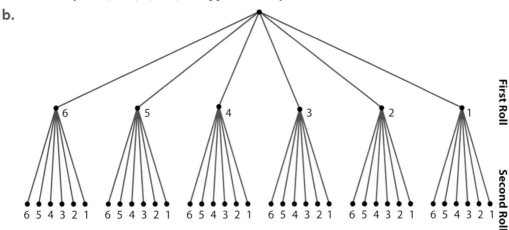

The probability of getting the same number twice is $\frac{6}{36}$.

c.

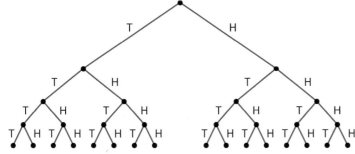

This tree has six paths with exactly two heads: HHTT, HTHT, HTTH, THHT, THTH, and TTHH. The probability of exactly two heads is $\frac{6}{16}$.

d. This tree has four branches (*bird of paradise, tiger, elephant,* and *crocodile*) for each of the three purchases (only the main *tiger* branch is shown below). Each main branch contains 16 possible outcomes of which 6 give three different stickers. So, 24 of the 64 paths give three different stickers. The probability that all three stickers will be different is $\frac{24}{64}$.

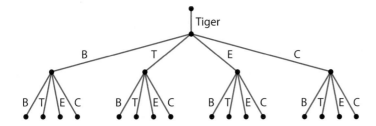

Suppose you are 5 spaces away from the next PAY DAY on the game board. You could land on the space by spinning a 5 on your next turn. Another way to land on the space is by spinning a 1 on your next turn, a 3 on the following turn, and a 1 on the turn after that.

a. Make a tree graph that shows all possible sequences of spins that would get you to this PAY DAY.

b. Make sure that you have 16 sequences in your tree graph and then compute the probability of each sequence.

c. What is the probability that you will land on this PAY DAY space on this trip around the board?

11 Consider the situation of rolling two dice. Give an example of events *A* and *B* in which the following is true:

a. $P(A) > P(A \mid B)$ **b.** $P(A) = P(A \mid B)$ **c.** $P(A) < P(A \mid B)$

12 If you select two random numbers that are both between 0 and 1, what is the probability that they are both greater than 0.5? You can think geometrically about this kind of problem, as shown at the right.

a. Explain how the shaded region represents the event that both numbers are greater than 0.5.

b. What is the probability that both numbers are greater than 0.5?

c. What is the probability that at least one of the numbers is greater than 0.5?

13 Use a copy of the coordinate grid below to help answer the following questions.

a. If you select two random numbers that are both between 0 and 1, what is the probability that they are both less than 0.25?

b. Suppose you select two random numbers that are both between 0 and 1.

    i. Make an area model and shade the region where their sum is less than 0.4.

    ii. What are the equations of the lines that border the region?

c. Suppose you select two random numbers that are both between 0 and 1.

    i. Make an area model and shade the region where their sum is greater than 1.5.

    ii. What are the equations of the lines that border the region that represents this event?

10 a.

| First Spin | Second Spin | Third Spin | Fourth Spin | Fifth Spin |

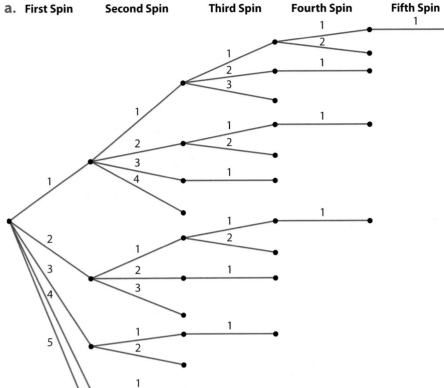

b. The table below summarizes the paths in the tree.

Path Length	Probability of Occurring	Number of Paths
1	0.1	1
2	$(0.1)^2$	4
3	$(0.1)^3$	6
4	$(0.1)^4$	4
5	$(0.1)^5$	1

c. To find the overall probability, sum the probabilities of the paths. Thus, the probability of landing on that PAY DAY space is $(0.1)^5 + 4(0.1)^4 + 6(0.1)^3 + 4(0.1)^2 + (0.1)$, or 0.14641.

11 Examples may vary. One possibility for each situation is given here.

a. Let event A be rolling doubles and event B be getting a sum of seven. Then $P(A) = \frac{1}{6} > P(A \mid B) = 0$.

b. Let event A be getting a 1 on the first die and event B be getting a sum of seven. Then $P(A) = \frac{1}{6} = P(A \mid B)$.

c. Let event A be getting a sum of eight and event B be getting doubles. Then $P(A) = \frac{5}{36} < P(A \mid B) = \frac{1}{6}$.

12 **a.** The right half of the square represents the event that the first number is greater than 0.5. The upper half represents the event that the second number is greater than 0.5. The upper-right quarter represents the intersection of these two events and gives the probability that both numbers are greater than 0.5.

b. $\frac{1}{4}$ **c.** $\frac{3}{4}$

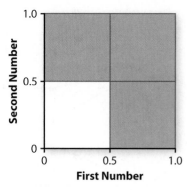

13 **a.** $\frac{1}{16}$

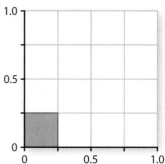

b. **i.** Find the area of the intersection of the solutions to the inequality $x + y < 0.4$ and the unit square with vertices $(0, 0)$, $(0, 1)$, $(1, 1)$, and $(1, 0)$. This gives a probability of 0.08. Students may find this probability by computing the area of the triangle with height 0.4 and base 0.4.

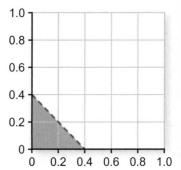

ii. The equations of the lines are $x + y = 0.4$, $x = 0$, and $y = 0$.

c. **i.** Find the area of the intersection of the solutions to the inequality $x + y > 1.5$ and the unit square with vertices $(0, 0)$, $(0, 1)$, $(1, 1)$, and $(1, 0)$. This gives a probability of $\frac{1}{8}$.

ii. The equations of the lines are $x + y = 1.5$, $x = 1$, and $y = 1$.

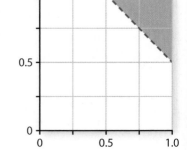

Teacher Notes

Reflections

14 If the probability that an event *A* will occur is *p* (that is, $P(A) = p$), what is the probability that the event will *not* occur, $P(not\ A)$? Explain why your conclusion makes sense.

15 Suppose you want to compute the proportion of students in your school who are sophomores and play a varsity sport. You know the proportion of students who are sophomores, and you know the proportion of students who play a varsity sport. To find the proportion of students who fit into both categories, you multiply the two proportions. Later, you discover that sophomores are less likely to play a varsity sport than are students in general. Is the proportion you computed correct, too large, too small, or could it be either too large or too small? Give an example to illustrate your answer.

16 In which of the following situations do you think it is reasonable to assume the events are independent?

a. Rolling a pair of dice twice in a row: the first event is not getting doubles on the first roll. The second event is getting doubles on the second roll.

b. Selecting two people at random: the first event is the first person pouring shampoo directly onto his or her hair. The second event is the second person pouring shampoo directly onto his or her hair.

c. Selecting a person at random: the first event is getting a person who puts catsup directly on his or her fries. The second event is getting a person who puts shampoo directly on his or her hair.

d. Selecting one person at random: the first event is getting a person with voice (singing) training. The second event is getting a person who can play a musical instrument.

e. Waiting for the results of next year's sports championships: the first event is the Celtics winning the NBA championship. The second event is the Red Sox winning the World Series.

f. Selecting a pair of best friends at random from a high school: the first event is the first friend attending the last football game. The second event is the second friend attending the last football game.

17 Can two events with nonzero probabilities be both independent and mutually exclusive? Explain.

18 The idea of independent events can be somewhat difficult to understand. Suppose that someone in your class has asked you to explain it. Write an explanation of the difference between independent events and dependent events. Include examples that would interest students in your high school.

Reflections

14 $P(not\ A) = 1 - p$. This makes sense because either A occurs or it does not, and so $P(A) + P(not\ A) = 1$. Thus, $P(not\ A) = 1 - P(A) = 1 - p$.

15 The number computed will be too large. For example, suppose that 25% of all students are sophomores, 15% of all students play a varsity sport, but only 10% of sophomores play a varsity sport. The number computed would be $(0.25)(0.15) = 0.0375$, but the correct proportion is 10% of 25% or $(0.25)(0.10) = 0.025$.

16 **a.** Independent. As students often say, "The dice don't remember."

b. Independent

c. Probably not independent. It may well be that a person who puts catsup directly on fries just likes to pour liquids on top of things and so may be more likely than other people to put shampoo directly on his or her head.

d. Not independent. People who have voice training are more likely to learn to play a musical instrument than people in general.

e. Independent

f. Not independent. Best friends tend to do things together. If we find that the first friend went to the football game, it increases the probability that the second friend went.

17 No. If A and B are mutually exclusive and you know that A happened, you know that the probability that B also happened is 0. That is, knowing that A happened changes your estimate of the probability that B happened, so A and B cannot be independent.

Formally, if A and B are mutually exclusive, then $P(B \mid A) = 0$. If they were independent also, then $P(B) = P(B \mid A) = 0$, but B is supposed to have nonzero probability.

18 Student examples will vary but should describe independent events A and B so that $P(A)$ stays the same whether B occurs or does not occur. For dependent events, knowing that one event has occurred changes the probability of the other event. So for example, when tossing two dice, $P(doubles) = \frac{1}{6}$ and $P(sum\ of\ 3) = \frac{2}{36}$. Since $P(doubles \mid sum\ of\ 3) = 0$, the two events are dependent.

Extensions

19 Some genetic diseases result only when a baby inherits a "disease" gene from both parents. Suppose that 1 in 30 people carry the gene for a certain disease and that the probability that a person who carries the gene passes it on to a baby is $\frac{1}{2}$. What proportion of babies will have the disease? What assumption must you make to do this computation?

20 Jesse read a report that said that 90% of carpool riders said they would go into the same carpool again, and 72% of carpool drivers said they would go into the same carpool again. He computed the probability that, for a random carpool, both the driver and the rider would say that they would go into the same carpool again as follows:

$$P(\textit{rider would and driver would}) = P(\textit{rider would}) \cdot P(\textit{driver would})$$
$$= (0.90)(0.72)$$
$$= 0.648$$

Is Jesse correct? Explain your reasoning.

21 Suppose you are sorting 100 items that have been donated for a charity auction. You classify each as antique (*A*) or not antique (*not A*) and as broken (*B*) or not broken (*not B*). You make a two-way table after you finish sorting and get the row and column totals in the table below. Keep these totals unchanged throughout this task. You will select one of these 100 items at random.

	B	Not B	Total
A			40
Not A			60
Total	10	90	100

a. Finish filling in the table so that events *A* and *B* are independent. Is there more than one way to do this?

b. Using your table from Part a:

   i. are event *not A* and event *B* independent?

   ii. are *A* and *not B* independent?

   iii. are *not A* and *not B* independent?

c. Can you fill in the table so that events *A* and *B* are independent, but none of the other three pairs of events are independent?

d. Next, fill in the table so that events *A* and *B* are not independent. Is there more than one way to do this?

e. Now fill in the table so that events *A* and *B* are mutually exclusive.

Extensions

19 To have the disease, the baby of two parents must inherit one "disease" gene from the mother and one from the father. The probability that the baby is the child of two carriers is $\left(\frac{1}{30}\right)\left(\frac{1}{30}\right) = \frac{1}{900}$. If both parents are carriers, the probability that the baby inherits the disease gene from each of them is $\left(\frac{1}{2}\right)\left(\frac{1}{2}\right) = \frac{1}{4}$. Thus, the probability the baby has two parents who are both carriers and gets the gene from both of them is $\left(\frac{1}{900}\right)\left(\frac{1}{4}\right) = \frac{1}{3,600}$.

Here is an alternative way to look at it: The probability that the mother is a carrier is $\frac{1}{30}$, and the probability that a carrier passes on the disease gene is $\frac{1}{2}$. So, the probability that the baby gets a disease gene from the mother is $\left(\frac{1}{30}\right)\left(\frac{1}{2}\right) = \frac{1}{60}$. The probability is the same for the father. The probability that the baby gets a disease gene from both parents is $\left(\frac{1}{60}\right)\left(\frac{1}{60}\right) = \frac{1}{3,600}$.

This computation assumes that the parents select each other independently of whether the other person carries the disease gene.

20 Jesse is not correct. He should not multiply the probabilities. He cannot assume that the event that the rider would go into the same carpool and the event that the driver would go into the same carpool are independent. If, for example, you knew that the rider would go into the same carpool, your estimate of the probability that the driver would go into the same carpool would be higher than 0.72. Since the rider is happy, it is more likely the driver is, too. In symbols, *P(driver would go into same carpool)* < *P(driver would go into same carpool | rider would go into same carpool)*.

21 **a.** There is only one way to fill in this table, keeping the marginal totals unchanged, because the *B* and *not B* columns have to be proportional to the Total column, and the *A* and *not A* rows have to be proportional to the Total row.

	B	Not B	Total
A	4	36	40
Not A	6	54	60
Total	10	90	100

  b. **i.** Events *not A* and *B* are independent because $P(not\ A) = \frac{60}{100}$ is equal to $P(not\ A \mid B) = \frac{6}{10}$.

  ii. Events *A* and *not B* are independent because $P(A) = \frac{40}{100}$ is equal to $P(A \mid not\ B) = \frac{36}{90} = \frac{4}{10}$.

  iii. Events *not A* and *not B* are independent because $P(not\ A) = \frac{60}{100}$ is equal to $P(not\ A \mid not\ B) = \frac{54}{90} = \frac{6}{10}$.

  c. No

  d. There are many ways to do this. Any table except the one in Part a will work.

  e. The table at the right is the only way to do this.

	B	Not B	Total
A	0	40	40
Not A	10	50	60
Total	10	90	100

Unit 8

Review

22 Use algebraic reasoning to solve each equation.

a. $3(t + 5) + 5(t - 3) = 6t + 12$

b. $3(2d^2) - 4d = (2d)^2$

c. $10^{x-3} = 592$

d. $(3x - 7)^2 = 121$

e. $2n^2 + 28n = 30$

23 When Daniel stands 20 feet from the base of the Veterans' Monument, he needs to look up at an angle of 68° to see the top of the monument. Daniel is 6 feet tall. About how tall is the monument?

24 Write each product in equivalent $ax^2 + bx + c$ form.

a. $(x + 5)(x + 8)$

b. $(3x + 1)^2$

c. $(6 - 2x)(5x + 3)$

d. $(10x - 4)(10x + 4)$

25 Write each quadratic expression in equivalent form as a product of linear factors.

a. $x^2 - 4x - 32$

b. $x^2 + 7x - 18$

c. $x^2 - 36$

d. $3x^2 + 30x + 75$

26 In late July and August of 2002, the Division of Visitor Services and Communications, National Wildlife Refuge System, U.S. Fish and Wildlife Service conducted a survey of visitors to 45 "high visitation" National Wildlife Refuges in order to gather information about visitor satisfaction. The table below gives the responses of 2,811 visitors to the statement: "Considering my overall experiences with this National Wildlife Refuge, I am satisfied with the quality of the recreational/educational experience."

Response	Frequency	Percent
Strongly disagree	60	2.1
Disagree	26	0.9
Neither agree nor disagree	71	2.5
Agree	1,065	37.9
Strongly agree	1,589	56.5

Source: *U.S. Fish and Wildlife Service National Wildlife Refuge Visitor Satisfaction Survey: Data Analysis and Report*, page 23. www.fws.gov/refuges/generalInterest/pdfs/VSS_part1.pdf

a. So that you can quickly compare responses from year to year, you plan to get a mean number for the visitors' responses. To do this, you must first turn the "Response" column into a numerical response. How could you do this? Make a new column with these numerical responses.

Review

22 **a.** $3(t + 5) + 5(t - 3) = 6t + 12$
  $3t + 15 + 5t - 15 = 6t + 12$
  $2t = 12$
  $t = 6$

b. $3(2d^2) - 4d = (2d)^2$
  $6d^2 - 4d = 4d^2$
  $2d^2 - 4d = 0$
  $2d(d - 2) = 0$
  $d = 0$ or $d = 2$

c. $10^{x - 3} = 592$
  $x - 3 = \log 592$
  $x = \log 592 + 3 \approx 5.77$

d. $(3x - 7)^2 = 121$
  $3x - 7 = \pm 11$
  $x = 6$ or $x = -\frac{4}{3}$

e. $2n^2 + 28n - 30 = 0$
  $2(n + 15)(n - 1) = 0$
  $n = -15$ or $n = 1$

23 $\tan 68° = \frac{x}{20}$; $x \approx 49.5$ ft
The Veterans' Monument is about 55.5 or 56 ft tall.

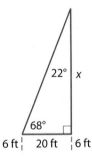

24 **a.** $x^2 + 13x + 40$ **b.** $9x^2 + 6x + 1$
  c. $-10x^2 + 24x + 18$ **d.** $100x^2 - 16$

25 **a.** $(x - 8)(x + 4)$ **b.** $(x + 9)(x - 2)$
  c. $(x - 6)(x + 6)$ **d.** $3(x + 5)^2$

26 **a.** Responses may vary. One option is to assign 0 to "Strongly Disagree," 1 to "Disagree," and so on, up to 4 for "Strongly Agree." In this rating system, a higher number indicates greater satisfaction with the recreational/educational experience.

b. Using your numerical responses and the frequency column, compute the mean response. On average, are people generally satisfied with their experience at the national wildlife refuges?

c. Make a new column, converting "Percent" to "Relative Frequency." Using your numerical responses and the relative frequency column, compute the mean response. Is your answer the same as that in Part b? Should it be the same?

27 Glendale and Arcadia High Schools both need to order new supplies for their math classrooms. Price information for ordering from School Central (SC) and Discount Educational Supplies (DES) is in the matrix below.

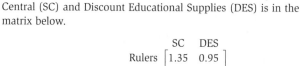

$$\begin{array}{c c} & \begin{array}{c c} \text{SC} & \text{DES} \end{array} \\ \begin{array}{r} \text{Rulers} \\ \text{Graph Paper Pads} \\ \text{Compasses} \end{array} & \begin{bmatrix} 1.35 & 0.95 \\ 3.50 & 4.15 \\ 1.75 & 1.25 \end{bmatrix} \end{array}$$

a. Glendale High needs 120 rulers, 15 graph paper pads, and 60 compasses. Arcadia High needs 60 rulers, 7 graph paper pads, and 90 compasses. Organize this information into a 2×3 matrix. Be sure to label the rows and columns of your matrix.

b. Use matrix multiplication to help you determine which supplier is less expensive for each school. What is the size of your product matrix?

28 The amount of time it takes to fill an empty tanker truck varies inversely with the number of gallons pumped per minute. When the pump is set at 8 gallons per minute, it takes 85 minutes to fill an empty tanker truck.

a. Write a general rule that describes the relationship between the amount of time it takes to fill the empty tanker and the pump rate in gallons per minute.

b. What is the constant of variation for your rule? What does this constant indicate about the tanker?

c. If the pump rate is doubled, how does the amount of time it takes to fill the empty tanker change? Explain your reasoning.

29 Determine to the nearest degree the measure of $\angle A$ in each triangle.

a.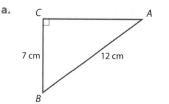

b.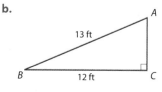

c.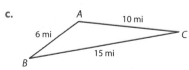

b. Responses will depend on the system described in Part a. For the numerical ratings we described, the mean response is $\frac{9{,}719}{2{,}811} \approx 3.46$. Using the rating scale from 0 to 4, on average, people rated their experience a 3.46. So, it is safe to conclude that, on average, the people were satisfied.

c.

Response	Frequency	Relative Frequency
Strongly Disagree	60	0.021
Disagree	26	0.009
Neither Agree nor Disagree	71	0.025
Agree	1,065	0.379
Strongly Agree	1,589	0.565

The mean response is $0.021(0) + 0.009(1) + 0.025(2) + 0.379(3) + 0.565(4) \approx 3.46$. This should be the same as the answer in Part b.

27 **a.**

$$\begin{array}{c} \\ \text{Glendale} \\ \text{Arcadia} \end{array} \begin{array}{ccc} \text{Rulers} & \text{Pads} & \text{Compasses} \\ \left[\begin{array}{ccc} 120 & 15 & 60 \\ 60 & 7 & 90 \end{array}\right] \end{array}$$

b.

$$\begin{array}{c} \\ \text{Glendale} \\ \text{Arcadia} \end{array} \begin{array}{cc} \text{SC} & \text{DES} \\ \left[\begin{array}{cc} 319.50 & 251.25 \\ 263.00 & 198.55 \end{array}\right] \end{array}$$

Matrix size: 2 by 2
DES is less expensive for both schools.

28 **a.** $T = \frac{k}{r}$, where T is the time to fill the empty tanker and r is the rate of filling.

b. $85 = \frac{k}{8}$; $k = 680$; The tanker holds 680 gallons.

c. Since $\frac{680}{2r} = \frac{1}{2}\left(\frac{680}{r}\right) = \frac{1}{2}T$, if the pump rate is doubled, the time it takes to fill the empty tanker is cut in half.

29 **a.** $\sin A = \frac{7}{12}$, so $m\angle A \approx 36°$.

b. $\sin A = \frac{12}{13}$, so $m\angle A \approx 67°$.

c. $15^2 = 6^2 + 10^2 - 2(6)(10)\cos A$, so $m\angle A \approx 138°$.

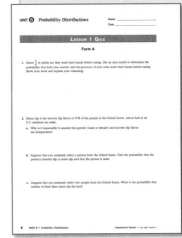

Teaching Resources

Assessment Masters 6–12.

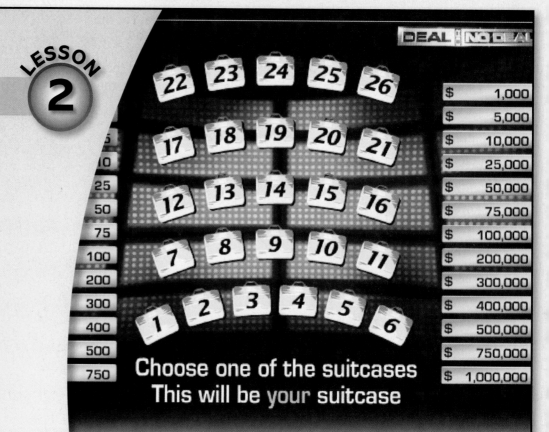

Choose one of the suitcases
This will be your suitcase

Expected Value

If you are like many people, you are probably intrigued by
television game shows that provide chances of winning large sums
of money. On one popular game show, the contestant chooses one
of 26 suitcases which remains unopened. The 26 suitcases contain
these amounts of money in dollars: 0.01, 1, 5, 10, 25, 50, 75, 100,
200, 300, 400, 500, 750, 1,000, 5,000, 10,000, 25,000, 50,000,
75,000, 100,000, 200,000, 300,000, 400,000, 500,000, 750,000,
1,000,000. The contestant then chooses six other suitcases, which
are opened.

At this stage, the player can either keep the suitcase she selected
or take the amount of money offered by the "bank." If she does
not take the money offered by the bank, more suitcases are
opened, and the bank gives new offers. The amount of each
offer depends on which amounts are left in the unopened
suitcases. Ultimately, the player either accepts one of the
bank's offers or keeps her suitcase.

Expected Value

In this lesson, students learn the concept of expected value, which is the term used for the mean of a probability distribution. In the first investigation, students use the concept of expected value to decide if the price charged for a game is a fair price. In the second investigation, they formalize the formula for the expected value, $EV = \Sigma x \cdot P(x)$.

Lesson Objectives

- Compute the fair price (expected value) of insurance and games of chance
- Develop a formula for the expected value of a probability distribution
- Compute the expected value of a probability distribution using the formula
- Estimate the expected value from the graph of the probability distribution

Consider the mathematics behind this television game.

a) What is the probability that the player picks a suitcase that contains at least half a million dollars? At the beginning of the game, what is the average amount the player can expect to win if she keeps the suitcase she selected?

b) After several rounds of this game one evening, a player got to the point where there were only four suitcases left unopened. The remaining suitcases contained $75, $5,000, $500,000, and $750,000. The bank offered her $212,050 for her suitcase. Was this a fair offer?

c) She refused the offer and opened one additional suitcase. It contained $750,000. Only three suitcases were left containing $75, $5,000, and $500,000. The bank's offer went down to $155,038. If you were the player, would you take the offer? Explain your thinking.

In this lesson, you will learn how to compute the average (**expected value**) of a probability distribution.

Investigation 1 — What's a Fair Price?

In mathematics, the **fair price** for a game is defined as the price that should be charged so that in the long run, the players come out even. In other words, in the long run, the amount won by the players is equal to the amount the players were charged to play. Of course, people who run carnival games or who sell insurance want to cover their expenses and make a profit so they charge more than the "fair price." To decide how much to charge, they must first compute the fair price. As you work on the problems of this investigation, look for answers to the following question:

How can you compute the fair price for a game or insurance policy?

1. Suppose your school decides to hold a raffle. The prizes in the raffle will be a bicycle that costs $400, an audio player that costs $175, and a video game that costs $100. Exactly 2,000 tickets will be sold. Three tickets will be drawn at random. The person who holds the first ticket drawn gets the bicycle, the second the audio player, and the third the video game.

   a. What is a fair price for a ticket?

   b. Write a procedure for finding the fair price of a raffle ticket.

Think About This Situation

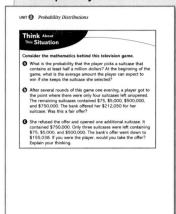

Note that the computations below depend on that fact that in this game, each amount is equally likely to be in the suitcase chosen by the contestant.

(a) $\frac{3}{26}$; The total amount in the 26 suitcases is $3,418,416.01. So, the average amount is $\frac{\$3,418,416.01}{26}$, or about $131,477.54.

(b) A fair offer would be the average amount she could win, or $\frac{\$75 + \$5,000 + \$500,000 + \$750,000}{4} \approx \$313,768.75$. Thus, the offer is too low to be fair.

(c) She can expect to win $\frac{\$75 + \$5,000 + \$500,000}{3} \approx \$168,358.33$. So, the bank's offer again is too low to be fair. On the other hand, she has only $\frac{1}{3}$ chance of winning more than $155,038. Students' ideas about whether or not to accept the bank's offer should fuel an interesting discussion. (This game can be played on-line at: www.nbc.com/Deal_or_No_Deal/)

Investigation 1 — What's a Fair Price?

In this investigation, students learn how to find the price that should be charged to play a game (or to buy insurance) so that, in the long run, the amount won by the players is equal to the amount the players were charged to play. This "fair price" is equal to the expected value, or mean amount won on each play, of the game.

You may occasionally have to remind your students that "fair" now has a mathematical meaning. When they are asked to find a fair price, the question is not asking for their opinion of a reasonable price for the operator to charge but rather for the mathematical calculation of the fair price. The fair price for a game is the price that should be charged so that, in the long run, the players expect to come out even.

1 **a.** $\frac{\$400 + \$100 + \$175}{2,000} = \frac{\$675}{2,000} = \$0.3375$

That is, if 2,000 tickets are sold at $0.3375 each, your school will take in $675. Because that is the value of the prizes, 34¢ is a fair price for a ticket.

b. Add up the value of all of the prizes and divide by the number of tickets to be sold.

Unit 8

② At a fund-raising carnival for a service organization, Renee is trying to get Leroy to play a game she has invented. Leroy would spin the spinner shown below and get a gift certificate worth the amount indicated. The organization charges $5 to play this game.

a. Leroy thinks he has the advantage because he has two chances of coming out ahead, one chance of coming out even, and only one chance of winning less than the game costs to play. What would you say to him?

b. How much would Leroy expect to win if he played 100 games? What is Leroy's expected net earnings?

c. Is $5 the fair price to play this game? If not, what would be the fair price?

d. Design a spinner that would make $5 a fair price to charge to play.

③ In a carnival game, a wheel is spun. The wheel has an equal chance of ending up in any one of 38 positions. The wheel has 18 red positions, 18 blue positions, and 2 white positions. Suppose a player picks red. If the wheel ends up on red, the player wins $2. The price to play this game is $1.

a. Complete the table below, which shows the outcomes and their probabilities for this game.

Outcome	Probability
Win $2	
Win $0	

b. Is $1 a fair price for playing this game? Why or why not?

④ The National Center for Health Statistics reports that the death rate for males aged 15–24 in the United States is 113 deaths for every 100,000 males in this age group. There are 43 deaths per year for every 100,000 females in that age group. (Source: www.cdc.gov/nchs/fastats/pdf/mortality/nvsr54_19t01.pdf) Use these statistics to answer the following.

a. Ignoring all factors other than gender, what would be the fair price for an insurance company to charge to insure the life of a male in that age group for one year for $50,000?

b. Ignoring all factors other than gender, what would be the fair price for an insurance company to charge to insure the life of a female in that age group for one year for $50,000?

Unit 8

2 **a.** Although Leroy does have two chances of winning, he does not net very much ($1 or $2) when he wins. However, when he loses, he loses the $5 that he bet. (Students also may suggest that Leroy observe the game for a while before playing.)

b. After playing the game 100 times, Leroy can expect to win each of the prizes 25 times each for a total of 25($6) + 25($7) + 25($5) + 25($0) = $450. However, it will cost him 100($5) or $500 to play. Thus, his expected loss is $50. Alternatively, his expected net earnings are −$50.

c. No, because Leroy expects to come out behind in the long run. On each spin, Leroy expects to win an average of $4.50 in gift certificates, so $4.50 would be the fair price for this game.

d. If the sectors are of equal sizes, the average value on the student's spinner should be $5. One such spinner appears at the right.

3 **a.**

Outcome	Probability
Win $2	$\frac{18}{38}$
Win $0	$\frac{20}{38}$

b. No. For every 38 players who pick red, you expect 18 winners. The carnival operators would pay out 18($2), or $36. However, the players would have paid $38 to play. A fair price to pay to play would be $\frac{\$36}{38}$, or approximately $0.95.

4 **NOTE** While discussing the Summarize the Mathematics, you may wish to ask students: "*How do you think insurance companies set their rates?*" Laws regarding setting insurance policy rates vary from state to state. When life insurance rates are based on the probability of dying at a given age, rates for males will be higher than rates for females of the same age.

Laws regarding automobile insurance rates for males and females vary from state to state. In Michigan, insurance companies may not set rates based on gender. In Georgia, automobile insurance rates first go down for women at age 21 but are not reduced for males until they are 30 years old.

a. For every 100,000 males, you expect 113 deaths. So, the insurance company expects to pay out 113($50,000) = $5,650,000. To break even, it would have to charge $\frac{\$5,650,000}{100,000}$ or $56.50 to insure each person for one year.

Alternatively, using algebra, let x be the fair price. Then, 113($50,000) = x(100,000). Thus, x = $56.50 per person.

b. $43\left(\frac{\$50,000}{100,000}\right)$ = $21.50 per person

c. If the insurance company is not allowed to have different rates for each gender, what would be the fair price for a $50,000 policy for one year? Assume that the same number of insurance policies are sold to males as to females.

d. Compare the procedure you used to answer Parts a and b with your procedure in Part b of Problem 1.

e. In what ways is insurance mathematically similar to a raffle? In what ways is it different?

Summarize
the Mathematics

In this investigation, you explored how to compute the fair price for games and insurance policies.

a What is the relationship between the fair price of a game and the average winnings of a player in the long run?

b Describe a general procedure for finding the fair price of raffle or lottery tickets.

c Describe a general procedure for finding the fair price of an insurance policy.

Be prepared to explain your ideas to the class.

✔ Check Your Understanding

Apply your method of finding a fair price to the three situations below.

a. After several rounds of the game show described at the beginning of this lesson, the contestant had opened all but five suitcases. The remaining suitcases contained $75, $500, $5,000, $500,000, and $750,000. The bank offered her $129,519 for her suitcase. Is this a fair offer?

b. The prizes in a raffle are ten $15 CDs and one $500 stereo. If 1,000 raffle tickets will be sold, what is the fair price for a ticket?

c. According to the Youth Risk Behavior Survey, about 30% of high school students reported that they had some property stolen or deliberately damaged at school within the previous year. Suppose the average value of the stolen or damaged property in that year was $60. Assuming these statistics stay the same each year, what would be the fair price to charge a student who wanted to be insured against theft or damage for one year of high school?
(Source: www.cdc.gov/mmwr/preview/mmwrhtml/ss5302a1.htm)

c. If 100,000 policies are sold to females and 100,000 to males, you expect a total of $113 + 43 = 156$ deaths out of the 200,000 policyholders. So, the insurance company expects to pay 156($50,000) or $7,800,000. A fair price for a policy would be $\frac{\$7,800,000}{200,000}$ or $39. (Note that this is the average of the fair price for males and the fair price for females. This is because you assumed that the same number of policies were sold to males as to females.)

d. The procedures are very similar to each other: divide the total payout by the number of "tickets" sold.

e. They are similar in that you can compute the fair price for a ticket or policy in the same way. However, in a raffle, the people running the game know exactly how much they will pay out in prizes. The insurance company is taking a much bigger chance. It never knows exactly how many deaths there will be for 100,000 policyholders.

Summarize
the Mathematics

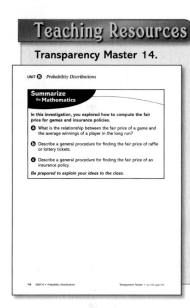

Teaching Resources

Transparency Master 14.

UNIT 8 *Probability Distributions*

Summarize
the **Mathematics**

In this investigation, you explored how to compute the fair price for games and insurance policies.

ⓐ What is the relationship between the fair price of a game and the average winnings of a player in the long run?

ⓑ Describe a general procedure for finding the fair price of raffle or lottery tickets.

ⓒ Describe a general procedure for finding the fair price of an insurance policy.

Be prepared to explain your ideas to the class.

ⓐ They are equal.

ⓑ Add the values of the prizes and divide this amount by the number of tickets to be sold.

ⓒ Multiply the value of the policy by the expected number of deaths per 100,000 customers and then divide by 100,000. (This is the same thing as multiplying the value of the policy by the probability of a death.)

✓ Check Your Understanding

a. Because the contestant is equally likely to win each of the five amounts, her expected winnings at this point is
$\frac{\$75 + \$500 + \$5,000 + \$500,000 + \$750,000}{5} = \$251,115$. This would be the fair offer. So, the offer she got was not fair.

b. The total value of the prizes is 10($15) + $500, or $650. The fair price for a ticket is $\frac{\$650}{1,000} = \$0.65$.

c. If 100 students each buy a policy, the insurance company expects 30 of them to have some property stolen or damaged. The company expects to pay 30($60), or $1,800. A fair price for a policy would be $\frac{\$1,800}{100}$, or $18.00.

Expected Value of a
Probability Distribution

You have learned how to find the fair price for games of chance and for
insurance. In this investigation, you will see how organizing your work in a
table leads to a formula for *expected value*. Keep in mind the following
questions as you work on the problems of this investigation:

How can you compute the fair price of a game if you are given
the probability distribution of the prizes?

In general, how can you find the expected value
of a probability distribution?

1 A game of chance has the probability distribution given in the
table below.

Prize Value, x	Probability, P(x)
$1	$\frac{1}{6}$
$2	$\frac{1}{6}$
$3	$\frac{1}{6}$
$4	$\frac{1}{6}$
$5	$\frac{1}{6}$
$6	$\frac{1}{6}$
Total	$\frac{6}{6}$

a. What is the fair price for this game?

b. Make a histogram of this probability distribution. Locate the fair
price on the histogram. How does this compare to the mean of the
distribution?

c. Complete a copy of this table, including the total.

Prize Value, x	Probability, P(x)	x · P(x)
$1	$\frac{1}{6}$	
$2	$\frac{1}{6}$	
$3	$\frac{1}{6}$	$\frac{3}{6}$
$4	$\frac{1}{6}$	
$5	$\frac{1}{6}$	
$6	$\frac{1}{6}$	
Total	$\frac{6}{6}$	

d. Compare your total from Part c to the fair price from Part a. What
do you notice?

Unit 8

Expected Value of a
Probability Distribution

In this investigation, students learn to compute the expected value (mean) of a
probability distribution and develop the formula, $EV = \Sigma x \cdot P(x)$.

INSTRUCTIONAL NOTE In Problem 1 Part b, ask students to center the labels under
the bars. If students label the units on the left side of the bar, they will likely get 4 for
the balance point. Also, you may need to remind students that the order of operations
for $\Sigma x \cdot P(x)$ is to multiply $x \cdot P(x)$ for each x before finding the sum.

1
a. Because each prize is equally likely, the average winnings will be
$3.50, so $3.50 is the fair price.

b. The balance point, or mean, of the histogram is 3.5, which is the same
as the fair price.

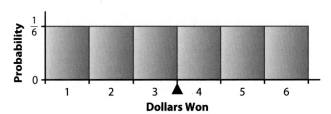

c.

Prize Value, x	Probability, $P(x)$	$x \cdot P(x)$
1	$\frac{1}{6}$	$\frac{1}{6}$
2	$\frac{1}{6}$	$\frac{2}{6}$
3	$\frac{1}{6}$	$\frac{3}{6}$
4	$\frac{1}{6}$	$\frac{4}{6}$
5	$\frac{1}{6}$	$\frac{5}{6}$
6	$\frac{1}{6}$	$\frac{6}{6}$
Total	$\frac{6}{6}$	$\frac{21}{6} = 3.5$

d. The total in Part c and the fair price in Part a are the same. (The
procedure in Part c is a method of computing the expected value.)

Teaching Resources

Student Master 15.

② The chart below gives the possible outcomes and their probabilities for a version of a scratch-off game played at a fast-food restaurant. What is the fair price of one scratch-off card?

Prize	Probability
Win free fries worth 90¢	$\frac{1}{6}$
Win nothing	$\frac{5}{6}$
Total	$\frac{6}{6}$

③ Here is the table for another scratch-off game.

Prize Value	Probability
$1	$\frac{4}{10}$
$2	$\frac{2}{10}$
$3	$\frac{2}{10}$
$5	$\frac{1}{10}$
Win nothing	$\frac{1}{10}$
Total	$\frac{10}{10}$

  a. What is the fair price of one scratch-off card?
  b. Make a histogram of this probability distribution.
  c. Estimate the balance point of the histogram. Compare this answer to the fair price of the card that you computed in Part a. What do you notice?

④ The mean of a probability distribution is called the **expected value** (*EV*).

  a. Suppose that your probability distribution represents the chances of winning the various prizes in a game. Explain why the expected value gives the fair price for a game.

  b. Describe how to implement a procedure for finding the expected value of a probability distribution in an efficient way on your calculator or computer.

  c. Use your method to find the expected value of the probability distribution table for the sum of two dice.

⑤ The table and histogram at the top of page 551 give the proportion of families in the United States that are a given size based on a census that tried to count all families in the United States.

  a. If you were to pick a family at random from the United States, what is the probability that it would have four people in it? What is the probability it would have four or fewer people in it?

  b. What is the mean number of people per family? (Count 7 or more as 7 people.)

2 A fair price (expected value) for a card would be
$0.90\left(\frac{1}{6}\right) + 0\left(\frac{5}{6}\right) = 0.15$, or 15¢.

3   **a.** The fair price is $1.90, as shown in the table below.

Prize Value	Probability	(Prize Value)(Probability)
$1	$\frac{4}{10}$	$0.40
$2	$\frac{2}{10}$	$0.40
$3	$\frac{2}{10}$	$0.60
$5	$\frac{1}{10}$	$0.50
Win nothing	$\frac{1}{10}$	$0.00
Total	$\frac{10}{10}$	$1.90

   b.

   c. The balance point is around $2, which is close to the fair price. (This result is no coincidence: the balance point of a probability distribution is equal to its mean or expected value.)

4   **a.** The expected value of a game is the average amount won on a single play. The fair price is the amount that should be charged to play the game so that in the long run, the players expect to come out even. The fair price and the expected value of a game are equal since the fair price is equal to the total amount expected to be won divided by the number of times the game will be played, which is the average amount won on a single play.

   b. One possibility is to make a table with three columns: column one has a heading Outcome x, column two is Probability $P(x)$, and column three is $x \cdot P(x)$. The total of column three is the expected value of the probability distribution. Or, succinctly, compute $\Sigma x \cdot P(x)$.

On a TI calculator, enter the first column of the table in List 1 and the second column in List 2. Define List 3 as the product of Lists 1 and 2 ($L_3 = L_1 \cdot L_2$). Finally, find the sum of List 3.

c. $EV = 7$

Sum on Dice	Probability	(Sum)(Probability)
2	$\frac{1}{36}$	$\frac{2}{36}$
3	$\frac{2}{36}$	$\frac{6}{36}$
4	$\frac{3}{36}$	$\frac{12}{36}$
5	$\frac{4}{36}$	$\frac{20}{36}$
6	$\frac{5}{36}$	$\frac{30}{36}$
7	$\frac{6}{36}$	$\frac{42}{36}$
8	$\frac{5}{36}$	$\frac{40}{36}$
9	$\frac{4}{36}$	$\frac{36}{36}$
10	$\frac{3}{36}$	$\frac{30}{36}$
11	$\frac{2}{36}$	$\frac{22}{36}$
12	$\frac{1}{36}$	$\frac{12}{36}$
Total	1	$\frac{252}{36} = 7$

5 **a.** Exactly four: 0.20
Four or fewer: 0.86

b. $\bar{x} = 2(0.43) + 3(0.23) + 4(0.20) + 5(0.09) + 6(0.03) + 7(0.02) = 3.12$

Teacher Notes

Size of Family	Relative Frequency
2	0.43
3	0.23
4	0.20
5	0.09
6	0.03
7 or more	0.02
Total	1.00

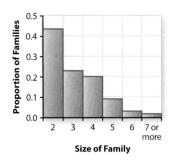

Source: *U.S. Bureau of the Census, Statistical Abstract of the United States: 2000 (120th edition).* Washington, D.C., 2000.

c. Is the standard deviation of this distribution closest to 1, 2, or 3? (A method for computing the standard deviation is outlined in Extensions Task 18.)

Summarize
the Mathematics

Look back at your method for finding the expected value of a probability distribution.

a How is the method for finding the expected value of a probability distribution similar to the method for finding the mean of a frequency table? How is it different?

b What property of a probability distribution explains the difference in the methods?

Be prepared to share your ideas with the class.

✓ Check Your Understanding

Find the expected value (fair price) of a ticket from the scratch-off game described in the following table.

Prize/Value	Probability
Small soft drink (89¢)	$\frac{15}{100}$
Small hamburger ($1.29)	$\frac{8}{100}$
T-shirt with restaurant logo ($7.50)	$\frac{3}{100}$
Movie passes ($15.00)	$\frac{1}{100}$
You lose! ($0.00)	$\frac{73}{100}$
Total	$\frac{100}{100}$

Unit 8

c. The standard deviation is closest to 1. The computed value is about 1.25. (See Extensions Task 18.)

INSTRUCTIONAL NOTE
If you plan to assign Extensions Task 18, do not provide the correct answer to Problem 5 Part c to students at this time.

Summarize
the Mathematics

Teaching Resources
Transparency Master 16.

UNIT 8   Probability Distributions

Summarize
the Mathematics

Look back at your method for finding the expected value of a probability distribution.

a How is the method for finding the expected value of a probability distribution similar to the method for finding the mean of a frequency table? How is it different?

b What property of a probability distribution explains the difference in the methods?

Be prepared to share your ideas with the class.

16   UNIT 8 • Probability Distributions   Transparency Master • use with page 551

a In both cases, you multiply the outcome by how often it occurs (frequency or probability) and add up these products. However, in a probability distribution, you do not need to "divide by the total frequency" because that number, in a sense, is the sum of the probabilities or 1. Compare these two tables:

Outcome	Frequency	(Outcome)(Frequency)
$1	6	6
$2	4	8
Total	10	14

The average is $\frac{14}{10} = 1.4$ or $1.40.

Outcome	Probability	(Outcome)(Probability)
$1	$\frac{6}{10}$	$\frac{6}{10}$
$2	$\frac{4}{10}$	$\frac{8}{10}$
Total	1	$\frac{14}{10}$

The expected value is $\frac{14}{10} = 1.4$ or $1.40.

b The property of a probability distribution that explains the difference is that the frequencies have already been divided by the total frequency, resulting in probabilities or relative frequencies. Thus, it is not necessary to divide again by the total frequency. This gives the same result as adding the (outcome)(frequency) values and then dividing by the total frequency. In the above example,

$$\frac{(\$1)(6) + (\$2)(4)}{10} = (\$1)\frac{6}{10} + (\$2)\frac{4}{10}.$$

MATH TOOLKIT What is the expected value of a probability distribution? How do you calculate it from a frequency table?

✓Check Your Understanding

The expected value of a ticket is $0.89\left(\frac{15}{100}\right) + 1.29\left(\frac{8}{100}\right) + 7.50\left(\frac{3}{100}\right) + 15\left(\frac{1}{100}\right) + 0\left(\frac{23}{100}\right)$, or about $0.61.

On Your Own

Applications

1. A charity raffle has five prizes: a car worth $25,000, a vacation worth $2,800, and three MP3 players, each worth $400.

   a. If 10,000 tickets are to be sold, what is the fair price of a ticket?

   b. If you buy 1 ticket, what is the probability that you win a prize?

   c. If you buy 10 tickets, what is the probability that you win the car?

2. The average claim for collision damage to a fairly new car involved in a collision is about $3,910. For every 100 fairly new cars that are insured, each year, there are about 7.8 collisions in which a claim is filed. (Source: Highway Loss Data Institute, www.iihs.org/research/hldi_facts/collision_coverage_trends.pdf)

   a. For every 100 fairly new cars that are insured, how much money would you expect to be paid out to insurance claims for collision damage?

   b. What is the fair price to charge for collision insurance for one year for a fairly new car?

3. If there is a 40% chance of rain today, it means that it rained on 40% of the days in the past that had weather conditions similar to those today.

   a. On 14 different days, the weather report says there is a 40% chance of rain. On how many of these days do you expect it to rain? On how many of these days do you expect it not to rain?

   b. On 20 different days, the weather report says there is a 50% chance of rain. It actually rained on 9 of those days. Do you think the meteorologist did a good job of predicting rain? Explain.

4. The table below is copied from the back of a ticket in a scratch-off state lottery game.

Prize	Probability of Winning
$0.75	$\frac{1}{10}$
$2.00	$\frac{1}{14.71}$
$4.00	$\frac{1}{50}$
$10.00	$\frac{1}{71}$
$20.00	$\frac{1}{417}$
$250.00	$\frac{1}{1,000}$

   a. What is the probability of winning nothing with one ticket? Add a line to a copy of the table that shows this outcome and its probability.

Applications

(1) **a.** The total value of the prizes is \$29,000, so the fair price of a ticket
   is $\dfrac{\$29,000}{\$10,000} = \$2.90$.

   b. Five chances out of 10,000, or 0.0005

   c. Ten chances out of 10,000, or 0.001

(2) **a.** $7.8(3,910) = \$30,498$

   b. $\dfrac{\$30,498}{100} = \$304.98$

(3) **a.** Rain: $14(0.4) = 5.6$ days
   No rain: $14(0.6) = 8.4$ days. Alternatively, $14 - 5.6 = 8.4$ days.

   b. Yes. Although you expect 10 days of rain, you know you will not
   always get exactly that many. It is like flipping a fair coin 20 times.
   You would not be surprised at all to get 9 heads.

(4) **a.** $1 - $ (the sum of the probabilities) ≈ 0.795

b. What is a fair price for a ticket?

c. The tickets in this lottery sell for $1.00 each. How much money does the state expect to make if 1,000,000 tickets are sold?

5 The player with the highest field goal percentage in the history of the National Basketball Association (NBA) is Artis Gilmore. In his career in the NBA, Gilmore attempted 9,570 field goals and made 5,732 of them.

a. What was Gilmore's field goal percentage?

b. During a typical game, Gilmore might attempt 25 field goals. In a typical game, how many field goals would you expect Gilmore to make?

The NBA player with the highest lifetime free throw percentage is Mark Price. Price had a free throw "percentage" of 0.904. He made a total of 2,135 free throws.

c. Why do you think the word percentage is in quotation marks above?

d. How many free throws did Price attempt?

e. How many free throws would you expect Price to make in 50 attempts?

f. Write an equation that relates the number of free throws T expected for a player who makes A attempts and whose free throw percentage is p.

6 A fast-food restaurant once had a scratch-off game in which a player picked just one of the four games on the card to play. In each game, the player stepped along a path, scratching off one of two adjacent boxes at each step. To win, the player had to get from start to finish without scratching off a "lose" box. Here's how the games on one card would have looked. (Of course, the words were covered until the player scratched off the covering.)

Game	Prize
A	free food worth 55¢
B	free food worth 69¢
C	free food worth $1.44
D	free food worth $1.99

Game A Start
GO	GO	
LOSE	GO	Finish

Game B Start
LOSE	GO	LOSE	
GO	GO	GO	Finish

Game C Start
LOSE	LOSE	LOSE	
GO	GO	GO	Finish

Game D Start
LOSE	GO	GO	GO	
GO	LOSE	LOSE	LOSE	Finish

a. What is the probability of winning each game?

b. For each game, make a probability distribution table and find the expected value.

b. $\Sigma prize \cdot probability \approx \$0.765$

c. The state expects to make $\$1.00 - \$0.765$, or $\$0.235$ per ticket. For every 1,000,000 tickets sold, the expected yield is $\$235,000$. (From this, the state must pay the costs of running the lottery including printing tickets and paying the stores that sell the tickets.)

5 **a.** $\dfrac{5,732}{9,570} \approx 0.599$, or 59.9%

b. $25(0.599) \approx 14.975$ field goals, assuming the attempts are independent.

c. The reported number is a proportion, not a percentage. To get a percentage, multiply the number by 100.

d. 2,362 free throws

e. $50(0.904) = 45.2$ free throws

f. $T = Ap$

6 **a.** Game A: $\left(\dfrac{1}{2}\right)(1) = \dfrac{1}{2}$

Game B: $\left(\dfrac{1}{2}\right)(1)\left(\dfrac{1}{2}\right) = \dfrac{1}{4}$

Game C: $\left(\dfrac{1}{2}\right)\left(\dfrac{1}{2}\right)\left(\dfrac{1}{2}\right) = \dfrac{1}{8}$

Game D: $\left(\dfrac{1}{2}\right)\left(\dfrac{1}{2}\right)\left(\dfrac{1}{2}\right)\left(\dfrac{1}{2}\right) = \dfrac{1}{16}$

b. **Game A**

Outcome	Probability
55¢	$\dfrac{1}{2}$
0	$\dfrac{1}{2}$

$EV = (55¢)\left(\dfrac{1}{2}\right) = 27.5¢$

Game B

Outcome	Probability
69¢	$\dfrac{1}{4}$
0	$\dfrac{3}{4}$

$EV = (69¢)\left(\dfrac{1}{4}\right) = 17.25¢$

Game C

Outcome	Probability
144¢	$\dfrac{1}{8}$
0	$\dfrac{7}{8}$

$EV = (144¢)\left(\dfrac{1}{8}\right) = 18¢$

Game D

Outcome	Probability
199¢	$\dfrac{1}{16}$
0	$\dfrac{15}{16}$

$EV = (199¢)\left(\dfrac{1}{16}\right) = 12.4375¢$

c. Which is the best game to pick if you just want to win something?

d. Which is the best game to pick if you want to have the largest expected value?

7 While a prisoner of war during World War II, J. Kerrich conducted an experiment in which he flipped a coin 10,000 times and kept a record of the outcomes. A portion of the results is given in the table below.

Number of Flips	Number of Heads
10	4
50	25
100	44
500	255
1,000	502
5,000	2,533
10,000	5,067

Source: J. Kerrich. *An Experimental Introduction to the Theory of Probability*. Copenhagen: J. Jorgenson and Co., 1964.

a. How many heads would you expect if you flip a coin 100 times? 32 times? 15 times?

b. After how many flips is the number of heads in Kerrich's table closest to the expected number of heads? Furthest?

c. Was the percentage of heads closer to the expected percentage of 50% after flipping 10 times or 10,000 times? Is this what you would expect? Explain.

Connections

8 Imagine an amateur archer shooting at the target below. The square board has a side length of six feet. Suppose the archer can always hit the board, but the spot on the board is random.

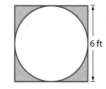

6 ft

a. Describe how to use a coordinate system and the **rand** function of your calculator to simulate the point where an arrow will land.

b. How can you tell whether the point is inside the circle?

c. Describe a simulation to estimate the probability that an arrow shot will land in the circle.

d. Simulate three arrow shots and tell whether each lands in the circle or not.

e. Describe another way to estimate the probability in Part c.

c. Game A has the highest probability of winning something.

d. Game A also has the largest expected value.

7 **a.** 50, 16, and 7.5. You would expect to get heads on half of your flips.

b. After 50 flips, exactly half of his flips were heads. He was farthest away after 10,000 flips. He had 67 extra heads.

c. After 10 flips, Kerrich had 40% heads. After 10,000 flips, he had 50.67% heads. His percentage was closer to the expected percentage after 10,000 flips. This is reasonable. As the number of flips increases, the percentage of heads tends to get closer to 50%. (However, the number of heads does not tend to get closer to half of the number of flips.)

Connections

8 **a.** **6rand** will give the first coordinate; **6rand** will give the second coordinate.

b. For example, suppose the point is (2.70, 1.72). This point will land in the circle if it is less than 3 units from the center at (3, 3). The distance between (3, 3) and (2.70, 1.72) is about 1.31, so the point is inside the circle. Thus, in this one run of the simulation, the arrow lands in the circle.

c. To simulate landing in the circle, you would use **6rand** twice to get the first and second coordinates. The equation of the circle with center at (3, 3) and radius 3 feet is $(x - 3)^2 + (y - 3)^2 = 9$. So, the arrow will land in the circle if the coordinates of the point randomly produced satisfy the inequality $(x - 3)^2 + (y - 3)^2 \leq 9$.

d. Points will vary.

e. Another way to estimate the probability the arrow lands in the circle would be to use an area model. The probability is the ratio of the area of the circle to the area of the square.

Unit 8

9 In this task, you will explore some of the geometry and algebra connected with the probability distribution for the sum of two dice.

   a. Make a probability distribution table for the sum of two octahedral dice (which have the numbers 1 through 8 on them).

   b. Plot the points given in your table $(x, P(x))$, where x is the sum and $P(x)$ is its probability.

   c. Write a single equation whose graph contains the points for $x = 2, 3, 4, 5, 6, 7, 8, 9$.

   d. Write another single equation whose graph contains the points for $x = 9, 10, 11, 12, 13, 14, 15, 16$.

   e. How are the slopes of these two graphs related?

   f. Use absolute value to write one equation whose graph contains all 15 points.

   g. Write an equation whose graph contains the points that represent the probability distribution for the sum of two regular polyhedral dice, each with n sides.

10 A summation sign, Σ, is useful in writing expressions involving expected value.

   a. Write an expression that uses a summation sign and gives the expected value of the probability distribution of a single roll of a die. Use x to represent the numbers in the faces of the die.

   b. Using the probability distribution table from Problem 1, Investigation 2, page 549, find each of the following sums.

     i. Σx **ii.** $\Sigma P(x)$ **iii.** $\Sigma[x^2 \cdot P(x)]$

   c. Using the probability distribution table from Problem 3, Investigation 2, page 550, find each of the sums above.

   d. Complete this sentence: In any probability distribution table, $\Sigma P(x) = $ _____ because _____.

Reflections

11 In this lesson, you calculated the expected value for various probability distributions. Expected value is another name for theoretical average.

   a. If you flip a fair coin 10 times, on average, how many heads would you expect to get?

   b. If you flip a coin 5 times, on average, you would expect to get 2.5 heads. Explain mathematically why that makes sense.

   c. If you roll a pair of dice 42 times, how many doubles do you expect? How many doubles do you expect if you roll 41 times?

9 **a.** In the chart for the octahedral dice below, the sum for each cell is included in parentheses.

Number on Second Die

Number on First Die	1	2	3	4	5	6	7	8
1	1, 1 (2)	1, 2 (3)	1, 3 (4)	1, 4 (5)	1, 5 (6)	1, 6 (7)	1, 7 (8)	1, 8 (9)
2	2, 1 (3)	2, 2 (4)	2, 3 (5)	2, 4 (6)	2, 5 (7)	2, 6 (8)	2, 7 (9)	2, 8 (10)
3	3, 1 (4)	3, 2 (5)	3, 3 (6)	3, 4 (7)	3, 5 (8)	3, 6 (9)	3, 7 (10)	3, 8 (11)
4	4, 1 (5)	4, 2 (6)	4, 3 (7)	4, 4 (8)	4, 5 (9)	4, 6 (10)	4, 7 (11)	4, 8 (12)
5	5, 1 (6)	5, 2 (7)	5, 3 (8)	5, 4 (9)	5, 5 (10)	5, 6 (11)	5, 7 (12)	5, 8 (13)
6	6, 1 (7)	6, 2 (8)	6, 3 (9)	6, 4 (10)	6, 5 (11)	6, 6 (12)	6, 7 (13)	6, 8 (14)
7	7, 1 (8)	7, 2 (9)	7, 3 (10)	7, 4 (11)	7, 5 (12)	7, 6 (13)	7, 7 (14)	7, 8 (15)
8	8, 1 (9)	8, 2 (10)	8, 3 (11)	8, 4 (12)	8, 5 (13)	8, 6 (14)	8, 7 (15)	8, 8 (16)

Sum, *x*	2	3	4	5	6	7	8	9	10	11	12	13	14	15	16
Probability, *P*(*x*)	$\frac{1}{64}$	$\frac{2}{64}$	$\frac{3}{64}$	$\frac{4}{64}$	$\frac{5}{64}$	$\frac{6}{64}$	$\frac{7}{64}$	$\frac{8}{64}$	$\frac{7}{64}$	$\frac{6}{64}$	$\frac{5}{64}$	$\frac{4}{64}$	$\frac{3}{64}$	$\frac{2}{64}$	$\frac{1}{64}$

b.

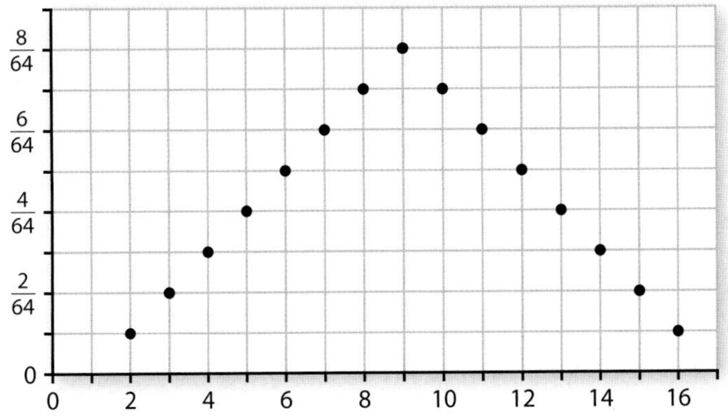

c. $y = \left(\frac{1}{64}\right)x - \frac{1}{64}$

d. $y = -\left(\frac{1}{64}\right)x + \frac{17}{64}$

e. The slopes are $\frac{1}{64}$ and $-\frac{1}{64}$; they are additive inverses.

f. $y = -\left(\frac{1}{64}\right)|9 - x| + \frac{8}{64}$

g. $y = -\left(\frac{1}{n^2}\right)|(n + 1) - x| + \frac{1}{n}$

10 **a.** $\Sigma x \cdot P(x)$

b. **i.** $\Sigma x = 21$

ii. $\Sigma P(x) = 1$

iii. $\Sigma x^2 \cdot P(x) = \frac{91}{6}$, or $15\frac{1}{6}$

c. **i.** $\Sigma x = 11$

ii. $\Sigma P(x) = 1$

iii. $\Sigma x^2 \cdot P(x) = \frac{55}{10}$, or 5.5

d. In any probability distribution table, $\Sigma P(x) = 1$ because the sum of the probabilities of all possible events is always 1.

INSTRUCTIONAL NOTE
Students might use calculator lists or spreadsheet software to do the calculations for Parts biii and ciii.

Reflections

11 **INSTRUCTIONAL NOTE** The solutions to this task should be discussed in class prior to doing Investigation 2. Students should understand that if you flip a fair coin 10 times, you expect to get 5 heads. However, you do not get 5 heads each time you flip a fair coin 10 times. Sometimes you get fewer; sometimes you get more. In the long run, however, the average number of heads will be 5. Expectation or expected value is another word for the theoretical average. For example, if you flip a coin 5 times, you might say in ordinary language that you expect to get 2 or 3 heads. However, in mathematics, you should say that you expect to get 2.5 heads because that is the number of heads you will get on average.

a. 5

b. Half of 5 is 2.5, and you expect half of the time to get heads.

c. $7; 6\frac{5}{6}$

Teacher Notes

d. About 45% of the U.S. population has type O blood. If 200 random people walk into a blood bank, how many do you expect to have type O blood? If 50 random people walk into a blood bank, how many do you expect to have type O blood?

e. If the probability of a success on each trial of a chance situation is p, how many successes would you expect to get in n trials?

12. Select one of the following projects and write a brief report summarizing your findings.

   a. If your state has a lottery, investigate the amount of money income from sales, the amount of money paid in prizes, the operating costs of the lottery, the profit your state makes, and what your state does with the profits of its lottery.

   b. Find the information about a scratch-off lottery ticket. Compute the expected value of a ticket.

13. Why don't gambling games charge the fair price for playing? Why do people gamble when the price of playing a game is always more than the expected value of the play?

14. According to the National Center for Health Statistics, in 2003, a newborn male in the United States could expect to live 74.8 years. A 20-year-old male could expect to live to the age of 75.9. A newborn female could expect to live to the age of 80.1 and a 20-year-old female to the age of 80.9.
(Source: www.cdc.gov/nchs/data/nvsr/nvsr53/nvsr53_15.pdf)

   a. In this case, what is meant by the words "expect to live to the age of"?

   b. Why is the life expectancy for a 20-year-old greater than for a newborn?

15. This probability distribution table gives the probability of getting a specified number of heads if a coin is tossed five times.

Number of Heads	Probability
0	$\frac{1}{32}$
1	$\frac{5}{32}$
2	$\frac{10}{32}$
3	$\frac{10}{32}$
4	$\frac{5}{32}$
5	$\frac{1}{32}$
Total	$\frac{32}{32}$

   a. What is the expected number of heads if a coin is tossed five times? Find the answer to this question in at least two different ways.

   b. José says that the answer to Part a cannot involve half a head. How would you help him understand why it can?

d. 90; 22.5

e. *np*

12 **a.** Reports will vary depending on the current law in your state. Many state lotteries pay out about 50 cents for every dollar bet.

b. For some states, information about scratch-off games may be found on Web sites. For example, those of New Jersey and Iowa are www.newjersey.gov/lottery and www.ialottery.com.

13 Gambling games are not fair because the operator wants to make money. People gamble for many reasons: it may be the gambler's only chance of ever getting a lot of money, it provides entertainment, a gambler may get addicted, a gambler may think that he or she has somehow outsmarted the operator, a gambler does not understand the probabilities involved and thinks he or she is more likely to win now because he or she has lost in the past. Compulsive gambling can be a serious problem. For information on compulsive gambling, see www.nlm.nih.gov/medlineplus/ency/article/001520.htm.

14 **a.** If you wait and determine the ages at death for all males who were 20 at the time of this report and average these ages, that average is predicted to be 75.9.

b. The newborn has a chance of dying before reaching his or her 20th birthday. The 20-year-old already has survived those years.

15 **a.** One way to solve this problem is to reason that you expect one-half of the 5 tosses to be heads, so you expect 2.5 heads.

Another way to solve the problem is to compute the expected value of the probability distribution by completing the third column in the table and finding its sum.

Number of Heads	Probability	(Number)(Probability)
0	$\frac{1}{32}$	0
1	$\frac{5}{32}$	$\frac{5}{32}$
2	$\frac{10}{32}$	$\frac{20}{32}$
3	$\frac{10}{32}$	$\frac{30}{32}$
4	$\frac{5}{32}$	$\frac{20}{32}$
5	$\frac{1}{32}$	$\frac{5}{32}$
Total	$\frac{32}{32}$	$\frac{80}{32} = 2.5$

A third way is to make a histogram of the probability distribution and find its balance point by noticing the symmetry around 2.5.

b. José does not understand the mathematical meaning of the word "expect." He needs to learn that to say that the expected value is 2.5 means that if the coin were repeatedly tossed five times, the average of the number of heads that would come up is 2.5. It may help to remind him that the mean does not have to be one of the values being averaged.

Extensions

16 In an episode of a television show, a man receives an anonymous letter that correctly predicts the winner of a sports event. In the next four weeks, similar letters arrive, each making a prediction that turns out to be correct. The fifth and final letter asks the man for money before he receives another prediction. The whole thing turns out to be a scam.

Two versions of the first letter had been sent out, each to a large number of people. Half of the people received letters that predicted Team A would win, and half of the people received letters that predicted Team B would win. Those people who received letters with the correct prediction were sent letters the second week. Again, half of the letters predicted Team C and half predicted Team D.

How many letters should have been sent out the first week so that exactly one person would be guaranteed to have all correct predictions at the end of the five weeks?

17 To help raise money for charity, a college service organization decided to run a carnival. In addition to rides, the college students planned games of skill and games of chance. For one of the booths, a member suggested using a large spinner wheel with the numbers from 1 to 10 on it. The group considered three different games that could be played. The games are described below. For each game, do the following:

a. Make a table showing all possible outcomes and their probabilities.

b. Calculate the expected value of the game, and compare that value to the price of playing the game.

c. Determine if the game will raise money, lose money, or break even in the long run. If the game will not make money, recommend a change that the group might consider.

Double Dare To play this game, the player must pay the booth attendant $1. The player then chooses two numbers from one to ten and gives the wheel a spin. If the wheel stops on either of the two numbers, the attendant gives the player a prize worth $15.

Extensions

16 32 letters. This may be easiest to understand if you work backwards: One correct letter was sent on the fifth week, so two correct letters were sent on the fourth week, four on the third week, eight on the second week, and sixteen correct letters on the first week. There would also be sixteen incorrect letters the first week for a total of 32.

You also can ask your students the total number of letters sent out: 62.

17 **Double Dare**

a.

Outcome	Probability	(Outcome)(Probability)
$15	$\frac{2}{10}$	$3.00
$0	$\frac{8}{10}$	$0.00
Total	$\frac{10}{10}$	$3.00

b. The expected value for this game is $3, but the price to play is only $1.

c. The game will lose an average of $2 per play in the long run. Either a less expensive prize must be given, or the group must charge more than $3 to play the game. Allowing the player to pick only one number reduces the probability of winning to $\frac{1}{10}$, but the game will still lose money.

Anything Goes For this game, the player can choose either one or two numbers. The player again must pay the attendant $1. After paying the attendant and choosing numbers, the player spins the wheel. If the wheel stops on a number the player chose, the attendant gives the player a prize. If the player selected only one number, the prize is worth $10. If the player selected two numbers, the prize is worth $5.

Triple Threat This game is a little more expensive to play. The player must pay $3 to spin the wheel. If the wheel stops on 1, 2, or 3, the player loses, receiving no prize. If the wheel stops on 4, 5, 6, or 7, the attendant gives the player a prize worth $2. If the wheel stops on 8, 9, or 10, the player gets a prize worth $6.

18. To find the standard deviation of a probability distribution given in a table, first compute the expected value, *EV.* Then complete columns as in the following table, or use the List feature of your calculator for the calculations. Finally, sum the numbers in the last column (or list) and take the square root.

Value, x	Probability, $P(x)$	$(x - EV)^2$	$(x - EV)^2 \cdot P(x)$
2	0.43		
3	0.23		
4	0.20		
5	0.09		
6	0.03		
7	0.02		

a. Find the standard deviation for the probability distribution above.

b. Check your answer to Problem 5 Part c (page 551) of Investigation 2.

c. Refer to Applications Task 2. Suppose that you insure just one car. Complete the probability distribution table of possible insurance claims below. Then find the expected value and standard deviation. Use these two numbers in a sentence about insurance.

Claim, x	Probability, $P(x)$
3,910	
0	

d. Write a formula for the standard deviation of a probability distribution.

Anything Goes

a. If the player selects one number, the probability distribution table is:

Outcome	Probability	(Outcome)(Probability)
$10	$\frac{1}{10}$	$1.00
$0	$\frac{9}{10}$	$0.00
Total	$\frac{10}{10}$	$1.00

If the player selects two numbers, the table now looks like this:

Outcome	Probability	(Outcome)(Probability)
$5	$\frac{2}{10}$	$1.00
$0	$\frac{8}{10}$	$0.00
Total	$\frac{10}{10}$	$1.00

b. In both cases, the expected value is $1, which is also the price to play the game.

c. The game will neither make money nor lose money in the long run because the price to play is the fair price. Lowering the value of the prize or raising the price to play will allow the game to make money.

Triple Threat

a.

Outcome	Probability	(Outcome)(Probability)
$0	$\frac{3}{10}$	$0.00
$2	$\frac{4}{10}$	$0.80
$6	$\frac{3}{10}$	$1.80
Total	$\frac{10}{10}$	$2.60

b. The expected value for this game is $2.60, and the group will charge $3.00 for each play.

c. In the long run, the group will make an average of $0.40 for each play. This is a good option for them to use without modification.

18 Note that this procedure is quickly implemented using the list functions of the calculator.

a. The *EV* is 3.12 and the standard deviation is about 1.25.

b. Students will now know that the correct response to that question is 1.

c. The *EV* is $304.98 and the standard deviation is about $1,048.55. An insurance company that insures just one car can expect to pay out $304.98 in collision claims, give or take about $1,048.55.

Claim, x	Probability, P(x)
3,910	0.078
0	0.922

d. $\sqrt{\Sigma(x - EV)^2 \cdot P(x)}$

Review

19 Javier bought a used car for $5,600. The value of his car is depreciating at the rate of 1.25% per month.

   a. How much is Javier's car worth after 6 months?

   b. Write a *NOW-NEXT* rule that indicates how the value of Javier's car changes from one month to the next.

   c. Write a function rule that can be used to find the value of Javier's car after any number of months.

   d. Javier took out a three-year loan to pay for his car. How much is his car worth when he makes his final payment?

   e. When is Javier's car first worth less than $2,500?

20 Suppose that you roll two dice and record the numbers showing on the top faces of the two dice. Find each of the following probabilities.

   a. *P(sum is 5)*   **b.** *P(sum is less than 4)*

   c. *P(sum is odd)*   **d.** *P(roll doubles)*

21 Write each expression in the simplest equivalent form that uses only positive exponents.

   a. $2x^3y(-3xy^{-2})$ **b.** $\dfrac{8a^4b^{10}}{2a^{-1}b^5c}$

   c. $2(-3x^2y^3)^3$ **d.** $3a^3b - 2a(a^2b + a)$

22 Consider the triangle shown below.

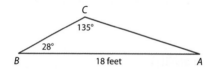

   a. Find *BC*.   **b.** Find *AC*.

23 Play the game below several times.

    In a game of matching, two people each flip a coin. If both coins match (both heads or both tails), Player B gets a point. If the coins don't match, Player A gets two points.

   a. What is the probability that Player A wins a round? That Player B wins?

   b. Explain why this is or is not a fair game.

24 Write rules for quadratic functions with graphs that have the following properties.

   a. opens down and has *y*-intercept at (0, 6)

   b. *x*-intercepts at (2, 0) and (8, 0) and opens up

   c. minimum point at (3, 0) and opens up

   d. *x*-intercepts at (−2, 0) and (4, 0) and maximum point at (1, 5)

Review

19 **a.** $5,600(1 - 0.0125)^6 \approx \$5,193$

b. $NEXT = 0.9875NOW$, starting at 5,600

c. $V(x) = 5,600(0.9875^x)$, where x is the months since purchase

d. $\$3,561$

e. After 65 months

Just in Time

20 **a.** $\frac{4}{36} = \frac{1}{9}$ **b.** $\frac{3}{36} = \frac{1}{12}$

c. $\frac{18}{36} = \frac{1}{2}$ **d.** $\frac{6}{36} = \frac{1}{6}$

21 **a.** $-\frac{6x^4}{y}$ **b.** $\frac{4a^5b^5}{c}$

c. $-54x^6y^9$ **d.** $a^3b - 2a^2$

22 **a.** $BC = \dfrac{18 \sin 17°}{\sin 135°} \approx 7.4 \approx 7$ feet

b. $AC = \dfrac{18 \sin 28°}{\sin 135°} \approx 11.95 \approx 12$ feet

23 **a.** The probability that Player A wins is $\frac{1}{2}$ because there are four equally likely outcomes (HH, HT, TH, TT) in the sample space, and two are wins for Player A. The probability that Player B wins is also $\frac{1}{2}$.

b. This game is not fair. Because Player A and Player B are equally likely to win, they should receive the same number of points when they win.

24 One possible function rule is given for Parts a–c. Part d has a unique answer.

a. $f(x) = -x^2 + 6$

b. $f(x) = (x - 2)(x - 8)$

c. $f(x) = (x - 3)^2$

d. $f(x) = -\frac{5}{9}(x + 2)(x - 4)$

Teaching Resources

Assessment Masters 17–21.

The Waiting-Time Distribution

Anita and her friends are playing a board game. Movement around the board is determined by rolling a pair of dice. Winning is based on a combination of chance and a sense for making smart real estate deals. While playing this game, Anita draws the card shown above. She must go directly to the "jail" space on the board.

Anita may get out of jail by rolling doubles on one of her next three turns. If she does not roll doubles on any of the three turns, Anita must pay a $50 fine to get out of jail. Anita takes her first turn and does not roll doubles. On her second turn, she does not roll doubles again. On her third and final try, Anita does not roll doubles yet again. She grudgingly pays the $50 to get out of jail. Anita is feeling very unlucky.

The Waiting-Time Distribution

One of the most common probabilistic situations is waiting for specific event to occur: waiting for red to come up in roulette, waiting for doubles to appear in backgammon or Monopoly, waiting for a day of rain on days when the weather forecaster says there is a 20% chance of rain, etc. In this lesson, students will be introduced to the idea of a waiting-time distribution (also called the geometric distribution). In a waiting-time situation, you conduct a series of independent trials in which the probability of a "success" is p for each trial and you count the number of trials needed until the first success.

Students will be able to use all the probability theory that they have learned so far to construct this distribution exactly and describe its shape and expected value.

In Investigation 1, students will construct waiting-time distributions, both by simulation and theoretically, and will discover that all have the same basic shape.

In Investigation 2, students will develop the formula that generates this distribution.

In the third investigation, students will discover the simple formula for the expected (average) waiting time, $\frac{1}{p}$, and are introduced to the idea of summing an infinite series.

The Importance of a Graph Throughout this lesson, emphasize to students that they will understand a probability problem if they can construct a histogram of its probability distribution. The histogram can be constructed theoretically or approximated by simulation. As usual, students should label all histograms so that they know what the distribution tells them.

Lesson Objectives

- Use simulation to construct an approximate waiting-time distribution and understand why the shape is skewed to the right
- Recognize rare events in a waiting-time situation
- Use the formula to construct the probability distribution for a waiting-time situation
- Discover the formula for the expected value of a waiting-time distribution
- Understand that some infinite series have a finite sum

Think About This Situation

Anita's situation suggests several questions.

a How likely is it that a player who is sent to jail (and does not have a "Get Out of Jail Free" card) will have to pay $50 to leave? As a class, think of as many ways to find the answer to this question as you can.

b In games and in real life, people are occasionally in the position of waiting for an event to happen. In some cases, the event becomes more and more likely to happen with each opportunity. In some cases, the event becomes less and less likely to happen with each opportunity. Does the chance of rolling doubles change each time Anita rolls the dice?

c On average, how many rolls will it take to roll doubles? Do you think Anita should feel unlucky? Explain your reasoning.

In this lesson, you will use the rules of probability that you have learned so far to analyze **waiting-time situations**, where you perform repeated, identical *trials* and are waiting for a specific event to happen.

Investigation 1 — Waiting for Doubles

In this investigation, you will explore several aspects of Anita's situation of waiting for doubles to get out of jail while playing the board game. For this investigation, assume that a player must stay in jail until he or she rolls doubles. That is, a player cannot pay $50 to get out of jail in this version of the game, and there is no "Get Out of Jail Free" card. As you work on the following problems, make notes of answers to the following questions:

How can you roll dice to estimate the probability that it will take a specified number of rolls to get doubles?

How can you calculate that probability exactly?

What is the shape of a waiting-time distribution?

You might want to begin this lesson by bringing in a Monopoly game and explaining the rules.

Although your students may say, in Part b, that Anita's chance of rolling doubles remains the same each time she rolls the dice (because that is what they have been told), many of them will not really believe it. If you want to test this, take a coin and try the following experiment with your students. Ask, "If I flip a coin ten times, how many heads do I expect to get, on the average?" (Most students will answer five. Be sure that they understand that, on the average, half of the flips of a fair coin will be heads.)

Flip the coin and announce that you got a head. Flip it again and announce that you got another head. This should not seem strange to the class. Now ask them, "When I have finished the ten flips, how many heads do you expect me to have?"

Almost every student will answer five. This answer indicates that the students expect the coin to "balance out" the first two flips of heads. In other words, they believe that tails are due and now have a probability greater than $\frac{1}{2}$. There are eight flips left, and they expect only three of them to be heads.

The correct answer is six. You have eight flips left, and with a fair coin, you expect four of them to be heads and four to be tails. With the first two flips of heads, that means you expect six heads for the ten flips.

Think About This Situation

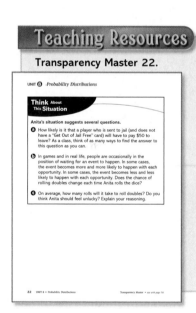

a First, students must recall or reconstruct the fact that the probability of getting doubles with a roll of the dice is $\frac{1}{6}$. To find the probability that Anita has to pay $50, students may suggest rolling dice. Others may suggest a simulation with random digits such as letting the digit 1 represent doubles, the digits 2, 3, 4, 5, and 6 represent not doubles, and ignore 0, 7, 8, and 9. Other students may realize they can use the Multiplication Rule to find the probability that Anita does not get out of jail in three tries: $\left(\frac{5}{6}\right)\left(\frac{5}{6}\right)\left(\frac{5}{6}\right) \approx 0.579$.

b The chances of rolling doubles remains the same each time.

c Student responses will vary. They may suggest trying an experiment or base their hunches on their game-playing experiences. (Students will not know that the theoretical answer is 6, and you do not need to tell them that yet. After completing Problem 1, students might want to look back at this question and see how the results from Problem 1 might help them decide whether or not Anita should feel unlucky.)

Unit 8

In Investigation 1, students will construct frequency distributions and histograms of waiting-time distributions, both by simulation and theoretically, and will discover that all have the same basic shape. Students learn that this distribution occurs when you conduct a series of independent trials in which the probability of a "success" is p for each trial and you count the number of trials needed until the first success. Waiting-time distributions have a characteristic shape, shown below, in which the first bar is the tallest (height p) and each succeeding bar is $(1 - p)$ times the height of the bar to its left.

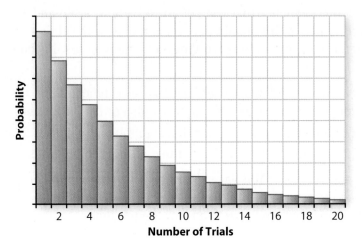

INSTRUCTIONAL NOTE
See the launch suggestions on page T561B.

Before beginning the investigation, you may want to perform the following demonstration in class:

Give each student a pair of dice. Alternatively, students could use a random digit table or the **randInt(1,6)** command on their calculators. Using the random digit table, assign, for example, the digit 0 to represent rolling doubles and the digits 1, 2, 3, 4, 5 to represent non-doubles (ignore the digits 6 through 9). Using **randInt(1,6)**, for example, the number 1 could represent doubles and the other numbers could represent not doubles. Students should count the number of times they have to press ENTER in order to get a 1.

First, ask students how many students they expect to roll doubles on the first try. Then have the students roll for the first time. Those students who roll doubles on the first try should go stand one behind the other at the side of the room.

Ask students how many of the remaining students they expect to roll doubles on the second try. Then have those students roll again. Students who roll doubles on this second try should go stand one behind the other to the right of the first group.

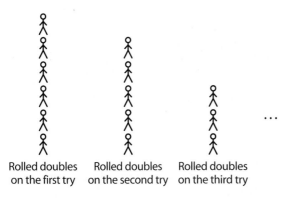

Rolled doubles   Rolled doubles   Rolled doubles
on the first try   on the second try   on the third try

Repeat this procedure until the class has formed a living histogram. (You may want to bring your camera!) Ask students why the lines keep getting shorter. (Because there are fewer students still trying to roll doubles each time.) Ask students approximately what proportion the length of each line is to the length of the preceding line. (Approximately $\frac{5}{6}$.)

1 Suppose you are playing Anita's game under this new rule and have just been sent to jail. Take your first turn and roll a pair of dice. Did you roll doubles and get out of jail? If so, stop. If not, roll again. Did you roll doubles and get out of jail on your second turn? If so, stop. If not, roll again. Did you roll doubles and get out of jail on your third turn? If so, stop. If not, keep rolling until you get doubles.

a. Copy the frequency table below and put a tally mark in the frequency column next to the event that happened to you. Add rows as needed.

Rolling Doubles

When First Rolled Doubles	Number of Rolls	Frequency
First try	1	
Second try	2	
Third try	3	
Fourth try	4	
⋮	⋮	
Total		100

b. With other members of your class, perform this experiment a total of 100 times. Record the results in your frequency table.

c. Do the events in the frequency table appear to be *equally likely*? That is, does each of the events have the same chance of happening?

d. Use your frequency table to estimate the probability that Anita will have to pay $50, or use a "Get Out of Jail Free" card, to get out of jail when playing a standard version of her game. Compare this estimate with your original estimate in Part a of the Think About This Situation.

e. Make a histogram of the data in your frequency table. Describe the shape of this histogram.

f. Explain why the frequencies in your table are decreasing even though the probability of rolling doubles on each attempt does not change.

2 Suppose you compared your class' histogram of the waiting time for rolling doubles with another class' histogram.

a. Explain why the histograms should or should not be exactly the same.

b. What characteristics do you think the histograms will have in common?

1 **INSTRUCTIONAL NOTE** There are many ways to have the class work together to complete this table. Assign each student a number of runs to conduct so that the class will have a total of 100 runs. Students enjoy making a histogram of their table on the wall of the classroom. To do this, give each student a removable sticker or sticky note for each run. Have students put their stickers on the wall of the classroom above stickers already marked with the numbers 1, 2, 3, 4, ... according to how many rolls it took them to get doubles.

a–b. A typical table might look like this:

Rolling Doubles

When First Rolled Doubles	Number of Rolls	Frequency
First try	1	17
Second try	2	14
Third try	3	12
Fourth try	4	10
⋮	⋮	
Total		100

Teaching Resources

Student Master 23.

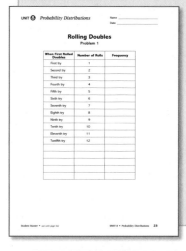

TECHNOLOGY NOTE
Rather than rolling dice, students could simulate the situation using the Simulation feature of *CPMP-Tools*.

c. The events in the table are not equally likely. The probability of rolling doubles for the first time on roll $k + 1$ is less than the probability for roll k. This is reflected in the table through the decreasing frequencies.

d. Probabilities will vary based on the results of the runs. Using the sample frequency table from Part b, the estimated probability that Anita will get out of jail in the first three rolls is $\frac{17 + 14 + 12}{100}$, or 0.43.

Thus, the estimated probability she will have to pay $50 is $1 - 0.43$, or 0.57. (The theoretical probability is 0.58, as students will learn later.) Comparisons will depend on the students' original estimate.

e. Histograms will vary. A sample histogram follows; most histograms will not be this smooth, and they will usually continue on to the right. The histogram is skewed right. The bars decrease in height. Each bar is about $\frac{5}{6}$ of the height of the bar to its left.

Rolling Doubles

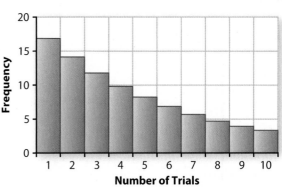

f. There will be fewer people who will roll doubles for the first time on their second roll than who will roll doubles for the first time on their first roll. One way to picture this is to imagine all 100 people taking their first roll simultaneously. Those who get doubles on this roll (about $\frac{1}{6}$ of the 100 people) leave the room. Everyone who remains then tries a second time to get doubles. About $\frac{1}{6}$ will succeed. This is not $\frac{1}{6}$ of 100 but $\frac{1}{6}$ of a smaller number.

2 **a.** Most likely, the histograms will not be exactly the same. They were created by rolling dice, and not every class will have the same rolls.

b. The overall pattern in the histograms should be that the bars gradually decrease in height as the number of rolls increases.

In Problem 1, you constructed an approximate *waiting-time distribution*. As you noted in Problem 2, two different groups could get quite different histograms when they constructed them by rolling dice. The two groups would then have different estimates of a probability. In the next problem, you will construct waiting-time distributions exactly, so everyone should get the same answers to the probability questions related to these distributions.

3 Imagine 36 students are playing a modification of Anita's game in a class tournament. All are sent to jail. A student cannot pay $50 to get out of jail but must roll doubles. (There is no other way out.)

a. How many of the 36 students do you expect to get out of jail by rolling doubles on the first try? (Remember that the word "expect" has a mathematical meaning.) How many students do you expect to remain in jail?

b. How many of the remaining students do you expect to get out of jail on the second try? How many students do you expect to remain in jail then?

c. How many of the remaining students do you expect to get out of jail on the third try? How many students do you expect to remain in jail then?

d. Complete a table like the one below. Round numbers to the nearest hundredth. The first three lines should agree with your answers to Parts a–c.

Rolling Dice to Get Doubles

Number of Rolls to Get Doubles	Expected Number of Students Released on the Given Number of Rolls	Expected Number of Students Still in Jail
1		
2		
3		
4		
5		
6		
7		
8		
9		
10		
11		
12		

e. What patterns of change do you see in this table? If possible, describe each pattern using the idea of *NOW* and *NEXT*.

INSTRUCTIONAL NOTE In the following problem, students will learn to construct a histogram of the theoretical frequencies for a waiting-time situation. To do this, students will use the fact that if you perform a binomial experiment n times and the probability of a success is p, then you expect np successes. For example, if you flip a coin 10 times, you expect 10(0.5) or 5 heads. Most people believe this intuitively. However, students may be uncomfortable with the statement that if you flip a coin 15 times, you expect 15(0.5) or 7.5 heads. You may have to remind them several times that "expect" means "on the average."

 a. $36 \cdot \frac{1}{6} = 6$ students get out of jail; 30 students remain in jail.

b. $30 \cdot \frac{1}{6} = 5$ students get out of jail; 25 students remain in jail.

c. $25 \cdot \frac{1}{6} \approx 4.17$ students get out of jail; 20.83 students remain in jail.

INSTRUCTIONAL NOTE You may wish to point out that this is an example where rounding (up, down, or truncating), even though you technically cannot have a part of a person, is not helpful in finding the pattern.

d. Rolling Dice to Get Doubles

Number of Rolls to Get Doubles	Expected Number of Students Released on the Given Number of Rolls	Expected Number of Students Still in Jail
1	6	30
2	5	25
3	4.17	20.83
4	3.47	17.36
5	2.89	14.47
6	2.41	12.06
7	2.01	10.05
8	1.67	8.37
9	1.40	6.98
10	1.16	5.81
11	0.97	4.85
12	0.81	4.04

e. In the first column, $NEXT = NOW + 1$.

In the second column, $NEXT = \frac{5}{6} NOW$.

In the third column, $NEXT = \frac{5}{6} NOW$.

UNIT 8 *Probability Distributions* Name
Date

Rolling Dice to Get Doubles
Problem 3

Number of Rolls to Get Doubles	Expected Number of Students Released on the Given Number of Rolls	Expected Number of Students Still in Jail
1		
2		
3		
4		
5		
6		
7		
8		
9		
10		
11		
12		

24 UNIT 8 • *Probability Distributions*   Student Master • *see sixth page (6a)*

4 The table you started in Problem 3 never really can be completed because there are infinitely many possible outcomes. That is, the rows could be continued indefinitely.

   a. How many of the 36 students do you expect to be in jail after 12 tries to roll doubles?

   b. Add a "13 or more" row to your table and write the expected number of students in the appropriate place.

5 Make a histogram of the "expected number of students released on the given number of rolls" from the frequency table you constructed in Problem 3.

   a. Compare this histogram to the one you constructed in Problem 1 of this investigation.

   b. Examine your histogram of the theoretical distribution. The height of each bar is what proportion of the height of the bar to its left?

   c. Using the balance point of your histogram, estimate the mean of the distribution.

   d. Using the frequency table from Problem 3, calculate the mean number of rolls of the dice it takes to get doubles. Compare your calculated mean to your estimate in Part c.

6 If there were 1,000 people (rather than 36) who had been sent to jail in Problem 3, how would the histogram change? How would the mean change? How many of these people would you expect to need 13 or more rolls to get out of jail?

Summarize
the Mathematics

In this investigation, you explored the distribution of the waiting time for rolling doubles.

a Suppose the probability of an event is p. How many times would you expect this event to happen in a series of n independent trials?

b Suppose the probability of an event is p and you have made a histogram of the waiting-time distribution for the event. How is the height of each bar of the histogram related to the height of the bar to its left?

Be prepared to share your ideas and reasoning with the class.

a. About 36 − 31.96 = 4.04 students are expected to still be in jail. (Answers may vary depending on how students round.)

b. Students should add a row like that below to the table in Problem 3, Part d:

13 or more	4.04	0

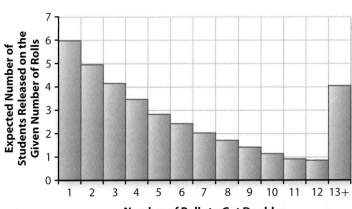

Number of Rolls to Get Doubles

a. This histogram is probably more "smooth" and less irregular looking than the histogram constructed following the activity in Problem 1, but the two histograms should have the same overall shape.

b. Except for the 13+ bar, each bar is $\frac{5}{6}$ of the height of the bar to its left.

c. The mean is about 6 rolls.

d. Students could use the formula $EV = \dfrac{\Sigma x \cdot f(x)}{n} = \dfrac{1(6) + 2(5) + 3(4.17) + \cdots}{36}$. If they use 13 for the *13 or more* row, they will get 5.44 for the mean. You may want to discuss how the mean will be too small when 13 is used to represent 13 or more. If students add more rows to the table, they will get answers that more closely approximate the theoretical mean of 6.

> **KEY IDEA** This is a crucial question. You may wish to have the full class discuss why this pattern occurs: with each round, there are $\frac{5}{6}$ as many students as in the previous round because $\frac{1}{6}$ of the students rolled doubles in the previous round and are no longer rolling.

6 The shape of the histogram would not change at all, but the frequencies would be different on the *y*-axis. The mean would not change either. After 12 rolls, you would expect $10,000\left(\dfrac{5}{6}\right)^{12} \approx 1,122$ people remain in jail.

Summarize
the Mathematics

Teaching Resources

Transparency Master 25.

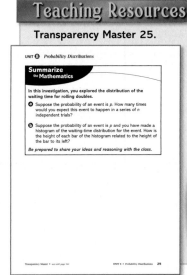

a *np* times

b It is $(1 − p)$ times as high. Students may be more comfortable giving a numerical example. For example: If the probability of a success is 20%, then the height of each bar is 80% of the height of the previous bar. Students may recognize this as exponential decay with decay factor equal to $1 − p$. Students will make this connection explicitly in Investigation 2.

✔ Check Your Understanding

Change the rules of Anita's game so that a player must flip a coin and get heads in order to get out of jail.

a. Is it harder or easier to get out of jail with this new rule instead of by rolling doubles? Explain your reasoning.

b. Play this version 24 times, either with a coin or by simulating the situation. Put your results in a table like the one in Problem 1. Then make a histogram of your results.

c. What is your estimate of the probability that a player will get out of jail in three flips or fewer?

d. Now, suppose you start with 1,000 people in jail. Make a table that shows the theoretical distribution of exactly how many you would expect to get out of jail on each flip. Continue until your table has four rows.

Investigation 2 — The Waiting-Time Formula

In Investigation 1, you created waiting-time distributions using simulation and theoretical probabilities. The theoretical distributions had a well-defined pattern. As you complete this investigation, keep in mind this basic question:

What general formula can be used to calculate the probability that it will take exactly x trials to get the first success in a waiting-time distribution?

1 Imagine that all students in your class are playing Anita's game. All are sent to jail. To get out of jail, a student must roll doubles. (You cannot pay $50 or use a Get Out of Jail Free card).

a. What is the probability of getting doubles on the first roll? Enter your answer as a fraction on the first line of a copy of the table at the right.

Number of Rolls to Get Doubles for the First Time	Probability
1	
2	
3	
4	
5	
6	
7	
8	
9	
10	
11	
12	
13 or more	

✓ Check Your Understanding

a. Much easier. The probability of getting heads, $\frac{1}{2}$, is quite a bit larger than the probability of getting doubles, $\frac{1}{6}$.

b. Tables and histograms will vary. The first bar will be the tallest. (About half of the time, heads will occur on the first flip.) The second bar will be about half as high as the first bar. The third bar will be about half as high as the second bar. This general pattern will continue with each bar being about half the height of the bar immediately to its left.

c. The theoretical answer is $\frac{7}{8}$, or 0.875. Students should respond based upon the results of their 24 runs.

d. Flipping Coin to Get Heads

Number of Flips to Get Heads	Expected Number of People Released on the Given Number of Flips	Expected Number of People Still in Jail
1	500	500
2	250	250
3	125	125
4	62.5	62.5

Investigation 2 The Waiting-Time Formula

In Investigation 2, students will develop the formula that generates the waiting-time distribution: the probability that it will take x tries to get the first success is

$$P(x) = (1 - p)^{x - 1}p$$

because there must be $(x - 1)$ failures followed by a success. The sequence of probabilities is indeed geometric with first term p and common ratio $(1 - p)$:

$$p, (1 - p)p, (1 - p)^2p, (1 - p)^3p, \ldots$$

In a standard waiting-time situation, the probability of a success on each trial is assumed to be the same, no matter what happened on previous trials. You may have to remind students to be sure that this assumption is reasonable before they use the formula.

 a. The portion of the table that students complete in this problem is shown below.

Number of Rolls to Get Doubles	Probability
1	$\frac{1}{6}$
2	$\left(\frac{5}{6}\right)\left(\frac{1}{6}\right)$
3	$\left(\frac{5}{6}\right)^2\left(\frac{1}{6}\right)$
4	$\left(\frac{5}{6}\right)^3\left(\frac{1}{6}\right)$

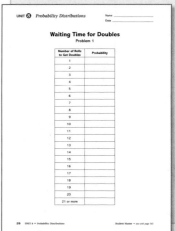

b. To get out of jail on the second roll, two events must happen. You must not roll doubles on the first roll, and you must roll doubles on the second roll.

   i. What rule of probability can you use to compute $P(A \text{ and } B)$ when A and B are independent events?

   ii. What is the probability of not getting doubles on the first roll and getting doubles on the second roll? Write your answer as a fraction on the second line of the table.

c. To get out of jail on the third roll, three events must happen.

   i. What are these three events?

   ii. What is the probability that all three events will happen? Write your answer as a fraction on the third row of the table.

d. To get out of jail on the fourth roll, four events must happen.

   i. What are these four events?

   ii. What is the probability that all four events will happen? Write your answer as a fraction on the fourth row of the table.

② Explain why your work for Problem 1 can be summarized in the following manner.

$$P(1) = \frac{1}{6}$$
$$P(2) = \left(\frac{5}{6}\right)\left(\frac{1}{6}\right)$$
$$P(3) = \left(\frac{5}{6}\right)^2\left(\frac{1}{6}\right)$$
$$P(4) = \left(\frac{5}{6}\right)^3\left(\frac{1}{6}\right)$$

③ Examine the equations in Problem 2.

a. What patterns do you see in the equations in Problem 2?

b. What is $P(5)$? $P(6)$? Explain the meaning of each of these probabilities.

c. What is $P(x)$? That is, what is the probability the first doubles will appear on the xth roll of the dice?

d. Use your formula in Part c to complete the rest of the probability distribution table. Leave the answers in the form of those in Problem 2. For the row "13 or more," include the probability that makes the total probability equal to 1.

e. Make another column, multiplying out the probabilities and expressing them as decimals to the nearest thousandth.

f. Make a graph from the probability distribution table in Part e. How does the height of each bar compare to the one on its left? Explain why this is the case.

g. When they have to wait longer than almost everyone else, lots of people begin to feel that something very unusual has happened. Thus, a **rare event** for a waiting-time distribution is defined as an event that falls in the upper 5% of a waiting-time distribution. Would it be a rare event to require 12 rolls to get doubles for the first time?

b. **i.** The Multiplication Rule for independent events:
$$P(A \text{ and } B) = P(A) \cdot P(B)$$

     ii. $\left(\frac{5}{6}\right)\left(\frac{1}{6}\right) = \frac{5}{36}$

c. **i.** You must not roll doubles on the first try, you must not roll doubles on the second try, and you must roll doubles on the third try.

     ii. $\left(\frac{5}{6}\right)\left(\frac{5}{6}\right)\left(\frac{1}{6}\right) = \frac{25}{216}$

d. **i.** You must not roll doubles on the first try, you must not roll doubles on the second try, you must not roll doubles on the third try, and you must roll doubles on the fourth try.

     ii. $\left(\frac{5}{6}\right)\left(\frac{5}{6}\right)\left(\frac{5}{6}\right)\left(\frac{1}{6}\right) = \frac{125}{1,296}$

(2) In each case, use the Multiplication Rule for independent events. There is another way to look at it. For example, the probability a person will roll doubles for the first time on the third roll is $\left(\frac{5}{6}\right)^2\left(\frac{1}{6}\right)$. We expect that $\frac{5}{6}$ of the people will not roll doubles on their first try and $\frac{5}{6}$ of that $\frac{5}{6}$ will not roll doubles on their second try. So, $\frac{5}{6}$ of $\frac{5}{6}$ of the people who started are left to try a third roll. We expect that $\frac{1}{6}$ of them, or $\frac{1}{6}$ of the $\frac{5}{6}$ of the $\frac{5}{6}$, will roll doubles for the first time on their third try.

(3) **a.** The right-hand side of the equation has an additional factor of $\frac{5}{6}$ for each increase of 1 in the number of rolls required on the left-hand side of the equation. (The sequence $\left(\frac{1}{6}\right)$, $\left(\frac{5}{6}\right)\left(\frac{1}{6}\right)$, $\left(\frac{5}{6}\right)^2\left(\frac{1}{6}\right)$, $\left(\frac{5}{6}\right)^3\left(\frac{1}{6}\right)$, ... is a geometric sequence with first term $\frac{1}{6}$ and common ratio $\frac{5}{6}$, which is why this distribution is called a geometric distribution. These sequences will be studied in Course 3 Unit 7, *Recursion and Iteration*.)

b. $P(5) = \left(\frac{5}{6}\right)^4\left(\frac{1}{6}\right)$; $P(6) = \left(\frac{5}{6}\right)^5\left(\frac{1}{6}\right)$; to get doubles for the first time on the fifth roll, you must fail to get doubles four times and then get doubles. To get doubles for the first time on the sixth roll, you must fail to get doubles five times and then get doubles.

c. $P(x) = \left(\frac{5}{6}\right)^{x-1}\left(\frac{1}{6}\right)$

d. See Part e.

e. Students can complete this table easily by using the list functions of their calculators. If the numbers of rolls are in L₁, then the probabilities can be placed in L₂ by placing the cursor on top of L₂ and typing **(1/6)*(5/6)^(L₁-1)** and pressing ⓔⓝⓣⓔⓡ.

See the table below.

Number of Rolls to Get Doubles	Probability	Probability (to thousandths)
1	$\frac{1}{6}$	0.167
2	$\left(\frac{5}{6}\right)\left(\frac{1}{6}\right)$	0.139
3	$\left(\frac{5}{6}\right)^2\left(\frac{1}{6}\right)$	0.116
4	$\left(\frac{5}{6}\right)^3\left(\frac{1}{6}\right)$	0.096
5	$\left(\frac{5}{6}\right)^4\left(\frac{1}{6}\right)$	0.080
6	$\left(\frac{5}{6}\right)^5\left(\frac{1}{6}\right)$	0.067
7	$\left(\frac{5}{6}\right)^6\left(\frac{1}{6}\right)$	0.056
8	$\left(\frac{5}{6}\right)^7\left(\frac{1}{6}\right)$	0.047
9	$\left(\frac{5}{6}\right)^8\left(\frac{1}{6}\right)$	0.039
10	$\left(\frac{5}{6}\right)^9\left(\frac{1}{6}\right)$	0.032
11	$\left(\frac{5}{6}\right)^{10}\left(\frac{1}{6}\right)$	0.027
12	$\left(\frac{5}{6}\right)^{11}\left(\frac{1}{6}\right)$	0.022
13 or more		0.112

The sum of the probabilities in rows 1 to 12 is approximately 0.888.

f.

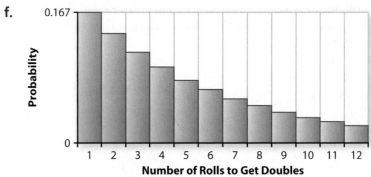

Each bar is $\frac{5}{6}$ the height of the bar to its left. This is because you expect $\frac{1}{6}$ of the people to roll doubles at any given stage, and so $\frac{5}{6}$ of those people remain in jail.

g. No, because the probability of requiring 12 or more rolls is 0.022 + 0.112, which is greater than 0.05.

Teacher Notes

④ Use your completed probability distribution table to find the following probabilities. "Rolls" stands for the number of rolls to get doubles for the first time.

  a. $P(rolls \leq 3)$

  b. $P(rolls > 3)$

  c. $P(rolls \geq 5)$

⑤ In this problem, you will develop a formula for waiting-time distributions. In this general case, use the letter p to represent the probability of getting the waited-for event. (In the situation of waiting for doubles on a pair of dice, $p \approx 0.167$ on each trial. In the situation of flipping a coin until a head appears, $p = 0.5$ on each trial.)

  a. The first row of the table below gives the probability that the waited-for event will occur on the first trial. On a copy of this table, fill in the first row.

Number of Trials to Get First Success, x	Probability, $P(x)$
1	
2	
3	
4	
5	
x	

  b. What is the probability of not getting the waited-for event on the first trial and then getting it on the second trial? Fill in the second row of the table.

  c. What is the probability of not getting the waited-for event on the first trial, not getting it on the second trial, and then getting it on the third trial? Fill in the third row of the table.

  d. Finish filling in the rows of the table. In the last row, write a general formula for the probability it will take x trials to get the first success. Compare your formula with those of your classmates. Resolve any differences.

  e. How is your general formula like an exponential function rule? How is it different?

Unit 8

④ The answers below use the rounded table entries from Problem 3.

 a. $P(rolls \leq 3) \approx 0.422$

 b. $P(rolls > 3) \approx 0.578$

 c. $P(rolls \geq 5) \approx 0.482$

⑤ **a–d.**

Number of Trials to Get First Success, x	Probability, $P(x)$
1	p
2	$(1 - p)p$
3	$(1 - p)^2 p$
4	$(1 - p)^3 p$
5	$(1 - p)^4 p$
x	$(1 - p)^{x - 1} p$

e. The general formula is like an exponential function rule in that the variable occurs in an exponent. The overall shapes of the two graphs are the same; but in this waiting-time situation, only positive integer values of x are in the domain.

INSTRUCTIONAL NOTE
The exponential models students studied in Course 1 were of the form $y = ab^x$, so you may need to help students recognize that $y = p(1 - p)^{x - 1}$ is also an exponential function.

6 Use your formula from Problem 5 to answer these questions.

a. The Current Population Survey of the U.S. Census Bureau recently found that 27% of adults over the age of 25 in the United States have at least a bachelor's degree. If a line of randomly-selected U.S. adults over the age of 25 is walking past you, what is the probability that the fifth person to pass will be the first with four or more years of college?

b. What is the probability that parents would have seven boys in a row and then have a girl? Use $P(boy) = 0.51$ and assume births are independent.

Summarize the Mathematics

In this investigation, you developed a formula for constructing a waiting-time distribution.

a Describe what each term in the formula represents.

b Explain how you know your formula gives the correct probability.

c How can you determine if a specific event in a waiting-time distribution is a rare event?

Be prepared to share your ideas and reasoning with the class.

Unit 8

6 **a.** $P(5) = (1 - 0.27)^{(5 - 1)}(0.27) \approx 0.077$

b. $P(8) = (0.51)^{7}(0.49) \approx 0.004$

Summarize
the Mathematics

Teaching Resources

Transparency Master 27.

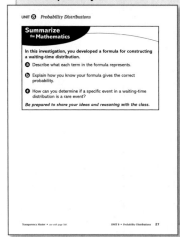

a $P(x) = (1 - p)^{x - 1}p$, where $P(x)$ is the probability that the first success occurs on the xth trial, p is the probability of a success on each trial, $1 - p$ is the probability of failure, and $x - 1$ is one fewer than the number of trials.

b The formula works because in order to get the first success on the xth trial, you first need to have $x - 1$ failures, each with probability $(1 - p)$, followed by a success, with probability p. You can use the Multiplication Rule for independent events to multiply because the trials are independent in a waiting-time situation.

c You add the probability of that many trials being needed to get the first success to the probabilities that it will take even more trials. If the sum is 0.05 or less, you have a rare event. Alternatively, add up the probabilities that it will take fewer trials. If the sum is greater than 0.95, you have a rare event.

MATH TOOLKIT Record the formula for constructing a waiting-time distribution. Indicate what the variables mean. Explain how to determine if an event is a rare event.

✓ *Check Your Understanding*

Complete a probability distribution table like the one below for the experiment of flipping a coin until a head appears. Complete the "Probability, $P(x)$" column using decimals rounded to the nearest thousandth.

Number of Flips to Get a Head, x	Probability, $P(x)$
1	
2	
3	
4	
5	
6	
7	
8	
9	
10	

a. Make a graph of your distribution.

b. What is the probability that the first head occurs on the second flip?

c. What is the formula for $P(x)$, the probability of getting the first head on flip number x? Simplify this formula.

d. What is the probability that Scott will require at most 5 flips to get a head?

e. What is the probability that Michele will require at least 8 flips to get a head?

f. What numbers of flips are considered rare events?

g. Suppose that the parents pictured had planned to have children until they had a boy. Did a rare event occur? Assume that the probability of getting a boy on each birth is 0.5.

Number of Flips to Get a Head, x	Probability, $P(x)$
1	0.500
2	0.250
3	0.125
4	0.063
5	0.031
6	0.016
7	0.008
8	0.004
9	0.002
10	0.001

a.

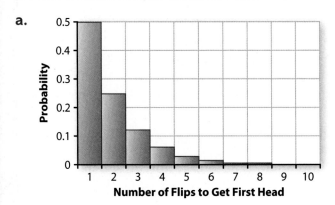

b. $P(2) = 0.250$

c. $P(x) = (1 - 0.5)^{x-1}(0.5) = 0.5^x$

d. 0.969

e. 0.007

f. 6 or more flips

g. This is a rare event. The probability of having more than 9 children to get the first boy is $\left(\frac{1}{2}\right)^9$, or approximately 0.002, because the first 9 children must be girls. If you count the event of getting all boys as equally extreme, the probability of getting a family this extreme is 2(0.002), or 0.004.

Expected Waiting Time

According to the company that makes them, M&M's® Milk Chocolate Candies are put randomly into bags from a large vat in which all the colors have been mixed. The percentage of different color coatings varies—20% are orange.

The probability distribution table below shows the waiting time to draw an orange one from a very large bag of the candies. In this situation, the probability of success on a single trial is 0.2. As you work on the problems in this investigation, look for an answer to this question:

How can you find the expected value of a waiting-time distribution?

Drawing Candies

Number of Draws to Get First Orange Candy	Probability
1	0.2
2	$(0.8)(0.2)$
3	$(0.8)^2(0.2)$
4	$(0.8)^3(0.2)$
5	$(0.8)^4(0.2)$
6	$(0.8)^5(0.2)$
7	$(0.8)^6(0.2)$
8	$(0.8)^7(0.2)$
9	$(0.8)^8(0.2)$
10	$(0.8)^9(0.2)$
11	$(0.8)^{10}(0.2)$
12	$(0.8)^{11}(0.2)$
⋮	

1. In this problem and the next one, you will explore how to find the expected number of draws until an orange candy appears. In other words, if a large number of people each draws candies until an orange one appears, what is the average number they draw?

    a. What is the difficulty in trying to find the expected value of this waiting-time distribution?

    b. Make an estimate of the expected value of the distribution by using just the first 25 rows of the table to compute the expected value. Keep at least 6 decimal places in all calculations.

    c. How much would adding the 26th row change your expected value?

    d. Is the real expected value larger or smaller than your estimate in Part b?

Expected Waiting Time

In this investigation, students find a theoretical way to calculate the expected value of a waiting-time distribution. At this point, students know how to calculate the individual probabilities and how to estimate the expected value from a table with many rows. They can compute the expected value (*EV*) for a probability distribution with a finite number of rows. In the case of a waiting-time distribution, the number of possibilities is endless (the histogram has an infinitely long tail) so that the mean that students calculated from a finite number of rows was not exact. In this investigation, students will use these estimates for distributions with various values of p to look for a pattern.

Launch

You may wish to do Problem 1 Part a as a class using calculator lists or spreadsheet software such as in *CPMP-Tools* and then divide up the work for the remaining values of p in the table asked for in Part b. When groups complete Problem 2 Part a, you can bring everyone back together to share all of the estimates and to make the graph. The model that fits best is the inverse function $y = \dfrac{1}{x}$ or $EV = \dfrac{1}{p}$.

1 The solutions below were found using lists and rounding to 6 decimal places.

a. Because the table actually has an infinite number of rows and you are using only the first 12 or so, you will be estimating the expected value.

b. 4.886663

c. A 26th row would increase the expected value by approximately 0.196450.

d. Larger because the missing rows would add to the sum.

Unit 8

(2) Place your estimated expected value from Problem 1, Part b in the appropriate space in a copy of the table below.

Expected Waiting Time

Probability of a Success, p, on Each Trial	Estimated Average Waiting Time (Expected Value)
0.10	10
0.20	
0.30	
0.40	
0.50	
0.60	
0.70	
0.80	
0.90	

a. The students in your class should regroup, if necessary, into seven groups, one for each of the remaining values of p in the table above. Each group should construct a waiting-time probability distribution table for its value of p. Tables should have at least 25 rows. Then estimate the expected waiting time for your value of p.

b. Get the expected waiting time from each of the groups and fill in the rest of the table.

c. Using a copy of this coordinate grid, make a scatterplot of the values from your table.

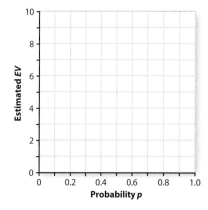

Unit 8

(2) **a–b. INSTRUCTIONAL NOTE** The completed table should look similar to this one that contains the theoretical expected values. However, each *EV* computed by the students will be a bit smaller than the theoretical ones because students can include only a finite number of rows.

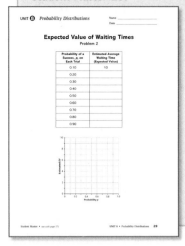
Expected Waiting Time

Probability of a Success, p, on Each Trial	Estimated Average Waiting Time (Expected Value)
0.10	10.00
0.20	5.00
0.30	3.33
0.40	2.50
0.50	2.00
0.60	1.67
0.70	1.43
0.80	1.25
0.90	1.11

c.

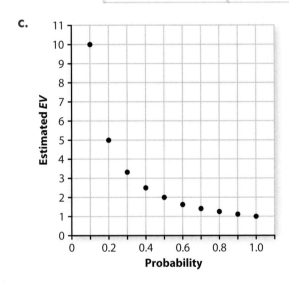

d. What is the expected value when $p = 1.00$? Plot the corresponding point on the scatterplot.

e. Describe the overall pattern relating probability p and expected value EV. Find an equation whose graph fits these points well.

f. According to your equation, how many candies would you expect to draw (from a large bag that contains 20% orange candies) until you get an orange one?

3 Use your equation from Problem 2 to answer the following questions.

a. Suppose you want a sum of 6. How many times do you expect to have to roll the dice?

b. About 25% of adults bite their fingernails. How many adults do you expect to have to choose at random until you find a fingernail biter?

c. There is about 1 chance in 14,000,000 of winning the California lottery with a single ticket. If a person buys one ticket a week, how many weeks do you expect to pass until he or she wins the lottery? How many years is this? If an average lifetime is 75 years, how many lifetimes is this?

Summarize
the Mathematics

In this investigation, you discovered the formula for the expected value of a waiting-time distribution. Suppose the probability of success on each trial of a waiting-time distribution is *p*.

a Write a formula for the expected value of this distribution. What information do you need to know about a distribution in order to use this formula?

b Explain what happens to the expected waiting time as *p* gets larger.

c How can you estimate the expected waiting time just using the histogram?

Be prepared to share your ideas and examples with the class.

✓Check Your Understanding

Suppose 30% of the beads in a very large bag are red.

a. How many beads would you expect to draw from the bag until you got a red one?

b. Can you conclude from Part a that about half of the people trying this experiment would need that many draws or even more to get a red bead? Explain.

d. Since the event is sure to happen on the first trial, the expected value is 1.

e. The points appear to lie near the graph of the equation of an inverse power function, $y = \frac{1}{x}$. Specifically, we have $EV = \frac{1}{p}$.

f. $EV = \frac{1}{0.2} = 5$ candies

NOTE A proof of the formula $EV = \frac{1}{p}$ for the case $p = \frac{1}{6}$ appears on page T583, following the solution for Extensions Task 23. This proof uses the formula for the sum of an infinite geometric series. Here is an informal justification that $EV = \frac{1}{p}$. Imagine, for example, that you are waiting for doubles while rolling a pair of dice. You repeat this over and over again, forming a long sequence of doubles (D) or not doubles (N): NNDNNNNNNNNNNDDNNNDNNNNNDNDNNNNND.

Then, p, the probability of getting doubles can be estimated by dividing the number of Ds by the total number of trials:

$$p \approx \frac{\text{number of Ds}}{\text{number of trials}}.$$

But the expected waiting time can be estimated by the reciprocal

$$\frac{\text{number of trials}}{\text{number of Ds}} \approx \frac{1}{p}.$$

(3) **a.** The probability of getting a sum of 6 on each roll is $\frac{5}{36}$,
$$EV = \frac{1}{\frac{5}{36}} = \frac{36}{5} = 7.2 \text{ rolls.}$$

b. $EV = \frac{1}{0.25} = 4$ adults

c. $EV = \dfrac{1}{\frac{1}{14,000,000}} = 14,000,000$ weeks;

This would be $\dfrac{14,000,000}{52} = 269,231$ years, or

$\dfrac{269,231}{75} = 3,590$ lifetimes.

DIFFERENTIATION The expected value formula can be derived by twice using the method outlined in Extensions Task 23 on page T583.

Summarize
the Mathematics

(a) $EV = \frac{1}{p}$. You need to know that you have a waiting-time distribution; that is, the trials are independent and the probability of a success remains the same for each trial. If these conditions are met, all you need to know to use the formula is the probability of success, p, on each trial.

(b) As p gets larger, the expected waiting time gets smaller. If p is large, you have a larger chance of getting a success than if p is small, and so you expect to get a success sooner on the average. This is an inverse variation relationship.

(c) Like any mean, the expected waiting time is the balance point of the histogram. When estimating the balance point, remember that the histogram has an infinitely long tail in which the bars get shorter and shorter as the number of trials increases.

Teaching Resources

Transparency Master 30.

UNIT 8 *Probability Distributions*

Summarize
the **Mathematics**

In this investigation, you discovered the formula for the expected value of a waiting-time distribution. Suppose the probability of success on each trial of a waiting-time distribution is p.

a Write a formula for the expected value of this distribution. What information do you need to know about a distribution in order to use this formula?

b Explain what happens to the expected waiting time as p gets larger.

c How can you estimate the expected waiting time just using the histogram?

Be prepared to share your ideas and examples with the class.

MATH TOOLKIT Record the formula for the expected value of a waiting-time distribution. Indicate what the variables mean.

NOTE The solutions to the Check Your Understanding are on page T573.

Unit 8

Applications

① Cereal manufacturers often place small prizes in their cereal boxes as a marketing scheme. Boxes of cereal once contained one of four endangered animal stickers: bird of paradise, tiger, African elephant, and crocodile. Suppose that these stickers were placed randomly into the boxes and that there were an equal number of each kind of animal sticker.

a. Polly likes birds and wanted the bird of paradise sticker. Describe a simulation to estimate the average number of boxes of cereal that Polly would have had to buy before she got a bird sticker.

b. Do five runs of your simulation. Add your results to those in the frequency table below so that there is a total of 100 runs. If needed, add additional rows.

Getting a Bird Sticker

Number of Boxes	Frequency	Number of Boxes	Frequency
1	19	15	0
2	14	16	2
3	15	17	1
4	13	18	0
5	11	19	1
6	6	20	0
7	4	21	0
8	2	22	0
9	1	23	0
10	1	24	0
11	1	25	0
12	3	26	1
13	0	Total	
14	0		

c. Make a histogram from the completed frequency table and describe its shape.

d. Use the completed frequency table to estimate the mean number of boxes a person would have to buy to get a bird of paradise sticker.

e. Estimate the chance that a person would need to buy more than 10 boxes.

✓ Check Your Understanding

a. $\dfrac{1}{\frac{1}{0.30}} = 3\frac{1}{3}$ beads

b. No. The *EV* computed in Part a is the mean while the question refers to the median. In fact, 0.30 of the people will get a red bead on the first draw and $(0.7)(0.3) = 0.21$ on the second draw. So, after the second draw, 51% of the people will have drawn a red bead. Thus, the median is 2, not 3 or more.

Applications

1
  a. One possible simulation is described here. Use a random digit table. Let the digit 1 represent a bird of paradise, 2 represent a tiger, 3 represent an African elephant, and 4 represent a crocodile. Ignore all other digits. Start at a random place on the table and count the number of digits (1 to 4) until a 1 appears.

  b. Student runs will vary.

  c. A typical histogram will look like the following. The histogram is skewed right with the first bar being the tallest and the bars generally decreasing in height.

Getting a Bird Sticker

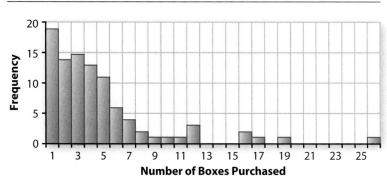

d. The average number of boxes using the runs in the table is $\dfrac{439}{95} \approx 4.62$. Students' answers will vary based on their 5 runs. (The theoretical mean is 4.)

e. Responses will vary according to the student's completed histogram. From the preceding histogram, the estimated probability of having to buy more than 10 boxes is equal to $\dfrac{9}{100}$, or 0.09.

2 Two statisticians have estimated that a penny has about a 6% chance of going out of circulation each year. About 10,000,000,000 pennies are minted each year in the United States. Assume that was the number minted the year you were born.

a. Complete this theoretical probability distribution table for the number of those pennies that go out of circulation each year. Add as many rows as you need to get to this year.

Circulation of Pennies from Your Birth Year

Years Since Your Birth	Number of Pennies That Go out of Circulation	Number of Pennies Still Left in Circulation
0	—	10,000,000,000
1	600,000,000	9,400,000,000
2		
3		
4		
5		

b. Write a *NOW-NEXT* equation describing the pattern of change in each of the last two columns.

c. Approximately what percentage of the pennies minted the year you were born are still in circulation?

d. Estimate the mean length of time until a penny goes out of circulation.

e. About how long will it (or did it) take for half of the pennies minted in the year you were born to go out of circulation? (This length of time is called the half-life of a penny.)

3 Suppose that you are drawing one card at a time from a deck of cards and want to get a heart.

a. Describe a simulation using random digits to estimate the mean number of draws from a regular deck of cards needed to get a heart if the card is replaced after each draw.

b. How would you modify your simulation model if the card is not replaced after each draw?

c. What is the probability that it will take you exactly 4 draws to get the first heart if the card is replaced after each draw?

2 **a.** Exact number of rows may vary, depending on the student's age.

Circulation of Pennies from Your Birth Year

Years Since Your Birth	Number of Pennies That Go out of Circulation	Number of Pennies Still Left in Circulation
0	—	10,000,000,000
1	600,000,000	9,400,000,000
2	564,000,000	8,836,000,000
3	530,160,000	8,305,840,000
4	498,350,400	7,807,489,600
5	468,449,376	7,339,040,224
6	440,342,413	6,898,697,811
7	413,921,869	6,484,775,942
8	389,086,557	6,095,689,385
9	365,741,363	5,729,948,022
10	343,796,881	5,386,151,141
11	323,169,069	5,062,982,072

b. Second column: *NEXT* = 0.94*NOW*
Third column: *NEXT* = 0.94*NOW*

c. Responses will vary, depending on the student's age. See the table to the right.

d. Estimates should be approximately 16.7 years but will vary depending on the length of the table.

e. About 11 years

Age	Percentage of Pennies Still in Circulation
12	$(0.94)^{12} \approx 0.476$
13	0.447
14	0.421
15	0.395
16	0.372
17	0.349
18	0.328
19	0.309

3 **a.** Simulations may vary. For example, a simulation might use a calculator to generate integers 1 through 52 (through a command such as **randInt(1,52)**. Let the integers 1 though 13 represent hearts. Count the number of integers until an integer in the interval 1 through 13 appears.

Alternatively, students could also use the random digit table and let 1 represent a heart. Digits 2, 3, and 4 could represent the other suits and then students can ignore all other digits. Start at a random place on the table and count the number of digits (1 to 4) until a 1 appears.

b. For the first simulation, after "drawing" the first card and finding it not to be a heart, one card is gone from the deck. So, to draw the second card, students should use **randInt(1,51)**. But, the integers 1 through 13 will always represent a heart. The third draw will be simulated using **randInt(1,50)**, and so on. If the student used only 4 digits, he or she will have to totally redesign their simulation.

c. $\left(\frac{3}{4}\right)^3\left(\frac{1}{4}\right) \approx 0.105$

d. What is the probability that it will take you no more than 4 draws to get the first heart if the card is replaced after each draw?

e. What is the probability that it will take you at least 4 draws to get the first heart if the card is replaced after each draw?

f. Would it be a rare event if it took you 5 draws to get the first heart?

4 Suppose there are 1,000 people who, like Polly in Applications Task 1, are buying boxes of cereal in order to get a bird of paradise sticker.

a. Make a chart with six rows that shows how many people you would expect to get a bird of paradise sticker with the first box, with the second box, etc.

b. Write a formula for $P(x)$, the probability of getting a tiger sticker on the xth purchase.

5 Sixteen percent of "M&M's®" Plain Chocolate Candies are green. Suppose that you are drawing candies one at a time from a very large bag of M&M's® in which all the colors have been mixed. (The bag has so many candies in it that you can assume that the probability of drawing a green candy is still about 0.16, no matter how many you have drawn before.)

a. Find the first five entries of the table for the waiting-time probability distribution for drawing a green candy.

b. What is the probability it takes you at least four draws to get a green candy?

6 Consider a situation in which a blood bank is testing people at random until it finds a person with type O blood. About 45% of the U.S. population has type O blood.

a. Make a probability distribution table with five rows for this situation.

b. Write a formula for $P(x)$, the probability that the xth person tested is the first with type O blood.

c. What is the probability that the 5th person tested is the first with type O blood?

d. What is the probability that it takes 5 or more people before getting one with type O blood?

e. Would it be a rare event if it takes 5 people before getting one with type O blood?

d. $P(\text{4 or fewer draws}) = \left(\frac{1}{4}\right) + \left(\frac{3}{4}\right)\left(\frac{1}{4}\right) + \left(\frac{3}{4}\right)^2\left(\frac{1}{4}\right) + \left(\frac{3}{4}\right)^3\left(\frac{1}{4}\right) \approx 0.684$

e. $P(\text{at least 4 draws}) = 1 - P(\text{3 or fewer draws}) =$
$1 - \left[\left(\frac{1}{4}\right) + \left(\frac{3}{4}\right)\left(\frac{1}{4}\right) + \left(\frac{3}{4}\right)^2\left(\frac{1}{4}\right)\right] \approx 0.422$

f. No, from Part d, the probability of requiring 5 draws or more is approximately $1 - 0.684 \approx 0.316$, and 0.316 is greater than 0.05.

④ a. Getting a Bird Sticker

Number of Boxes	Expected Number Who Get the Sticker
1	250
2	187.5
3	140.625
4	105.469
5	79.102
6	59.326

b. $P(x) = (1 - 0.25)^{x-1}(0.25)$

⑤ a. Drawing M&M Candies

Number of Draws to Get First Green Candy	Probability
1	0.16
2	$(0.84)(0.16) = 0.1344$
3	$(0.84)^2(0.16) \approx 0.1129$
4	$(0.84)^3(0.16) \approx 0.0948$
5	$(0.84)^4(0.16) \approx 0.0797$

b. $P(\text{4 or more draws}) = 1 - P(\text{fewer than 4 draws}) \approx 1 - 0.4073 = 0.5927$. Alternatively, to require 4 or more draws, you must fail on the first 3, which happens with probability $(0.84)^3 \approx 0.5927$.

⑥ a. Probability Distribution for Waiting for Type O Blood

Number of Draws to Get Type O Blood	Probability
1	0.45
2	$(0.55)(0.45) = 0.2475$
3	$(0.55)^2(0.45) \approx 0.1361$
4	$(0.55)^3(0.45) \approx 0.0749$
5	$(0.55)^4(0.45) \approx 0.0412$

b. $P(x) = (0.55)^{x-1}(0.45)$

c. 0.0412

d. $P(\text{5 or more}) = 1 - (0.45 + 0.2475 + 0.1361 + 0.0749) = 1 - 0.9085$
$= 0.0915$. Alternatively, to require 5 or more people, you need to begin with four failures and the probability of that is $(0.55)^4 \approx 0.0915$.

e. No. From Part d, the probability of needing 5 or more people is 0.0915, which is greater than 0.05.

7. Painkillers are often given as shots to people who have sustained injuries. The time that it takes for a person's body to get the medicine out of his or her system varies from person to person. Suppose one person is given 400 mg of a medicine, and her body metabolizes the medicine so 35% is removed from her bloodstream each hour.

   a. Complete the following chart.

Hours	Milligrams of Medicine Leaving the Blood	Milligrams of Medicine Left in the Blood
0	0	400
1		
2		
3		
4		
5		
6		

   b. How is this situation similar to and different from a waiting-time distribution?

   c. On average, how long does a milligram of medicine stay in the blood?

   d. What is the approximate half-life of medicine in the blood? That is, how long does it take for half of the medicine to be gone?

8. In the 1986 nuclear reactor disaster at Chernobyl in the former Soviet Union, radioactive atoms of strontium-90 were released. Strontium-90 decays at the rate of 2.5% a year.

   a. What is the average time it takes for a strontium-90 atom to decay?

   b. Supposedly, it will be safe again for people to live in the area after 100 years. What percentage of the strontium-90 released will still be present after 100 years?

7 **a.**

Hours	Milligrams of Medicine Leaving the Blood	Milligrams of Medicine Left in the Blood
0	0	400
1	140.00	260.00
2	91.00	169.00
3	59.15	109.85
4	38.45	71.40
5	24.99	46.41
6	16.24	30.17

b. The first two columns define a waiting-time distribution that is much like the others such as the waiting time to get doubles. There is a difference, however. The medicine does not leave the blood all at once at the end of 1 hour. This is a continuous process. The medicine leaves gradually throughout the hour. Further, there is no randomness or probability in this situation.

c. Expected (mean) length of time in the blood is $\frac{1}{0.35}$, or 2.857 hours.

d. The half-life is between 1 and 2 hours.

8 **a.** The average time for a strontium-90 atom to decay is $\frac{1}{0.025}$, or 40 years.

b. After 100 years, 0.975^{100}, or about 7.95%, of the radioactive strontium-90 will remain.

Connections

9 Refer to the table for waiting for doubles in Problem 3 of Investigation 1 on page 563.

    a. Make a scatterplot of the points (*number of rolls to get doubles, expected number of students who get out of jail on this roll*).

    b. Find an algebraic model of the form "$y = \dots$" that is a good fit for these points.

    c. Let *NOW* be the number of people who are expected to get doubles on a roll, and let *NEXT* be the number of people who are expected to get doubles on the next roll. Write a rule relating *NOW* and *NEXT*.

10 Let A be the event of requiring exactly 5 rolls of a pair of dice to get doubles for the first time. Let B be the event that the first four rolls are not doubles. Find the following probabilities.

    a. $P(A)$ **b.** $P(B)$

    c. $P(A \mid B)$ **d.** $P(B \mid A)$

    e. $P(A \text{ and } B)$ **f.** $P(A \text{ or } B)$

11 Consider the median as a measure of center of a probability distribution.

    a. Find the median of the waiting-time-for-doubles probability distribution produced in Problems 1–3 of Investigation 2. In this situation, what does the median tell you?

    b. Describe how to find the median of any probability distribution.

    c. Make a rough sketch of the box plot of a waiting-time distribution.

12 You have studied many different models for expressing relationships between quantitative variables, including linear, exponential, power, and quadratic.

    a. When examining the pattern in your scatterplot from Problem 2 of Investigation 3, which of these models could you immediately rule out as not reasonable? Explain your reasoning.

    b. Refer to Applications Task 7. Write an equation that represents the number of milligrams of medicine left in the blood at any hour x.

    c. Refer to Applications Task 2. Write an equation that represents the number of pennies minted in your birth year that are still in circulation x years later.

Connections

9 **a.**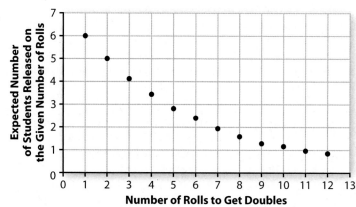

b. The best algebraic model will be an exponential equation. The exponential equation that passes through these points is $y = 7.2\left(\frac{5}{6}\right)^x$, where $x = 1, 2, 3, \ldots$.

c. $NEXT = \frac{5}{6}\, NOW$

10 **a.** $P(A) = \left(\frac{5}{6}\right)^4\left(\frac{1}{6}\right) = 0.080$ **b.** $P(B) = \left(\frac{5}{6}\right)^4 \approx 0.482$

c. $P(A \mid B) = \frac{1}{6}$ **d.** $P(B \mid A) = 1$

e. $P(A \text{ and } B) = 0.080$ **f.** $P(A \text{ or } B) = 0.482$

11 **a.** The median is 4. Roughly half of the time it will take 4 or fewer rolls to get doubles and half the time it will take 4 or more rolls to get doubles.

b. Add the probabilities until the sum is 0.5 or greater. The row with the last probability that was added gives the median.

c. The box plot should be skewed right. The box plots at the right show the waiting-time distributions to get a tiger sticker when there are four stickers available, heads when a coin is flipped, and doubles when two dice are rolled.

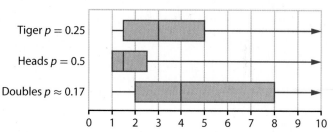

Situation	min	Q_1	median	Q_3	max
Tiger Sticker $p = 0.25$	1	1.5	3	5	infinite
Heads on Coin Flip $p = 0.5$	1	1	1.5	2.5	infinite
Rolling Doubles $p = \frac{1}{6} \approx 0.17$	1	2	4	8	infinite

12 **a.** Because the points follow a curve, the relationship is not linear. It cannot be exponential or quadratic because it has a vertical asymptote at $x = 0$. Possible equations include $y = \frac{1}{x}$ and $y = \frac{1}{x^2}$.

b. $y = 400(0.65^x)$

c. $y = 10{,}000{,}000{,}000(0.94^x)$

Unit 8

(13) When given some information about a waiting-time distribution, you can use connections to reason to other information.

   a. If the expected value of a waiting-time distribution is 6.5, what is the probability p of success on each trial?

   b. James draws marbles one at a time from a bag of green and white marbles. He replaces each marble before drawing the next. If the probability that he gets his first green marble on the second draw is 0.24, what percentage of the marbles in the bag are green?

(14) Most of the waiting-time distributions that you investigated in this unit could be represented by formulas of the form $P(x) = pq^{x-1}$.

   a. For a given situation, what would the symbols $P(x)$, p, and q represent? How are p and q related?

   b. What is the expected value of this distribution?

(15) The waiting-time distribution below was constructed by a computer simulation.

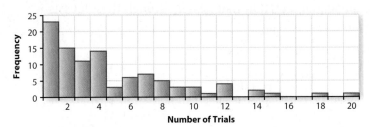

   Think of at least two methods that you could use to estimate p, the probability of the event occurring on each trial. What is your estimate of p with each method?

Reflections

(16) April and May are playing Anita's game (See page 561.) and are both in jail. April has tried twice to roll doubles and failed both times. May has tried only once, and she was also unsuccessful. Who has the better chance of rolling doubles on her next turn? Explain your reasoning.

13 **a.** Solve the equation $6.5 = \frac{1}{p}$ for p. Multiplying both sides by p gives $6.5p = 1$. Finally, dividing both sides by 6.5 gives $p = \frac{1}{6.5} \approx 0.154$.

b. Solve the quadratic equation $(1 - p)p = 0.24$ for p. The two solutions are 0.6 and 0.4. So, either 60% or 40% of the marbles in the bag are green.

14 **a.** $P(x)$ is the probability that success will happen first on the xth trial. p is the probability of a success on any given trial, all of which are independent in a waiting-time distribution. q is the probability of not having success on any given trial. Thus, $p + q = 1$.

b. $\frac{1}{p}$

15 Adding up the heights of all of the bars gives a total of 100 runs. Since 23 of the runs were successful on the first trial, a good estimate is $p = 0.23$. Alternatively, there were 23 successes on the first trial and 15 on the second trial. The second bar is 0.65 times the first. The estimate of p would then be $1.00 - 0.65$, or 0.35. A third strategy would be to count the total number of trials, which is 479. One hundred of these were successful trials. The estimate of p in this case is $\frac{100}{479}$, or approximately 0.21. Your students may think of other methods (such as finding the exponential regression equation) or doing simulations with various values of p to find the value of p that gives a distribution like this one. In fact, this distribution was simulated with $p = 0.2$.

Reflections

POSSIBLE MISCONCEPTION If your students are not sure of the response to Reflections Task 16, you may wish to have them carry out the following activity. The workload should be divided among groups of students.

- One group of students will represent May trying to roll doubles on her first roll of the dice. That group will roll the dice many times, for example, 400 times, each time a "first try," and count the number of doubles. This group now has an approximation of the probability of rolling doubles on the first try.

- The second group, representing April, will roll the dice until they did not get doubles twice in a row. The group will then try to get doubles on the third roll. Counting only the times the group tried a third roll, they shall repeat this process 400 times (not doubles, not doubles, try to roll doubles). This group now has an approximation of the probability of rolling doubles on the third try, given that doubles did not happen on the first or second try.

The two groups probably will not get exactly the same probability. Before the experiment, discuss with the class how close the relative frequencies will have to be so that they believe the theoretical probabilities are the same and how far apart the relative frequencies will have to be so that they believe the theoretical probabilities are different. (With 400 repetitions, there is a 95% chance that the probabilities will be within 0.05 of each other.)

TECHNOLOGY NOTE *CPMP-Tools* Simulation software can be used to quickly generate thousands of flips of a coin to help address this misconception.

NOTE Continued misconception information and the solution to Task 16 are on page T579.

Unit 8

17 Suppose that two dice are rolled repeatedly.

a. What is the probability of getting doubles on the first roll? On the fourth roll?

b. What is the probability of getting doubles for the first time on the first roll? What is the probability of getting doubles for the first time on the fourth roll?

c. Compare your answers to Parts a and b. Why is the probability of getting doubles for the first time on the fourth roll less than the probability of getting doubles on the fourth roll?

18 The table and histogram below give the mileage at which each of 191 buses had its first major motor failure. Is the shape of the distribution the same as that of other waiting-time distributions you have seen? Explain why this makes sense.

Mileage before Failure	Number of Buses
0 to 19,999	6
20,000 to 39,999	11
40,000 to 59,999	16
60,000 to 79,999	25
80,000 to 99,999	34
100,000 to 119,999	46
120,000 to 139,999	33
140,000 to 159,999	16
160,000 and up	4
Total	**191**

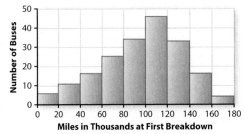

Source: Mudholkar, G.S., D.K. Srivastava, and M. Freimer.
"The Exponential Weibull Family: A Reanalysis of the Bus-Motor-Failure Data."
Technometrics 37 (Nov. 1995): 436–445.

CONTINUED FROM PAGE T578

One of the difficulties of simulation is the large number of runs needed to convince students that two probabilities are the same. If, for example, one student flips a nickel 100 times and another flips a penny 100 times, there is a very good chance that there will be a difference of 0.10 or more in the proportion of heads with the nickel and with the penny. One of the students could easily get 45 heads out of 100 and the other get 56 out of 100, for a difference of 0.11. Very roughly, if each coin is flipped n times, there is a 95% chance that the two estimates will be no farther apart than $\frac{\sqrt{2}}{\sqrt{n}}$.

16 Both April and May have the same probability of rolling doubles, $\frac{1}{6}$, on her next turn. The rolls of the dice are independent and probabilities do not change depending on what has been rolled before.

17 a. $\frac{1}{6}; \frac{1}{6}$

b. $\frac{1}{6}; \left(\frac{5}{6}\right)^3\left(\frac{1}{6}\right)$

c. The probability of getting doubles on the fourth roll is independent of what happens on the first three rolls. The probability of getting doubles for the first time on the fourth roll means that all three of the other rolls must not be doubles. Thus, only one outcome from the sample space of four rolls of a pair of dice would involve getting doubles for the first time on the fourth roll, while many outcomes will involve getting doubles on the fourth roll.

18 The histogram is not the same shape as that of a waiting-time distribution and we would not expect it to be. The probability of a breakdown is not the same on each mile the bus is driven. The probability of a breakdown increases as the bus gets older. The bars eventually decrease after almost all buses have had their first breakdown.

19 Examine each of the following probability distributions.

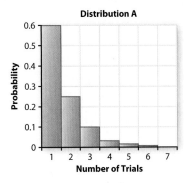

Distribution A

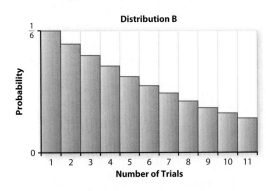

Distribution B

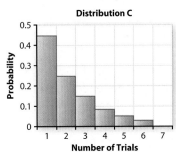

Distribution C

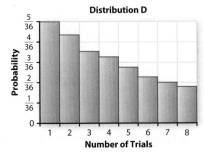

Distribution D

a. Match the following descriptions to the probability distributions.

- rolling a die until a 6 appears
- rolling two dice until a sum of 6 appears
- counting the days on which the weather report states there is a 60% chance of rain until there is a rainy day
- selecting a person at random until one with type O blood appears (About 45% of the U.S. population has type O blood.)

b. What is the height of the second bar (representing 2 trials) in each case? The third bar?

20 Which of the following, if any, are correct interpretations of the expected value (*EV*) of a waiting-time distribution?

- Half of the people wait longer than the EV and half shorter.
- The EV is the most likely time to wait.
- More than half of the people will wait longer than the *EV*.

19 **a.** • Rolling a die until a 6 appears: Distribution B

  • Rolling two dice until a sum of 6 appears: Distribution D

  • Counting the days on which the weather report says there is a 60% chance of rain until there is a rainy day: Distribution A

  • Selecting a person at random until one with type O blood appears: Distribution C

b.

Distribution	Height of Second Bar	Height of Third Bar
A	$(0.4)(0.6) = 0.24$	$(0.4)^2(0.6) = 0.096$
B	$\left(\frac{5}{6}\right)\left(\frac{1}{6}\right) = \frac{5}{36} \approx 0.139$	$\left(\frac{5}{6}\right)^2\left(\frac{1}{6}\right) = \frac{25}{216} \approx 0.116$
C	$(0.55)(0.45) = 0.2475$	$(0.55)^2(0.45) \approx 0.136$
D	$\left(\frac{31}{36}\right)\left(\frac{5}{36}\right) = \frac{155}{1,296} \approx 0.120$	$\left(\frac{31}{36}\right)^2\left(\frac{5}{36}\right) = \frac{4,805}{46,656} \approx 0.103$

20 None of the three is a correct interpretation. For example, suppose that 100 people are flipping a coin until heads lands face up. Since $p = 0.5$ in this case, the *EV* is $\frac{1}{0.5}$, or 2. But, we expect 50 people to get heads on the first flip and 25 to get heads on the second flip for a total of 75 people on or before the *EV*. Therefore, neither the first nor the third statement holds. The "most likely" time to wait is one flip because more people got heads on their first flip than got heads on any other flip. So, the second statement does not hold either.

Extensions

21 Now that you can describe waiting-time probability distributions with an algebraic formula, you can use a calculator to help analyze situations modeled by these distributions. A helpful calculator procedure to produce a waiting-time probability distribution table makes use of a sequence command found on some graphing calculators. The command is usually of the form **seq(*formula*, *variable*, *begin*, *end*, *increment*)**. The following keystroke procedure uses *A* for the variable and 1 for both the beginning value and the increment. (The exact structure of this command and how to access it vary among calculator models. You may need to refer to the manual for your calculator.)

First, you need to access the sequence command. For example, from the home screen on a TI-84, press **2nd** **STAT** **▶** **5**. Then, complete the command by entering the following example:

Store the resulting values in a list for easier access. The following are sample display screens for this procedure.

The list now holds the first 12 probabilities of the waiting-time probability distribution for rolling doubles. (Note that the decimal display was set to show only two digits.)

a. Compare the probabilities produced by this procedure with those you calculated in Problem 1 of Investigation 2.

b. Compare the sequence command with the general formula you wrote in Problem 5, Part d of Investigation 2. How are they similar and how are they different?

c. Modify the sequence command to produce the first ten probabilities of the waiting-time probability distribution for drawing a green M&M® as in Applications Task 5. If you completed that task, compare the first five entries.

d. Write a summary of what you need to know in order to use this procedure for producing a waiting-time probability distribution.

e. How could this calculator procedure help you analyze questions about rare events associated with waiting-time probability distributions?

Extensions

21 **a.** The entries stored in List 1 should be equal to those in Problem 1 if they are rounded to two decimal places.

   b. The first part of the command uses the formula for the waiting-time distribution, although the variable used is A instead of x. The command provides only the first 12 entries, whereas the formula can be used to get any one particular entry.

   c. **seq(0.16*(0.84)^(A-1),A,1,10,1)** Actual commands may vary. Entries in the table below are rounded to four decimal places.

Number of Draws to Get Green M&M	Probability
1	0.16
2	0.1344
3	0.1129
4	0.0948
5	0.0797
6	0.0669
7	0.0562
8	0.0472
9	0.0397
10	0.0333

The first five entries generated by the command should be equal to the five entries in the table in Applications Task 5 unless rounded differently.

   d. You need to know the probability that the event you are waiting for will occur on any given trial. In addition, you must decide how many rows you want in the list. If the probability of a success on each trial is p, then the formula will be $(1 - p)^{A - 1}p$ and the command for N rows stored in List 1 will be **seq((1-p)^(A-1)*p,A,1,N,1)→L1**.

   e. Most calculators will give the sum of the elements in a list. You could use this procedure to place probabilities into a list and then find the length of the list needed to get the sum to be greater than 0.95.

Unit 8

22 You have seen two ways to compute the expected value of the waiting-time distribution for rolling doubles. The first is to use the formula $\Sigma x \cdot P(x)$, which gives an *infinite series*:

$$1\left(\frac{1}{6}\right) + 2\left(\frac{5}{6}\right)\left(\frac{1}{6}\right) + 3\left(\frac{5}{6}\right)^2\left(\frac{1}{6}\right) + 4\left(\frac{5}{6}\right)^3\left(\frac{1}{6}\right) + 5\left(\frac{5}{6}\right)^4\left(\frac{1}{6}\right) + \cdots$$

The second way is to use the formula you discovered in this investigation:

$$EV = \frac{1}{\frac{1}{6}} = 6$$

Because these two methods give the same expected value, you can set them equal. So,

$$6 = 1\left(\frac{1}{6}\right) + 2\left(\frac{5}{6}\right)\left(\frac{1}{6}\right) + 3\left(\frac{5}{6}\right)^2\left(\frac{1}{6}\right) + 4\left(\frac{5}{6}\right)^3\left(\frac{1}{6}\right) + 5\left(\frac{5}{6}\right)^4\left(\frac{1}{6}\right) + \cdots$$

It is rather amazing that a series can keep going forever and still add up to 6.

a. Write the next three terms of the infinite series above.

b. Here is another example of an infinite series:

  i. Show by dividing 3 into 1 that $\frac{1}{3} = 0.333333333\ldots$.

  ii. Why can you then write
  $$\frac{1}{3} = \frac{3}{10} + \frac{3}{100} + \frac{3}{1,000} + \frac{3}{10,000} + \frac{3}{100,000} + \cdots ?$$

  iii. Multiply both sides of $\frac{1}{3} = 0.3333333\ldots$ by 3.

  What do you conclude?

c. Write $\frac{2}{3}$ as an infinite series.

d. The following square is 1 unit on each side.

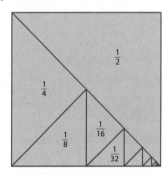

  i. What is the area of the square?

  ii. Describe its area by adding the areas of the (infinitely many) individual triangles.

  iii. What can you conclude?

22 **a.** $6\left(\frac{5}{6}\right)^5\left(\frac{1}{6}\right) + 7\left(\frac{5}{6}\right)^6\left(\frac{1}{6}\right) + 8\left(\frac{5}{6}\right)^7\left(\frac{1}{6}\right)$

b. **i.** $3\overline{)1.0000...}^{\,0.3333...}$

  ii. By the definition of place value, 0.03, for example, is equal to $\frac{3}{100}$. Thus, $\frac{1}{3} = 0.33333... = \frac{3}{10} + \frac{3}{100} + \frac{3}{1,000} + \frac{3}{10,000} + \frac{3}{100,000} + \cdots$.

  iii. $0.99999... = 1$

c. $\frac{2}{3} = 0.66666... = \frac{6}{10} + \frac{6}{100} + \frac{6}{1,000} + \frac{6}{10,000} + \frac{6}{100,000} + \cdots$

d. **i.** 1 square unit

  ii. $\frac{1}{2} + \frac{1}{4} + \frac{1}{8} + \frac{1}{16} + \frac{1}{32} + \cdots$

  iii. $1 = \frac{1}{2} + \frac{1}{4} + \frac{1}{8} + \frac{1}{16} + \frac{1}{32} + \cdots$

23 Study the following method to find the sum of one kind of an *infinite geometric series*:

To find the sum of a series like $\frac{1}{2} + \frac{1}{4} + \frac{1}{8} + \frac{1}{16} + \frac{1}{32} + \cdots$ first, set the sum of the series equal to S:

$$S = \frac{1}{2} + \frac{1}{4} + \frac{1}{8} + \frac{1}{16} + \frac{1}{32} + \cdots \qquad \textbf{Equation I}$$

Multiply both sides by 2:

$$2S = 2\left(\frac{1}{2} + \frac{1}{4} + \frac{1}{8} + \frac{1}{16} + \frac{1}{32} + \cdots\right)$$
$$2S = \frac{2}{2} + \frac{2}{4} + \frac{2}{8} + \frac{2}{16} + \frac{2}{32} + \cdots$$
$$2S = 1 + \frac{1}{2} + \frac{1}{4} + \frac{1}{8} + \frac{1}{16} + \cdots \qquad \textbf{Equation II}$$

Finally, subtract each side of Equation I from the corresponding side of Equation II:

$$2S = 1 + \frac{1}{2} + \frac{1}{4} + \frac{1}{8} + \frac{1}{16} + \cdots$$
$$-S = -\left(\frac{1}{2} + \frac{1}{4} + \frac{1}{8} + \frac{1}{16} + \cdots\right)$$
$$\overline{S = 1}$$

In this example, both sides of Equation I were multiplied by 2. With other infinite sums of this type, other numbers must be used.

a. Use the method above to find the sum of each of the infinite series below. You must first find the number to use for the multiplication.

    i. $S = \frac{1}{3} + \frac{1}{9} + \frac{1}{27} + \frac{1}{81} + \cdots$

    ii. $S = \frac{7}{10} + \frac{7}{100} + \frac{7}{1,000} + \cdots$

b. Why doesn't the method work with the following infinite series?
$$\frac{1}{2} + \frac{1}{3} + \frac{1}{4} + \frac{1}{5} + \frac{1}{6} + \frac{1}{7} + \cdots$$

c. Show that the sum of the probabilities in the waiting-time distribution for rolling doubles is equal to 1.

Review

24 Consider the function $f(x) = \frac{64}{x^2}$.

a. Sketch a graph of $f(x)$.

b. Evaluate $f(4)$.

c. Evaluate $f\left(-\frac{1}{2}\right)$.

d. Solve the equation $f(x) = 4$.

23 a. i. $3S = 3\left(\frac{1}{3} + \frac{1}{9} + \frac{1}{27} + \frac{1}{81} + \cdots\right)$

$$3S = \frac{3}{3} + \frac{3}{9} + \frac{3}{27} + \frac{3}{81} + \cdots$$

$$3S = 1 + \frac{1}{3} + \frac{1}{9} + \frac{1}{27} + \cdots$$

Subtract S from $3S$:

$$3S = 1 + \frac{1}{3} + \frac{1}{9} + \frac{1}{27} + \cdots$$

$$\underline{-S = \qquad -\frac{1}{3} - \frac{1}{9} - \frac{1}{27} - \frac{1}{81} + \cdots}$$

$$2S = 1 \qquad\qquad\qquad\qquad\text{So, } S = \frac{1}{2}$$

ii. $S = \frac{7}{9}$. This is obtained by multiplying both sides of the equation by 10 and then subtracting to get $9S = 7$.

b. There is no multiplier that results in all terms canceling during the subtraction. This is the harmonic series which diverges (grows larger than any given positive number, given enough terms).

c. $S = \frac{1}{6} + \frac{1}{6}\left(\frac{5}{6}\right) + \frac{1}{6}\left(\frac{5}{6}\right)^2 + \frac{1}{6}\left(\frac{5}{6}\right)^3 + \cdots$

$$\frac{6}{5}S = \frac{1}{5} + \frac{1}{6} + \frac{1}{6}\left(\frac{5}{6}\right) + \frac{1}{6}\left(\frac{5}{6}\right)^2 + \frac{1}{6}\left(\frac{5}{6}\right)^3 + \cdots .$$

Subtracting the first equation from the second gives $\frac{1}{5}S = \frac{1}{5}$, so $S = 1$.

How to Sum an Infinite Series for the Expected Value of a Waiting-Time Distribution

If your students liked the trick given for summing the infinite series, they will enjoy learning to sum the infinite series for the expected value of a waiting-time distribution. For example, the infinite sum for the expected waiting time to roll doubles is $S = 1\left(\frac{1}{6}\right) + 2\left(\frac{5}{6}\right)\left(\frac{1}{6}\right) + 3\left(\frac{5}{6}\right)^2\left(\frac{1}{6}\right) + 4\left(\frac{5}{6}\right)^3\left(\frac{1}{6}\right) + \cdots .$

It is necessary to use the trick twice. First, multiply S by $\frac{6}{5}$.

$$\left(\frac{6}{5}\right)S = \left(\frac{1}{5}\right) + 2\left(\frac{1}{6}\right) + 3\left(\frac{5}{6}\right)\left(\frac{1}{6}\right) + 4\left(\frac{5}{6}\right)^2\left(\frac{1}{6}\right) + 5\left(\frac{5}{6}\right)^3\left(\frac{1}{6}\right) + \cdots$$

Subtracting S from $\left(\frac{6}{5}\right)S$ gives the following:

$$\left(\frac{1}{5}\right)S = \left(\frac{1}{5}\right) + \left(\frac{1}{6}\right) + \left(\frac{5}{6}\right)\left(\frac{1}{6}\right) + \left(\frac{5}{6}\right)^2\left(\frac{1}{6}\right) + \left(\frac{5}{6}\right)^3\left(\frac{1}{6}\right) + \cdots$$

Since $\left(\frac{1}{6}\right) + \left(\frac{5}{6}\right)\left(\frac{1}{6}\right) + \left(\frac{5}{6}\right)^2\left(\frac{1}{6}\right) + \left(\frac{5}{6}\right)^3\left(\frac{1}{6}\right) + \cdots$ is an infinite geometric series, which can be summed in the usual way to get 1, we have $\left(\frac{1}{5}\right)S = \left(\frac{1}{5}\right) + 1$, or $S = 6$.

Review

24 a.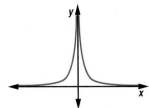

b. $f(4) = \frac{64}{4^2} = 4$

c. $f\left(-\frac{1}{2}\right) = \frac{64}{\left(-\frac{1}{2}\right)^2} = 256$

d. $4 = \frac{64}{x^2}$ when $x = \pm 4$.

25 Shown below is a scatterplot matrix of information about the number of cell phones, main line telephones, and personal computers per 100 persons in 13 different countries. (Source: *Statistical Abstract of the United States: 2007*. U.S. Census Bureau)

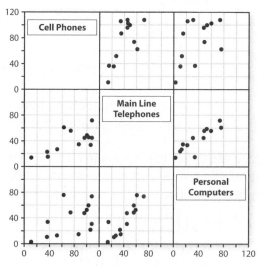

a. Which pair of variables has the strongest association? The weakest association? Explain your reasoning.

b. Which of the following is the correlation for the (*main line telephones, personal computers*) data pairs?

$$r = 0.43 \qquad r = -0.85 \qquad r = 0.88 \qquad r = 1.15$$

c. Saudi Arabia has 15 telephones and 34 personal computers per 100 persons. If Saudi Arabia were deleted from the data set, would the correlation for the (*main line telephones, personal computers*) data pairs increase or decrease?

d. If you convert the data so that it gives the number of cell phones, main line telephones, and personal computers per person rather than per 100 persons will the correlation for the (*main line telephones, personal computers*) data pairs be the same, larger, or smaller? Explain your reasoning.

26 Systems of equations can have no solutions, exactly one solution, or an infinitely many solutions. Consider the following system of equations.

$$4x + 18y = 32$$
$$2x + ky = c$$

a. Find values for k and c so that the system has exactly one solution.

b. Find values for k and c so that the system has no solution.

c. Find values for k and c so that the system has infinitely many solutions.

Unit 8

25 **a.** The strongest association is between main line telephones and personal computers and the weakest association is between cell phones and personal computers.

b. $r = 0.88$

c. The correlation would increase because Saudi Arabia is far from the general trend.

d. The correlation would stay the same since rescaling does not affect the correlation.

 26 **a.** The system has exactly one solution for any value of k such that $k \neq 9$ and any value for c.

b. In order for the system to have no solution, the lines must be parallel. Therefore, $\frac{-2}{k} = \frac{-4}{18}$. Then $k = 9$ and $c \neq 16$.

c. There are infinitely many solutions for $k = 9$ and $c = 16$.

Unit 8

27 Namid is considering using regular pentagons with sides of length 10 cm as part of the pattern on her quilt.

   a. How could she find the measure of each angle of the regular pentagon? What is the angle measure?

   b. How could she find the area of each pentagon? What is the area?

   c. Namid has lots of squares of material left over from a previous project. Each square has sides of length 20 cm. Could she use these scraps to make her pentagons?

   d. Could she make her entire quilt using just regular pentagons sewn side-to-side? Explain your reasoning.

28 Solve each equation by reasoning with the symbols themselves.

   a. $(x - 5)(x + 3) = 9$

   b. $-3(2x + 7) + 2(12 - x) = 21$

   c. $\frac{3}{x} = x - 2$

   d. $2x^2 + 6x = 4$

29 Consider $\triangle ABC$ with vertices at $A(-2, 5)$, $B(2, 8)$ and $C(7, 8)$.

   a. Is $\triangle ABC$ an isosceles triangle?

   b. Find the measure of all three angles of $\triangle ABC$.

   c. Find the coordinates of the vertices of the final image of $\triangle ABC$ if it is first reflected across the line $y = x$ and then the image is rotated clockwise 90° about the origin.

   d. Write a coordinate rule for the composite transformation described in Part c.

   e. Represent $\triangle ABC$ with a matrix. What matrices could you use to find the image of $\triangle ABC$ in Part c?

30 Write each radical expression in equivalent form so that the number under the radical sign is the smallest possible whole number.

   a. $\sqrt{49}$

   b. $\sqrt{50}$

   c. $\sqrt{52}$

   d. $5\sqrt{24}$

Unit 8

27 **a.** A regular pentagon can be subdivided into 3 triangles as shown at the right. Since there are 5 conguent angles in the regular pentagon, each angle measure is equal to $\frac{3(180°)}{5} = 108°$.

b. The pentagon can be divided into 5 isosceles triangles—each with a base of 10 cm and base angles of 54° (as shown at the right). The height of each triangle is 5 tan 54° ≈ 6.88. Thus, the area of each triangle is $\frac{1}{2}(10)(6.88) \approx 34.4$ cm², and the area of the pentagon is 5(34.4) = 172 cm².

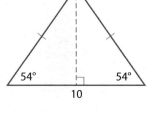

c. The greatest length across the pentagon is the length of a diagonal.

$d^2 = 10^2 + 10^2 - 2(10)(10)\cos 108°$

$d^2 \approx 261.8$

$d \approx 16.2$ cm

Since the squares of material have sides of length 20 cm, Namid can make her pentagons.

d. No. Regular pentagons do not tile the plane because 108 is not a factor of 360.

28 **a.** $x = 6$ or $x = -4$

b. $x = -2.25$

c. $x = 3$ or $x = -1$

d. $x = -1.5 \pm \frac{\sqrt{17}}{2}$

29 **a.** Yes. $AB = BC = 5$

b. $AC = \sqrt{9^2 + 3^2} = \sqrt{90}$. Then using the Law of Cosines,

$(\sqrt{90})^2 = 5^2 + 5^2 - 2(5)(5)\cos B$. So, m∠B ≈ 143°. Then since the triangle is isosceles, the measure of each base angle is

$\frac{180° - 143°}{2} = 18.5°$.

c. $A'(-2, -5); B'(2, -8); C'(7, -8)$

d. $(x, y) \rightarrow (x, -y)$

e. $\triangle ABC = \begin{bmatrix} -2 & 2 & 7 \\ 5 & 8 & 8 \end{bmatrix}$

To find the image of △ABC under the transformation described in

Part c, multiply $\begin{bmatrix} 0 & 1 \\ 1 & 0 \end{bmatrix}$ by $\begin{bmatrix} -2 & 2 & 7 \\ 5 & 8 & 8 \end{bmatrix}$ with the point matrix on the

right. Then, multiply $\begin{bmatrix} 0 & 1 \\ -1 & 0 \end{bmatrix}$ by the point matrix result of the first transformation.

30 **a.** 7

b. $5\sqrt{2}$

c. $2\sqrt{13}$

d. $10\sqrt{6}$

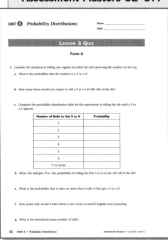
Unit 8

Looking Back

I n this unit, you learned about probability
distributions and the rules used to construct them. Among
the concepts you investigated were the Multiplication Rule,
independent events, conditional probability, fair price, and
expected value. You used these concepts to construct the
probability distribution table for a waiting-time situation. In
this lesson, you will review and apply many of these ideas
in new contexts.

1 North Carolina collects data on all bicycle crashes with motor
vehicles that are reported to the police. The table below gives the
injury status and whether the bicyclist was wearing a helmet for all
crashes in a recent year. Children and young adults are the most
frequent victims.

	Killed/ Disabling Injury	Less Serious or No Injury	Total
Helmet Not Used	68	598	666
Helmet Used	2	27	29
Total	70	625	695

Source: www.pedbikeinfo.org/pbcat/bike_main.htm

Suppose you pick a crash at random.

a. Compare *P*(*killed/disabled* | *helmet not used*) with
P(*killed/disabled* | *helmet used*). What can you conclude about
helmet use?

b. Are being killed or getting a disabling injury and using a helmet
independent events? Are they mutually exclusive events?

c. Use the Multiplication Rule to find *P*(*killed/disabled* and
helmet used). Check your answer by using the table directly.

d. Use the Addition Rule to find *P*(*killed/disabled* or *helmet
used*). Check your answer by using the table directly.

Looking Back

1   **a.** $P(killed/disabled \mid helmet\ not\ used) = \frac{68}{666} \approx 0.102$

$P(killed/disabled \mid helmet\ used) = \frac{2}{29} \approx 0.069$

The probability that the bicyclist was killed or had a disabling injury is higher when a helmet was not used than when a helmet was used, just as we would expect. However, we cannot conclude from these observational data that wearing a helmet reduced the chance of injury. First, the number of helmet-wearers was very small. Second, there may be a lurking variable such as helmet-wearers may be younger than non-helmet wearers and so less likely to be seriously injured in a crash.

b. They are not independent events because

$P(killed/disabled \mid helmet\ used) = \frac{2}{29} \approx 0.069$

is not equal to $P(killed/disabled) = \frac{70}{695} \approx 0.101$.

If you look just at the bicyclists wearing helmets, the probability that they were killed or had a disabling injury is less than for bicyclists overall. These are not mutually exclusive events because there were 2 people who were killed or had a disabling injury *and* were using a helmet.

(Students may notice that because few of the bicyclists who had crashes with motor vehicles were wearing helmets, the overall probability that the bicyclist was killed or injured is about the same overall as when a helmet was not used.)

c. $P(killed/disabled$ and $helmet\ used) =$
$P(killed/disabled) \cdot P(helmet\ used \mid killed/disabled)$
$= \frac{70}{695} \cdot \frac{2}{70} = \frac{2}{695} \approx 0.0029$. From the table, the cell in the lower left gives 2 bicyclists who were killed/disabled and were wearing helmets, so $P(killed/disabled$ and
$helmet\ used) = \frac{2}{695} \approx 0.0029$, as from the formula.

d. $P(killed/disabled$ or $helmet\ used) = P(killed/disabled)$
$+ P(helmet\ used) - P(killed/disabled$ and $helmet\ used)$
$= \frac{70}{695} + \frac{29}{695} - \frac{2}{695} = \frac{97}{695} \approx 0.140$. Adding the three cells in the table where either a helmet was used or the bicyclist was killed or had a disabling injury gives
$\frac{68 + 2 + 27}{695} = \frac{97}{695} \approx 0.140$.

② Throughout the basketball season, Delsin has maintained a 60% free-throw shooting average.

a. Suppose in the first game of the post-season tournament, Delsin is in a two-shot foul situation. That is, he gets two attempts to make a free throw, which are worth one point each. Use an area model to determine:

   i. P(*Delsin scores 2 points*)

   ii. P(*Delsin scores 1 point*)

   iii. P(*Delsin scores 0 points*)

b. Show how to use a formula to determine the probability that Delsin will score 2 points.

c. What is the expected number of points Delsin will score?

d. Suppose that later in the game, Delsin is in a one-and-one free throw situation. That is, if he makes the free throw on his first try, he gets a second free throw. If he misses the first free throw, he does not get a second attempt. Determine the expected number of points Delsin will score in this situation.

③ The Bonus Lotto game described below is similar to those played in many states. The jackpot starts at $4,000,000. On Saturday, 6 numbers from 1 through 47 are drawn. A seventh number, called the Bonus Ball, is then drawn from the remaining numbers. A player wins if the numbers he or she selects match the Bonus Ball and at least two of the numbers drawn.

The probabilities of winning various prizes are given in the following table.

Match	Winnings	Probability
6 of 6	$4,000,000	$\frac{1}{10,737,573}$
5 of 6 + bonus ball	$50,000	$\frac{1}{1,789,595}$
4 of 6 + bonus ball	$1,000	$\frac{1}{17,896}$
3 of 6 + bonus ball	$100	$\frac{1}{688}$
2 of 6 + bonus ball	$4	$\frac{1}{72}$
Other	0	

a. What is the probability of winning nothing? Write your answer in decimal form.

b. What would be a fair price to pay for a ticket?

c. Bonus Lotto costs $2 to play. How much does the state expect to earn on every 1,000,000 tickets sold?

2 **a.**

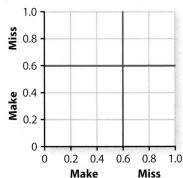

- $P(\text{Delsin scores 2 points}) = (0.6)(0.6) = 0.36$
- $P(\text{Delsin scores 1 point}) = (0.6)(0.4) + (0.4)(0.6) = 0.48$
- $P(\text{Delsin scores 0 points}) = (0.4)(0.4) = 0.16$

b. Assuming the two shots are independent and using the Multiplication Rule, $P(\text{Delsin scores 2 points}) = P(\text{Delsin makes the first shot}) \cdot P(\text{Delsin makes the second shot}) = (0.6)(0.6) = 0.36$.

c. $EV = \Sigma x \cdot P(x) = 0(0.16) + 1(0.48) + 2(0.36) = 1.2$

d. The probability that Delsin misses the first shot and so scores no points is 0.4. The probability that he makes the first shot and then misses the second and so scores 1 point is $(0.6)(0.4)$. The probability that he makes both shots and so scores 2 points is $(0.60)(0.60)$. Thus, his expected number of points is

$$EV = \Sigma x \cdot P(x) = 0(0.4) + 1(0.60)(0.40) + 2(0.60)(0.60) = 0.96.$$

3 **a.** Add the probabilities in the right column to get 0.0154. Since the sum of all probabilities must be 1, the probability of winning nothing is $1 - 0.0154$ or 0.9846.

b. The fair price is about $0.658. See the following table.

Match	Winnings	Probability	(Winnings)(Probability)
6 of 6	$4,000,000	$\frac{1}{10,737,573}$	0.373
5 of 6 + bonus ball	$50,000	$\frac{1}{1,789,595}$	0.028
4 of 6 + bonus ball	$1,000	$\frac{1}{17,896}$	0.056
3 of 6 + bonus ball	$100	$\frac{1}{688}$	0.145
2 of 6 + bonus ball	$4	$\frac{1}{72}$	0.056
Other	0	0.9846	0
		Total	0.658

c. $(1,000,000)(2 - 0.658) = \$1,342,000$

d. If the jackpot is not won on the Saturday drawing, it grows by $4,000,000 for the next week. Other prize winnings remain the same. If you buy one ticket that second week, what is the probability of winning the jackpot?

e. What is a fair price for a ticket the second week?

f. What is the probability that a person who plays Bonus Lotto once this week and once next week will not win anything either week?

g. Suppose a person buys one ticket a week. What is the expected number of weeks he or she will have to wait before winning the jackpot? How many years is this? How much money will have been spent on ticket purchases?

h. The table above actually simplified the situation. In fact, if there is more than one winner, the $4,000,000 jackpot is shared. Explain why this fact makes the answer to Part b even smaller.

④ In the *Patterns in Chance* unit in Course 1, one investigation focused on the population issues in China. In 2000, the population of China was more than 1,200,000,000. To control population growth, the government of China has attempted to limit parents to one child each. This decision has been unpopular in the areas of rural China where the culture is such that many parents desire a son.

Suppose that a new policy has been suggested by which parents are allowed to continue having children until they have a boy. For the following problems, assume that the probability that a child born will be a boy is 0.51 and that births are independent.

a. Describe a method using random digits to simulate the situation of parents having children until they get a boy.

b. Out of every 100 sets of parents, how many would you expect to get the first boy with the first baby? With the second baby? With the third baby?

c. Construct a theoretical probability distribution table for this situation, using a copy of the table below.

Number of Children to Get First Boy	Probability
1	
2	
3	
4	
5	
6	
7	
8 or more	

d. $\frac{1}{10,737,573} \approx 9.3 \times 10^{-8}$

e. The fair price is about $1.03. See the following table.

Match	Winnings	Probability	(Winnings)(Probability)
6 of 6	$8,000,000	$\frac{1}{10,737,573}$	0.745
5 of 6 + bonus ball	$50,000	$\frac{1}{1,789,595}$	0.028
4 of 6 + bonus ball	$1,000	$\frac{1}{17,896}$	0.056
3 of 6 + bonus ball	$100	$\frac{1}{688}$	0.145
2 of 6 + bonus ball	$4	$\frac{1}{72}$	0.056
Other	0	0.9846	0
		Total	1.03

f. $(0.9846)(0.9846) \approx 0.9694$

g. $EV = \dfrac{1}{p} = \dfrac{1}{\frac{1}{10,737,573}} = 10{,}737{,}573$ weeks or almost 206,492 years.

At $2 a week, $21,475,146 would have been spent on tickets.

h. One chance in 10,737,573 is actually the probability of matching 6 of 6, not the probability of winning $4,000,000. That is the largest amount you could win. There is a chance you will have to share the prize with others, which lowers the expected value.

4

a. One possible simulation: Let the pairs of digits 00, 01, 02, ... , 50 represent a boy and the pairs of digits 51, 52, ... , 99 represent a girl. Enter the table at a random spot and count the number of pairs of digits needed until a "boy" appears.

b. $(0.51)(100) = 51$
$(0.49)(0.51)(100) = 24.99$
$(0.49)(0.49)(0.51)(100) = 12.2451$

c.

Number of Children to Get First Boy	Probability
1	0.510
2	0.250
3	0.122
4	0.060
5	0.029
6	0.014
7	0.007
8 or more	0.008

(Answers may vary depending on how students round.)

d. From your table, estimate the mean number of children two parents will have.

e. From the formula for expected value, what is the expected number of children?

f. Explain whether the population will increase, decrease, or stay the same under this plan.

g. If this new policy were adhered to, what percentage of the population would be boys? Explain your reasoning.

Summarize the Mathematics

In this unit, you explored the multiplication rules of probability and used those rules to construct a theoretical waiting-time distribution.

a Give an example that illustrates the difference between $P(A)$ and $P(A|B)$.

b How can you find $P(A$ and $B)$ when events A and B are independent? When they are not?

c What is the expected value of a probability distribution? How do you compute it?

d Describe a waiting-time distribution. Include:
- how to construct the probability distribution table.
- how to develop the formula.
- what the shape of the distribution looks like.
- ways to find the average waiting time.

Be prepared to share your ideas and examples with the class.

✓ Check Your Understanding

Write, in outline form, a summary of the important mathematical concepts and methods developed in this unit. Organize your summary so that it can be used as a quick reference in future units and courses.

d. Using the table, as below, an (under)estimate of the average number of children is 1.958.

Number of Children to Get First Boy	Probability	(Number)(Probability)
1	0.510	0.510
2	0.250	0.500
3	0.122	0.366
4	0.060	0.240
5	0.029	0.145
6	0.014	0.084
7	0.007	0.049
8 or more	0.008	0.064
	Total	1.958

e. The expected number using the formula is $EV = \dfrac{1}{0.51} \approx 1.96$.

f. The population will decrease if all adults pair up and follow the plan of having children until they get a boy. Each pair of adults produces an average of only 1.96 children, not quite replacing themselves.

g. 51% of all children born will be boys. Since the chance of a boy is 0.51 on each birth, the proportion of boys will be 0.51. This ignores differences in mortality rates after birth of boys and girls.

Summarize the Mathematics

Teaching Resources

Transparency Master 38.

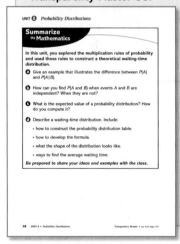

UNIT 8   *Probability Distributions*

Summarize the Mathematics

In this unit, you explored the multiplication rules of probability and used those rules to construct a theoretical waiting-time distribution.

ⓐ Give an example that illustrates the difference between $P(A)$ and $P(A|B)$.

ⓑ How can you find $P(A$ and $B)$ when events A and B are independent? When they are not?

ⓒ What is the expected value of a probability distribution? How do you compute it?

ⓓ Describe a waiting-time distribution. Include:
• how to construct the probability distribution table.
• how to develop the formula.
• what the shape of the distribution looks like.
• ways to find the average waiting time.

Be prepared to share your ideas and examples with the class.

38   UNIT 8 • *Probability Distributions*   *Transparency Master • see text page 169*

ⓐ Examples will vary. For example, in Task 1, *P(killed/disabled)* means the probability of selecting a person at random who was killed or disabled out of the 695 accidents. But to find *P(killed/disabled | helmet used)*, you are looking only at the 29 people who used a helmet and counting the number who were killed or disabled.

ⓑ The Multiplication Rule is used when you want to find the probability that two (or more) events both occur. When the events are independent, $P(A$ and $B) = P(A) \cdot P(B)$. When the events are dependent, $P(A$ and $B) = P(A) \cdot P(B \mid A)$.

ⓒ The expected value of a probability distribution is another term for the mean or average outcome. You compute it using the formula $EV = \Sigma x \cdot P(x)$. That is, you multiply each numerical outcome by its probability and add up all the products.

Unit 8

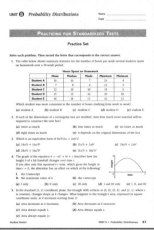

Summarize the Mathematics

(d) A waiting-time distribution occurs in situations where someone is watching a sequence of independent trials and waiting for a certain event to occur. The probability that the event occurs remains the same for each trial. The formula for $P(x)$, the probability that the event first occurs on the xth trial, is $P(x) = (1 - p)^{x-1}p$, where p is the probability that the event occurs on any one trial. This formula was developed using the Multiplication Rule for independent events. In order to get the first success on the xth trial, you have to have $x - 1$ failures, each with probability $1 - p$, followed by a success, which has probability p. The histogram of a waiting-time distribution has the highest bar on the left, and the height of each bar is $(1 - p)$ times the height of the bar to its left. To find the average waiting time, or expected value, you can find the balance point of the histogram, or evaluate $EV = \Sigma x \cdot P(x) = \dfrac{1}{p}$.

Be prepared to share your ideas and examples with the class.

✔ Check Your Understanding

You may wish to have students use the Teaching Master, *Probability Distributions* Unit Summary, to help them organize the information. Above all, this should be something that is useful to the individual student.

Practicing for Standardized Tests

Each Practicing for Standardized Tests master presents 10 questions in the multiple-choice format of test items similar to how they often appear in standardized tests. Answers are provided below.

Answers to Practice Set 8

1. (e)	**2.** (b)	**3.** (d)	**4.** (e)	**5.** (a)
6. (c)	**7.** (d)	**8.** (d)	**9.** (a)	**10.** (c)

Teacher Notes

Glossary/Glosario

Math Online A mathematics multilingual glossary is available at www.math.glencoe.com/multilingual_glossary. The Glossary includes the following languages:

Arabic	English	Korean	Tagalog
Bengali	Hatian Creole	Russian	Urdu
Cantonese	Hmong	Spanish	Vietnamese

English

Español

A

Addition Rule Formula for the probability that event A occurs, or event B occurs, or both events occur: $P(A \text{ or } B) = P(A) + P(B) - P(A \text{ and } B)$.

Addition Rule for Mutually Exclusive Events Simplified form of the Addition Rule that can be used only when event A and event B are mutually exclusive: $P(A \text{ or } B) = P(A) + P(B)$.

Additive identity matrix (p. 134) An $m \times n$ matrix E such that $B + E = B = E + B$, for all $m \times n$ matrices B. (Also called a *zero matrix*, since every entry in an additive identity matrix is 0.)

Additive inverse matrix (p. 134) The matrix which when added to a given matrix yields the zero matrix.

Adjacency matrix for a digraph (p. 93) Matrix representation of a digraph in which the vertices are used as labels for the rows and columns of a matrix and each entry of the matrix is a "1" or a "0" depending on whether or not there is a directed edge from the row vertex to the column vertex. (Sometimes an adjacency matrix is constructed such that each entry is the *number* of directed edges from the row vertex to the column vertex, thus an entry could be larger than 1.)

Algorithm (p. 167) A list of step-by-step instructions, or a systematic step-by-step procedure.

Angle in standard position (p. 461) A directed angle with vertex at the origin of a rectangular coordinate system and initial side the positive x-axis.

Angle of depression (p. 476) The acute angle between the line of sight and the horizontal when sighting from one point downward to a second point.

Angle of elevation (also called *angle of inclination*) (p. 481) The acute angle between the line of sight and the horizontal when sighting from one point upward to a second point.

Regla de adición Fórmula para encontrar la probabilidad que el evento A ocurra o que el evento B ocurra, o que ambos eventos ocurran: $P(A \text{ ó } B) = P(A) + P(B) - P(A \text{ y } B)$.

Regla de adición para eventos mutuamente excluyentes Forma simplificada de la Regla de adición que puede usarse solamente cuando el evento A y el evento B son mutuamente excluyentes: $P(A \text{ ó } B) = P(A) + P(B)$.

Matriz identidad aditiva (pág. 134) Una E matriz $m \times n$ de modo que $B + E = B = E + B$, para todas las B matrices $m \times n$. (También se le llama *matriz cero*, debido a que cada entrada en una matriz de identidad aditiva es 0.)

Matriz inversa aditiva (pág. 134) Matriz que al sumarla a una matriz dada da como resultado la matriz cero.

Matriz de adyacencia para un dígrafo (pág. 93) La representación de una matriz de un dígrafo en el cual los vértices se usan como rótulos para las filas y columnas de una matriz y cada entrada de la matriz es un "1" o un "0" dependiendo de si hay o no una arista dirigida de la fila del vértice hacia la columna del vértice. (Algunas veces una matriz de adyacencia se construye de tal manera que cada entrada es el *número* de aristas dirigidas de la fila del vértice a la columna del vértice, por lo tanto una entrada puede ser mayor que 1.)

Algoritmo (pág. 167) Lista de instrucciones detalladas o procedimiento detallado.

Ángulo en posición estándar (pág. 461) Un ángulo dirigido con vértice en el origen de un sistema rectangular de coordenadas y lado inicial del eje x positivo.

Ángulo de depresión (pág. 476) Ángulo agudo entre la línea de visión y la horizontal cuando se aprecia de un punto hacia abajo a un segundo punto.

Ángulo de elevación (también llamado *ángulo de inclinación*) (pág. 481) Ángulo agudo entre la línea de visión y la horizontal cuando se aprecia de un punto hacia arriba a un segundo punto.

Glossary/Glosario

Association (p. 299) A relationship between two variables. Association can be positive or negative, weak or strong, curved or linear. Compare with *correlation*.

Asociación (pág. 299) Una relación entre dos variables. La asociación puede ser positiva o negativa, débil o fuerte, curva o lineal. Comparar con *correlación*.

· (B) ·

Bivariate data (p. 257) Data consisting of ordered pairs that are responses for two variables for each person or object of study, such as age and height for each tree in a park.

Datos covariantes (pág. 257) Datos que constan de pares ordenados que son las respuestas para dos variables para cada persona u objeto de estudio, tales como edad y altura para cada árbol de un parque.

Brute-force method (p. 409) A problem-solving method that involves finding and checking all possibilities.

Método de la fuerza bruta (pág. 409) Método de resolución de problemas relacionado con hallar y comprobar todas las posibilidades.

· (C) ·

Cause-and-effect relationship (p. 299) A change in the value of one variable (called the *explanatory* or *independent variable*) tends to cause a change in the value of a second variable (called the *response* or *dependent variable*).

Relación de causa y efecto (pág. 299) Un cambio en el valor de una variable (llamada la *variable explicativa* o *independiente*) tiende a causar un cambio en el valor de una segunda variable (llamada *variable de respuesta* o *dependiente*).

Centroid (p. 286) On a scatterplot of points (x, y), the point $(\overline{x}, \overline{y})$, where $\overline{x}$ is the mean of the values of x and $\overline{y}$ is the mean of the values of y. (In a polygon, the point that is the "center of gravity.")

Centroide (pág. 286) En una gráfica de dispersión, de los puntos (x, y), el punto $(\overline{x}, \overline{y})$, donde $\overline{x}$ es la media de los valores de x, y $\overline{y}$ es la media de los valores de y. (En un polígono, el punto que es el "centro de gravedad.")

Circle The set of all points in a plane that are a fixed distance r, called the *radius*, from a given point O, called the *center* of the circle.

Círculo Conjunto de todos los puntos de un plano que están a una distancia dada r, llamada *radio*, de un punto O dado, denominado *centro* del círculo.

Circuit (p. 403) A route through a vertex-edge graph that starts and ends at the same vertex and does not repeat any edges.

Circuito (pág. 403) Una ruta a través de un grafo que empieza y termina en el mismo vértice y no repite ningún vértice.

Closed interval A continuous interval of real numbers that includes the endpoints of the interval; the interval from a to b, including a and b, is denoted $[a, b]$ or $\{x: a \leq x \leq b\}$.

Intervalo cerrado Intervalo continuo de números reales que incluye todos sus puntos límite; el intervalo de a a b, incluyendo a y b, se denota como $[a, b]$ ó $\{x: a \leq x \leq b\}$.

Column matrix (p. 119) A matrix consisting of one column. (Also called a *column vector* or a *one-column matrix*.)

Matriz columna (pág. 119) Matriz formada por una columna. (También llamada *vector de columna* o *matriz de una columna*.)

Column of an $m \times n$ matrix (p. 76) A vertical array of m numbers in the matrix.

Columna de una matriz $m \times n$ (pág. 76) Matriz o conjunto vertical de m números en la matriz.

Column sum of a matrix (p. 81) The sum of all numbers in a column of a matrix.

Suma de columna de una matriz (pág. 81) La suma de todos los números en la columna de una matriz.

Glossary/Glosario

English	Español

Complementary angles (p. 481) Two angles whose measures sum to 90°.

Ángulos complementarios (pág. 481) Dos ángulos cuyas medidas suman 90°.

Components of a translation (p. 199) The horizontal and vertical directed distances (left or right, up or down) through which all points in the plane are moved by the translation.

Componentes de una traslación (pág. 199) Distancias dirigidas horizontal y vertical (izquierda o derecha, arriba o abajo) por las cuales se mueven todos los puntos en un plano por una traslación.

Composition of transformations (p. 213) The result of applying two transformations in succession. The transformation that maps the *original preimage* to the *final image* is called the *composite transformation*.

Composición de transformaciones (pág. 213) Resultado de aplicar dos transformaciones en sucesión. La transformación que traza la *figura geométrica original* (o preimage) a la *imagen final* se llama *transformación compuesta*.

Conditional probability (p. 528) The probability that an event A occurs given that another event B occurs, written $P(A \mid B)$. When $P(B) > 0$,
$P(A \mid B) = \dfrac{P(A \text{ and } B)}{P(B)}$.

Probabilidad condicional (pág. 528) La probabilidad que un suceso A ocurra a condición de que otro suceso B ocurra, de manera escrita es $P(A \mid B)$. Cuando $P(B) > 0$, $P(A \mid B) = \dfrac{P(A \text{ y } B)}{P(B)}$.

Congruent figures Figures that have the same shape and size, regardless of position or orientation. (For angles: having the same measure; for segments: having the same length.)

Figuras congruentes Figuras de la misma forma y tamaño, sin importar su posición u orientación. (Para los ángulos: tener la misma medida; para los segmentos: tener la misma longitud.)

Connected graph (p. 406) A vertex-edge graph that is all in one piece; that is, from each vertex there is at least one path to every other vertex.

Grafo conexo (pág. 406) Un grafo que es de una sola pieza, o sea, de cada vértice hay por lo menos un camino a cada uno de los otros vértices.

Correlation (p. 257) A measure, usually Pearson's r, of the linear association between two variables. A number between -1 and 1 that tells how closely the points on a scatterplot cluster about the regression line.

Correlación (pág. 257) Una medida, usualmente la r de Pearson, de la asociación lineal entre dos variables. Un número entre -1 y 1 que indica qué tan cerca los puntos en una gráfica de dispersión se agrupan acerca de la línea de regresión.

Cosine function (p. 457) If $P(x, y)$ is a point (not the origin) on the terminal side of an angle θ in standard position and $r = \sqrt{x^2 + y^2}$, then $\cos \theta = \frac{x}{r}$. If A is an acute angle in a right triangle, then $\cos A = \dfrac{\text{length of side } adjacent \text{ to } \angle A}{\text{length of } hypotenuse}$.

Función de coseno (pág. 457) Si $P(x, y)$ es un punto (no el origen) en el lado terminal de un ángulo θ en posición estándar y $r = \sqrt{x^2 + y^2}$, entonces $\text{coseno } \theta = \frac{x}{r}$. Si A es un ángulo agudo en un triángulo rectángulo, entonces $\cos A = \dfrac{\text{medida del cateto } adyacente \text{ a } \angle A}{\text{medida de la } hipotenusa}$.

Critical path (p. 434) A path through a *project digraph* that corresponds to the earliest finish time for the project.

Trayectoria crítica (pág. 434) Una trayectoria a través de un *dígrafo de proyecto* que corresponde al tiempo más temprano del final para el proyecto.

Glossary/Glosario

|

Critical Path Method (CPM) (p. 437) A method using critical path analysis to optimally schedule large projects consisting of many subtasks; developed at about the same time as and similar to the Program Evaluation and Review Technique (PERT).

Método de Trayectoria Crítica (CPM por sus siglas en inglés) (pág. 437) Método que emplea un análisis crítico de trayectoria para programar de manera óptima proyectos grandes compuestos de muchos subproyectos; desarrolladas aproximadamente al mismo tiempo y similares a la Evaluación de Programa y Técnica de Revisión (PERT por sus siglas en inglés).

Critical task (p. 440) A task on a *critical path*.

Tarea crítica (pág. 440) Tarea o trabajo en una *trayectoria crítica*.

— — — — — — — — — — — — — — (D) — — — — — — — — — — — — — —

Dart A nonconvex quadrilateral with two pairs of congruent consecutive sides.

Dardo Cuadrilátero no convexo con dos pares de lados consecutivos congruentes.

Degree of a vertex The number of edges touching the vertex. If an edge loops back to the same vertex, that counts as two edge-touchings.

Grado de un vértice Número de aristas que concurren en el vértice. Si un extremo se regresa al mismo vértice, eso cuenta como dos veces.

Dependent variable (p. 3) A variable whose value changes in response to change in one or more related independent variables. (Also called a *response variable*.)

Variable dependiente (pág. 3) Variable cuyo valor cambia en respuesta a cambios en una o más variables independientes relacionadas. (También llamada *variable de respuesta*.)

Diagonal of a polygon A line segment connecting two vertices that are not adjacent.

Diagonal de un polígono Un segmento de recta que conecta dos vértices que no son adyacentes.

Digraph (p. 93) A vertex-edge graph in which all the edges are directed, that is, the edges have arrows indicating a direction. (Also called a *directed graph*.)

Dígrafo (pág. 93) Grafo en el cual todas las aristas están dirigidas, es decir, las aristas tienen flechas que indican una dirección. (También se le llama *gráfico dirigido*.)

Direct variation (p. 1) If variables x and y are related by an equation in the form $y = kx$ or $\frac{y}{x} = k$, then y is said to vary directly with x, or be directly proportional to x.

Variación directa (pág. 1) Si las variables x y y están relacionadas por una ecuación en la forma $y = kx$ o $\frac{y}{x} = k$, entonces se dice que y varía directamente con x, o que es directamente proporcional a x.

Directed edge (p. 93) An edge in a vertex-edge graph with a direction indicated.

Arista dirigida (pág. 93) Arista de un grafo en que se indica la dirección de la misma.

Directed graph See *digraph*.

Grafo dirigido Véase *dígrafo*.

Distance Formula (p. 171) Formula for calculating the distance between two points in the coordinate plane.

Fórmula de distancia (pág. 171) Fórmula para calcular la distancia entre dos puntos en un plano de coordenadas.

Distance matrix (p. 414) A matrix representation of a weighted graph in which the vertices are labels for the rows and columns and each entry is the length of a shortest path between the corresponding vertices.

Matriz distancia (pág. 414) Representación de una matriz de un gráfico cargado en el cual los vértices son rótulos para las filas y columnas y cada entrada es el largo de la trayectoria más corta entre los vértices correspondientes.

Glossary/Glosario

English	Español

Domain of a function (p. 330) For a function f, all values of the independent variable x that have corresponding $f(x)$ values. (Also called *input values* for the function.)

Dominio de una función (pág. 330) Para una función f, todos los valores de la variable independiente x que tienen valores $f(x)$ correspondientes. (También llamados *valores de entrada* para la función.)

(E)

Earliest Finish Time (EFT) (p. 438) The minimum amount of time needed to complete a large project that consists of numerous subtasks.

Tiempo mínimo de resolución (EFT por sus siglas en inglés) (pág. 438) La cantidad mínima de tiempo necesario para terminar un proyecto grande compuesto por varios subproyectos.

Elimination method (p. 55) A method used to solve a system of linear equations. One or both of the equations may be multiplied by a nonzero constant so that the coefficient of one of the variables is the same in both equations, subtracting the equations eliminates that variable.

Método de eliminación (pág. 55) Método que se utiliza para resolver un sistema de ecuaciones lineales. Una o ambas ecuaciones se pueden multiplicar por una constante no-cero para que el coeficiente de una de las variables sea el mismo en ambas ecuaciones, restar las ecuaciones elimina esa variable.

Equally likely outcomes (p. 562) Outcomes that all have the same probability of occurring.

Resultados equiprobables (pág. 562) Resultados que tienen la misma oportunidad de ocurrir.

Equation of a line An equation that can be expressed as $ax + by = c$ where a and b are not both 0.

Ecuación de una línea Una ecuación que puede expresarse como $ax + by = c$ en donde a y b no son ambas 0.

Error in prediction (p. 283) For points not used to calculate the regression equation, the difference between the observed value of y and the value of y predicted by the regression equation.

Error en la predicción (pág. 283) Para aquellos puntos no utilizados para calcular la ecuación de regresión, la diferencia entre el valor observado de y y el valor de y predicho por la ecuación de regresión.

Euler circuit A route through a connected graph such that (1) each edge is used exactly once, and (2) the route starts and ends at the same vertex.

Circuito de Euler Camino en un grafo conexo de modo que (1) cada arista se recorre sólo una vez y (2) el camino empieza y termina en el mismo vértice.

Expected value or expectation (p. 525) The mean, or average, of a probability distribution.

Valor previsto o de expectativa (pág. 525) Media, o promedio, de una distribución de probabilidad.

Experiment (p. 4) A research study in which subjects are randomly assigned to two or more different treatments in order to compare how the responses to the treatments differ.

Experimento (pág. 4) Estudio de investigación en el cual se asignan sujetos al azar a dos o más tratamientos diferentes para comparar cómo se diferencian las respuestas a los tratamientos.

Explanatory variable See *independent variable*.

Variable explicativa Véase *variable independiente*.

Exponential function A function with rule of correspondence that can be expressed in the algebraic form $f(x) = a(b^x)$ ($a, b > 0$).

Función exponencial Función con regla de correspondencia que se puede expresar en forma algebraica $f(x) = a(b^x)$ ($a, b > 0$).

Glossary/Glosario

English	Español

(F)

Fair price (p. 546) The price that should be charged to play a game so that, in the long run, the player wins the same amount that he or she pays to play.

Precio justo (pág. 546) Precio que se debe cobrar para jugar un juego de modo que, a la larga, el jugador gane la misma cantidad que éste paga por jugar.

Function (p. 161) A relationship between two variables in which each value of the independent variable x corresponds to exactly one value of the dependent variable y. The notation $y = f(x)$ is often used to denote that y is a function of x.

Función (pág. 161) Una relación entre dos variables en la cual cada valor de la variable independiente x corresponde exactamente a un valor de la variable dependiente y. La notación $y = f(x)$ comúnmente se usa para denotar que y es una función de x.

(G)

Glide-reflection (p. 224) A rigid transformation that is the composition of a reflection across a line and a translation in a direction parallel to the line.

Reflexión del deslizamiento (pág. 224) Transformación rígida que es la composición de una reflexión en una recta y una traslación en dirección paralela a esa recta.

Graph See *vertex-edge graph*.

Gráfica Véase *grafo*.

(H)

Half-turn (p. 229) A 180° rotation about a point.

Media vuelta (pág. 229) Rotación de 180° con relación de un punto.

Hamilton circuit (p. 408) A route through a vertex-edge graph that starts at one vertex, visits all the other vertices exactly once, and ends at the starting vertex.

Circuito de Hamilton (pág. 408) Camino a través de un grafo que empieza en una vértice, visita todas las demás vértices exactamente una vez y termina en el vértice inicial.

(I)

Identity matrix (p. 135) An $n \times n$ square matrix I such that $A \times I = I \times A = A$ for all $n \times n$ matrices A. (Also sometimes called a *multiplicative identity matrix*.)

Matriz identidad (pág. 135) Una matriz I cuadrada $n \times n$ de modo que $A \times I = I \times A = A$ para todas las matrices A $n \times n$. (También llamada en ocasiones una *matriz multiplicativa de identidad*.)

Identity transformation A rigid transformation that maps each point of the plane onto itself.

Transformación de identidad Transformación rígida que traza cada punto de un plano en sí mismo.

Immediate prerequisite table (p. 436) A table showing the immediate prerequisites for each task within a large project.

Tabla de prerrequisitos inmediatos (pág. 436) Tabla que muestra los prerrequisitos inmediatos para cada tarea dentro de un proyecto grande.

Independent events (p. 523) Two events A and B are independent if the occurrence of one of the events does not change the probability that the other event occurs. That is, $P(A \mid B) = P(A)$. Alternatively, events A and B with nonzero probabilities are independent if $P(A \text{ and } B) = P(A) \cdot P(B)$.

Eventos independientes (pág. 523) Dos eventos A y B son independientes si el que uno ocurra no afecta la probabilidad de que el otro ocurra. Es decir, $P(A \mid B) = P(A)$. Igualmente, los eventos A y B con probabilidad no-cero son independientes si $P(A \text{ y } B) = P(A) \cdot P(B)$.

Glossary/Glosario

English	Español

English

Independent variable (p. 3) Variables whose values are restricted only by the context of the problem or by mathematical restrictions on allowed values. These variables influence the values of other variables called *dependent variables*. (Also called an *explanatory variable*.)

Influential point (p. 287) On a scatterplot, an outlier such that when it is removed from the data set, the slope or *y*-intercept of the regression line changes quite a bit, where "quite a bit" must be determined by the real-life situation.

Initial side of an angle (p. 461) The position of a ray that is one side of the angle before it rotates about the angle's vertex to the terminal side.

Inscribed angle (p. 178) An angle whose vertex is on the circumference of a circle and whose sides are segments connecting the vertex to two other points on the circumference.

Inverse matrix (p. 137) For a given square matrix A, the matrix denoted A^{-1} (if it exists) that satisfies $A \times A^{-1} = A^{-1} \times A = I$, where I is the identity matrix. (Also called *multiplicative inverse matrix*.)

Inverse variation (p. 42) If variables x and y are related by an equation in the form $y = \frac{k}{x}$ or $yx = k$, then y is said to vary inversely with x, or be inversely proportional to x.

Isosceles triangle A triangle with at least two congruent sides. The side that joins the congruent sides is called the *base*, and the angles that lie opposite the congruent sides are called the *base angles*.

Español

Variable Independiente (pág. 3) Variable cuyos valores están restringidos solamente por el contexto de un problema o por restricciones matemáticas sobre los valores permitidos. Estas variables influyen en los valores de otras variables, las llamadas *variables dependientes*. (También llamada *variable explicativa*.)

Punto influyente (pág. 287) En una gráfica de dispersión, un valor atípico dado que cuando se elimina del conjunto de datos, la pendiente o intersección *y* de la línea de regresión cambia un poco, situación en la cual "un poco" debe determinarse de acuerdo con la situación real.

Lado inicial de un ángulo (pág. 461) Posición de una semirrecta que está en un lado del ángulo antes de rotar en el vértice de un ángulo al lado terminal.

Ángulo inscrito (pág. 178) Ángulo cuyo vértice está en la circunferencia de un círculo y cuyos lados son segmentos que conectan el vértice con otros dos puntos en la circunferencia.

Matriz inversa (pág. 137) Para una matriz cuadrada dada A, la matriz denominada A^{-1} (si existe) que satisface $A \times A^{-1} = A^{-1} \times A = I$, donde I es la matriz identidad. (También llamada *matriz inversa multiplicativa*.)

Variación inversa (pág. 42) Si las variables x y y están relacionadas por una ecuación en la forma de $y = \frac{k}{x}$ o $yx = k$, entonces se dice que y está inversamente con x, o que es inversamente proporcional a x.

Triángulo isósceles Triángulo con por lo menos dos lados congruentes. El lado que une a los lados congruentes se llama *base* y los ángulos opuestos a los lados congruentes se llaman *ángulos basales*.

Kite A convex quadrilateral with two distinct pairs of congruent consecutive sides.

Kruskal's Algorithm (p. 405) An algorithm for finding a minimum spanning tree in a connected graph.

Deltoide Cuadrilátero convexo con exactamente dos pares de lados congruentes consecutivos.

Algoritmo de Kruskal (pág. 405) Algoritmo para hallar un árbol de expansión en un grafo conectado.

Glossary/Glosario

English	Español

L

Law of Cosines (p. 457) In any triangle ABC with sides of lengths a, b, and c opposite $\angle A$, $\angle B$, and $\angle C$, respectively: $c^2 = a^2 + b^2 - 2ab \cos C$.

Ley de cosenos (pág. 457) En cualquier triángulo ABC con longitudes de sus lados a, b, y c opuestos $\angle A$, $\angle B$, y $\angle C$, respectivamente: $c^2 = a^2 + b^2 - 2ab \cos C$.

Law of Large Numbers In a simulation, the more runs there are, the closer the probability determined by the simulation tends to the theoretical probability.

Ley de números grandes En una simulación, si el número de repeticiones es mayor, más cercana a la probabilidad teorética tiende a ser la probabilidad determinada por la situación

Law of Sines (p. 457) In any triangle ABC with sides of lengths a, b, and c opposite $\angle A$, $\angle B$, and $\angle C$, respectively: $\frac{\sin A}{a} = \frac{\sin B}{b} = \frac{\sin C}{c}$.

Ley de senos (pág. 457) En un triángulo ABC con longitudes de sus lados a, b, y c opuesto $\angle A$, $\angle B$, y $\angle C$, respectivamente: $\frac{\sin A}{a} = \frac{\sin B}{b} = \frac{\sin C}{c}$.

Least squares regression line (p. 257) The line on a scatterplot that has the smallest sum of squared residuals (SSE). (Also called the *regression line*.)

Línea de regresión de cuadrados mínimos (pág. 257) La línea en una gráfica de dispersión que tiene la menor suma de residuos cuadrados (SSE por sus siglas en inglés). (También llamada *línea de regresión*.)

Line reflection (p. 201) A rigid transformation which associates with each point P in a plane an image point P' such that the "mirror line" (or line of reflection) is the perpendicular bisector of the segment $\overline{PP'}$ if P is not on the line of reflection. A point on the line of reflection is its own image.

Línea reflexión (pág. 201) Una transformación rígida que se relaciona con cada punto P en un plano con un punto de imagen P' de modo que la "línea de espejo" (o línea de reflexión) es el bisector perpendicular del segmento $\overline{PP'}$ si P no está en la línea de reflexión. Un punto en la línea de reflexión es su propia imagen.

Linear data (p. 264) The points on a scatterplot are called "linear" if they form an elliptical cluster so that a line is an appropriate summary.

Datos lineales (pág. 264) Los puntos en una gráfica de dispersión se llaman "lineales" si forman un grupo elíptico para que una recta sea un resumen apropiado.

Linear function A function with rule of correspondence that can be expressed in the algebraic form $f(x) = mx + b$.

Función lineal Función con regla de correspondencia que puede expresarse en la forma algebraica $f(x) = mx + b$.

Linear scale (p. 388) A scale for which the difference between equally spaced scale points is a constant.

Escala lineal (pág. 388) Escala para la cual la diferencia entre los puntos de la misma están separados por igual.

Logarithm (p. 325) If $y = 10^x$ then x is the common or base-10 logarithm of y. This relationship is often indicated by the notation $y = \log x$ or $y = \log_{10} x$.

Logaritmo (pág. 325) Si $y = 10^x$ entonces x es el logaritmo común o de base 10 de y. La notación $y = \log x$ ó $y = \log_{10} x$ usualmente indica esta relación.

Logarithmic function (p. 381) A function with rule of correspondence that can be expressed in the form $f(x) = \log x$.

Función logarítmica (pág. 381) Función con regla de correspondencia que puede expresarse en la forma $f(x) = \log x$.

Glossary/Glosario

English	**Español**

Logarithmic scale (p. 388) A scale for which the ratio between consecutive scale points is a constant.

Lurking variable (p. 300) When explaining the association between two variables, a third variable that affects both of the original variables.

Escala logarítmica (pág. 388) Escala para la cual el radio entre puntos consecutivos de la escala es constante.

Variable latente (pág. 300) Al explicar la asociación entre dos variables, una tercera variable que afecta a ambas variables originales.

· ·

Main diagonal of a square matrix (p. 80) The entries in the matrix that run from the top-left corner of the matrix to the bottom-right corner.

Matrix (p. 73) A rectangular array of numbers (plural: *matrices*).

Matrix addition (p. 134) Two matrices A and B, having the same size, are combined by adding their corresponding entries to produce the sum matrix, $A + B$.

Matrix multiplication (p. 105) An $m \times k$ matrix A and a $k \times n$ matrix B are multiplied to produce the $m \times n$ product matrix, $A \times B$, in which the entries of $A \times B$ are computed by a specific method of combining rows of A with columns of B.

Matrix of coefficients of a system of linear equations (p. 133) A matrix whose entries are the coefficients of the variables in the system of linear equations.

Midpoint (p. 163) The point on a segment that is equidistant from the endpoints of the segment.

Midpoint Formula (p. 169) Formula for calculating the coordinates of the midpoint of the segment connecting two points in the coordinate plane.

Minimum spanning tree (p. 403) A spanning tree in a vertex-edge graph that has minimum total weight.

Multiplication rule (p. 532) If A and B are two events, $P(A \text{ and } B) = P(A)P(B \mid A)$.

Multiplication Rule for Independent Events (p. 523) When events A and B are independent, the multiplication rule simplifies to $P(A \text{ and } B) = P(A) \cdot P(B)$.

Diagonal principal de una matriz cuadrada (pág. 80) Entradas de una matriz que van de la esquina superior izquierda de la matriz a la esquina inferior derecha.

Matriz (pág. 73) Arreglo rectangular de números (plural: *matrices*).

Adición de la matriz (pág. 134) Dos matrices A y B, que tienen el mismo tamaño, se combinan al sumar sus entradas correspondientes para producir la suma de la matriz, $A + B$.

Multiplicación de la matriz (pág. 105) Una matriz A $m \times k$ y una matriz B $k \times n$ se multiplican para producir el producto $m \times n$ de matriz, $A \times B$, en el cual las entradas de $A \times B$ se computan con un método específico de combinación de filas de A con columnas de B.

Matriz de coeficientes de un sistema de ecuaciones lineales (pág. 133) Matriz cuyas entradas son los coeficientes de las variables en el sistema de ecuaciones lineales.

Punto medio (pág. 163) El punto en un segmento que está a la misma distancia de los extremos del segmento.

Fórmula de punto medio (pág. 169) Fórmula para calcular las coordenadas de un punto medio de los segmentos que conectan dos puntos en el plano de coordenadas.

Árbol de expansión mínima (pág. 403) Árbol que atraviesa en un grafo que tiene peso total mínimo.

Regla de multiplicación (pág. 532) Si A y B son dos eventos, $P(A \text{ y } B) = P(A)P(B \mid A)$.

Regla de multiplicación para eventos independientes (pág. 523) Cuando los eventos A y B son independientes, la regla de multiplicación se simplifica a $P(A \text{ y } B) = P(A) \cdot P(B)$.

Glossary/Glosario

English	Español

Multiplicative inverse matrix See *inverse matrix.*

Matriz inversa multiplicativa Véase *matriz inversa.*

Multiply a matrix by a number (p. 85) Multiply each entry in a matrix, A, by the same number, k, to generate the entries in a new matrix, kA. (Also called *scalar multiplication.*)

Multiplicar una matriz por un número (pág. 85) Multiplicar cada entrada en una matriz, A, por el mismo número, k, para generar las entradas en una nueva matriz, kA. (También conocida como *multiplicación escalar.*)

Mutually exclusive events (or *disjoint events*) (p. 523) Events that cannot occur on the same outcome.

Eventos mutuamente excluyentes (disjuntos) (pág. 523) Eventos que no pueden ocurrir en el mismo resultado.

— N —

Negative correlation (p. 264) The points on a scatterplot have a downwards trend from left to right and so the slope of the regression line is negative.

Correlación negativa (pág. 264) Los puntos en un diagrama de dispersión tienden a bajar de izquierda a derecha y por lo tanto la pendiente de la línea de regresión es negativa.

— O —

One-to-one function (p. 354) A function f for which each value of $f(x)$ in the range of f corresponds to exactly one value of x in the domain of f.

Función biunívoca (pág. 354) Función f para la cual cada valor de $f(x)$ en el rango de f corresponde exactamente al valor de x en el dominio de f.

Orientation of a figure (p. 212) Can be determined by clockwise or counterclockwise labeling of consecutive vertices of a figure.

Orientación de una figura (pág. 212) Se puede determinar por los rótulos de los vértices consecutivos de una figura en dirección de las manecillas del reloj o contrario a éstas.

Outlier on a scatterplot (p. 77) A point that does not follow the trend of the other points and so lies outside the main cluster of points.

Valor atípico (o Dato aberrante) en una gráfica de dispersión (pág. 77) Punto que no sigue la tendencia de los demás puntos y queda fuera del grupo principal de puntos.

— P —

Parallel lines Lines that are coplanar and do not intersect.

Rectas paralelas Rectas coplanarias que no se intersecan.

Parallelogram (p. 154) A quadrilateral with opposite sides congruent.

Paralelogramo (pág. 154) Cuadrilátero de lados opuestos congruentes.

Perfect correlation (p. 260) All points on a scatterplot fall on the regression line so that the correlation is 1 or -1.

Correlación perfecta (pág. 260) Todos los puntos en una gráfica de dispersión recaen en la recta de regresión de modo que la correlación es biunívoca.

Perpendicular lines Lines that intersect at right angles.

Rectas perpendiculares Rectas que se intersecan en ángulos rectos.

Point matrix (p. 233) A one-column matrix whose entries are coordinates of a point in the plane. (See also *column matrix.*)

Matriz punto (pág. 233) Matriz de una columna cuyas entradas son coordenadas un punto en el plano. (Véase también *columna de matriz.*)

Glossary/Glosario

Positive correlation (p. 264) The points on a scatterplot have an upwards trend from left to right and so the slope of the regression line is positive.

Power function (p. 10) A function with rule of correspondence that can be expressed in the algebraic form $f(x) = ax^r$ $(r \neq 0)$.

Preimage (p. 199) If point A' is the image of a point A under a transformation, then point A is the preimage of point A'.

Probability distribution A description of all possible quantitative (numerical) outcomes of a chance situation, along with the probability of each outcome; the distribution may be in table, formula, or graphical form.

Program Evaluation and Review Technique (PERT) (p. 435) A technique using critical path analysis to optimally schedule large projects consisting of many subtasks; developed in the 1950s to help create military defense systems. (See also *Critical Path Method*.)

Project digraph (p. 437) A digraph representing a large project, in which the vertices represent the subtasks of the project and the directed edges show the immediate prerequisite(s) for each task.

Correlación positiva (pág. 264) Los puntos en un diagrama de dispersión muestran una tendencia hacia arriba de izquierda a derecha y por lo tanto la inclinación de la línea de regresión es positiva.

Función exponencial (pág. 10) Función con regla de correspondencia que puede expresarse con la forma algebraica $f(x) = ax^r$ $(r \neq 0)$.

Preimagen (pág. 199) Si el punto A' es la imagen de un punto A después de una transformación, entonces el punto A es la preimagen del punto A'.

Distribución probabilística Descripción de todos los resultados posibles de una situación aleatoria, junto con la probabilidad de cada uno; la distribución puede estar en forma de tabla, fórmula o gráfica.

Técnica de Evaluación y Revisión de Programa (PERT, por sus siglas en inglés) (pág. 435) Técnica que utiliza el análisis de trayectoria crítico para programar de manera óptima proyectos grandes compuestos de muchos subproyectos; desarrollado en la década de 1950 como ayuda para crear sistemas de defensa militar. (Véase también *Método de trayectoria crítica*.)

Dígrafo del proyecto (pág. 437) Grafo que representa un proyecto grande, en el cual los vértices representan los sub-proyectos del proyecto y las aristas dirigidas muestran los prerrequisito(s) para cada trabajo.

· (Q) ·

Quadratic equation An equation that can be expressed in the form $ax^2 + bx + c = 0$ $(a \neq 0)$.

Quadratic formula (p. 340) A formula for the solutions of a quadratic equation in the form $ax^2 + bx + c = 0$: $x = \dfrac{-b}{2a} \pm \dfrac{\sqrt{b^2 - 4ac}}{2a}$.

Quadratic function A function with rule of correspondence that can be expressed in the algebraic form $f(x) = ax^2 + bx + c$ $(a \neq 0)$.

Ecuación cuadrática Ecuación que puede expresarse en la forma $ax^2 + bx + c = 0$ $(a \neq 0)$.

Formula cuadrática (pág. 340) Fórmula para las soluciones a una ecuación cuadrática que puede expresarse en la forma $ax^2 + bx + c = 0$: $x = \dfrac{-b}{2a} \pm \dfrac{\sqrt{b^2 - 4ac}}{2a}$.

Función cuadrática Función con regla de correspondencia que puede expresarse en la forma algebraica $f(x) = ax^2 + bx + c$ $(a \neq 0)$.

Glossary/Glosario

English	Español

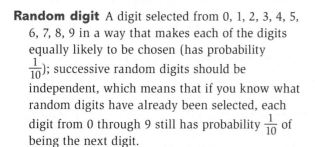

Random digit A digit selected from 0, 1, 2, 3, 4, 5, 6, 7, 8, 9 in a way that makes each of the digits equally likely to be chosen (has probability $\frac{1}{10}$); successive random digits should be independent, which means that if you know what random digits have already been selected, each digit from 0 through 9 still has probability $\frac{1}{10}$ of being the next digit.

Dígito aleatorio Dígito escogido de 0, 1, 2, 3, 4, 5, 6, 7, 8, 9 de modo que cada uno tenga la misma probabilidad de elegirse que cualquier otro (tiene probabilidad $\frac{1}{10}$); los dígitos aleatorios consecutivos deben ser independientes, o sea, se conocen los dígitos aleatorios ya escogidos, cada dígito de 0 a 9 aún tiene $\frac{1}{10}$ de escogerse cono el dígito siguiente.

Range of a function (p. 330) For a function f, the values of the dependent variable y corresponding to values of x in the domain of f. (Also called *output values* of the function.)

Rango de una función (pág. 330) Para una función f, los valores de las variables dependientes y que corresponden con los valores de x en el dominio de f. (También llamada *valores de salida* de la función.)

Rank correlation (p. 259) A correlation based on two different rankings of the same items. Two types of rank correlation are Spearman's and Kendall's.

Correlación de rango (pág. 259) Correlación basada en dos diferentes rangos del mismo objeto. Dos tipos de rangos son los de Spearman y de Kendall.

Rare event (p. 566) In a waiting-time distribution, an event that falls in the upper 5% of the distribution.

Evento raro (pág. 566) En una distribución de espera de tiempo, un evento que está en el 5% superior de la distribución.

Rectangle A quadrilateral with opposite sides congruent and four right angles.

Rectángulo Cuadrilátero con lados opuestos congruentes y cuatro ángulos rectos.

Regression equation (p. 282) The equation of the least squares regression line for the points on a scatterplot.

Ecuación de regresión (pág. 282) Ecuación de la recta de regresión de los mínimos cuadrados para los puntos en una gráfica de dispersión.

Regression line See *least squares regression line.*

Recta de regresión Véase *línea de regresión de mínimos cuadrados.*

Regular polygon A polygon in which all sides are congruent and all angles are congruent.

Polígono regular Polígono cuyos lados y ángulos son todos congruentes.

Residual (error) (p. 283) For points used to calculate the regression equation, the difference between the observed value of y and the value of y predicted by the regression equation, $y - \hat{y}$.

Residuo (error) (pág. 283) Para puntos que se usan para calcular la ecuación de la regresión, la diferencia entre el valor observado de y y el valor y predicho por la ecuación de la regresión, $y - \hat{y}$.

Response variable See *dependent variable.*

Variable respuesta Véase *variable dependiente.*

Rhombus A quadrilateral with all four sides congruent.

Rombo Cuadrilátero con cuatro lados congruentes.

Rigid transformation (p. 196) A transformation of points in the plane that repositions figures without changing their shape or size.

Transformación rígida (pág. 196) Una transformación de puntos en un plano que vuelve a colocar figuras sin cambiar su forma o tamaño.

Glossary/Glosario

|

Rotation (p. 161) A rigid transformation of points in the plane that rotates (or turns) figures about a specified point, called the *center of rotation*, through a specified angle, called the *directed angle of rotation*.

Rotation matrix (p. 232) A matrix, which when multiplied on the right by a point matrix, has the effect of rotating the point about the origin through a specified angle.

Row matrix (p. 105) A matrix consisting of one row. (Also called a *one-row matrix* or a *row vector.*)

Row of an *m* × *n* matrix (p. 76) A horizontal array of *n* numbers in the matrix.

Row sum of a matrix (p. 81) The sum of all the numbers in a row of a matrix.

Rotación (pág. 161) Transformación rígida de puntos en un plano en la que una figura gira en torno a un punto fijo, llamado *centro de rotación*, y a través de un ángulo especificado, llamado *ángulo dirigido de rotación*.

Matriz rotación (pág. 232) Matriz que al multiplicarse a la derecha por un punto de matriz tiene el efecto de rotar el punto del origen a través de un ángulo dado.

Matriz fila (pág. 105) Matriz que consta de una fila. (También llamada *matriz de una fila* o *vector fila.*)

Fila de una matriz *m* × *n* (pág. 76) Arreglo horizontal de *n* números en la matriz.

Suma de fila de una matriz (pág. 81) Suma de todos los números de la fila de una matriz.

······················ **S** ······················

Sample space A list of all possible outcomes of a chance situation.

Scalar multiplication See *multiply a matrix by a number.*

Scale factor of a size (or similarity) transformation (p. 215) The ratio of the distance between any two image points and the distance between their preimages under the transformation.

Scatterplot matrix (p. 266) A matrix where each entry is a scatterplot formed using a pair of variables from a set of multivariate data.

Similar figures (p. 215) Figures that are related by a similarity transformation. These figures have the same shape, regardless of position or orientation, but may be of different scales.

Similarity transformation (p. 196) Composition of a size transformation and a rigid transformation (possibly the *identity transformation*). Such a transformation resizes a figure in the plane without changing its shape.

Simulation Imitating a real-life situation by creating a mathematical model that captures the situation's essential characteristics.

Espacio muestral Lista de todos los resultados posibles de un suceso.

Multiplicación escalar Véase *multiplicar una matriz por un número.*

Factor de escala de una transformación de tamaño (o similitud) (pág. 215) Radio de distancia entre cualquiera dos puntos de una imagen y la distancia entre sus preimagenes bajo la transformación.

Matriz de gráfica de dispersión (pág. 266) Matriz en la cual cada entrada es una gráfica de dispersión formada usando un par de variables de un conjunto de datos multivariados.

Figuras semejantes (pág. 215) Figuras que se relacionan por una transformación de similitud. Estas figuras tienen la misma forma, sin importar la posición u orientación pero pueden ser de diferentes escalas.

Transformación de similitud (pág. 196) Composición de una transformación de tamaño y una transformación rígida (posiblemente la *transformación de identidad*). Tal transformación cambia de tamaño en el plano sin cambiar su forma.

Simulación Imitación de una situación real al crear un modelo matemático que captura las características esenciales de la situación.

Glossary/Glosario

Sine function (p. 457) If $P(x, y)$ is a point (not the origin) on the terminal side of an angle θ in standard position and $r = \sqrt{x^2 + y^2}$, then $\sin \theta = \dfrac{y}{r}$. If A is an acute angle in a right triangle, then $\sin A = \dfrac{\text{length of side } \textit{opposite} \angle A}{\text{length of } \textit{hypotenuse}}$.

Función de seno (pág. 457) Si $P(x, y)$ es un punto (no el origen) en el lado terminal de un ángulo θ en posición estándar y $r = \sqrt{x^2 + y^2}$, entonces $\sin \theta = \dfrac{y}{r}$. Si A es un ángulo agudo en un triángulo rectángulo, entonces $\sin A = \dfrac{\text{medida del cateto } \textit{opuesto a } \angle A}{\text{medida de la } \textit{hipotenusa}}$.

Size of a matrix (p. 76) The number of rows and columns in a matrix, denoted by (*number of rows*) × (*number of columns*).

Tamaño de una matriz (pág. 76) Número de filas y columnas en una matriz, indicado por (*número de filas*) × (*número de columnas*).

Size transformation (or *dilation*) (p. 205) A transformation that moves each point P in the plane along a ray through P from a specified point O, called the *center of the transformation*, according to the rule $OP' = kOP$, where P' is the image of P and $k \neq 0$ (k is called the *scale factor* or *magnitude* of the transformation).

Transformación de tamaño (o *dilatación*) (pág. 205) Transformación que mueve cada punto P en el plano a lo largo de una semirrecta a través de P del punto dado O, llamado *centro de la transformación*, según la regla $OP' = kOP$, donde P' es la imagen de P y $k \neq 0$ (k se llama el *factor de posicionamiento* o *magnitud* de la transformación.

Slope of a line Ratio of change in y-coordinates to change in x-coordinates between any two points on a nonvertical line; $\dfrac{\textit{change in y}}{\textit{change in x}}$ or $\dfrac{\Delta y}{\Delta x}$; indicates the direction and steepness of a line.

Pendiente de una recta Radio de cambio en las coordenadas y para cambiar en las coordenadas x entre dos puntos cualesquiera en una recta no vertical; $\dfrac{\textit{cambio en y}}{\textit{cambio en x}}$ o $\dfrac{\Delta y}{\Delta x}$; indica la dirección e inclinación de una recta.

Square matrix (p. 138) A matrix with the same number of rows and columns.

Matriz cuadrada (pág. 138) Matriz con el mismo número de filas y columnas.

Spanning tree (p. 403) A tree in a vertex-edge graph that includes all the vertices of the graph.

Árbol de expansión (pág. 403) Árbol en un grafo que incluye todos los vértices de la gráfica.

Strength of a correlation (p. 260) The association between two variables is strong if the points cluster closely to the regression line and weak if the distances from the regression line to the points tend to be large.

Fuerza de una correlación (pág. 260) La asociación entre dos variables es fuerte si los puntos se agrupan cerca de la recta de regresión y débil si las distancias de la recta de regresión a los puntos tiende a ser grande.

Subscript notation (p. 189) A letter or number displayed slightly below a variable. Subscripts are used to discriminate between variables that have the same letter symbol.

Notación de subíndice (pág. 189) Una letra o número que aparece ligeramente debajo de una variable. Las notaciones de subíndice se usan para discriminar entre variables que tienen el mismo símbolo de la letra.

Substitution method (p. 51) A method used to solve a system of linear equations. Two equations with two variables are combined into a single equation with only one variable by *substituting* an expression for a variable from one equation into the other.

Método de substitución (pág. 51) Método que se utiliza para resolver un sistema de ecuaciones lineales. Dos ecuaciones con dos variables se combinan en una sola ecuación con únicamente una variable al *sustituir* una expresión por una variable de una ecuación a la otra.

Glossary/Glosario

English	Español

Sum of squared errors (SSE or sum of squared residuals) (p. 285) The sum of the squared residuals, $SSE = \Sigma(y - \hat{y})^2$.

Suma de cuadrados debido al error (SSE, por sus siglas en inglés, o suma de residuales cuadrados) (pág. 285) La suma de residuos cuadrados, $SSE = \Sigma(y - \hat{y})^2$.

Symmetric matrix (p. 92) A square matrix that exhibits reflection symmetry about its main diagonal.

Matriz simétrica (pág. 92) Matriz cuadrada que muestra simetría de reflexión de su diagonal principal.

System of equations A set of two or more equations with two or more variables for which common solution(s) are sought.

Sistema de ecuaciones Conjunto de dos o más ecuaciones con dos o más variables para las cuales se buscan solución(es) en común.

— — — — — — — — — — — (T) — — — — — — — — — — —

Tangent (p. 180) A line is *tangent* to a given curve at a point, called the *point of tangency*, if the line touches the curve at that point, but does not cross the curve at that point.

Tangente (pág. 180) Una recta es *tangente* de una curva dada en un punto, llamado *punto de tangencia*, si la recta pasa a través de la curva en sólo un punto pero no cruza la curva en ese punto.

Tangent function (p. 462) If $P(x, y)$ is a point (not the origin) on the terminal side of an angle θ in standard position and $r = \sqrt{x^2 + y^2}$, then $\tan \theta = \frac{y}{x}$ $(x \neq 0)$. If A is an acute angle in a right triangle, then $\tan A = \frac{\text{length of side } opposite \angle A}{\text{length of side } adjacent \text{ to } \angle A}$.

Función de tangente (pág. 462) Si $P(x, y)$ es un punto (no el origen) en el lado terminal de un ángulo θ en posición estándar y $r = \sqrt{x^2 + y^2}$, entonces $\tan \theta = \frac{y}{x}$ $(x \neq 0)$. Si A es un ángulo agudo en un triángulo rectángulo, entonces, $\tan A = \frac{\text{la medida del cateto } opuesto \text{ a } \angle A}{\text{la medida del cateto } adyacente \text{ a } \angle A}$.

Taxi-distance (p. 191) The shortest distance between two locations following a path along the edges of a square grid (or parallel to those edges).

Distancia taxi (pág. 191) La menor distancia entre dos posiciones seguida de un camino a lo largo de las aristas de una cuadrícula cuadrada (o paralela a esas aristas).

Terminal side of an angle (p. 461) The position of a ray that is the side of an angle after rotating about the angle's vertex from the initial position.

Lado terminal de un ángulo (pág. 461) La posición de una semirrecta que es el lado de un ángulo después de rotar en torno al vértice del ángulo de una posición inicial.

Transformation (p. 161) A one-to-one correspondence (function) between points of a plane.

Transformación (pág. 161) Correspondencia (función) biunívoca entre dos puntos de un plano.

Translation (p. 197) A rigid transformation that shifts all points in the plane a specified distance and direction, determined by the *translation vector*.

Traslación (pág. 197) Transformación rígida que cambia todos los puntos en el plano a una distancia y dirección dadas, determinadas por el *vector de traslación*.

Transpose of a matrix (p. 126) The matrix obtained from a given matrix A by interchanging the rows and columns of A. Denoted by A^T.

Trasposición de una matriz (pág. 126) Matriz que se obtiene de una matriz dada A al intercambiar las filas y columnas de A, la cual se denomina A^T.

Glossary/Glosario

English	Español

Traveling Salesperson Problem (p. 407) A problem related to vertex-edge graphs stated informally as follows: A sales representative wants to visit several different cities, each exactly once, and then return home. Among the possible routes, which will minimize the total distance traveled? (Also called the *Traveling Salesman Problem* or the *TSP.*)

Problema del vendedor viajero (pág. 407) Problema relacionado informalmente con grafos de la siguiente manera: un vendedor quiere visitar diferentes ciudades, solamente una vez cada una, y después regresar a casa. De entre los resultados posibles, ¿cuál minimizará la distancia total que se viaja? (También conocido como *TSP*, por sus siglas en inglés.)

Tree (p. 403) A connected graph that has no circuits.

Árbol (pág. 403) Gráfica conectada que no tiene circuitos.

Trial (or sometimes *run*) One repetition of a simulation.

Prueba Repetición de un simulacro.

Trigonometric functions (p. 457) The sine, cosine, and tangent functions and (to be defined in a later course) their reciprocals.

Funciones trigonométricas (pág. 457) Funciones de seno, coseno y tangente y (se definirán en un curso posterior) sus recíprocos.

TSP See *Traveling Salesperson Problem.*

TSP Véase *Problema del vendedor viajero.*

Venn diagram A diagram where mutually exclusive events are represented by non-overlapping circles and events that are not mutually exclusive are represented by overlapping circles.

Diagrama de Venn Diagrama en el cual los eventos mutuamente excluyentes se presentan por círculos no sobrepuestos y los eventos que no son mutuamente excluyentes se presentan por círculos sobrepuestos.

Vertex-edge graph (p. 68) A diagram consisting of points (called *vertices*) along with segments or arcs (called *edges*) joining some of the points. (Also simply called a *graph*.)

Grafo (pág. 68) Diagrama que consta de un conjunto de puntos (los *vértices*) junto con segmentos o arcos (las *artistas*) que unen algunos de los puntos. (También llamada simplemente una *gráfica*.)

Waiting-time (geometric) distribution (p. 525) A probability distribution of the number of independent trials required to get a specified outcome called a "success." The probability that a success will occur must be the same on every trial.

Distribución (geométrica) del tiempo de espera (pág. 525) Distribución probabilística del número de pruebas independientes requeridas para obtener un resultado especificado llamado "éxito." La probabilidad de que un éxito suceda debe ser la misma en cada prueba.

Weighted graph (p. 403) A vertex-edge graph with numbers (*weights*) on its edges.

Gráfico cargado (pág. 403) Grafo con números (*pesos*) en sus aristas.

Weights (p. 403) Numbers that are placed on the edges (or vertices) of a vertex-edge graph.

Pesos (pág. 403) Números que se colocan en las artistas (o vértices) de un grafo.

With replacement Selecting a sample from a set so that each selection is replaced before selecting the next; thus, a member of the set can be selected more than once.

Con devolución Selección de una muestra de un conjunto de modo que cada selección se devuelve antes de elegir la siguiente; así cada miembro del conjunto puede escogerse más de una vez.

Glossary/Glosario

English	Español

Without replacement Selecting a sample from a set so that each selection is not replaced before selecting the next; no member of the set can be selected more than once.

Sin devolución Selección de una muestra de un conjunto de modo que cada selección no se devuelve antes de elegir la siguiente; así cada miembro del conjunto no puede escogerse más de una vez.

• (X) •

x-**intercept(s) of a graph** The point(s) where the graph intersects the *x*-axis.

Intersección(es) *x* de una gráfica El punto o los puntos en que una gráfica interseca el eje *x*.

• (Y) •

y-**intercept(s) of a graph** The point(s) where the graph intersects the *y*-axis.

Intersección(es) *y* de una gráfica El punto o los puntos en que una gráfica interseca el eje *y*.

• (Z) •

Zero matrix (p. 134) A matrix in which every entry is 0. See *additive identity matrix*.

Matriz cero (pág. 134) Matriz en la cual cada entrada es cero. Véase *matriz identidad aditiva*.

Index of Mathematical Topics

Index of Mathematical Topics *(continued)*

Index of Mathematical Topics (continued)

Index of Mathematical Topics *(continued)*

Index of Mathematical Topics (continued)

Index of Contexts

Index of Contexts (continued)

Index of Contexts *(continued)*

Index of Contexts (continued)

Index of Contexts (continued)

Index of Contexts (continued)

Index of Contexts (continued)